A bold, sweeping epic of blood and passion by Kyle Onstott, who wrote the towering MANDINGO, and Lance Horner, who collaborated with Onstott on the famous bestsellers FALCONHURST FANCY and THE TATTOOED ROOD.

In THE BLACK SUN, the background is no longer the slave-breeding farms of the pre-Civil War South, but the lush and violent island of Haiti, where a handsome, brawny young New Englander has come to claim his Caribbean plantation. Here on his island in the sun, Armes Holbrook falls in love with another man's wife, becomes enmeshed with a lovely half-caste who initiates him into the strange and sensual rights of voodoo, and plays a blazing and tumultuous role in the bloody revolution led by the giant slave, Henry Christophe . . .

Another Fawcett Gold Medal Book by
Lance Horner & Kyle Onstott:

FALCONHURST FANCY

THE
BLACK
SUN

Lance Horner & Kyle Onstott

A FAWCETT GOLD MEDAL BOOK

Fawcett Publications, Inc., Greenwich, Conn.
Member of American Book Publishers Council, Inc.

To my good friend
ALEXANDER G. BOCK
who first gave me the idea of visiting Haiti—and
to whom I shall always be grateful for having introduced me to the beauty of the country and
the charm of its people.

Qui in solem venit, licet
non in hoc vererit, colorabitur.

"He, who comes in the sun, though
he walk not for that purpose must
needs become darkened."

Seneca
Epistulae ad Luculilium
Epis. CXIII—4

1

ARMES Holbrook was never a man to shrink from a disagreeable duty. Do it and get it over with! That was his theory and the more disagreeable the duty, the more quickly it should be dispatched, gotten out of the way, finished, ended, over with—*finis*, as he had learned to say it in Latin. Sometimes, however, it took a little thinking and planning to get through these difficult tasks. At other times it was better to barge right in and get the matter over with quickly and the devil take the hindmost.

He walked across the bare, wide-boarded floor to the small-paned window of his room in Massachusetts Hall and looked out over the leafy elms of Harvard Yard. This was his last night in the little room with its starkly whitewashed walls, its rather primitive furniture, and its sterile air of a monastic cell. The room's austerity seemed to symbolize the New England that he had always known and frankly hated. He was not a Puritan—not Armes Holbrook! This day had marked his graduation from Harvard and, he hoped, from New England. His sheepskin informed the world that he was a Bachelor of Arts. In truth he was a bachelor, and so he intended to stay, for a while at least. But he did want to do something about the *arts*. He knew what kind of arts, too—nothing like poetry or painting. He had other things in mind.

Tomorrow would be his twenty-first birthday and that was far more important to him than any number of engraved sheepskins. Tomorrow his inheritance would be safely in his own name and he could quit this scheduled life of bells, classes, puerile restrictions, and do exactly what he pleased, when he pleased, and where he pleased. He'd be free! Yes, damn it, free!

All the more important then to get rid of Kitty, and to do it tonight. Start in tomorrow with a clean slate. Kitty had served her small purpose and served it admirably, but now it was time to write *finis* to that chapter in his life, too. The little house in Cambridgeport was no longer a necessity, and

7

certainly Kitty in her present condition had no place in his life. Kitty with a baby! Good God, what did he want with any squalling brat?

It might be a rough hour: Kitty would probably weep and wail and try to play upon his feelings with all her Irish histrionics. But he had only to lay down the law and stand pat. Sooner or later she would come around to his way of thinking. She'd have to! What else could she do but accept? He wouldn't take orders from an Irish hired girl who only a couple of years ago had been washing out chamber pots in Mr. Frothingham's Boston house. She'd accept! She loved him too much to make any trouble. First she'd go into a temper and call him all sorts of names. Then she'd relent and tell him how much she loved him, and in the end she would grow defiant but calm, and bring up the matter of their unborn child—her unborn child—and try to foist it off on him. He wanted no part of it.

He smiled to himself. Fifteen minutes for the teary business of her great love for him, fifteen minutes for the histrionics, fifteen minutes for the business of his duty to the child. Three quarters of an hour in all. And then the last fifteen minutes he would devote to giving her the deed to the house and the money he had planned to turn over to her, and damned generous of him, too! A half-hour to walk there, a half hour to return, and an hour to finish up the business with Kitty— two hours in all. He'd have plenty of time to finish his packing and get to bed early for his morning appointment with Mr. Frothingham in his office. Then, no more guardians! Never!

So . . . better get started and get the unpleasant business over with.

The drizzle outside and the damp chill in the air had made the small fire in the grate welcome even in June, but now the few pieces of wood had burned themselves out and only the glowing coals illuminated the room. Armes took one of the twisted paper spills out of the glass on the mantelpiece, held it to the coals until it burst into flame, and lighted the candles in the room—two on the mantelpiece and two in sconces on either side of the tall mahogany pier glass. That large and elaborate piece of furniture looked strangely out of place in the cell-like room. It had been one of the few things that Armes had purchased for his school days and it had been the principal piece of furniture in all the rooms he had occupied during his four years in Harvard Yard. No man, he insisted, could dress correctly unless he were able to see himself from head to toe.

The light of the candles showed him that he was quite presentable now, sufficiently so at least for his quick visit to shabby Cambridgeport. His tallness and bigness stared back at him from the watery depths of the mirror. The shoulders, so broad they filled the entire glass, stretched the blue broadcloth of his coat. The yellow nankeen trousers fitted him like his skin, and the waistcoat of sprigged taffeta smoothed over his flat stomach so tautly that the gold watch chain depended from it rather than rested upon it. The black silk stock was a little askew and he tightened the ends of it and straightened it, then ran his fingers over his chin. The sooty outlines of a beard were plainly visible on his olive skin, but he knew that the darkness would not disappear with shaving. It was there even when he had just finished with the razor. As his fingers explored his chin he smiled at himself in the mirror, quite satisfied with his own reflection. The white teeth gleamed brightly between the moist, rather full red lips; the wide nostrils of the short nose flared in an upswept curve; and the gray eyes were a distinct contrast to the dark olive skin and the black brows above them. He was glad that he had cut his hair short, for now it took only a rake of the comb to set the crisp curls in place and bring out the widow's peak that came down low on his forehead. Again he smiled. He sure was a hairy bastard, but the women seemed to like him that way.

Before he opened the door to the plain deal wardrobe, he looked out the window. The drizzle had now turned into rain. He took out the caped greatcoat and the white beaver hat, slipping his long arms into the satin-lined sleeves and tipping the hat at a jaunty angle on his head. Once more he regarded himself in the mirror, changed the angle of his hat a little more to one side, and then winked at his reflection in the mirror.

"Good luck, Armes boy." The reflection winked back at him confidently. He blew out the candles. Hurriedly, he took the stairs two at a time and then was out the door and in the Yard, sniffing the damp fresh air, so welcome after the close, dusty smell of the dormitory. Well, he was leaving tomorrow. Just where he might be going he did not know, except that it would be away from Boston. Of one thing he was absolutely certain: it would not be to the little house in Cambridgeport where Kitty was waiting for him.

9

He started off with a brisk step, letting his long legs carry him out of Harvard Yard onto Massachusetts Ave., and along its uneven brick sidewalks until he turned off to leave the big Cambridge houses with their wide lawns behind and enter the narrow streets and the modest cheek-by-jowl wooden houses of the "port."

Long accustomed to the way, for he had made the same trip night and morning for the past two years, he paid little attention to the street turnings. He found that he was walking so fast and the caped coat was so heavy for June that he was beginning to sweat, and he could feel a trickle of moisture creeping down the sides of his body from his armpits. Then he slowed his pace; he was anxious to get the matter over with, but he felt a certain amount of dread in commencing it. Kitty had been a pleasant interlude and he had never intended that it should go as far as it had—certainly not to the point of Kitty's having a child, but that, of course, was something nobody could plan or prevent. It was going to complicate matters.

His thoughts went back to the first time he had seen her. It was during Christmas vacation two years ago when he left his room at Harvard to spend the holidays with Mr. Frothingham, his guardian, and his wife at their home on Beacon Street in Boston. At Christmas one certainly missed having parents and a home of one's own, but Mr. and Mrs. Frothingham had always stood in lieu of a family. They were the only family he had, so he felt free to go there, knowing that a room was always waiting for him even without an invitation. To his surprise, he had met Kitty, a new maid, slipping noiselessly through the dark corridors and up the steep stairs of the Boston house. She always lowered her head when she passed him but once or twice he had caught her looking up from under the long lashes of her lowered lids. Armes had always accepted his own good looks as an asset and he knew that he had made an impression on the girl. She was good-looking, too. Even the long black dress and the stiffly starched white apron had failed to disguise her alluring curves, and her bowed head with the little white lace cap perched on her dark-red hair had not been able to hide the heart-shaped face with the red cheeks and the dark-green eyes.

Her seduction had not been too difficult. Armes Holbrook had never found any woman difficult to seduce once he had put his mind to it. One of his greatest difficulties had been to keep women away from him. With Kitty it had worked out exactly as he had planned, with a minimum of effort.

Late one wintry afternoon, while he was dressing for dinner, he had noticed that the fire had to be replenished in his room. Boston houses at Christmastime consumed a lot of fuel. As if by design, Armes had been in his long velvet dressing gown and nothing else, when he rang for service. Kitty had appeared, breathless from carrying the big brass coal scuttle up the stairs, and Armes had been all sympathy, taking the heavy burden and bringing it into the room. He insisted that she sit down, at least long enough to regain her breath, and although Kitty told him that it was against Mrs. Frothingham's rules for her to sit, she let his strong hand guide her to a chair and allowed herself to be pushed down onto it.

Then, of course, came his carefully rehearsed speech about how no girl as delicate as she should be forced to carry heavy buckets of coal up so many flights of stairs. It was all wrong, he asserted. All the time he was coming nearer and nearer to her, standing beside her chair while he talked and finally laying one of his large hands on her shoulder, lightly of course, so that its reassuring pats would be interpreted only as an expression of sympathy.

She allowed the hand to remain there, and with this encouragement the fingers of his hand reached up to twist a lock of her hair and then to squeeze the lobe of her ear. This sortie having been successfully accomplished, it was only natural that he gently pull her head over until her cheek rested against the smooth velvet of his robe. Now, quite in possession, his fingers strayed from the lobe of her ear down her throat and commenced slowly and quietly to unbutton the high black collar. Not being repulsed, they traced their tantalizing way down under the front of her dress, finding all sorts of thick underclothes to impede their progress, but finally managing to slip under them to the soft, warm skin below.

Only when they had discovered that which they sought, the swelling globes under the black dress, had Kitty pulled away, but Armes knew that her heart was not in this required gesture of maidenly virtue. It was only a token to preserve her own feeling that she was not yielding too quickly, and soon her head was once again resting against the velvet. His other hand reached down for hers and there was a moment when their fingers were intertwined before he coaxed her

11

hand in his inside the warmth of his dressing gown, where her fingers, guided by his own, started on an exploring journey. When they had encountered that to which he was guiding them, they shrank away, but he held them firm and soon they were willing to remain by themselves. Once having found the courage to remain, they were not anxious to leave, but their continued stay was creating a dangerous situation as Armes did not want to rush matters. Almost unwillingly he disengaged her fingers and lifted her up to him, bending his head until his lips reached hers. Now he knew his conquest was complete. Her lips were as avid as his and her body in its rough black woolen dress pressed closely against his own.

"How lovely you are, Kitty darling, and how wonderful it would be if only we were alone together. However," he said, releasing her, "Mrs. Frothingham will surely wonder why it is taking her pretty little maid so long to put a few coals on Armes Holbrook's fire. See what a fire you have already started in me, Kitty darling. And there is only one way to put out a fire of that sort. Only you can do it. Tonight, I'll leave my door ajar. There is nobody else on this floor. All you will have to do is creep down the back stairs about midnight. . . ." He kissed her again.

Kitty had crept down the back stairs. She was all that Armes had hoped she would be, but the brief fortnight of the Christmas holidays had proved scarcely enough. At his suggestion, she had given up her work at Mrs. Frothingham's and taken up residence in the little house in Cambridgeport. He had had a devil of a time getting the money to buy the house from Mr. Frothingham, but Armes had explained it by saying that the money was for gambling debts. Of course, he had explained to Mr. Frothingham, he had had no intention of losing so much, and Mr. Frothingham finally agreed that a gambling debt was a debt of honor and must be paid. Armes had to listen to a long dissertation on extravagance and how a young man should hang onto his money. The lecture took all of ten minutes, and Armes stared at Mr. Frothingham most appealingly, as though he intended to profit by every word. His patience paid off in the end, for Mr. Frothingham sent his clerk for the money and Armes sallied forth to buy the house. Kitty was installed and thereafter, although Armes nominally lived in his bleak little cell at Massachusetts Hall, he spent most of his time and practically all of his nights in the cozy little house in Cambridgeport with Kitty to warm his bed.

It had turned out to be a good investment. Kitty was a good cook and an economical one, so he had far better food than he would have had at Commons. She was a neat housekeeper and washed and ironed his shirts much better than any hired laundress, in addition to lovingly and most meticulous mending his socks and sewing on his buttons. Actually, Armes figured, he had saved money on the venture, for Kitty loved to make him fine cambric shirts, embroider his waistcoats, and fuss about him in a hundred different ways. . . .

Yes, it had indeed been a pleasant interlude, but like all pleasant interludes it had to end, and he couldn't really regret that it was ending tonight. He hoped that Kitty would be grateful for the past two years and realize that it had to end eventually and it was better for it to end pleasantly. She certainly would not be the loser. She would have the house in her own name, and five hundred dollars was quite a fortune for an ignorant Irish girl who could write her own name only with difficulty. And, besides all this, she had had his love for two years—that was something she could not buy for money.

He turned the last corner and followed the narrow sidewalk passing the identical houses, each with its wooden picket fence, its two steps to the front door, and its two windows facing the street. The lilac bush that Kitty had planted in her front yard had already bloomed, and its few remaining blossoms were now faded and soot-stained. There was a light between the stiffly starched curtains of the front room, and when Armes' key turned in the lock, he heard Kitty's steps in the hall—not the light running steps she formerly used but slow, heavy ones adapted to her swelling body. He opened the door to find her smiling up at him, her hands running up under the soggy capes of his coat to where it was dry and warm underneath, pulling his big shoulders down until his face touched hers.

"You're late tonight, Armes darling." She touched the tip of his nose with her finger. "And me keeping the stew warm for over an hour so that it's probably spoiled by now and you won't be able to eat it."

Armes' finger touched her nose with an identical gesture. "Wouldn't be able to eat it anyway, Kitty child, because

13

Billy Boy Brooks had a big feed in his rooms this afternoon and I'm stuffed."

"And it was such a good stew," she sighed, "made the way you like it." She was helping him off with his coat. "Never mind, we'll have it warmed over for breakfast. Stew's good for breakfast and it's better when it's warmed over."

He followed her out into the kitchen while she spread his coat over a kitchen chair and moved it up close to the stove. The stew was simmering in a kettle on the back of the stove and she pushed it still further back.

"Afraid I'll not be here tomorrow, Kitty girl." He felt this was as good a time as any to break the news. "I'm leaving Boston."

"How long will you be gone?" Her underlip was trembling.

"A long time." He smiled at her.

"Over a week?" She was thinking of the longest time they had ever been separated.

He nodded in assent.

"Two weeks?" This seemed almost unbelievable.

"More."

"Where are you going, Armes darling?" She was frightened now.

"Just don't rightly know, Kitty, but I've been cooped up for four years. I've got to get away and see something different. Perhaps I'll go to Europe. I don't know, but I can't hang around Cambridge all my life, girl. You must have known that. But I want you to know how grateful I am for these past two years, Kitty girl. Having you has meant a lot to me."

She still did not understand or, if she did, she did not want to realize the full meaning of his words.

"You mean you are going away—going to leave me—not going to marry me?"

"Now, Kitty girl, when did I ever say anything about marrying you?"

"You never did." She was trying hard to keep the tears back. "But now things are different. Now I'm going to bear your child."

"Your child, Kitty. I intend to provide for that child of yours."

She turned to face him, completely forgetting how much he meant to her as she loosed her ready temper on him. He stood, smiling faintly, until he was sure she had exhausted

14

her entire repertoire of vituperations, awaiting the storm of tears which he knew would follow.

He was not disappointed. She paused in her stream of invective, and the tears came just as he had expected. She came toward him, forgiving and humble, throwing herself in his arms and telling him over and over again how much she loved him and how much he loved her. His arms enfolded her protectively and, feeling them around her, she felt she had won her case, although he had said nothing. Her sobbing quieted and she pulled away from him, smiling a bit through her tears.

"Oh, darling Armes, I knew you wouldn't leave me. I knew you would stand by me."

"And so I shall, Kitty girl." He reached in the inside pocket of his fine blue coat and pulled out a long envelope which he opened carefully.

"Now let's talk things over sensibly, Kitty. You know and I know that it would be impossible for you and me to marry. I never promised you marriage and you never asked for it. It was no part of our bargain. Of course we never expected a child, but it's as much your fault as mine. Remember, girl, there were times you wanted it even more than I did. So that's the chance we took." He touched her swollen belly. "I'm not just walking out on you, Kitty. I'm not abandoning you. Look!" He pulled out a folded paper from the envelope. "Here's the deed to this house, made out all proper and legally to Mrs. Kitty O'Banion. See, Kitty, M—r—s, making you a proper widow. And here—he drew a thick sheaf of banknotes from the envelope—"here's five hundred dollars. It's far more, I'm sure, than you would ever have otherwise, and then of course you'll have the little fellow to remember me by. Some day soon, you'll meet a fine Irish lad who'll be only too glad to get a pretty Kitty with a house of her own and five hundred dollars in the bank."

Still smiling, he laid the envelope on the kitchen table and then, surprising even himself, he stepped close to her and kissed her gently on the forehead.

"Good luck, Kitty girl."

He reached for his still damp coat on the chair, picked up the white beaver hat, and walked through the little sitting room to the front door. With his hand on the door, he remembered something and reached in his pocket for the key, which he tossed lightly on the table in the hall. He saw her, standing in the kitchen and still staring at him as though she could not believe that what was happening was a reality. The latch on the front door lifted easily and the door swung open. Strange that he would not be coming here again. The rush of fresh damp air took away the hearty smell of stew which had filled the house. Kitty was a good cook—he would miss her meals.

The door closed behind him and he pulled the collar of his coat up around his neck to keep out the rain. It had been easier than he thought. Kitty was a sensible girl. He'd been right in choosing her, and certainly he'd done handsomely by her. Well, that episode was closed.

A closed hack passed him at the corner and he hailed it. No use in wasting any more time. He was anxious to get back to his room. There was still some packing to do before he went to bed. He must be up early tomorrow. Ah! Tomorrow! Surely it was going to be the most important day of his life. But he could hire the porter to do the packing and he needed something to remove the image of Kitty, mutely staring at him beside the kitchen stove. He rapped on the little sliding door in the front of the hack and the door slid open. The coachman spoke.

"Where to now, young gentleman?"

"Take me to Mother Carey's in Boston," Armes said.

The coachman clucked enviously.

"Best girls in the city, she has. Wishin' I was a young blood like you. Sure wishin' it, I am."

Armes sank back on the aromatic cushions and smiled. He knew that the desires of his own hot young blood would be soon satisfied—professionally. The whole thing had turned out far easier than he had expected and he was due for a little reward for all his trouble.

2

THE evening at Mother Carey's had been both successful and entertaining. Even the nameless girl had enjoyed it, and her evident appreciation caused Armes to take particular pains to please her. But he had quitted her after an hour, and had already forgotten her face when he closed Mother Carey's door, to return and spend his last night in Massachusetts Hall. Now on this new day—this all-important day

16

—he had left Harvard, Cambridge, and Kitty forever. His furniture and belongings were sent to Mr. Frothingham's Beacon Street house by a hired dray, and he took a hack to Mr. Frothingham's office.

After he had paid the hack driver, he stopped for a moment on the narrow brick sidewalk that ran along Boston's School Street before he entered Mr. Frothingham's office. He felt in need of that extra moment. He needed it to anticipate the full joy of the occasion; to realize it in its entirety and to draw the fullest measure of happiness from it. That moment was necessary to reassure him that at long last the day and the month of that anticipated year of 1791 had finally arrived, and he was his own master. Today he was *Mister* Armes Holbrook, twenty-one years of age, and he was standing on the threshold of a new life. This new life was to be entirely his own, lived in any manner he might want, free at last of the restricting guidance of his guardian; free of all the petty discipline he had been compelled to suffer under his father's trustee. Truly it was a wonderful feeling. From now on he would be free to live, free to love, free to shake the gray mud of Boston from his boots, as he damned well intended to do.

He looked down at his varnished boots on the dull granite step, stamped his feet to free their soles of the clinging mud. It seemed to make him feel better. It was as though he were being liberated from the propriety and Puritanism which had always enveloped him. Despite his stamping, a little mud remained on the polished leather, so he leaned over and flicked it off with a linen handkerchief. He must be absolutely free of it—this clammy Boston grayness. As he straightened up, his eyes were level for a moment with the polished brass sign, across which a row of letters marched most sedately. It read "Jno. Frothingham, Att'y at law." How like Mr. Frothingham to economize even on the letters of his name! *John* was only one letter more than the abbreviated *Jno.*, but it had meant one less letter to engrave —one more shilling saved.

One hand reached up for the brass ball which dangled on a bell chain beside the door. When he pulled it, he could hear a bell tinkle somewhere in the building. It was a very genteel bell—a most undisturbing bell. In fact, it sounded old and tired, like Mr. Frothingham himself, with his cautious nods and his "Now, Armes, I do not know if I would exactly advise that." But the sound, feeble though it was,

17

did produce results. The door opened slowly, only enough to disclose a pallid face topped by a wisp of white hair and attached to a figure clad in an indeterminate shade of worn homespun. The watery blue eyes lighted up when they recognized Armes and the door opened wide. The figure bowed like an automaton.

"Mr. Holbrook, sir." He bobbed again. "Won't you come in?"

Armes entered. It seemed even damper and chillier inside than it had been outside. The man minced down the hall and up a flight of uncarpeted stairs, with Armes following him. On the second floor they passed opened doors which showed a line of rust-suited clerks bent over high desks, scraping away at ledgers with scratching quills. Then up another flight of uncarpeted stairs and down another hall at the end of which the man opened a door and motioned Armes inside. He walked in and faced Mr. Frothingham across a long green baize-covered table. Without rising, the old man looked up and smiled a frigid greeting, while his long tapering fingers nervously stroked a portfolio of worn red morocco. Although his smile was scarcely inviting, there was a hint of warmth in his voice.

"Armes, my dear boy! So nice to see you, and"—he glanced at the tall clock in the corner—"only fifteen minutes late for a wonder. It's exactly a quarter past nine."

As if to corroborate his words, the clock wheezed and whirred inside, then slowly struck the quarter chimes. Mr. Frothingham motioned to a tall-backed Chippendale chair facing him across the table. Though Armes sat down gingerly, the thin legs creaked under his weight. He leaned his arms on the table and the table also groaned.

Mr. Frothingham produced a pair of steel-rimmed spectacles from a drawer of the table, polished them meticulously with a handkerchief, and then adjusted them carefully over his ears and straightened them on the high bridge of his nose. He pursed his lips and regarded the young man in front of him.

"What a big fellow you are, Armes! I suppose I should call you a man today." His lips lifted at the corners sufficiently to indicate a smile. "Take after your mother's folks, you do. The Winslows were all big men—all over six feet— and they were all dark like you. 'The Black Winslows,' we used to call them. You're more Winslow than Holbrook, Armes. Unfortunate, because the Winslows were wild ones.

18

But, you've got Holbrook blood in you, too, and they were settled folk, contented to sit in their counting rooms and invest their money to see if they couldn't double it in six months. They usually did"—he really smiled this time—"and demned lucky for you they did, boy. I'm about to turn over a sizable estate to you today. You're going to be a rich man, Armes, not just rich but very rich, and I hope you'll know how to handle great wealth. All this money will be a big responsibility."

Armes grinned back at him. "At least I've had plenty of advice from you, Mr. Frothingham—"

"None of which you ever took very willingly."

"But some of it must have penetrated this thick skull of mine."

"Let's hope so," the old man sighed. "And now . . ." He opened the leather portfolio. "It's all here, to the last penny, since the day your father and mother died over ten years ago and left you an orphan."

Armes sat there, facing the man who had played such an important part in guiding his life. How well he could visualize the boy he used to be, sitting in this same chair, straight and uncomfortable in his sober gray suit with the steel buttons, looking across the same table at the same man who had changed so little over the years. He remembered how often he had begged and pleaded for something which, at the moment, had seemed of paramount importance to him. It might have been a catboat to sail at Scituate, a visit to a school friend's home in Maine, or a fishing trip to Cape Cod. The more he pleaded, the more judiciously Mr. Frothingham would shake his head in refusal. Now, however, he was able to feel a modicum of gratitude toward the old man. Surely some of his schemes had been harebrained and rattleheaded, and Armes could see that Mr. Frothingham had used patience and wisdom in treating the headstrong and impetuous boy he had been. In a sudden gesture of gratitude he reached across the table and took the slender, blue-veined hand in his own. The white skin looked almost transparent in contrast to the smooth olive of his own, and the hand itself looked frail as it lay inert in his powerful fingers.

"You've been good to me, Mr. Frothingham, and I appreciate it. Yes, I do. Both you and Mrs. Frothingham! Why, Aunt Martha has been the only mother I can remember much about, and you, Mr. Frothingham, you've been a father to me."

The old man fumbled in his sleeve for his handkerchief and blew his nose. He managed to wipe his eyes at the same time. For a moment he was silent as he regarded the young man across the table from him.

He saw a big man, for Armes Holbrook was a big fellow —"a strappin' big fellow," they called men of his size in New England. Despite his obvious breeding and gentility there was something of the peasant about him—a certain thickness of hands and a sensuality of features. The black curls crept down a little too low over the forehead, lowering the line of the brow, and Mr. Frothingham firmly believed that a pale high brow denoted intelligence. Yet he had to admit that Armes was intelligent. The same black curls grew vigorously back from the temples to the crown of his head, and his hair looked so alive one could almost see it growing in curling tendrils, so unruly that it was impossible to restrain it with comb or brush. The clear, white light from the windows scattered blue highlights across it.

Armes' thick black brows curved upward abruptly from his nose, then slanted down in a straight line toward his ears. His nose was scarcely patrician, for it was short and a little too flat with nostrils that were just a trifle too wide. The lips were too wide also; too red and far, far too sensual. But . . . the chin was strong, and Mr. Frothingham could trace the dark line of the beard from one temple to the other in spite of the fact that Armes had so recently shaven. The ears were small, rather pointed, and close to his head, rising above the white stock that set off the deep tone of his skin. The buttons of his taffeta waistcoat strained over his chest, and caught in the top button of his shirt was a tendril of black hair, like a little vine that was struggling to grow out toward the light and refused to be confined.

Mr. Frothingham shook his head with impatience and abandoned his inventory of the man in front of him. He was not a man given to sentimental daydreams. Therefore he got down to business, opening the red leather portfolio.

"Now here, Armes, is a strict accounting of your estate," he began. "I'm glad to say that in the ten years I have handled your father's business, everything has showed much progress. Here's a complete list of your investments. As you will see by the first item, there is a sum of $12,852.37 in ready cash in Mr. Armitage's counting house. And the second item shows £20,000 invested with Messrs. Masterson of Liverpool—a most worthy company."

"Which was formerly engaged in the slave trade."

"Formerly, yes formerly." Mr. Frothingham cleared his throat. "But a good investment, nevertheless," he added sharply.

Armes reached impatiently across the table for the paper, took it from Mr. Frothingham's hands, and started to read the long list.

"Fifty thousand, five hundred dollars in bonds of the United States of America."

"Safe and sure, my lad."

"Eighty thousand, two hundred and fifty-four dollars in farm mortgages."

"All at six per centum."

"Twenty thousand dollars invested in Childer's Rope Walk."

"A growing concern in Gloucester."

"Four hundred shares of stock in Harper Brothers."

"An excellent importing house here in Boston."

Armes read several other items, then stopped abruptly and considered one in particular.

He read it slowly, hesitating between the words.

"Sans Souci Plantation in Saint Domingue. A loss of three thousand francs last year."

Mr. Frothingham sighed. "And that, boy, is the only poor investment we have. Sell it! Get rid of it! Take whatever you can get for it! I should have sold it myself for you. It used to make money—big money. Your father took it over as a debt from Monsieur Patenaud of St. Domingue. Some matter of slaves which the man owed for, I believe. Then Patenaud died and your father operated it *in absentia*. He got it cheap. As I say, it paid off well until the last few years. Then it started to fall off. Can't seem to get a good manager. These French—can't depend on them."

Armes regarded the item carefully. The tip of his tongue circled his lips and he considered the words—Though they were inscribed with black ink on white paper, to him they were illuminated in color. His finger touched them as though trying to pin them down on the paper to keep them from flying away.

"I didn't know I had a plantation in St. Domingue." He spoke more to himself than to Mr. Frothingham.

"Well, well, let's not bother about that. Now about the stock in the Hawthorne Mills . . ."

Armes held up his hand. He didn't want to hear about

the Hawthorne Mills. He gazed past Mr. Frothingham, out through the small-paned window behind the lawyer's gray head. Over the tops of the buildings on Washington Street, he could see a far-off cluster of masts down in the harbor. They beckoned to him and he felt an overwhelming desire to see them at closer range—the masts and the stout ships that supported them. They called to him to leave this red-brick, gray-granite stability of Boston. In response to their skyward-pointing fingers, he half rose in his chair, then forced his mind back into the little office; back to Mr. Frothingham; back to the paper he held in his hand.

"Now, the Hawthorne Mills . . ." Mr. Frothingham had no desire to waste time. "They turned out to be an excellent investment. Paid almost twelve per centum last year."

Armes interrupted him. "Tell me more about this Sans Souci Plantation," he said eagerly.

Mr. Frothingham took a long breath, pushed his spectacles down on his nose, and glared across them at Armes.

"Not much I know about the place. Raises sugar. Fairly decent house, I understand, and all furnished. Used to have a good man for a manager; showed a profit every year; kept the place in good condition. Hard on the slaves, I heard, but a good businessman. Guess he made enough to go back to France. Left anyway, and since then we've had two or three managers—but not one of them a demned bit of good. Fellow there now by the name of Fabre. He's always writing whining letters, making excuses. Says the slaves are deserting and dying and repairs have to be made." He pushed his glasses back up. "That's that. Sell the demned thing. Just an expense. Get rid of it."

The masts still beckoned through the window to Armes. This time he got up out of his chair and walked over to the window. He pointed through it, over the rooftops.

"See those ships, Mr. Frothingham?"

The old man shifted his weight in his chair and nodded. He'd been looking at the far-off masts most of his life without seeing them. He nodded again, dismissing the matter. But Armes was not to be dismissed so easily.

"Well, maybe one of those ships is going to leave Boston tomorrow, Mr. Frothingham," Armes said excitedly. "That very mast which we see anchored now at "T" Wharf here in Boston will be heading out across the Atlantic. Or maybe it will be heading south, calling at Rio, Havana, or Panama. In a week or two weeks or three weeks, it will be

22

anchored again, that same mast, only then it will not be in Boston. It will be somewhere where a tropic sun shines hotly down on it. It will be where the air smells differently—smells of coffee or sugar or spices. Colored birds will come and roost in it and at night different stars will shine down on it. Soft winds will play about it and summer rains fall on it. But you, Mr. Forthingham, you'll be sitting right here in this same office, right in that same chair."

"Thank God for that, Armes," sighed the old man, and he nodded his head in grateful assent.

"But I won't be here, Mr. Frothingham. I'm going on that ship. I'll feel the tropic sun on my face. I'll know that smell of coffee or rum or spices in my nostrils. I'll feel that soft breeze—"

"And have colored birds roosting in your hair." Mr. Frothingham harrumphed grimly and scowled. "No, Armes, I do not like the idea. In fact, I forbid it."

Armes walked back to the table and faced his guardian again. This time he did not sit down but spread both hands on the edge of the table and leaned across it.

"Forbid and be damned!" He straightened up and allowed a trace of a smile to curve his lips. "For the first time in my life I can say that to you. There always has to be a first time, you know."

Mr. Frothingham started to speak, but Armes silenced him with a wave of his hand. "Yes, I'm going to take one of those ships—one that is heading for St. Domingue, and I'm going to see that plantation at least once before I sell it. Maybe I'll stay there a while. Maybe I'll enjoy having a host of niggers to wait on me—a hundred black slaves to do my bidding. Yes, maybe I'll stay a while and then I'll probably sell it and come back to Boston. Then, when I've got it out of my system, I'll take a little office down the hall from you and I'll get me a big mahogany table just like yours. I'll sit behind it day after day and figure out how to make two shillings grow where there was only one before. But until that time, Mr. Frothingham, I'm going to live. And something tells me I can really *live* in St. Domingue."

Mr. Frothingham assumed his usual frown of disapproval, but as he looked up at the eager young face above him, the frown turned into a very small smile. Slowly, as though unaccustomed to such a process, the smile broadened. He stood up and walked toward the door, opened it, and offered his hand to Armes.

"You know, my boy," he whispered, looking up and down the hall to make sure that nobody was eavesdropping, "You know, I've always wondered what those mulatto wenches look like myself!"

3

THE sea, which had beckoned to him so alluringly, turned out to be a most unkind mistress to Armes. She did not reciprocate his affection. For three days and nights after he sailed from Boston, the capricious Atlantic did everything in her power to make life unbearable for him. He was seasick —utterly, violently, hopelessly, and most nastily seasick. The narrow berth cramped his wide shoulders; his feet dangled helplessly over the foot; his pillow seemed stuffed with gravel; and the pale green light which filtered through his porthole only made the cell-like cabin more confining and more unpleasant.

During the first day, the violent pitching and tossing of the ship frightened him, although Armes did not easily frighten. At first he had sufficient strength to lean over the edge of the bunk and vomit in the white chamber pot while holding its one handle. But, as his sickness increased, all strength vanished, and he cared not if he retched in his bunk and remained in his own sour stinking vomit. What difference did it make? He was certain that the ominous groans and creaking mutterings of the ship's timbers presaged the end of both the ship and himself. All he could do was stare, with glazed eyes, at the swaying lantern which oscillated from the ceiling of his cabin, listening to the screaming of the wind in the rigging, punctuated by the battering-ram crash of his chests and boxes as they slid across the floor and pounded against the thin board walls. By the third day he had given up hope entirely and had only one overwhelming desire—that the ship would sink to the bottom and take him along with it.

At times he was conscious that someone entered his room to change the stinking sheets, adjust the scratchy blankets, smooth the rock-like surface of the pillow, and wipe the encrusted puke from his face with a damp cloth, but who it might be or if there really were anyone at all, he could not be entirely sure. He only knew that in his absolute misery he wanted to die. Either that or get his feet planted firmly once again on land—something that did not sway, rock, or tremble.

Somewhere in his consciousness there was a half-formed irritation caused by frequent loud quarrels, plainly heard through the thin boards of his cabin wall. He had a recollection of ugly words but he was unable to place their origin, and in his illness he could not concentrate on translating the vituperative words, which he knew must be French. The frequency of these quarrels and their very bitterness disturbed him as much as did the smell of food cooking in the nearby galley and the clatter of knives and forks in the dining salon outside his cabin door.

Then, sometime during the third night, he fell asleep, oblivious to the shouting, screaming, and sobbing which was going on next door. At first he slept fitfully, waking often, but little by little the mattress grew softer, the pillow more yielding, the blankets less scratchy, and the narrow berth wider and more comfortable. He slept with his huge body curled in an embryonic curve, his face toward the wall. When he finally awoke, he was amazed at the great quiet like a vast expanse of peace, coupled with the blessed stability of the cabin. Instead of the limpid sea-green light from the porthole, he could see sunshine, streaking the floor with white light.

The heavy blankets were too warm on his body and he threw them off, welcoming the warm air that came in through the porthole and caressed his sweaty skin. Contentedly now, his hands roamed his body, encountering for the first time in days the hard tumescence of maleness which had been so conspicuously absent. With his hands' discovery came a resurgence of desire and he lay back on his pillow, his eyes closed and his mind given over to a voluptuous fantasy, which was interrupted by the sound of the door opening. He did not have time to clutch the protecting blanket around his nakedness, and the glistening island of white teeth in a black face gave him only a momentary glimpse of the intruder before the door was hastily closed again. After a long second, there came a knock. Armes grasped the blanket and pulled it up to his chin before calling out, "Come in." The door opened and the same black face appeared, now ashamedly lowered.

"I'm Jupiter." The white teeth grinned again and Armes

25

recognized the Negro boy who had carried his boxes on board in Boston.

"A visitation from the Immortal Gods, no less." Armes grinned back. "Well, come in, Jupiter. Do you by any chance have a Juno with you? I could use her just now."

"I don't have any Juno, Master Holbrook sir. Sure wish I did, though. I'd bring her in to you, because I guess you could use her. We don't have any wenches on this ship."

"Should have thought of that before I left Boston."

"Yes sir, Master Holbrook sir."

"And who are you, Jupiter?"

"I'm the captain's boy, Master Holbrook sir. He bought me in the Cap, last time he was in St. Domingue. This is the first time I've been back to St. Domingue for five years. I belongs to the captain, but I'm your steward."

Armes saw a neat-looking boy, probably around seventeen, prune-black, with a glossy sheen to his skin. His head was covered with a wiry cap of black wool, his lips were broad and purple, his nose wide with two enormous nostrils, but the eyes, large, brown and gentle, were kind and trusting.

"You've been very sick, Master Holbrook sir. Yes sir, very sick."

Armes remembered the gentle ministrations, the cool cloths on his face, the straightened sheets.

"So you're the one who's been taking care of me? I wasn't dreaming after all."

"Tried to, Master Holbrook, sir, but you're a very powerful man. Yes sir, very powerful. Tried to lift you to make your bed, but couldn't. If I could've, I'd have made your bed better."

"Did the best you could. Thank you, Jupiter."

"They call me Jupe, mostly, Master Holbrook sir. I've never seen anyone as seasick as you were. I sure thought you'd bust a gut, the way you were puking. You must've puked everything in you up. You must be awfully empty.

"That about describes how I'm feeling, Jupe." Armes ran his hand over his belly, sensing the emptiness that he had not been entirely aware of.

"Then you'd better eat something, because you've got a big hole to fill up. How about having some food now? Cook's got something good today."

Armes shuddered at the word *food*. Strangely enough, however, it didn't seem to nauseate him anymore. Suddenly he

26

realized he was hungry—hungrier than he had ever been before. And he was dirty. His fingers came out from under the blanket and touched the three-day growth of beard. He needed a bath, he needed a shave, he needed food, and he needed a woman—but where would he find her? He felt sure he could satisfy his needs for the first three, but he was uncertain about the latter, even though it seemed the most important.

"You're a smart boy, Jupiter." Armes regarded the boy. "And thank you for taking care of me. I guess you're right, food is something I need; but I need something else, too—a bath and a shave. How do I go about getting them in this little two-by-four?"

"Now, that's easy, Master Holbrook, sir. First off, I'll get things organized. I'll go to the galley and get that lazy goddam cook bastard to put on a pot of coffee for you, sir." He spread his hands in an expressive gesture. "Real coffee from St. Domingue! Best you ever tasted. Then, some nice *pain-rôti,* a couple of eggs, and a nice slice of ham. How's that soun'?"

"Fine! And the bath?"

"That's easy too, Master Holbrook sir. While that goddam cook's getting your breakfast, I'll drop a bucket over the side of the ship, haul up some sea water, and heat it up for you. I'll bring down a wooden tub for you to scrooch down in. "Can't get all of you in at once," he giggled, "but enough of you. Then I'll scrub your back and leave you sitting there while I go to fetch your breakfast. When I get back, you'll be all done soaping yourself and I'll pour a little bucket of fresh water over you to wash the salt off. How's that?"

Armes stretched out in his bunk and regarded the boy, marveling at his willingness and cheerfulness.

"Sounds practically perfect, Jupiter, my lad. Let's get organized."

Jupiter had his fingers on the door latch and was about to open the door when it was wrenched out of his hands. He stumbled backward a step or two, then lurched forward, nearly falling into the arms of the man who stood in the doorway.

"Look out, you goddamned nigger!" The words were harsh and brutal, but even more brutal was the slash across the cheek which the intruder gave Jupiter. "Get out, you stinking nigger! Get out!"

Jupiter ducked under his arms and slid out the door.

Armes jumped up from the bed, forgetting in his sudden anger to clutch the blanket around him. His eyes were blazing as he groped for words. Finally they came in a torrent.

"Who the hell are you?" he demanded. "What do you mean by barging into my cabin without knocking and what do you mean by hitting that poor boy in the face? It wasn't his fault. Had you possessed the simple decency to knock, it would not have happened. Now, get out of here yourself, whoever you are!"

The man in the doorway did not move for a moment, but carefully inventoried Armes. Without replying, he stepped inside the cabin and closed the door softly behind him. In direct opposition to Armes' anger, he smiled—a most engaging smile which completely obliterated his annoyance of the moment before. His English was slow, halting, and quite heavily accented, but entirely correct.

"A thousand pardons, Monsieur Holbrook. I happen to be your neighbor—there!" He pointed to the wall behind Armes' bunk. "The walls are so thin we are denied much privacy, and I could not help but hear from your conversation with that black imp, Jupiter, that you were feeling better. So, I came to pay my respects and to say that I shall be happy to make your acquaintance. Permit me to introduce myself."

Armes did not reply, but sat down on the bunk and drew the blanket around him. Despite the now-engaging smile of the other he was still angry, but he listened as the young man continued.

"I am the Vicomte de St. Gabriel, *ci-devant*. For the last two years, I have had no very definite idea of just who I am but as I possess no other name, I must needs stick to the one I had before the Revolution—the one in France, I mean." His smile broadened. He seemed to have lost all trace of anger or annoyance. It was as though the little incident with Jupiter had never happened. He advanced a couple of steps until he stood directly in front of Armes. His air of ingenuousness was intended to charm and it partly succeeded. Armes stifled his anger and looked up at him. There was such an air of complete self-possession about the young Vicomte with his thin face now so disarmingly pleasant, his eyes so brimming with good humor, that Armes extended his hand reluctantly.

The Vicomte took it and shook it heartily.

28

"Sometimes they say a poor beginning makes a good ending. I hope it augurs well for our friendship."

Armes freed his hand from the overlong clasp.

"You seem to know my name," he said, "but I'll introduce myself anyway. I am Armes Holbrook of Boston, bound for Cap François."

"Exactly where my wife and I are going."

"You're a fortunate man to have your wife with you." Armes remembered his recently interrupted fantasy.

The Vicomte shrugged his shoulders with a look of annoyance. "Perhaps." He spoke without enthusiasm. Then his face brightened. "It will be nice to have your company on this voyage, Monsieur Holbrook. You and my wife and I are the only three passengers on board."

"Thank you, Vicomte."

"How about René? The Vicomte is a rather empty title just now."

"Very well, if you will return the compliment by calling me Armes."

"*Certainement!* And by the way, Armes, do you speak French? My English is not very good."

"I studied it four years at Harvard," Armes replied, "and I spent two summers with a French family in Quebec. It's rather rusty and you will have to discount the New England accent, but the words will all be there."

"*Enchanté de faire votre connaissance.*"

"*Et vous même.*"

The Vicomte snapped his fingers, then spread out both hands in an all-embracing gesture.

"How happy I am to have a man of my own age on board. Our good captain is elderly and so are most of the other officers."

Armes did not immediately respond to the Vicomte's enthusiasm. His ingrained New England reserve, no matter how much he wished to deny it, cautioned him against too immediate a friendship or too immediate an acceptance of one. Yet, as he observed the Vicomte, he saw that the fellow was young, cultured, and entertaining. He was also good-looking with his patrician face, narrow green eyes, and slender body like a fencing master. As they were on ship together and would, of necessity, be seeing much of each other during the voyage, it would be only politic to accept the proffered friendship. Yes . . . but accept it with reservations. Armes offered his friendship with his hand, and this time he shook the

29

Vicomte's hand wholeheartedly. He had no sooner finished when there was a rap on the door, which signaled Jupiter's re-entry.

There was no trace of resentment on the boy's face as he wheeled in the wooden tub. There was, however, a streak of dull purple across his cheek. He smiled apologetically at the Vicomte, and as he leaned over to pour the hot water into the tub, René patted the boy's kinky hair.

"Jupiter's a good boy." His pat became a playful tweaking of the boy's ears. "They're like children, these niggers. Always keep the upper hand with them. Don't let them get away with anything." He pulled the crouching boy over to him, and let his hand wander down the neck and under his shirt.

Jupiter suffered the attentions silently, and Armes could see that he had entirely forgotten the punishment. But as René released him and he resumed pouring water into the tub, Armes observed that the black hands were trembling.

"You angry with me, Jupiter?" René asked.

"No sir, Master René sir. You can slap me again if you want to."

"Slap you goddam good and hard if you don't watch out and mind your manners, and if slapping doesn't do it, I'll have the captain string you up. A taste of the cat on your back will teach you."

"Yes sir, Master René sir, only don't tell the captain. Don't want that cat clawing at my back."

René winked at Armes, as though informing him that he should adopt the same treatment with Jupiter.

"And now—" René opened the door—"a pleasant bath and an appetizing breakfast, *mon ami,* after which I shall anticipate the pleasure of seeing you on deck."

"Merci." Armes tested the heat of the water in the tub with his fingers, and as he straightened up he met René's eyes. "And I shall be happy to meet the Vicomtesse."

René hesitated with his hand on the door latch. The smile disappeared and he looked at Armes as though he wondered how much Armes might have heard through the thin partition.

"A thousand regrets, *mon ami,* but the Vicomtesse is indisposed. A touch of *mal de mer* such as has visited you." He closed the door behind him.

Armes dropped his blanket to the floor and stepped into the tub. At Jupiter's urging, he squatted there, finding the water just the right temperature. Jupe soaped his back vigor-

ously, and the warm water and the scrubbing seemed to put
new life into his pores. As the accumulation of dirt disappeared from his body in the voluptuous caress of the warm
water, Armes' thoughts returned to the fantasies which Jupe
had interrupted when he had opened the door so precipitately,
and these thoughts led him to the Vicomtesse next door. Even
if there was only one woman on board, it would be pleasant
at least to talk to her. As René's wife, she must be young,
and from Armes' knowledge of young women, there was
always a chance for a flirtation, serious or otherwise. At
least it would be amusing, certainly entertaining and . . . it
might lead to something else. It had before.

"What does the Vicomtesse look like?" he inquired of
Jupiter.

"I've never seen that woman, Master Holbrook sir. I
haven't seen hide nor hair of her since she came on board
in Boston."

"Well, what did she look like then?"

"Didn't see her then, either. She came on with something
white wrapped around her head, and she hasn't been out of
her cabin since. I haven't been in either. I take her tray to
the door and Master René takes it in." He gently prodded
Armes. "If you'll stand up now, Master Holbrook sir, I'll
wash your legs."

Armes stood up in the tub, balancing himself with his
hand on Jupe's head.

"You like the Vicomte, Jupe?"

It took the boy a minute to answer.

"Sure, Master Holbrook sir. Master René's a fine man."

Armes leaned down to look into the boy's face.

"You're a goddam liar, Jupe. You hate his guts. If you
could have managed it, you would have killed him this
morning when he struck you."

"You're a white man, Master Holbrook sir. If you say so,
I sure do hate him." The strong hands which were scrubbing
Armes' legs suddenly lost their vigor and Jupe sank down on
his haunches. There were tears in his eyes. He looked up at
Armes.

"You're a good man, Master Holbrook sir. I like you. I'd
like to be your slave, I would."

All his life Armes had heard of slaves, but never before
had he come in contact with one. This boy kneeling before
him was a slave, a piece of property, a chattel. Armes suddenly realized what slavery meant. Dripping water onto the

31

floor, he stepped out of the tub and walked the few steps to the wardrobe. He opened it, took a wallet out of his trousers pocket and brought forth two shiny silver shillings.

"When we get to Cap François, Jupe, you go and buy yourself something with this."

The two silver coins gleamed in Jupe's wet pink palm. He was overcome by Armes' kindness and quite unable to speak. He reached for one of Armes' hands and pressed his lips against it.

"Thank you, Master Holbrook sir. Thank you."

4

SHIPBOARD days pass quickly and shipboard acquaintances ripen quickly, if not always into real friendship at least into a sort of interdependence. Nowhere else on earth can a man get to know his fellow man more thoroughly and in a shorter time than on board ship. On that small island of life, adrift in the vastness of the ocean, isolated from all the rest of the world, human companionship becomes a far greater necessity than on shore. Certainly Armes needed companionship, and he had no other choice but the debonair René. However, as the days passed, Armes forgot his initial dislike of the young Frenchman.

René turned out to be good company. He was an engaging rogue with a sharp mind and an inexhaustible fund of clever, prurient anecdotes which were entertaining and many of which Armes was inclined to believe despite himself. They were all amusing and most of them were concerned with the multitude of enemies René had vanquished with his sword or the multitude of women he had satisfied. René's liking for Armes was apparent, and in turn Armes began to like him. At least it was better than being alone.

They were together constantly. In the morning, often before Armes was awake, René tapped on his door, and as time went on, René spent more of his waking hours in Armes' cabin than he did in his own. There was always some reason why the Vicomtesse could not appear. She was seasick—she was ill—she had a headache—she had not slept well the night before. The repetition of René's excuses caused them to grow thin and lose their credibility. Armes knew that René was lying, but with a new England respect for other people's privacy he did not pry. He realized that there was some definite reason why the Vicomtesse never appeared at meals or on deck. So, if René were lying, as Armes was sure he was, it was René's own business, and Armes had to admit that René lied with charm.

Nevertheless Armes thought of the woman often even though he had never seen her. He was curious about her, more especially as he was a forced eavesdropper on the nightly quarrels which seeped through the thin partition. He heard the woman sobbing frequently as an aftermath of René's shouts of anger and scurrilous words. Sometimes there was self-abasement and pleading on her part. At other times, she expressed her opinion of René in words as loud if not as obscene as his. Several times Armes heard the abrupt crack of a vigorous slap, always followed by a strangled weeping. Then gradually the weeping would die away and the mechanical sounds of lovemaking would begin, interspersed with René's words and the woman's moans, all so close—so very close—that Armes felt he was sharing the same bed. Then, after René's quick gasp and his sudden expulsion of breath there would be nothing but quiet whimpering until Armes heard René settle himself in the upper berth. After this Armes would seek his own relief and eventually sleep, but he was conscious that the woman did not sleep because whenever he awoke during the night he could hear the restless sounds of her wakefulness.

At first he blamed the woman, cursing her for a weak and frigid hypochondriac who was never willing to comply with her husband's demands but, after listening night after night to René's obscenities and brutalities, Armes came to pity her and blame René. He longed to rip away one of the boards from the partition and thrust his hand through to comfort her. Instead he slept, wanting her.

Regardless of the night before, René would appear each morning at Armes' door, freshly shaven, with the skin of his lean face shining from the razor, his linen sharply white, and his blue-black hair smooth and unruffled. Armes would stifle his anger, engendered the night before, and together they would go out into the salon and devour huge breakfasts. A secluded spot on the stern, behind the carpenter's shop, had become their retreat, and here they would strip to the waist and soak up the hot sun on their already bronzed skin. Later they might wrestle, or lift heavy weights in competition with

33

each other, their muscles bulging in the sun and the sweat pearling the hair on their bodies. Such contests always went to Armes, as René's whiplash body could not compete with the huge chunks of muscle which enabled Armes to lift an anvil high over his head with one hand. But when one day René produced a pair of foils and started to teach Armes the art of fencing, René was the master. His lithe quickness enabled him to spin around Armes like a fox terrier around a St. Bernard and, although Armes became somewhat adept, he was no competitor for René.

Sometimes they would climb aloft into the rigging and watch the prow of the ship churn the deep blue of the Gulf Stream into white foam. At other times, they would spread a blanket on the deck and lie in the sun, talking about their past and confiding their hopes for the future. René was always the voluble one. Armes did more listening than talking.

"My mother was a Condé," René stated matter-of-factly, as though it were an everyday matter, "a princess in her own right."

Armes listened, as René stretched his arms behind his head, closing his eyes against the brilliance of the sun.

"My mother was a favorite of the Queen—she and the Princesse de Lamballe. So, my parents were always at court and I was brought up at Versailles. *Hélas!* Certain business on my father's estates in Normandie needed his attention and my mother and I accompanied him to the château. While we were there, the Bastille was stormed."

"And the Revolution began." Armes turned on his side to face René.

"Mais oui! The Revolution began and my life nearly ended." René paused and Armes could see the young man's lips tremble. It was the first time he had ever seen the volatile Frenchman display any unhappiness.

"Don't talk about it if it saddens you."

"But I want to talk about it to you," René insisted. "When the news of the fall of the Bastille reached our little village, the peasants marched on the château. The *intendant* who was in authority during my father's absence had a hobby of crucifying peasants on the barn doors and they were tired of seeing their people spread-eagled to die, so they were out for his blood. Their *sortie* netted even bigger game than the *intendant*, for they found my father and mother too. Well, to even things up they nailed the *intendant* and his wife and my mother and father up on the barn doors. I saw them."

34

Armes let his big hand rest on René's shoulder in a gesture of sympathy. "And you?" he asked.

"My *valet de chambre,* a boy a few years older than I, was madly in love with me. He was the son of the blacksmith in the village and he and his father saved me. They hid me in the smokehouse at the château among the hams, and then later helped me to escape to Holland. I owe my life to them."

"I too am an orphan," Armes said. "I've never known what it is like to have parents. I was brought up by a guardian and as far as I know I have no relatives in the world."

"Do not regret, *mon cher ami."* René opened his eyes and smiled. "Relatives can be a damned nuisance. They are always demanding money, coming around with some sort of pitiful story. That's what mine did, particularly after I married Athenée. They knew she was rich and they wanted me to support them. *Merde!* Support them? What Athenée has I shall use for myself. Take my advice, Armes, stay single. Although"—he winked at Armes—"I sometimes wonder what a man like you does on a long voyage like this. Certainly a wife is better than no woman at all."

Armes doubled up the fingers of his right hand into a fist and shook it at René, who winked at him.

"Not a very satisfactory solution. Use the nigger boy, Jupe. He's willing." He looked out of the corner of his eye to gauge Armes' reaction. "And adept, too."

Armes did not answer, although he had been aware of Jupe's willingness. He waited for René to continue, for he was anxious to find out something about the mysterious Athenée.

"There's never been any love lost between Athenée and me." René spat on the deck. "Her parents were planters in St. Domingue. But rich! *Mon Dieu,* so very rich for commoners. But like so many of the *bourgeoisie,* they were ardent royalists with a great reverence for titles. They were visiting in France when the Revolution broke out and left, but the old man had the good sense to transfer all his money into good, solid Dutch guilders. Finally they ended up in Hesse-Nassau, where I was."

"And what were you doing there?" Armes' question was more of a spur to further conversation than anything else.

"Oh, the old Grand Duchess was a cousin of my mother's. She permitted me to stay there out of charity. *Merde!* What charity! Three meals a day and an unheated room in the at-

35

tic, until one of her ladies invited me to share her featherbed which was warmer. *Mon Dieu!* How the old turkey's breath stank! But I was a beggar and I had no choice. Then, in some way, Athenée's parents wangled a presentation to the Grand Ducal Court. I heard about the gold that lined their *porte-monnaie* and immediately became interested in the daughter. I figured sleeping with her would not be quite as bad as it had been with the old Countess. At least she was young and the golden aura which surrounded her made her most attractive. She had no use for me, but the thought of marrying their daughter to a cousin of the Grand Duchess, even though he was nothing but a penniless *ci-devant* vicomte, was so much higher than her parents had ever dared aim that they took me as a son-in-law. And paid well for it, too! So here I am, saddled with her and she with me, and now we go to St. Domingue to revive the money-making power of her plantation, which is now mine."

Armes stood up and stretched himself. He knew little more about the Vicomtesse now than he had before, except that her parents had sold her into marriage. He wandered over to the rail and looked down at the churning water.

René followed him. "Looks like we're in the same boat, *mon ami,* and I do not mean that as a pun. You have a plantation and so have I. Neither of us has ever seen our property before. The only difference is that I'm saddled with Athenée and you're free. Not that it will make much difference to me. I've heard about these St. Domingue women."

"Apparently everyone has," Armes laughed. "Even my staid old guardian in Boston got a lecherous look in his eyes, just thinking about them. But I cannot see how a white man could be interested in a colored girl."

René lifted his hand and slapped Armes smartly on the back.

"Why not, *mon brave?*"

"Somehow the idea is repulsive to me, but by the time we reach the Cap I shall probably not care if she is black, white, green, or striped like a zebra, as long as she has that one certain something."

"You can have the striped ones, Armes. As for me, I intend to get myself a little cinnamon-colored wench within a day after I arrive. I've already seen one in France. A friend of my father's brought her back from St. Domingue." René closed his eyes. "Glorious, Armes, she was glorious! Skin the color of dark honey, hair in ripples of midnight. And when she looked at you"—he expelled his breath in a long erotic sigh—"*mon Dieu,* you got hot as hell, and wondered how that lush tan flesh would look spread out on a white sheet."

"Wait a minute, wait a minute!" Armes took René by the shoulders and shook him. "If you keep on like this, poor Jupe is going to suffer. Come! I'll race you to the crow's nest and if I win, you'll pay me a forfeit."

"Such as?" René looked up quickly, a question in his eyes.

"First let's see who wins." Armes made a leap for the rigging, pulling himself up hand over hand. René followed him, but Armes had the lead. He tumbled into the crow's nest seconds before René even got his hand on the edge. They were both panting. When René caught his breath, he looked up at Armes through his lashes.

"I must pay the forfeit," he grinned. "Will it be a hard one?"

"Very easy."

"Easy?" René smiled. Their faces were close together. The crow's nest, built for one man, hardly accommodated Armes' bulk and René's, too. René insinuated one leg between Armes' and pressed his body against Armes. His eyes regarded Armes expectantly.

"Yes, easy," Armes answered. "Introduce me to your wife."

René withdrew his leg and the color drained from his face. He bit his underlip in vexation and disappointment.

"You should have asked a bigger forfeit, *mon ami,* and it would have been granted. The one you did ask is altogether insignificant but, *hélas,* I doubt if I can grant it unless she's willing, and the bitch never will be."

5

IT had been an uneventful day—a flashing, blue-and-white day—with the deep blue of the Gulf Stream flecked with white foam and the blue sky dotted with fleecy white clouds which shadowed the white sails that billowed in the steady breeze. Armes and René had breakfasted together, then wrestled each other, and later, finding no particular topic of conversation which they had not already threshed out, they had idled at the rail, watching the water slip by. After lunch, with the languor of the Tropics already creeping upon them,

37

they had decided on a *siesta,* preparing themselves in advance for the custom of St. Domingue.

It was quiet in Armes' cabin. The sun-spattered patterns on the ceiling reflected the movement of the water through the open port. Jupiter turned down the white sheet of the bunk, helped Armes off with his sweaty clothes, and gathered them into a bundle. As he looked down at Armes, stretched out on the narrow bunk, he seemed to be waiting for some word from him. His broad grin invited Armes' acceptance of his willingness to be of further service, but the boy's black masculinity did not appeal to Armes, particularly not the musky scent of him. He dismissed Jupe, and almost before the door was closed behind the boy, Armes was asleep. When he awoke, the sun pattern had disappeared from the ceiling and violet shadows were already gathering in the corners of the cabin.

He stretched lazily, hating to come back to the world of reality and desiring once again the oblivion of sleep and the series of voluptuous fantasies which had drained his body and relaxed him. But now he was awake and the luxury of dreaming past, there was nothing left to do but ring for Jupiter to bring lights and dress himself for dinner, eat, try to find something to talk about with René, and eventually go to bed again. For the first time since he had left Boston, he wondered about Kitty and wished that he might walk into the little house in Cambridgeport. But no! The thought of Kitty's swollen body repelled him.

He turned over on his side, hoping that he could woo another respite from boredom by sleep, but it was useless. He had just decided to forego it as an impossibility when he caught the murmur of voices on the other side of the partition. Armes was quite willing to eavesdrop—it was something to do—and he strained his ears to hear the muted voices on the other side. The words were indistinct at first, for René and his wife were conversing in low whispers, quite cognizant that they might be overheard, but as they continued they raised their voices and their words came through the wall plainly.

"Did it ever occur to you, René, that I might hate you?" The woman's voice was low and well-modulated. It might have been a pleasant voice without the sharp edge of anger. Armes tried to visualize the woman who was speaking. What did she look like? Was she tall or short, blonde or brunette? Was she beautiful or ugly? At least her voice was pleasing.

"Hate me, Athenée?" There was a short laugh, and Armes could picture René's thin lips curling in mock amusement. "Hate me? Why not? I hate you! I even hate to look at you. Let's be honest—we hate each other. The devil himself threw us together and he seems bound to keep us that way. So let's go on hating each other. At least we have that much in common." Again Armes was able to picture René, probably standing there in front of her, arrogant, his feet wide apart, his hands on his slender hips and a mocking smile on his face.

René continued: "After all, my dear wife, you are now a vicomtesse and that is something you never thought you would be. That at least must be worth something to you."

"What?"

"How the hell should I know? At least your stupid father thought it might. And I'm much richer than I ever was before. As for you, my dear wife, you haven't a *sou* to your name. You're absolutely dependent on me. So, unless you wish to starve to death in St. Domingue, you'd better keep up our little bargain. But there is one thing I cannot understand."

"Just one thing, René?"

Armes could hear him laugh. "The one important thing at this moment."

"And that is why I fight against your sleeping with me?"

"How delicately you put it. I could say it more precisely and in fewer words. Come on! Look at me! You can see I do not intend to be put off any longer. At least you should be grateful for what you are getting for nothing. Princesses have paid me for it. Look at me, Athenée. Look at my perfection and then . . . take a look at yourself. Here!"

Something hit the floor with a thud and there was the sound of glass splintering, which was drowned out by a sob.

René's voice was heard above the sobbing.

"You should feel flattered, Athenée, yes, flattered that I should even look at you, much less think of bedding you. Not that I want you. You know damn well you can never satisfy me." René's voice dropped and Armes strained to listen. "But, this has been a long voyage and in spite of your stubbornness and obstinacy, I'm going to take you. You're better than nothing."

"You beast!" Athenée's sobs almost drowned her words.

"Why not? I'm a goat, a satyr, a bull, a stallion, anything you want to call me. But, as you can see, I need something

39

and you are the most convenient. It would be a generous gesture on your part if you made it pleasant for me. I might even be grateful to you."

Armes looked at his hands. They were trembling. He too had felt the strain of the long voyage, the enforced absence from the company of women, and the monotony of René's companionship. He lifted his shoulders from the bunk and started to get up. He had heard enough. To listen to more would be torture. Suddenly there was a low scream from the cabin next door.

"René, you wouldn't dare."

"Oh yes I would."

"Keep away from me. Keep away from me, René!"

It was quiet for a second, but for a second only. Then there was the unmistakable sound of the swish of a whip through the air, a sharp crack as it landed on flesh, then another and another and another. A stillness. There were no more screams.

Armes breathed deeply. His feet felt unsteady on the cool boards of the cabin floor, and there seemed to be no strength in his hands as he reached down for his trousers and drew them on. The creaking of the ropes and the rustlings in the bunk next door informed him of what was going on, and he could no longer stay in his cabin and listen. He had a longing for fresh air, for open spaces, for the motion of the waves beneath the bow of the boat. He wanted to saturate his body with the cleanliness of salt spray and evening air. Without waiting to put on his shirt, he hurried from his cabin up to the dark coolness of the deck.

The sun had just sunk beneath the sea, leaving clouds of red, purple and green which suffused the water with myriad colors. He was aware of a strange noise which grated on his ears—a noise which rose above the whistling of the wind in the ropes. It was a sound which he had not heard before on the ship, and when he looked up he saw the dark shapes of gulls flying about the masts, dipping down into the purple sea, and rising again in long slow parabolas. Gulls meant land and land meant St. Domingue and the end of the long voyage.

His appetite had fled and he had no desire to eat, particularly if he had to make conversation with René across the table. The episode in the cabin had confused his thoughts—confused them to such an extent that he did not know how long he stood there, following the ever-changing pattern of the gulls and the darkening water. He wanted something that was beyond food or drink. There was a strange vitality welling up in his body that demanded release. To conquer it he would have to run many miles on a road of hard-packed earth until he dropped from exhaustion or—his thoughts returned to the inevitable—have a woman. His hands gripped the rail tightly, clutching at the wood until the knuckles whitened, and the veins in his arms were choked and swollen with blood, as though by their very force they might expend this restless energy.

The tropic night fell suddenly and still he remained at the rail. He became aware of motion on the deck beside him, but he did not turn, as he did not want to talk to René. He was relieved when a gleam of white teeth in the darkness revealed the person to be Jupe.

"St. Domingue." The colored boy's voice was rich and low, vibrating with the joy of being near land. He pointed ahead. "Look, Master Holbrook sir, you can see it."

"Looks mighty black to me, Jupe." Somehow the boy's presence relaxed Armes.

"You're right, Master Holbrook sir. St. Domingue sure is mighty black. More goddam black than white."

Jupe uttered the high throaty laugh of the Negro and edged along the rail until he stood besides Armes, their elbows touching on the rail. The smooth warmth of the boy's flesh against his arm was welcome and stimulating, and Armes did not move away. His eyes strained in the darkness, but he could make out only a dim line of high horizon— sharp mountain peaks which were a deeper purple than the wine-colored sky.

"Tomorrow morning, Master Holbrook sir, we'll be in Cap François early. This here's our last night on the ship. You won't be needing Jupe anymore." He sidled closer to Armes and almost unconsciously Armes lifted one arm and let it rest around Jupe's neck. The boy snuggled up to him and Armes' hand slid down under the neckband of the opened shirt, gliding along the glabrous flesh. His fingers found the protuberance of a nipple and squeezed. He had quite forgotten that Jupe was a boy—the feeling of flesh under his fingers was strangely satisfying as he pulled Jupe closer.

"I like you, Master Holbrook sir. If you want, I'll come down to your cabin tonight." Suddenly Jupe pulled away, separating himself from Armes, only to lay a restraining hand on Armes' shoulder.

"Sh-h-h, don' move, Master Holbrook sir." Jupe whispered close to Armes' ear and pointed aft. "Someone's here."

Armes turned and looked in the direction in which Jupe's finger was pointed. It was true, they were not alone. A woman was standing at the rail some little distance from them. About her was an air of utter dejection, apparent in the very way her hand clutched at the rail, the manner in which the gossamer white veil swathed her forehead, and the spiritless droop of her head.

"Must be the Vicomtesse," Jupe whispered. "She's the only woman on board."

They stood there, none of them moving in the shadows. Apparently the Vicomtesse was unaware that she was not alone. Slowly she turned so that the flickering light of the companionway lantern fell on her, and one hand listlessly loosened her veil, letting it stream out behind her in the wind. As though its release freed her spirit, she raised her head and eagerly drank in the fresh coolness of the air. Armes could see her profile plainly in the dim light—a cameo perfection of face, chiseled against the onyx background of darkness. He noticed the black eyebrow, like a bird poised in flight; the deep, lustrous dark eye beneath it; the finely sculptured line of her nose; her full red lips; and her softly rounded chin. He had never seen such beauty before. Now he knew the answer to his great yearning, and it certainly was not the boy beside him. It was a woman he wanted. This woman! Not some black slut or a professional whore, but this woman whom he had never seen before. Every part of him longed for her.

"So that is the Vicomtesse." Armes lips were so dry he had to moisten them with his tongue before he spoke.

"Must be, Master Holbrook sir. I've never seen her before, but must be."

"There's something strange here." Armes was speaking more to himself than to Jupe. "Something very strange. Either René is crazy, which I do not think he is, or stupid, which I know he is not, or there's something I do not understand and never shall." He took another step forward, moving toward her. She heard him then, but could not identify him in the shadows. Startled, she gathered the veil about her face and ran to the lighted companionway, disappearing down the steps without turning back. Armes stood still, wondering, now that she was gone, if he had really seen her.

"Aren't you going to eat any supper, Master Holbrook sir?" Jupe's voice brought Armes back to reality.

"Supper, Jupe? No, I've already had more than I can digest now. Leave me alone now, but come down to my cabin in about half an hour. Bring me two or three bottles of wine. I'm going to celebrate my last night on board ship by getting drunk, so goddamned drunk I'll not care whether we ever get to St. Domingue or not."

"I'll come, Master Holbrook sir. Sure will be there. But rum's better than wine to get drunk on. You go ahead and get yourself good and drunk and then, Master Holbrook sir . . ." Jupe's hand again sought Armes' shoulder.

"Then what, Jupe?"

"Can I undress you and put you to bed?"

"Why the hell not?" Armes looked over the rail, tracing the pattern of the white foam against the black water. "Yes, Jupe, why the hell not?"

6

ARMES did get drunk, so wholeheartedly and so completely that he was only dimly aware of Jupiter's coming to his cabin, undressing him, and the boy's subsequent ministrations, to which he did not object but suffered passively. However, when he awoke the next morning and remembered, even though fragmentarily, he was quite thoroughly disgusted with himself. His head was bursting; he reeked sourly of rum; and he cursed himself, the memory of the Vicomtesse, René, and most especially Jupe, until he saw that the latter had left a pitcher of cold water beside his bunk. For that one thoughtful action he almost forgave Jupe, and gulped the water down in huge mouthfuls. It watered his parched throat, and cleared his thoughts sufficiently to enable him to maneuver his legs over the side of the bunk. This momentous feat having been accomplished, he stretched his legs straight out in front of him, focusing his eyes on them and studying them carefully with the intention of finding out how he might use them to stand up on. Then, having decided his strategy, he carefully tested his weight on his feet. He managed a few halting steps over to the porthole and stuck his head out. He blinked. It was true! He could see land.

43

What could be more wonderful after days and weeks of water? He had forgotten, during the watery days at sea, that land could be so beautiful. It was a miracle that trees still grew, that mountains reared their heights, that houses existed, and that life went on on land. Yes, here it was—land! And such a land! Never before had he seen such a stupendous, towering, impossible land with mountains tumbling down into the sea, with everything so green, so deeply green that it paled all other greens he had ever seen before. Behind this wall of verdure there were other walls, even more perpendicular, which shaded into purple and blue, dark and menacing even in the blinding sunshine. Far behind there was a dim line of other mountains which were only a misty violet in the distance. A froth of white houses cascaded down one of the mountains to meet the sea, and here and there other spots twinkled white in the devouring greenness. Plantations, Armes thought.

He dressed quickly, and found that his excitement had dispelled his vertigo. By the time he came on deck, the ship was near enough to Cap François to enable him to distinguish houses and to make out people on the distant quay. René came up on deck and stood beside him. Neither spoke. Both were enchanted with the surprising vista of this tropical land, the like of which neither had ever seen before, and both watched it closely as the ship drew nearer and nearer. Soon the houses became more detailed and, as they came closer, they could see people walking on the roads near the city.

They had lost the smell of the sea! Gone was the salty cleanness. In its place was a sweet, overpowering odor wafted out from the land. It combined jasmine with tuberoses; the heady scent of roasted coffee with neglected privies; the moist smell of fertile earth and the nauseating odor of sewage. It was at once repellent and agreeable. It was like an exotic perfume that tried hard to mask the sweaty stench of unwashed bodies, yet at the same time it was invigorating, sensuous, and erotic. It promised much and withheld nothing.

Armes soon discovered that the sun was a force to be reckoned with, here in Cap François. It belabored him with a burning white radiance that robbed his limbs of movement. It was a powerful weapon, wielded by an unseen hand, ready to smite while it caressed. It beat down upon his hands with a scorching heat—a heat that penetrated the skin and fevered the blood beneath it. It started beads of perspiration on his forehead. It dampened his clothes and caused a rivulet of

44

sweat to course down his back. His whole body was mois-
tened, and he had the uncomfortable feeling that the hair of
his body was plastered to his skin. The wetness of his groin
produced an unbearable itch. The clean shirt he had so recently donned now clung clammily to his back, and his tight
woolen pantaloons seemed to shrink and tighten on his thighs.

"It's hot!" René complained, and initiated the eternal male
fumbling and adjustment which is the masculine trademark
of the islands of the Indies. "It's damned hot," he asserted.

Armes agreed. "Hot as hell and perhaps even hotter. Still,
in this horrible heat, we see, spread before us, one of the richest cities of the richest colony in the world. Here is Cap
François, the gold mine of France, the most beautiful . . .

"Mon Dieu, how it stinks." René held both fingers to his
nose.

Armes agreed as he twitched the muscles of his back, trying
to divert the channel of sweat that dripped down his spine.
He stared ahead at the quay, which was now a blaze of color,
like a bed of nodding tulips. As he looked more closely, the
gigantic flowers resolved themselves into the gay headcloths
of the Negresses on the pier—red, violet, magenta, green,
blue, and white, each one a bobbing, moving blot of sheer
color against the whiteness of their dresses. Here and there
in the undulating sea of color were the brilliant uniforms of
the French Army, the varicolored suits of gentlemen, the
glistening black nude torsos of the stevedores, and the shiny
black, brown, and yellow bodies of naked boys who were
diving into the sea from small boats and swimming out to
the ship. It was a pandemonium of noise, color, violent activity, and confusing odors. Behind the brilliance of the scene
—above it and shadowing it—was the unwholesome greenness of the hills, and in back of them the menacing deep
amethyst of the mountains. The combination of sight, sound,
and odor overwhelmed the senses.

René scanned the quay, his hand over his eyes to shield
them from the sun.

"If my letter was delivered by the boat that sailed two
weeks before we did, there should be a carriage here to meet
us."

The remark did not seem to call for an answer, and Armes
was glad he did not have to reply. He was relieved that he
and René were separating. He had entirely exhausted the
Frenchman's conversational depths, and was thoroughly bored
with the other's conceits and vanities. A few days more of en-

45

forced companionship and Armes knew they would have grated on each other to the point of bitter words.

René regarded him half-apologetically. "I have not invited you to stay with us, *mon ami*. It is not lack of hospitality on my part, but my wife, as you know, is not well and it would be difficult for her . . ." His voice trailed off as though he were unable to think of any valid excuse.

"I quite understand." Armes was inwardly grateful that he did not have to make excuses. "Your companionship made the voyage much pleasanter, and I regret that the Vicomtesse has been indisposed."

René put his arm around Armes' shoulders. "I have enjoyed knowing you, Armes, *mon ami*. You do not understand me very well or you might not have desired my friendship. Perhaps some day you will really know me and dislike me for what I am. This voyage has been a little interlude in my life, with neither past nor future."

René's arm was hot and heavy on his shoulder and Armes resented the intimacy it implied. He wished that the other would remove it, but René made no move to do so. Armes leaned further over the rail to dislodge the unwelcome pressure. René's arm fell to his side and as it did so, he looked questioningly at Armes. Armes chose to ignore the glance. Outside of the necessary formalities of bidding him good-bye, Armes was quite willing for René to know that their acquaintanceship was ended.

The ship was slowly warped up to the quay.

"Well, here we are at last, René."

René nodded.

"And if you have a carriage to meet you, surely I must have some sort of a reception, too. My guardian wrote to a hotel here. There must be someone from there down here to transport me and my baggage."

"Perhaps that is it." René pointed to the quay, to a carriage that stood alone in gaudy isolation.

Armes followed the direction of his finger. He could hardly believe his eyes. Surely it was the most beautiful woman he had ever seen. She sat alone in the carriage, with a tiny white sunshade that cast a deep shadow over her face. But beautiful as she was, there were so many distracting features around her, it was difficult at first to concentrate on her beauty. There was the carriage itself—an ornate barouche of deep crimson with white leather upholstery and white wheels. There was the coachman, sitting high on the box in white livery and gold buttons, keeping a tight rein on the two restless black horses. There was the scintillating shine of varnish on the carriage, and the gleam of silver on the harnesses. But the woman herself put all the gaudy splendor around her to shame.

She sat alone and upright, entirely oblivious to the noise and movement around her. In her splendid isolation she was almost regal. Her bare arms and face were a soft gold in color—a gold with lavender shadings where the sun cast soft rounded shadows, but a gold with pale green highlights where the sun kissed her skin. The shadow of the parasol made her face almost mauve, and her full red lips looked like dark grapes when the movement of the parasol temporarily obscured the light.

Armes stared at her open-mouthed, conscious that René was as stunned as he was. Then, through that curious telepathy which draws eyes together, she stared at both of them. It was a bold look—a look of appraisal. First her eyes undressed René. She inventoried his lithe body, the whipcord muscles of his arms, his slender hips, and his youthfulness. Her eyes returned to his face, and she granted him the ghost of a smile as though to say, "You'll do."

But, when her eyes shifted to Armes, they devoured him. This time she made a far more complete inventory. She noted the black hair, tightly curled from the dampness of perspiration; the olive cheeks with the underlying blue of his beard. Her eyes lingered for a moment on the smooth, strong column of his neck and then, without the least trace of embarrassment, she continued her appraisal. She hesitated for a moment at the shirt, opened at the neck, then proceeded to the sweeping muscles of the chest, damply outlined under the thin fabric, down to the narrow waist and hips. Her look stripped him of trousers and smallclothes and left him naked before her gaze. She smiled in approval and then lifted her eyes to meet his. He returned her look and, as their eyes met, the distance between them seemed to vanish. It seemed they were only inches apart and he could almost feel the warmth of her body and the pressure of those full red lips. He smiled back at her, but she did not return his smile this time. Instead, with her eyes still fastened on him, she leaned forward and spoke to the coachman. The carriage started to move, and as it passed down the crowded quay, she turned in her seat, keeping her gaze riveted on Armes. It was not

47

until the carriage reached the street that she abandoned him and turned.

"Well, I'll be damned!" Armes' breath exploded

René looked at him, but Armes was still traveling in the carriage. He watched it until it disappeared and then stood like a man in a trance. Finally he shook his head violently and stamped his foot on the deck.

He was exhausted, drained of all emotion. He felt that he had lain with ten women.

"Tell me, René, was that real?"

"Certainement! But I do not wonder that you ask, *mon ami*. It could well have been a vision."

"I wonder who she is, what she is, where she comes from, and what she is doing here."

A voice beside him spoke. He turned to see Jupe grinning up at him. Remembering last night, Armes felt a sudden revulsion for the boy. But this was immediately dissipated by the boy's good nature.

"That, Master Holbrook sir, was Topaze. That's her name! Who is she? She is a mulatto. What is she? She's a goddam whore. What's she doing here? She came down to the ship to see what it would bring her. She's looking for a man and she wants a man who'll give her more than she's getting now. Topaze is St. Domingue—pretty to look at but bad, Master Holbrook sir, bad, bad, bad."

Armes was scarcely aware that they had docked, that the gangplank now connected the ship with the quay, and that René was shaking his hand with promises to see him soon. He was still with Topaze in the carriage, or rather he and Topaze had traveled somewhere in the carriage and he was alone with her, reaching out his arms to her, crushing her to him. . . . But again, he shook himself back to the present. Good God! He wondered if all the women in St. Domingue were like her. Suddenly he was glad he had come; he felt that of all places on earth fate had brought him to this island.

The gangplank was bringing half the population of Cap François on board, or so it seemed, and the activity around him helped Armes to banish the disturbing image of Topaze from his thoughts. The entire deck was now a mass of white skirts, black faces, and bright bandanas. The women were offering baskets of brightly colored tropical fruits, exotic flowers, and crude handcrafts. Armes saw a round, black, moonlike face, set off by a violently green madras. She grinned and held up a cucumberish fruit which he declined. Another pressed close to him and offered a garland of orange flowers, another more fruit, and as he pushed his way through the press of closely packed bodies, he felt dark hands slithering along his thighs, accompanied by low Creole words of invitation. He managed to fight them all off and gained the companionway. Below deck, things were quieter. Jupe had already packed his belongings and the valises stood, closed and strapped, ready to go, but how and to what destination, Armes did not know.

He heard a commotion in the passageway, and the thundering voice of a man, raging like a bellowing bull, speaking French with a curiously slurred accent.

"Out of my way, you black bitch. Keep your hands away from my breeches. You wouldn't interest me if you were the only woman I could ever sleep with. Get going before I slap your black ass."

"Who're you, Henry Christophe, to be getting so high and mighty? Who do you think you are? You're just as goddam black as I am. You're just as much a slave as I am. Besides, you've got a black master. My master's white. I don't want you, anyway. Black master!" Armes could hear the woman spit. There was the sound of a well-directed slap, a yelp of surprise from the woman, and then the doorway of his cabin darkened. It was filled by a huge man. It seemed to Armes that for the first time in his life, he was looking at a man bigger than he. He saw a fellow of about his own age, whose black face was patently Negroid yet savagely handsome. The servile smile seemed ill at ease on the bold face, as though it had been merely assumed for the moment. The hair clustered tight to his head, like a layer of thick, curly black moss, creeping down over a low forehead which shadowed eyes under heavy brows. The eyes were dark and intelligent, although now clouded with anger. The nose was short, with wide flattened nostrils. The lips were perhaps the most Negroid feature, for they were thick and wide, wet and the color of ripe eggplant. Under the face, a taurine neck showed a pulsing artery which bespoke a powerful heartbeat. The thin cotton shirt strained above a thin flat belly, over swelling chest and arm muscles. The man had to duck his head to enter the cabin door.

"You are Monsieur Holbrook from Boston?" He was speaking now in good French instead of Creole, but there was a belligerency in his voice which defied Armes to disagree with him.

"Yes, and you?"

"Christophe from the Hotel Couronne. I have come to fetch you. Monsieur Coidovic, the owner of the Couronne, sent me. He is expecting you."

There was something about the fellow that Armes liked. Perhaps it was his size, or perhaps it was the swagger of independence. Whatever it was, it caused Armes to sense a personality similar to his own, and with this recognition he smiled and extended his hand.

"Glad to know you, Christophe. You are the first person from St. Domingue to greet me." His hand remained extended, grasping only thin air. He looked at it, then up to Christophe.

"Well, I'll be good goddamned." Armes' voice shook with anger. "You refuse my hand, monsieur?"

Christophe looked at him, baffled, and Armes could see the sensitive nostrils of the big Negro's face quiver.

"Hospitable place, this St. Domingue," Armes muttered. "I travel two thousand miles to get here and the first man I meet refuses to shake hands with me."

Christophe's eyes did not leave those of Armes. He reached out slowly, even timidly, and took Armes' hand. The white hand, large as it was, was completely engulfed in the warm, moist expanse of the black one. Armes saw the pink tip of Christophe's tongue wet his lips nervously. He noticed the strange look in the Negro's eyes, and was aware of a disturbing tension between them. To cover it, Armes smiled embarrassedly, and his smile removed the fear from Christophe's eyes. Suddenly the clasp on his hand tightened and his hand was shaken vigorously.

"I thank you, M'sieu." Christophe's brazen bellow had sunk to a whisper. He glanced over his shoulder to see if there was anyone outside the door. *"Je vous remercie beaucoup, m'sieu.* You might be interested to know that I am twenty-four years old."

"Yes?" Armes could not quite account for the strange statement.

"Yes, and this is the first time in my life that a white man ever offered me his hand or ever called me 'monsieur.' Believe me, I have no right to accept either. I am a slave, and here in St. Domingue, a white man does not offer his hand to a slave, nor would a slave dare to accept it if such an unusual thing were to happen. Nor does a man address a slave as *monsieur.* Yet you have done both of these things.

50

I do not understand but I appreciate it. I do, M'sieu Holbrook, I do."

Armes laughed casually. "I mean it, Christophe. Where I come from, when I meet a man for the first time and I tell him my name and he tells me his, we shake hands. That's all there is to it. You are a man and your name is Christophe. I am a man and my name is Armes. So . . . we shook hands."

"Yes, but your hand is white, m'sieu, and look at mine." Christophe spread his hand before him. "Mine is black."

Armes reached out and took it again. "It sure is, Christophe. But it is a clean hand, a powerful hand, and, I hope, a friendly hand. Someday, Christophe, I may be glad that I shook your hand. It might do me a big favor, might even save my life. So, here's a real handshake, and let me say I'm proud to shake hands with a man like you."

The strain was gone. They both laughed. Christophe picked up the heavy bags, two in each hand, and sidled out the cabin door. Armes looked back for a moment to see if he had forgotten anything. The cabin was empty now, but it had held some strange dreams and some new and novel experiences for him. He was almost loath to leave it and enter into an unknown world, but he followed Christophe up the narrow stairway. Christophe looked back over his shoulder.

"Will you be staying long at the Couronne, m'sieu?"

"That I do not know, Christophe."

"I hope you will stay a long time, m'sieu."

"You do? Why?"

"Because, m'sieu, you are a *gentilhomme*. A real one. I am very proud that you shook my hand. Henry Christophe is a very happy man. He will show you what it is to have a real friend in St. Domingue."

"Thank you, Christophe, or did you say 'Henry' just now?"

Christophe did not hear him. He was having difficulty with the bags on the narrow stairs. They ascended into the blinding sunlight.

Just across the gangplank Armes saw René helping the Vicomtesse into a carriage. He noticed Armes on deck and waved to him. Armes waved back. Despite the fact that the Vicomtesse was heavily veiled, she must have seen him wave, for she politely fluttered her hand in his direction. René glared at her, jumped into the carriage, and they were gone. Armes walked across the gangplank and Christophe followed him. Once more his feet were on solid earth. Somewhere in his mind he recalled the Latin phrase *terra firma*. Yes, this was *terra firma*, good firm land, and he was satisfied once more to find land under his feet.

Christophe sweated with the bags, his neat white shirt clinging damply to his back. On ahead there was a carriage waiting. It was an ordinary sort of conveyance, shabby and a bit decrepit but polished and shining, with a pair of beautifully groomed horses.

Christophe piled the luggage in front, waited for Armes to enter, then jumped up on the driver's seat and cracked the whip. The horses started with a sudden bolt, but Christophe had them admirably under control. They trotted down the quay at a fast pace, passing the white skirts and the gay turbans. Off the quay, the carriage turned into a roughly paved street, then into an imposing square surrounded by colonnaded white buildings. Another turn and they came to a low, rambling white building with a large golden crown swinging from two chains in front of the entrance.

"This is the Hotel Couronne, Monsieur Holbrook." Christophe pointed his whip in the direction of a gray-haired Negro, dressed in black, who was standing in the doorway. "And this is Monsieur Coidovic, your host and my master."

For a moment the proprietor's color confused Armes. He had considered the man merely another slave. Then he remembered that René had told him that some of the Negroes had purchased their freedom and now in turn owned slaves. He recalled René saying that a slave felt it a disgrace to be owned by another Negro and that usually the Negroes were the most brutal masters, far worse than the free mulattoes or whites. Armes remembered the taunt of the woman on board ship that Christophe was the slave of a Negro. But Christophe did not appear unhappy over it, and there seemed to be no animosity in his greeting of his master when he came down the steps to meet Armes. He appeared to be a kindly, intelligent man.

Coidovic bowed. "We are at your service, Monsieur Holbrook. We shall be delighted to have you as our guest."

Armes noticed that the man did not offer his hand. After his experience with Christophe, he did not want to cause embarrassment again, so he too refrained. Coidovic turned from Armes to Christophe.

"Henry, take Monsieur Holbrook's baggage to Number Three. Monsieur Holbrook, if you will follow Henry."

"You mean Christophe?"

"Ah yes, monsieur," Coidovic smiled. "That is Henry

Christophe. During the afternoon and evening, he has charge of my billiard room and he is a waiter, too. This morning I took him away from his usual chores to meet you. Henry is a fine young man."

"You called him Henry, Monsieur Coidovic. That is an English name. I learned to say Henri in French—Ân-ree."

Coidovic laughed and shook his head. "But Henry Christophe is Henry, not Henri." He walked up the broad steps beside Armes. "The man is really English. He was born on the island of St. Christopher, although sometimes he changes his birthplace to Grenada. I do not believe he really knows. However, as he was born on English soil, he insists that his name is Henry and not Henri." He put his hand before his mouth and whispered confidentially to Armes. "It's the only English word he knows, poor Henry Christophe, and he's mighty proud of it."

"Then, from now on I shall call him Henry." Armes took his leave from Coidovic and ascended the wide mahogany staircase. Henry was standing in the doorway of a room down the hall and motioned with a welcoming gesture for Armes to enter.

After the cramped confines of the ship's cabin, the room seemed enormous. Wide boards of polished mahogany made a dark mirror of the floor. The tall windows reached from floor to ceiling and through them, Armes could see balcony railings and a bright fringe of potted plants. There was a high, four-poster mahogany bed, shrouded in white netting; a monumental armoire; a broad expanse of table; and several large chairs which looked as though they would be quite impossible for anyone to move except Henry Christophe. All the furniture was the rich, glowing, dark red of native mahogany, crudely crafted by hand but highly polished.

It was cool in the room. A soft breeze played through the windows, ruffled the bed hangings, and made tiny ripples in the big white china bowl of water on the commode. Several large vases were filled with strange, colorful flowers which Armes had never seen before. The clean, wholesome scent of beeswax and fresh linen mingled with the heavy odor of the flowers and the insistent smell of Cap François which Armes and René had first noticed on the ship.

Henry Christophe opened the bags on the floor.

"A maid will come to do your unpacking, Monsieur Holbrook."

"Thank you, Henry."

Henry looked up and smiled and the smile broadened to show his teeth. Then it progressed into a hearty laugh.

"Yes, from now on, it will be 'Henry' and not 'Christophe,' " Armes said, "and, by the way, Henry, 'Monsieur Holbrook' is quite a mouthful for a Frenchman, even for a mouth as big as yours or mine. So as long as we have agreed to be friends, let's make it just 'Armes' after this."

Henry's laugh died in his throat and he became preoccupied with the fastenings of Armes' valise. When he looked up, Armes was surprised to see tears in the big fellow's eyes. They looked strange in the eyes of a man so large and powerful as Henry Christophe, but tears they were, and he wiped them away with the back of his hand, unabashed at the display of such emotion.

"*Merci, mon ami,*" he said, and his voice caught in his throat. "Do they not have slaves where you come from?"

"Damn few slaves in Boston, Henry. Outside of the boy Jupe on board ship, I've never met any. I've never thought much about this matter of slaves. To me, a man's a man. Some men I like, some I do not. I happen to like you, Henry, and it makes little difference to me whether you are slave or free, white or black. I'm going to need friends here in St. Domingue, and I'd like to think of you as the first friend I've made."

"I never heard a man talk like you before. *Merci!* If I could address you as 'Armes' I would consider it a great honor—the greatest honor anyone ever paid Henry Christophe. And, if you will allow me, I shall do it when we are alone, but when anyone else is around it must be 'Monsieur Holbrook.' St. Domingue would condemn you more than it would me if the people here heard me call you by your first name. May we leave it that way"—Henry hesitated— "Armes?"

"That we can, Henry. And now, how about a cup of that St. Domingue coffee I've heard so much about? I'm starved."

"Right away, Armes." Again Henry hesitated over the name, then grinned and whispered, "And judging by your size, which is about the same as mine, just a cup of coffee won't be enough, will it?"

"Right you are, and if you can discover a nice steak in St. Domingue, it wouldn't be bad. No—not bad at all."

"The best steak in St. Domingue for you, *mon ami* Armes, just as soon as I can get the cook to fix it." He started for the door and turned around. One eyelid dropped slowly. "Nothing's too good for Henry Christophe's friend."

Armes could hear his chuckles as he ran down the hall. He closed the door, stripped himself of his damp, sweaty clothes, and threw himself down on the bed, which to his weary mind seemed to sway as much as did his bunk on the ship. His thoughts immediately centered on the strangely exotic woman whom he had seen on the quay. Never before had he desired a woman so completely; he was determined to have her. She occupied his thoughts until he heard a rap on the door and Henry Christophe entered, a large covered tray in his hand.

"Resting, *mon ami?*" He pulled a small table over beside the bed and placed the tray on it.

"Beefsteak." He pulled the white napkin off and released the succulent aroma. "And wine." He pointed to a tall thin bottle, liberally covered with cobwebs. "The best in the cellar. Now, *mon ami,* you eat, you drink, you rest, and you be happy."

"Sometimes it takes more than food and drink and a comfortable bed to make a man happy," Armes answered.

Henry grinned back at him. "You mean it takes someone to share that bed with you?"

"Exactly." Armes nodded his head.

"What my friend wants, my friend shall have. Now you eat, and when you have finished . . ." Henry closed his eyes, threw his head back, and whistled. "You are a big man like me, my friend. We big fellows—we have hot blood and lots of it. I expected you to ask for a woman before you asked for food."

"So you can help me?"

"Certainement! No place on earth you can get such a choice as here at Cap François. Anything from black as ink to almost white. How do you like your women?"

"Mostly white, I guess. I've never slept with a Negro girl."

"Best there is." Henry winked. "Lively they are, because they enjoy it. Once you lay a nigger wench, you'll never want a white one again."

Armes' thoughts immediately turned to Topaze. "Seems to me I'd prefer one on the light side, Henry."

"Cost more than the black ones and aren't worth half as much."

"But I still think I'd like one."

Henry considered the matter for a moment. "There's a

Justine who lives right next door to the hotel. Can't recommend her, because I never had her. She's too expensive for me. Should I bring her here or do you want to go there?"

"Can you bring her here?"

"Sure can. Early in the morning like this, she's not busy."

"Then go fetch her while I'm eating."

Henry shook his head vehemently.

"Not good for a man to eat hearty and then bed a wench. This is the Tropics, friend Armes. Better to wait an hour after eating.

"Never bothered me before," Armes asserted, "and a whole hour is too goddamned long to wait."

Henry shrugged his shoulders.

"Then I'll go fetch her if you want. After all that time on ship without a woman, you're not going to last too long anyway. It will be over before you know it. Then you get a chance to rest before the second time."

"The second time?" Armes looked up at Henry and laughed.

"Sure, my friend. You're like me. First time, second time, third time, fourth time. After that you begin to feel a little tired. We're both big fellows, friend Armes."

"But something tells me you're bigger than I am."

Once again Armes listened to Henry's chuckles as Henry ran down the hall.

7

THE languorous charm of St. Domingue, following the long monotonous days on shipboard, robbed Armes of all ambition, and in his pleasant lethargy, he found it easy to defer everything, especially his visit to his plantation, despite the fact that it was located only about ten miles inland from Cap François. Each day he found himself manufacturing excuses to delay it until the morrow. It was far too pleasant just to laze at the Couronne, talk with Henry, enjoy M. Coidovic's sumptuous meals, and do absolutely nothing else.

One sunny, idle day slipped into another effortlessly. He awoke late in the mornings to the jasmine-scented air with the full blaze of the tropic sun coming in slanted shafts of light through the jalousies. A pot of Henry's strong, rich, black coffee would clear his head, and soon after Henry would wheel in the cumbersome tub, which he would fill with warm water. When Armes finished with his bath, he did not bother to dress but stretched out on his bed until Henry brought his noon meal. After that he would read a while and sleep again, waking late in the afternoon when the room was cool, anticipating Henry's knock on the door signaling that he had brought Justine. Then followed an interval with the professionally adept mulatto who, if not as charming and exotic as the girl of the carriage, was handsome, willing, and already madly in love with Armes, despite her professional status. Consequently she tried, and most successfully too, to please him. But he had not forgotten Topaze, and when he was making love to Justine he tried to imagine that she was Topaze. Much against Henry's advice, Armes had sent him to seek Topaze, but Henry had returned almost too gleefully with the discouraging news that Topaze was visiting on a rather distant plantation. It was plain to see that Henry did not approve of her.

After Justine departed, Armes dressed, dined in his room, and, during the early evenings, engaged Henry to drive him around the city. Thus he passed his days.

For the first few days, while his ship was still in port, Armes had borrowed Jupe, who came to the hotel and tended to his wants, keeping his clothes in order, sending out his laundry, and helping him dress. Then, after Jupe had bidden him a tearful farewell and the ship had sailed, Henry had taken over, performing various personal tasks for Armes in between his other duties in the billiard room. But this, Armes realized, could be only a temporary measure. He must make other arrangements. There were two things he needed. First a servant and then a horse. As usual, he found himself turning to Henry for advice.

"I want to hire a servant, Henry"—Armes was filling Henry's arms with soiled linen—"someone to take care of my things and look out for me the way you have been doing. How do I go about hiring a servant in Cap François?"

Henry was counting the shirts, drawers and small clothes that Armes was pulling out of the armoire. "Six, seven, eight! That's eight shirts and you want them without starch, *mon ami?*"

Armes nodded. "Now, if I were back in Boston, I would put an advertisement in the paper: 'Wanted: Young man, alert, intelligent, and honest, as personal servant. Experience desirable.' That, Henry, is what I would do in Boston. But what do I do here in Cap François?"

"You don't."

"I don't what?"

"You don't go around putting any silly advertisement in the paper. It would be ridiculous. All of Cap François would be laughing at you."

"Then what do I do?"

"You just go out and buy yourself one, if you got the money."

Armes laughed, "I've got the money, but I don't particularly want to own a slave, Henry."

It was Henry's turn to laugh. "If you've got a plantation, you already own hundreds of them."

Armes had never considered that aspect before. That he was actually a slave owner had never occurred to him.

"You know, Henry, I never thought about that. I guess I do own some. I must. I'll have to wait until I go out to the plantation, and I must go soon. But before I go, I must have a horse—in order to get the servant."

"The horse is easy." Henry was confident. "I can attend to that for you. After all the years I spent as a boy in the Couronne stables, I know every horse within fifty miles of Cap François. I can pick the finest for you if you'll give me time to look around. But the matter of a servant is different. May I advise you?"

"Why not?"

"Well, it's this way." Henry stuffed the soiled linen into a capacious white bag and motioned to Armes to be seated, while he remained standing. Regardless of his friendship with Armes, he never felt totally at ease in the white man's presence. "Those slaves at your plantation are probably all field slaves—ignorant black bastards who've never been in a house before. They're not even housebroken. If one of them wanted to piss, he'd piss in the middle of the floor just like he'd piss in the middle of a field. You couldn't use one of them for a servant unless you trained him, and that would take time. You'd better buy one here in Cap François. Now, Monsieur duCharme has a fine young griffe wench that is up for sale. She'd serve you by day and you could serve her by night."

Armes stood up quickly, shaking his head. "No wench, Henry. If I bedded her at night I wouldn't want her waiting

58

on me daytimes. No, I'd rather have a man for this job. Seems more fitting. At home every man has a man servant. Only women have wenches."

"But here in St. Domingue most men prefer wenches."

Armes laughed. "So do I, but not for helping me dress. With a wench helping me put on my breeches, I'd never get them on."

"*Mon Dieu,* you are right. And we can't have you going around without breeches. No! A man it is." He stopped laughing and became serious. "I know what we can do."

"Then tell me."

"Well, this morning the Portuguese ship *Dom Joao* arrived in Cap François with a cargo of slaves on board. I don't think they've been unloaded yet. The *Dom Joao* has a reputation for fine stock—Mandingos, Hausas, Ibo, Fantees, and fancies—fine upstanding young bucks and handsome wenches. We could go there now and you could pick one out first hand. Monsieur Coidovic will grant me time to go with you."

Armes groaned. "I suppose it's the only way."

Henry nodded.

"Well then, let's go now."

"I'll have to speak to Monsieur Coidovic first. Then there are a few things I must attend to. In about an hour?"

"I'll meet you in the bar in about an hour."

Armes dressed by himself and descended to the cool darkness of the big tavern room with its sweeping length of mahogany bar and its multitude of tables. Though still quite early in the morning it was partially filled with men from the Cap and others who were obviously planters in from the country. As Armes entered, a man at the bar looked up from his drink and stared overlong at him. He kept his eyes fastened on Armes, scowled, and then deliberately spat on the floor. Another of the white-coated planters took up the stare and then still another. By the time Armes had seated himself at a table, he was conscious that everyone in the room was looking at him and that every look was malignant. Feeling somewhat ill at ease, he ordered a rum punch, and as he waited to be served, he became increasingly aware of the unpleasant undercurrent of hostility that ran through the room. Those at the tables were staring along with those at the bar and their scowls revealed the same animosity.

The waiter brought his drink. Armes noticed that the man advanced to his table with more than a little timidity. Suddenly Armes didn't want the drink. He wanted only to clear up the mystery. He had never been treated in such an insulting manner before and he had to know the cause of the trouble.

With the drink in one hand, he walked slowly toward the bar. Those at the bar moved aside, and where there had been a group of men, there was now only an empty space where he stood alone. He smashed the drink down on the bar with such force that the glass broke and the liquid ran over the polished wood, spattering onto his shirt front. Armes was angry. He walked over to one of the men—the same who had first stared at him when he entered the room. It was difficult for Armes to control his temper as the man turned his back, quickly and rudely. But he was not quick enough. Armes' hand grabbed for his shoulder and spun him around. The fellow's face flushed suddenly, the red stain mounting into his cheeks. He shook Armes' hand away and muttered something under his breath.

"Your pardon, monsieur," Armes said, trying hard to speak calmly. "My presence seems to disturb you and your friends."

The man looked him straight in the eyes and again turned away without answering.

The temper which had been boiling inside Armes could no longer be controlled. This time his long arm reached out, caught the man's coat, and swung him around. The unexpected motion upset the other's balance and he started to fall, but Armes caught him and lifted him up. He kept his grip on the thin fabric of the coat.

"I no longer beg your pardon." Armes measured every word. "Goddamn it, you are rude! You turned your back on me. You refused to answer a civil question. Nobody does that to me."

"Take your black hands off me, you *affranchi* bastard!" The fellow was almost screaming at Armes in his rage. "In the eyes of the law you may be as free as we are. We won't deny it. As a mulatto you are legally a free man. But don't come here. Don't try to mix with us. You may be free, but to us you're just a goddamned nigger."

Armes released him and the very absurdity of the situation made him laugh. The more he laughed—and he laughed loudly and boisterously—the more puzzled and angry his audience became. This was an unanticipated reaction. They had expected either an abject apology or a swaggering defiance. Least of all had they expected ridicule. Finally one of them spoke.

60

"It's no laughing matter, *affranchi*, whoever you are. We mean what we say. No fraternization between whites and mulattoes."

"But that's what's so funny, monsieur. It's so funny and you're all so stupid. Me? An *affranchi*? Good God, why? Do I look like a half-breed nigger?"

The first man, the one whom Armes had grabbed, pointed to the suit that Armes was wearing.

"That monsieur!" He fired the words like a pistol.

"That what?"

"That suit!"

"*Mon Dieu*, my suit? But what of that? It was tailored by Mr. Bowman of Boston. His place on Cornhill is quite the fashion with the young fellows of Boston and Cambridge."

"You said *Boston*? You mean the United States?"

"Certainly, Boston! And where else but in the United States?"

The man came closer and peered into Armes' face. He looked long and searchingly, carefully noting him feature by feature. He drew in a long breath and looked at his companions.

"The man is white. We've made a terrible mistake." Turning to Armes he said, "Monsieur, we regret our stupidity—but did you not know when you put on that suit . . ."

"Know what?"

"That that particular shade of bottle-green which you are wearing is the mark of an *affranchi*, a color reserved for mulattoes only?"

"Hell, no!"

The man bowed low. "*Quelle méprise.* There has been a mistake, monsieur. I take it you are an American and not familiar with our customs. Allow me to apologize for our rudeness."

"And we all add our apologies." The others bowed in unison and one by one they came forward and awkwardly offered their hands to Armes.

He shook hands with all of them.

"Now, messieurs, that we can talk like civilized persons, let us straighten the matter out. I buy a suit in Boston. I wear it for the first time in St. Domingue. I enter this bar and immediately I am ostracized."

"Because we thought you were a mulatto," one of them said.

"Do I look like a mulatto?" Armes pursued the question.

61

The fellow shrugged his shoulders. "Who can tell what the hybrid bastards look like? Some of them are whiter and, goddamn it, better-looking than we are. As for you, monsieur, in the first place you are a big man—far bigger than most white men—and we associate great height and unusual strength with Negroes. Then, too, you have black hair and an olive complexion, both of which are a common characteristic of mulattoes. But no! You do not look like a mulatto, but you must admit, the suit is misleading."

"So it is all on account of my suit. I chose the color in Boston. It seemed a dark, conservative color, quite in style at home. But it nearly precipitated a most unhappy affair, possibly a duel."

"Oh no, monsieur, we would not have crossed swords with an *affranchi*." They all started to laugh and crowded around Armes. Now they were as friendly as they had been hostile a few moments before. Someone called for champagne. The corks popped from half a dozen bottles. A young man disengaged himself from the crowd and came up and laid his hand on Armes' shoulder.

"Allow me. I am Edouard Granville of Côte des Fleurs Plantation."

"Armes Holbrook of Boston, at your service."

Granville recognized the name. He clapped Armes heartily on the back. "We have heard of you, monsieur. You are the man who owns Sans Souci."

"I am."

"Oh, a thousand pardons, Monsieur Holbrook. I speak for myself and all my friends." His gesture took in the whole room. "What an unfortunate occurrence! Why, we are neighbors you and I. The lands of Sans Souci border my own. Here!" He offered Armes a bubbling glass of wine. "Let us drown our unfortunate introduction in this toast to neighborliness."

Armes accepted the glass and drank with them.

"But now," Armes said, "my curiosity is still unanswered. What is the mystery about this ill-fated suit?"

"Oh yes, the bottle-green suit." Granville fingered the sleeve and laughed. "Monsieur Holbrook's famous bottle-green suit! You see, that particular color is reserved for the mulattoes here in Cap François. We have many of them here and many of them would like to pass for white and could if we didn't know them. However, it is necessary to make a distinction."

"Damn necessary!" another interrupted. "The cheeky bastards want to push their way into white society. If we allowed them, soon they'd be marrying white women."

"So," Granville continued, "in order to make a distinction, our local legislature recently passed a law, limiting the colors the damned *affranchis* may wear. In that way they are immediately recognized and cannot usurp the position of whites. We whites may wear any color we choose except the three colors the mulattoes are permitted—dark gray, dark brown, and dark green. *Naturellement*, when we see a man, if he is wearing a dark green suit, we immediately take it for granted that he is an *affranchi*—a free mulatto. We do not encourage their mixing with us and they are not permitted to enter the Couronne, which is for whites only."

Armes' glass had been refilled again. "What a shame to waste my new suit," he said between sips. "I shall go and change immediately. I shall give it to Henry Christophe. He is only a little larger than I and it might fit him."

Granville shook his head and raised his hands in mock horror. "*Hélas,* Monsieur Holbrook, that you cannot do. Henry Christophe is a Negro and not a mulatto. He could not wear it because the *affranchis* would be offended. They would tear it from his back."

"I imagine it would be pretty difficult to tear anything from Henry's back. But I'll throw the damned thing away. Thank you, gentlemen, for setting me right. I shall now change. Good day to you all and especially to you, Monsieur Granville. I hope that we shall be very good neighbors."

They all bowed as he left the room. On the stairs he met Henry, who told him that he was now ready to go and that the carriage was waiting. Armes pointed to his clothes. Henry gaped in amazement and then chuckled. He caught up with Armes on the stairs and entered his room with him. Henry drew Armes over to the window, looked at him again, and then doubled up with laughter.

"What a fine *affranchi,* you make, *mon ami.* Did you get kicked out of the bar?"

"Almost. I didn't know that that suit would cause all that trouble."

Henry suddenly straightened up and his face became solemn. He turned and looked out the window. His hands were clenched so tightly that the knuckles were pale. He turned back quickly, his face contorted.

"Damn them, Armes! Damn them, damn them, damn'

them! May the curse of death, the curse of Baron Samedi, be upon them. But Armes, is there nothing we can do about it?"

"We, Henry?"

"Not you and I, Armes, but we, the thousands of blacks on this island. We have no rights, no voice. We are dumb stupid cattle. We are bought and sold; we are whipped, lashed and tortured; we work from sunup to sunset; we make money for the whites to throw away. But what can we do about it? I ask you, what can we do?"

Armes looked at him in surprise. Now, for the first time, he was seeing the real Henry. This was not the grinning, affable young fellow who always went about his tasks so cheerfully, who waited on Armes so gladly and pimped so willingly for him. This was not the Henry who helped him dress, shined his shoes, carried away his dirty linen, brought Justine to his room, and always smiled at him in return. This was another man—a man whose soul was showing for a brief moment! Armes saw the brief flash of pride, mingled with defeat in Henry's eyes. And then, he suddenly saw the man before him, powerful in his potentialities. This proud, young Negro was no longer a servant, no longer the obsequious, bowing Henry, but a new man, a forceful, dominant man, a man who was capable of leading other men, and dangerous because he was an intelligent man.

There was nothing Armes could think of to say. He walked across the room and poured a glass of Madeira from the decanter on the table and carried it over to Henry. He pushed him down into a chair and put the glass in Henry's hand.

Henry looked first at the glass of wine and then at Armes. He shook his head in wonderment. "For me? You brought this to me? First you shake my hand, then you become my friend, and now you bring me this glass of wine?"

"And why not? You know, Henry, I saw something a moment ago. I saw *you*, Henry. Perhaps it frightened me a bit. I saw a new Henry Christophe and I liked him. You may be a slave, but first of all you're a man, and I respect you for it. Someday, Henry, you are going to do something about it."

Henry shook his head sadly. "It is better for me to forget all about it for now. There is nothing I can do now, but perhaps"—he looked up at Armes—"someday I shall be able to do something. I hope that when that day comes you will still be my friend, even if you are white and I am black."

"And I hope you will still be mine even if you are black and I am white. Come, drink your wine, Henry, and let's get started. Have you forgotten we have business to attend to? We're going to buy a slave, Henry, another man."

"Another poor devil starting on the long road to hell. But no, not this one! This one will be lucky. He'll have you for a master. Let him thank his gods for that."

"*Allons,* Henry! We'll buy the slave, you and I. But I'll promise you one thing, and I'll swear it on our friendship. If he deserves it and he serves me well, I'll give him his freedom someday."

"And if he doesn't serve you well, I'll break his god-damned neck," Henry said, rising slowly from the chair. He placed the glass carefully on the table and went and opened the door for Armes. He waited for Armes to pass through and followed him silently down the hall. At the head of the stairs Armes waited for him, and then they walked down the stairs together, side by side.

Henry cast a sidelong glance at Armes and winked. *"Mon ami,* I couldn't like you any better if you were as black as I am." Armes winked back. "Or I you, if you were white."

8

"THAT," said Henry, pointing with his whip to an ornate and somewhat dilapidated confection of white stucco, hung with magenta bougainvillea, "is the Villa Topaze, where she lives." The iron-shod wheels of the carriage made such a clatter on the cobbles that Armes had to bend forward in the seat to hear him.

The house sat back from the street, shut off by a high wall, pierced with elaborately gilded wrought-iron gates. Wide verandahs, screened by red and white sailcloth, surrounded it. On closer inspection its gaudy shabbiness was even more apparent, particularly the garden, which was overgrown and neglected. Through the gates Armes could see a statue of

Eros, poised drunkenly over a dry fountain; ropes of vines hung from the trees and dead palm fronds littered the driveway. The whitewash was peeling from the house, and it had the tawdry look of a slattern dressed in greasy satin.

"She lives there," Henry repeated, raising his voice so Armes could hear.

"And she is Topaze." Armes had never been able to forget the disturbing thoughts which had taken possession of him when he first glimpsed the mulatto on the quay. "Yes, she is Topaze. And she is beautiful."

"There are those who say a snake is beautiful. How come you still want her? Doesn't Justine satisfy?"

"Marvelously, but I doubt if any man has ever seen Topaze without wanting her."

"I'm a man and I don't want her. Keep your distance, *mon ami*. She is poison, that one. I'd rather be bitten by the *fer de lance* of Martiníque than have anything to do with her. God knows how many of the men of St. Domingue the slut has ruined. She strips them bare in a matter of months. Then she spends the money so fast, she has to look for another. They say that there's only one man in the world who can really satisfy her, and that's a renegade slave by the name of Bouckmann, black as smoke, who lives up in the hills. She's in love with him and uses white men only for what she can get out of them. There was young Armand Lamartinière who hanged himself when she left him, after he had spent every sou on her. The old Chevalier de Brunac, who cadges drinks in every bar in the Cap, was once a rich man and her lover. Aristide Caron mortgaged his plantation and slaves trying to buy her love; and Williams, the English ship owner, just returned to England, his passage paid by friends who took up a collection for him. Now she'll be on the prowl for another victim, I've heard, after she gets back from visiting her black stallion in the hills. She'll be back soon, meeting the boats again to see if she can find another victim. Most everyone in the Cap is afraid of her, so she has to look for strangers." Henry turned and pointed the butt of his whip at Armes. "Like you."

Despite Henry's warning, Armes continued to look at the house. There was no sign of life about the villa, and yet there was a brooding personality about it, an air of mystery which was heightened by the closed shutters that provoked unlicensed imaginings about what must have taken place behind them. Armes closed his eyes. How well he could picture her! Now, confronted by the actuality of her house, he imagined her moving behind those closed shutters with the sunlight from the jalousies striping her golden body with bands of fire. He could see the tumbled bed with the damp, sweaty sheets and the panting, exhausted lover who resembled himself. He opened his eyes and turned his face from the slatternly mansion. Damn it! Of course he didn't want her. But, damn it! Of course he did.

The Villa Topaze was not the only pretentious house in Cap François. There were many others, more beautiful and more carefully tended than that of Topaze. Here were the town mansions of the wealthy planters—those who lived too far away from Cap François to drive back and forth to the opera. Yes, Cap François had an opera, and during the season there were brilliant balls, *soirées*, and entertainments. It was a city of wealth and squalor, riches and poverty, white domination and black subjection. It was, so everyone in the Cap insisted, the Paris of the new world.

The sun blazed on walls of white, pistachio, rose, and pale blue stucco. Armes thought of Boston and the bricks of Pinckney Street and Louisburg Square, washed pale in the dismal spattering of New England summer showers. He saw the wet, slippery cobbles of Tremont Street and the elms on the Common with their sparse verdure, so different from the lush vegetation of the Tropics.

Boston was a pale, anemic spinster compared to the overblown Creole beauty of St. Domingue. Here the flamboyants were just beginning to bloom and every tree gave promise of being a fountain of fiery flowers. The bougainvillea wreathed pillars and walls in cascades of purple, carmine, and magenta. Swags of jasmine hung from the trees; huge white calla lilies trumpeted among their green leaves; waxy white orange blossoms cloyed the air with an overpowering sweetness; brilliant-leaved crotons made harlequin patterns of hedgerows. Over all—vital, throbbing, and burning, was the sun. It caressed the earth with an intensity that produced an eruptive climax of uncontrolled growth. It beat down upon man and fired his passions to the point where they melted his reason, and no sooner were the fires quenched than they were rekindled with greater intensity.

They had passed the overblown *bocage* that threatened to engulf the Villa Topaze, and Armes looked up at Henry's broad back, towering above him from the driver's seat. He saw the tight wrinkles of the blue coat as it stretched across the man's wide shoulders and the dark circles of sweat spreading under the armpits. He noted the life and vigor of the ebony column of Henry's neck and the movement of muscles under the coat sleeves as Henry flicked the whip above the horses' heads. In Henry, Armes saw the force and power of St. Domingue, an overgrowth that compared with everything else in the Tropics, where everything was too big, too beautiful, too odorous, too rank, and too lush. Like Topaze— too beautiful! Once again he closed his eyes and communed with Topaze in an uncensored, voluptuous fantasy. Topaze belonged in St. Domingue—she was a part of it, as much a part of it as Henry and the burgeoning vegetation. And he wanted her, he needed her. Every fiber of his flesh desired her. The consequences were not to be considered, his need for her must be satiated.

They drove on and the jolting of the carriage caused Armes to open his eyes. Now they had passed out of the city and were driving along a road that skirted the shore. Dusty palms gave scanty shade and instead of the multi-colored mansions, there were only crude thatched huts with naked children running in and out of doorways. They followed the road for about two miles to where the slave barracoons were located at a sufficient distance from the town so that their stench would not offend delicate white nostrils. Some distance offshore, Armes could see the long, low, rakish lines of a ship which he took to be the *Dom Joao*, the slave ship that could not anchor at the quay but had to take its living, breathing cargo somewhere beyond the sight of the whites.

Their destination was apparently reached, for Henry stopped the horses and tied them to a multi-rooted banyan tree, waited for Armes to dismount, and then led the way from under the dense shade of the tree along a dusty path to a little wooden pier that ran, in sagging decrepitude, out into the blue water. From inside the slave sheds which stretched away on both sides of the pier came sounds of activity and voices, wailing in a strange, low, minor key. Through the wattled walls they could see moving shadows. Between the stockades there was a house of substantial masonry and as they passed it, a white came and stood in the doorway. He called out to them, or rather to Armes.

"Looking for someone, m'sieu?" Henry answered for him. "Monsieur Holbrook seeks the captain of the *Dom Joao*. He has business with him."

The man lifted a languid hand and pointed to a small boat tied at the end of the sagging wharf. "He's out on the ship. Use the boat if you wish, but if it's slaves you're looking for, they've all been unloaded. Come in here if you want to see them."

"My business is with the Captain," Armes answered.

The white man shrugged his shoulders and again pointed to the boat. "Can your nigger row?"

Henry nodded assent and waited for Armes to precede him down the pier. Armes could hear him muttering under his breath. He knew that Henry didn't like to be called a nigger, and the curses that rolled from Henry's lips were already consigning the white man to some bottomless hell. But Henry walked straight and, after untying the boat, he helped Armes in, still muttering curses whose very ripeness caused Armes to laugh. As they rowed away, they got a better view of the barracoons. They were nothing more than rough palisades of palm trunks, interwoven with branches and daubed here and there with mud. Several armed guards in ragged pantaloons passed back and forth on a beaten path outside the enclosure, and in the jerry-built watchtowers on the corner, other guards lolled, watching, Armes supposed, the milling about of the human cattle inside.

Henry's powerful muscles propelled the boat quickly toward the *Dom Joao*. As they came alongside, a black on board threw them a rope and a second later a rope ladder snaked down the side. Henry motioned for Armes to go first, and although he had some difficulty in negotiating the swaying ladder, Armes climbed up and over the rail, Henry following him. The first thing that Armes noticed was the sickening stench of the ship, and the second was the brilliant luster of the deck. Instead of being scrubbed white, the boards were of dark, polished oak—the result, as he was afterward to learn, of the countless passing of the bare feet over the boards. Although the exercise period of each slave was brief, each hour of the day saw a new contingent arrive on deck for a few moments of sun and air. Then they were crowded back down into the dark hold where they lay, chained together "spoon fashion," unable to sit or stand.

A seaman, lounging nearby, clad only in spotless white pantaloons, snapped to attention and advanced smartly to-

69

ward them. His small blue eyes regarded them quizzically. With a glance at Armes' clothes and bearing, his manner took on respect and politeness. He disregarded Henry entirely and addressed himself to Armes in a strangely accented English that Armes could scarcely understand.

"You'll be looking for someone, sir?"

"The Captain," Armes answered.

"Then follow me, sir." He led the way aft to an immaculately white deckhouse. Armes was astounded by the hygienic cleanliness of the ship. Despite the putrid odor, the entire ship was spotless—scrubbed, painted and polished. It was entirely at variance with his expectations of what a slave ship would be like.

The pantalooned sailor knocked at a door of varnished oak. From inside a cultured voice replied in English, asking who was there. The sailor made the appropriate reply and the door opened. Again Armes was surprised. He was greeted by a tall, blond, young man, who was so obviously English that he could not possibly be anything else. He started to address Armes in French, but Armes interrupted him.

"You are English, sir?"

"Is it as obvious as all that?" The captain laughed. "But—naturally you hardly expected to find an Englishman as captain of a Portuguese slaver. However, the slave trade recognizes no nationality, and although we fly a Portuguese flag we are really an English ship."

"It's good to hear English words again." Armes extended his hand. "Armes Holbrook of Boston, at your service."

"Ah, one of our late enemies, the dauntless New Englanders. And from Boston, the hotbed of revolution! But we are too young to have been enemies. I'm Alonzo Tait of Liverpool, captain of this ship, at your service." He invited Armes inside and pointed to a chair. Armes beckoned for Henry to follow, and he came in and stood behind Armes' chair.

It was a cheerful cabin. The sun glinted through the open portholes onto the polished floor, onto the stout oak table and chairs, the framed hunting prints on the walls, and the red serge draperies hung before the bed. Armes' eyes betrayed his puzzlement and surprise.

"Yes, Mr. Holbrook, this is a slaver. Have you ever been aboard a slaver before? No? Then probably it is a surprise to you. Perhaps it does not coincide with what your idea of a slave ship might be. 'Floating hells,' I think we are called,

70

and some of the slavers were and still are, but not the *Dom Joao*. It's a difficult business, and yet we do the best we can. You see, Mr. Holbrook, we carry a valuable cargo, and it is our business to keep that cargo in good condition. Every slave we lose during the middle passage is a direct financial loss. Therefore we do all we can to keep them in good shape, and a clean ship is a prime necessity. On this last voyage we didn't lose a single man, and when we docked, each one was strong, in good health, without a sore on him. Worth five to ten pounds more that way, so it's good business. Ah, pardon me, Mr. Holbrook, I am digressing—talking shop—and I know you didn't come out here for that."

"I find it most interesting," Armes said sincerely.

"Permit me then to show you around the ship. Just now we are fumigating and cleaning, as we landed practically all our slaves this morning. No matter how clean we keep the ship there is always an odor, engendered by the niggers themselves. Their sweat seems to be composed of different chemicals from ours. But if you care to see the ship . . ."

"My thanks, Captain. It would be a new experience and I am sure an interesting one, but it happens that I have other business with you. I am looking for a slave for myself. Henry"—his thumb pointed behind his chair—"who has been my mentor since I landed in St. Domingue, advised me to come out here and see you. He seems to think that I would be more satisfied dealing with you than if I were to go through regular channels."

Captain Tait took notice of Henry for the first time. "He's quite right. Smart boy, your slave."

"Hardly a boy and not my slave. I call him my friend."

Tait regarded Armes and a faint smile showed at the corners of his mouth. "You are but recently come to St. Domingue, Mr. Holbrook? You must entertain very democratic ideas in Boston."

Armes caught his meaning and nodded.

"Do you mind?" Captain Tait asked Armes, but then, without waiting for an answer, he beckoned Henry to come over to him. He ran his hands over Henry's arms, felt of his biceps, the muscles of his back, hit him sharply on the chest, and then tested his leg muscles with his fingers.

"A prime specimen. Unusually fine. We don't get that kind anymore. Looks like Mandingo or Hausa, possibly Ibo. Speaks French, I suppose. I'll offer fifty pounds for him, but I'll have to see him stripped down before I buy him."

71

Apparently Henry did not mind being appraised so frankly. He merely grinned and looked at Armes.

"He's not for sale," Armes answered curtly," and if he were I'd buy him myself, and I'd give a lot more than fifty for him. But I came here to buy and not to sell."

Tait was most apologetic. "Quite right! Forgive my enthusiasm, but we rarely see so fine a specimen. Yes, Mr. Holbrook, you've come to the right place. On every voyage we have a few special slaves which we do not send to the barracoons along with the others. Fancies, you might say. Special merchandise for which we have special buyers! Now, let's see what we have to offer. I have an unusual Dahomey, a fine buck in his twenties, superb body, strong, intelligent and gentle. Speaks a little English. Make a fine stud for some plantation that wants to improve its breed."

Armes and Henry spoke to each other in French for a moment.

"He might do," Armes said in English.

"Then there is a girl who, I believe, is Egyptian. She's about sixteen, beautiful and accomplished. Also I have an unusual young buck who's hung like a stallion"—he winked at Armes—"bought to order for a gentleman in Port-au-Prince. This gentleman's had me keep my eye out for a buck of this type for several voyages, so I really couldn't let you have him, since I'll make a handsome profit on him. I don't find bucks equipped like him very often."

"Wouldn't be interested anyway." Armes had caught the drift of the captain's conversation. "But how about the Dahomey fellow? Could he be trained as a personal servant?"

The captain considered the matter a moment. "Why not? He's a smart boy. Tell you what, I'll have him brought here. Better have him washed up first, as he's probably pretty musky. While we are waiting will you join me in a glass of wine? We're a Portuguese ship and have some excellent port." Tait turned in his chair and pulled a bellcord behind him.

In a few moments the door opened and a young man appeared.

"You rang, sir?" he said in English, and while he addressed the captain, his glance wandered to Armes, and he gave him an intimate and almost impudent smile.

Immediately Armes was fascinated by the appearance of the lad. He might have been anywhere between sixteen and twenty, slender, delicately formed, with an intelligent oval face. He was bare from the waist up and his skin was a *café-au-lait* color—*café* with an overdose of *lait*. His eyes held Armes' attention. They were large and dark, fringed by extremely long lashes that curled up to finely penciled brows. The nose was short and slightly aquiline. His pate was covered with a mass of dark brown curls which escaped from under a battered fez that sported a frayed black tassel. The boy was dressed only in voluminous white trousers of some thin muslin stuff which were not really trousers at all, but seemingly made of one piece of cloth drawn up between his legs and tucked into a wide red leather belt. The muscles of his chest were smoothly rounded with almost a girlish contour to his breasts, and his skin was entirely smooth and glabrous. He was fully conscious of Armes' appraisal of him and after it, when their eyes met again, he lowered one eyelid in a surreptitious wink that matched the impudence of his smile. He was entirely aware of his beauty.

"Now that is what I am looking for." Armes nodded his head in the direction of the boy. "This young fellow is exactly what I would like."

"I rather had an idea that once you had seen Ali you would be interested in him. And, Mr. Holbrook, Ali *is* for sale. I can recommend him most highly. He's been with me for three voyages and I've come to depend on him, particularly since he's learned English. But, I'm in the slave business and I'm always ready to buy or sell if I can make a profit. I never let sentiment stand in my way, Mr. Holbrook, because I always know that any slave can be replaced."

Armes motioned to the boy to come across the room to him. Ali walked over and stood in front of him, servile yet at the same time insolently independent.

"Look at me, boy!" The brusqueness of Armes' voice concealed his embarrassment. Buying a slave was a new experience for him. "As long as you are for sale I am going to buy you."

"In-sha-Allah." The boy bowed low before him and straightened up. His fingers sought the buckle of his belt, undid it and, as the belt fell to the floor, the trousers floated down to his feet, like a deflated balloon.

Armes' surprise showed in his face. He looked at Tait.

"He means, 'It is the will of Allah.' Ali is a Mussulman from Morocco. He says he was captured by a tribe of

Arab raiders and taken from his father's palace at Marrakech. According to him, his father was a Moorish sheik . . ."

"An emir, begging your pardon, Captain Tait," Ali interrupted softly.

"But why does he take his clothes off?" Armes still could not understand.

"For you to examine him. Take my advice, Mr. Holbrook, never buy a slave without stripping him down. You can never be sure of hidden defects. You're free to finger him as you wish. Examine him carefully. He does have one defect, however. You'll note that he is circumcised, a Moorish custom. I'll admit that it's a trifle disfiguring, but it doesn't harm his value."

"I'll waive the examination," Armes said. "The boy seems to be in good condition." He turned and spoke rapidly to Henry in French.

Henry nodded slowly and spoke only one word. *"Certainement."*

"Come, come, Mr. Holbrook. There is no need to ask anyone for advice. You decided the moment Ali walked into the room. I saw it in your eyes that you were going to buy him, and I saw it in his eyes that he wanted to be sold to you. I've considered selling him before, but every time I did, he wept and wailed and threw himself at my feet and pleaded with me. Foolishly I gave in to him. But you will notice that this time he has not said a word nor wept a tear. But I warn you, Mr. Holbrook. His price is high. A hundred and fifty pounds—good solid English pounds, too—no French livres that are not worth the Revolutionary paper they are printed on."

Henry's hand pressed Armes' shoulder slightly, and the pressure caused Armes to hesitate. He pursed his lips in thought.

Tait leaned forward in his chair, beckoned Ali to him, and slapped the boy softly on his rounded rump.

"He's worth it, Mr. Holbrook. Look at him. Prettiest boy you've ever seen. Smart, too! He's no dumb nigger. As a matter of fact, I don't believe there's a drop of black blood in the boy." His arm reached out and encircled Ali's waist and drew him a bit closer. "It's going to be a real sacrifice to me to sell him, Mr. Holbrook, and although I said one hundred and fifty pounds, I might shade it a little. Let's say one-thirty. That's my lowest price—take it or leave it."

Henry's big thumb nudged Armes' back. It was a go-ahead signal. Armes looked at the boy and then at Tait.

"Very well, one-thirty it shall be, although I do not have that amount of money on me. However, I shall make a draft, payable to you at the offices of Durham, Brown and Company, the English factors in Cap François. I am sure you will find my credit good."

"I am so sure, Mr. Holbrook, that I shall not bother to clear your draft before I allow you to take Ali. Take him along with you now and I will send you a bill of sale for him tomorrow. Go dress yourself, Ali, and put on some civilized clothes—the suit I bought you."

Ali gathered up the cloud of muslin at his feet and started to leave, but Tait detained him.

"Tell me something, boy. Why is it you don't mind being sold to this gentleman? Why aren't you weeping and carrying on and throwing yourself at my feet?"

Ali crossed the room, and with as much dignity as he could muster in his bare skin, he bowed stiffly from the waist to the captain.

"You are a very fine man, Captain Tait. Ali is so happy to be with you so long a time. You very kind to Ali. Now Ali no longer your slave, what?"

"No, you imp of Satan, you're no longer my slave, and believe me, the next slave I get will certainly not be an impudent little self-willed son-of-a-bitch like you."

"Then this little son-of-a-bitch now belongs to this fine gentleman." He turned and bowed to Armes.

"For heaven's sake, come to the point. Say what you're going to say and spit it out quick, because even if I don't own you, I'll wallop you." Tait glanced at Armes. "Like all Moors, he can talk around any given point for an hour and not hit it once. Tell Mr. Holbrook what you want to say."

"Just this, my captain. I do not mind that you sell me to Mr. Holbrook because he is a fine man. He is a bigger man, a stronger man, a handsomer man, and I think a richer man than you. So, with Mr. Holbrook Ali is a bigger, stronger, handsomer, and richer boy."

Tait reached out and cuffed him, but it was a playful blow that only ruffled Ali's curls.

"Mr. Holbrook," Tait laughed, "I hope the first thing you do with this little bastard is to take his breeches down and blister his little ass good, so he won't be able to sit down for

75

a week. I've been negligent, Mr. Holbrook. I should have strung him up and let him have a good taste of the cat, but I didn't. So, take my advice. Buy yourself a nice little whip—one with a good bite in it, and use it often."

"I hardly think that will be necessary," Armes said.

"Oh yes it will. If you don't by the time a month passes you'll not be owning Ali—he'll be owning you. He's an engaging young devil who always manages to get his own way come hell or high water. So, blister his ass night and morning and let him know who's master."

"As you did, Captain Tait?" Although Armes addressed the captain, he was held by Ali's dancing eyes.

"Hell no! That's why I'm warning you."

Ali grinned as he walked to the door. At the door he hesitated for a moment.

"Ali won't mind, Mr. Holbrook, if you do blister his ass every night and every morning." He left, trailing the cloud of muslin behind him.

9

JUST as Henry Christophe had been instrumental in Armes' purchase of Ali, so did he manage a purchase of a horse. It was as good a horse as Ali was a slave—which is to say, excellent. Henry knew horses. His years as a stable boy at the Couronne had taught him to love them and judge them well, and consequently the horse he bought for Armes was a magnificent specimen—a black stallion with a white star on his forehead. But one horse was not enough, Armes quickly learned. Ali was determined that he should have one also, and when Ali decided on something it was next to impossible to gainsay him. He marshaled an array of well-founded arguments and kept at them so persistently, begged so consistently, and pleaded so pitifully that Armes finally yielded, as much to keep the boy quiet as any other reason.

"It is not fitting for you to be alone on the road, my master. A master as important as you should never travel without his servant, otherwise people will think you are too poor to afford such a fine slave as Ali. What is the use of owning the handsomest slave in all St. Domingue if you do not show him off and make every other man jealous of you?"

76

"So, you are the handsomest slave in all St. Domingue?" Armes teased him.

"But naturally, my master, did you not yourself buy Ali? Would you settle for second best? And besides, my master, if I do not have a horse and cannot accompany you wherever you go, I will be separated from you, and that Ali cannot bear. Whip Ali, work Ali, starve Ali, my master, but never separate Ali from you or Ali will die."

So Ali got his way. Henry found a little chestnut mare for him. Then came the christening of the horses. After choosing and rejecting many names, Armes decided on "Tom" for his stallion because, as he said, "he reminds me of a black tomcat Mrs. Frothingham used to have." Ali spurned such a plebeian name and chose "Lalla" for his mare— "Lady" in Arabic.

Armes was quick to admit Ali's proficiency with horse-flesh. The boy was a born rider. Evidently he had been brought up in a saddle and the intervening years on ship-board had not caused him to forget. He and Lalla moved as one, whereas Armes, never an experienced horseman, had to hold Tom down to a slow, jogging trot, and for several days after the purchase he found some difficulty in sitting down to meals. In fact, his whole body ached so that he was forced to dispense with Justine for two after-noons, a circumstance which made Ali extremely happy. He resented the beautiful mulatto and the closed door of Armes' room which denied admittance while she was there. Equally he resented Henry's office in bringing her, and the only slaps he suffered from Armes were the results of his spiteful re-marks about the both of them.

"Niggers!" Ali was contemptuous. "How can you stand those dirty stinking black niggers around you, my master? How can you let that yellow whore in your bed? After she goes I have to change the sheets, they smell so."

But when Armes had recovered sufficiently and was able to ride with some degree of comfort, the first place he planned to go was out to Sans Souci to inspect his planta-tion. Henry gave them explicit directions as to how to get there and one morning, shortly after dawn, Armes and Ali started out. Although it was only a short distance from Cap François, Armes was still experiencing some difficulty in riding, so he decided not to return the same day but to find some overnight accommodation at the plantation.

Nowhere in the world are the hours just after dawn more

beautiful or exhilarating than in Haiti. The cool freshness which has crept down from the mountains during the night still overlies the coastal cities and towns. There is a vital clarity in the air—a translucence which makes all objects seem intimately close. A palm tree down the road stands out in minute detail, its green fronds so distinct and seemingly close at hand that one feels almost able to touch them. A faint odor of wood smoke mingles with the other perfumes in the air, as fires are being lighted in the peasant *cailles* for morning coffee. The fresh breeze causes a restless movement of trees, leaves, vines, and grasses against the mother-of-pearl sky, which soon turns to aquamarine and then to an overpowering blue as the sun ascends higher. And always, in the background, are the purple mountains of Haiti. No matter how early it may be, a cavalcade of peasants are walking along the road in single file, their black feet powdered by the dust of the road, their heavy burdens expertly balanced on their heads. *Marchandes,* peasant women from the hills, will be coming down to the city market, laden with baskets of vegetables. Little *bourriques* raise the dust with their dainty hooves as they labor under huge panniers of fruits and sugar cane or, occasionally, a high pile of crude wooden chairs. The long procession of poor, honest, hardworking people who, despite their poverty and adversity, have been traveling the roads of Haiti for over two hundred years, fill the roads with gaiety and happiness, always ready with a smile, a jest, a laugh, or *bon jour.*

So it was that morning in St. Domingue. As Armes and Ali passed them, they noticed that the slaves had momentarily lost their hangdog manner and their obsequiousness. Walking along the roads, away from their white masters, they seemed to forget their misery and their captivity. Once again they were free, treading the leafy trails of Africa, and for these few moments they were happy again, grinning and giggling at Armes and Ali as they passed. Ali had been following behind until Armes turned in the saddle and motioned him to come alongside. They trotted along abreast.

"Well, boy," Armes asked, "don't you wish you were back on board the *Dom Joao,* sailing across the Atlantic with your Captain Tait?"

"No, milord."

"I'm no *'milord,'* Ali. Just an American, and in the United States we do not have English titles."

"To me you are milord," Ali insisted, looking sidelong

at Armes from under his lashes. "I called Captain Tait *'my captain,'* and he was. But you are more than Captain Tait! You are—how do you say it—my lord and master, so I call you *'milord.'*"

Armes flicked his whip at the boy. Ali ducked and grinned, showing his white teeth. "Milord this! Milord that! Milord has Ali and Ali is a good boy and Ali loves his milord and his milord loves Ali and—"

"Whoa there." Armes scowled at him. "Now just a moment. My liking you depends on one thing and that is that you do what I tell you when I tell you and how I tell you, understand?"

Armes' scowl did not frighten Ali. He was now speaking in a lilting chant and he continued with his singsong.

"And Ali understands everything that Milord wants even before he asks for it. Milord is strong and rich, and he will always look out for Ali and take him back to Marrakech, and then Ali's father will give Milord ten beautiful slave girls, all more beautiful than that stinking nigger Justine, but Milord will not love any of them as much as he loves Ali."

"You and your Marrakech and your slave girls! What is this Marrakech, anyway? You're always talking about it."

"Milord does not know? Oh, what a great pity! Marrakech is the most beautiful city of the Moors, therefore Marrakech is the most beautiful city of the whole world. Oh, milord, you should see it, with the pink tower of the Koutoubia rising against the white snow of the Atlas and the date palms and the palace of my father, the emir."

Armes was becoming accustomed to Ali's exaggerations. He realized that the boy did not deliberately lie, but that he delighted in embroidering facts. Armes usually discounted about half of what Ali said.

"Well, if your father was such a great man, how come you are a slave—my slave?"

Ali's smile disappeared. He rode on a few steps in silence. Then he laughed again. "Yes, by the will of Allah, your slave now, milord, but once Ali had his own slaves. My father was a rich man with a big harem and many hundreds of children. He had many castles—we call them *casbahs*—up in the mountains behind Marrakech, and one day my father and all his harem and all his children, we leave Marrakech to go to one of the *casbahs*."

"How old were you then?"

Ali counted on his fingers. "That was four years ago and I was fourteen years old. I rode with some of the other boys in the baggage carts. On the way, there was an accident with my cart, a wheel came off, but the whole caravan could not wait for one baggage wagon, so they left us behind while the driver fixed the wheel. A band of Blue Men—Berbers from the High Atlas and enemies of my father—had been following the caravan. They caught up with us, killed the driver, and took all of us children with them. We rode for many days, each one of us behind a saddle. Then, at last we came to the coast and the Blue Men sold us to a Portuguese trader. That was the last I ever saw of my brothers. Pretty soon along comes the *Dom Joao* with Captain Tait and he buys me and I go with him and learn to talk his language. Then along comes Milord and buys me, and here I am in St. Domingue and now I learn to speak French. *Bon jour, monsieur. Comment vous portez-vous? Voulez-vous coucher avec moi?* Ali tapped Lalla with the whip and galloped ahead of Armes, only to return in a few moments, standing high in his stirrups. "Al-la-la-la-la-la-la, whew!" he yelled as he came tearing down the road with a cloud of white dust streaming out behind. He reined Lalla in and stopped her within a foot of Tom's nose. Poor Tom, who was ordinarily placid and even-tempered, reared and nearly unseated Armes, who had to cling to the bridle to keep from falling.

"Damn you for the little devil you are!" He shook his fist at Ali. "I promise you that if ever we get to Sans Souci, I'll fix you so you'll have to stand in your saddle to ride back."

"Ali is sorry, milord. He is only showing off because he feels so happy. He promises to be good, but if milord wishes to whip him, milord may do so now, for Ali deserves it." His contrition was made even more disarming by his smile, and Armes could not remain angry with him; his good humor was too infectious. They rode on up together through the foothills. Ali sang snatches of song that he remembered from his Moorish youth, interspersed with some obscene English songs he had learned on shipboard. When they had reached the top of a high hill, they turned and looked below. Cap François was spread out before them, a cluster of tiny houses nestled against the blue sea. Ahead of them lay more mountains with fertile valleys in between, valleys which waved with shimmering green seas of sugar cane. As they went on, the road continued through huge stands of mahogany trees, then down into cultivated valleys with big white houses sitting in majestic isolation at the end of long avenues. Once or twice they passed carriages with wigged and powdered black footmen and delicately clad ladies inside. They met other riders who bowed courteously, but they never lost the constant stream of slaves, trudging along in the white dust.

According to Henry's directions, they knew they must be near the plantation. The heat was now becoming unbearable. Each spot of shade along the road was an island of refuge which they strained to attain, enjoyed for a brief moment, and relinquished reluctantly. They asked directions several times, and within the half-hour, they arrived at a crossroads where a leaning signpost, engulfed in lianas, drunkenly proclaimed "Sans Souci" in faded letters which had once been gilded.

They rode between crumbling white masonry gateposts, each with a gilded wrought-iron lantern standing askew on the top, and up what had once been a long avenue of royal palms. The roadway was now overgrown with weeds and overrun with vines which had crept in between the trees, some of which were broken off and stood like weathered pillars of rotting cement. Those that had survived were unkempt and cluttered with dead fronds. Look where they might, there was an air of disheveled desolation about the approach which was not lessened when they reached the peeling white stucco mansion that appeared between the trees.

It was certainly not a palace—it never had been. But it was solidly constructed of heavy masonry with good lines and some achitectural pretensions in its two stories. A sweeping horseshoe staircase in front led up to a wide balcony which encircled the entire second floor. Square white pillars, quite devoid of capitals or ornament, supported the balcony, but those between the balcony and the overhanging tilted roof were more elaborate, with carved Ionic capitals. It gave the impression of two entirely unrelated houses, one sitting atop the other.

Armes and Ali dismounted and climbed the lichen-encrusted staircase. Lizards scuttled in every direction, dried leaves rustled underfoot. The whitewash had long since disappeared from the balustrade. Thick festoons of green vines wrapped dense verdure around some of the pillars.

At the head of the stairs, two huge carved mahogany doors were solidly set in the deep masonry. These were locked, as were the thick, planked window shutters. Together they circled the balcony which went around the four sides of the building, trying each window in turn; but none yielded. When they descended to the ground floor, they found that the windows there were protected by heavy iron grilles as well as shutters. The place seemed as impregnable as a fortress.

While they were examining the house, a child appeared from around the back, obviously male in his nakedness, stared at them for a moment with his finger in his mouth, then ran back through the dense growth. They followed him along an overgrown path which led to a clearing in the rear of the house. Here they found another house of solid masonry in far better repair than the big house, although it too needed a coat of stucco over the rough bricks. As they approached, a mulatto woman appeared in the doorway. Heads of vari-colored children peeped around her skirts like chicks around a mother hen.

Armes addressed her from the clearing. "You are Madame Fabre?"

She nodded assent.

"Is your husband here?"

She shook her head stupidly. "He's over the hill at the Granville plantation. He won't come back till tomorrow morning."

"I am Armes Holbrook, the owner of this plantation."

She seemed to recognize the name. Her eyes clouded with fear and she started apologizing breathlessly about many things. From her mumbled words, there was, it seemed, a lack of help on the plantation. It was difficult to keep things going. Her husband's health was not too good and she herself was ailing. The fields did not yield well. The slaves were running away. Armes held up his hand and dammed her torrent of words with another question.

"Have you the keys to the house? We must remain overnight."

She quitted the doorway, shooing her brood before her, but returned in a moment with a big bunch of keys dangling from a steel ring. "All here, m'sieu." She bobbed in an attempt at a curtsy. "We never touch them, never go inside the big house. Never stole anything."

Armes took the keys, surprised at their jangling weight.

"Can you furnish us with some food?"

"*Oui*, m'sieu. I'll bring it over to the big house later."

They returned by the same little path to the mansion. Armes chose the largest of the keys, a huge wrought-iron affair. His guess turned out to be correct, for after a period of screeching manipulation, the doors opened. Ali made a wry face at the musty smell which poured out of the doorway to greet them.

"Hurry, Ali! You go that way," Armes pointed with his left hand, "and I'll go this. Open all the window shutters."

They separated in the dim light and one by one, the windows on both sides came open. Some stuck, some were difficult to open, but it was not long before they met at the rear of the house.

"And now, Ali," Armes exclaimed, "let's see what the place looks like. We'll go back to the front door and make a grand tour of my new home."

"And mine too, milord."

"Only as long as you behave yourself," Armes reminded him.

Surprisingly enough, the interior of the house appeared to be in very good condition, although, according to Armes' estimate, it had been several years since the original owners had left. Apparently little had been disturbed, although he noticed that some wooden cases had been broken into. On the right of the hall, which ran from one end of the house to the other, directly through the center, there was a large, high-ceilinged drawing room. The floor was of wide, mahogany boards, as were all the other floors in the house. No expense had been spared on the decorations. The walls were paneled in carved mahogany with details picked out in gold leaf. There was a decorated plaster ceiling and what looked to be an imposing chandelier, swathed in sheets. The furniture also was wrapped in sheets; on removing them, Armes discovered that the *fauteuils* and sofas were in good condition. A large Aubusson rug, however, rolled and tied, was badly chewed by insects. There was a fireplace of sea-green marble upheld by simpering nymphs and bearded satyrs, and the swathed ornaments thereon turned out to be an ormolu clock and matching candelabra. . . .

A large pillared archway led them into the dining room. Here the walls were also paneled but painted white. There was a large round table, upon which Ali scribbled some Arabic characters in the thick dust, many chairs against the wall, and several mirrored consoles. From this a door led into what seemed to be a butler's pantry; there was a dumb-waiter connection with the room below. From here a door led them back into the center hallway again, past a small flight of steps which led to the ground floor. They found several large bedrooms on the other side of the hall, each with its own bathing and dressing room. When they had finished their tour of these they were back at the front door again.

Together they descended the stairs to the ground floor. Here, under the pantry above, was another small room, whose door led into a covered passageway and thence to a smaller building which, from the charcoal stove and the copper pans on the wall, Armes assumed to be the kitchen. All the other rooms on the ground floor were empty, and those under the bedrooms above were small, damp, cell-like compartments. Armes thought that these must have been the quarters of the household slaves. He mentioned this to Ali.

Ali stood still in the doorway of one of the small rooms, looking frightened. "But, milord, you do not intend that Ali sleep in one of these awful places, do you?"

"Why not? Slaves have slept here before."

Ali shook his head. "But not slaves like Ali. Beside the big room upstairs where Milord will sleep, there is a small room. It's a very tiny room and milord would not use it for any-thing. Ali could sleep there. That would be better because, milord, if Ali were far away down here, he could not hear milord call in the night."

"And what makes you think I call in the night?"

"Oh but you do, milord, you do. And you always mention a name which sounds like "Topaze" in your sleep. Then I get up in the night and come to your bed, and when I put my hand on your head it is wet with sweat. Then I stroke your head very slowly and after a while you do not cry out anymore and you sleep again."

Armes looked at him with disbelief. "You do that? You hear me in the night? You get up to see if I am all right? He shook his head in wonderment. You take pretty good care of me, don't you, Ali?"

"Yes, milord."

"I never realized that, boy." Armes put his hand on Ali's shoulder. "Yes, if you want to, little fellow, you may sleep in the room upstairs—at least for tonight."

"And always when we are here, promise me, milord."

"I promise, if it means so much to you." Armes could feel the thin shoulder tremble under his hand. He had not realized the utter devotion the boy felt for him. Now, even more important, he realized that this devotion was given freely—it had not been purchased.

"Then, milord, we go upstairs now." Ali wiped his eyes with the sleeve of his shirt. "Ali will find a broom and sweep out our rooms. Ali will make this place like a real home. Come, milord. This is Ali's home and he loves it. Wait and see, milord, Ali will make it all clean and shining, and milord will love it and love Ali, too."

They started back up the stairs, but suddenly Ali turned and ran back to the doorway of one of the small rooms. Armes saw him standing there on the threshold. Ali made up a face and then deliberately spat into the room, slammed the door shut, and skipped back to Armes.

"Nasty, stinking nigger's room." He made a long face at Armes. "Not good enough for milord's Ali." Without waiting for Armes, he dashed up the stairs, down the hall, and into the big bedroom at the front of the house.

Immediately he became all activity. He yanked the dust covers off the big bed and carried them out onto the balcony and threw them over the railing. Armes uncovered an armchair and sat there, watching him. Ali reached for the last covering and pulled it off, disclosing a satin bedspread over the pillows. The boy was delighted and ran his hands over its silken smoothness. He turned to Armes, exclaiming over the beauty of the spread. Still chattering to Armes, he pulled down the sheet and was turning to gather it up in his arms, when he shrieked. There was genuine fear in his scream. Ali was not playacting.

"Milord, milord, come quick, milord! There's a snake in the middle of the bed."

Armes jumped up and ran to the bed. A quick glance satisfied him that whatever it was it was not a real snake. It was lifeless. He reached over and took up the object which was coiled on the bed. It was a length of sisal rope, dyed green, about two feet long and nearly as thick as a man's wrist. The ends were bound together to keep them from fraying with bits of colored wool and cotton. Fastened into the binding were feathers, chicken feathers, white ones on one end and red ones on the other. One end of the rope was covered with a dried white residue which flaked off into Armes' hands as he touched it. The other end was coated with a thick coagulation,

85

dried and blackened on top but still wet and sticky where it adhered to the counterpane. Armes recognized it as blood. Then it dawned on him that the dried white substance on the other end was semen. He dropped the piece of rope in disgust.

Ali's face was livid under the warm tan of his cheeks. "What is it, milord?"

"I don't know, little fellow." Armes looked at the rope where it lay, coiled on the bed. "I don't know, but this much I do know. It has been put here recently—yesterday, or perhaps even this morning, for the blood is still wet and that is surely blood at that end. As for the other end, it has dried and I had rather not tell you what I suspect it to be. Pick it up, Ali." Ali shrank from it but Armes persisted. "Pick it up and put it in the fireplace in the drawing room. Then burn it. I'll ask Henry about it. He'll know if anyone does. There's something goddamned strange about this. Perhaps it's just as well that you are sleeping up here tonight."

"It's a djinn," Ali muttered as he gathered the rope into a torn fragment of cloth and carried it out of the room. He paused at the door. "Ali can keep the djinns away from milord. Ali knows powerful magic that the djinns are afraid of. Nothing can harm milord with Ali here."

Armes sat down in his chair. He was laughing. "You'll be a great protection, Ali, you and those mighty arms of yours."

Ali hesitated. "Sometimes, milord, love can be a greater protection than strong arms."

10

ALI had never exerted himself overmuch during the short period he had belonged to Armes. He had been most meticulous in his care of Armes' clothes as well as his own. He had badgered the maids in the hotel to keep the room clean, lording it over them with a superiority which they resented from another slave but which, nevertheless, they obeyed. Most important of all, he had always been on hand to anticipate and gratify any wish that Armes might express, and as he occupied a small cot in Armes' room, he was on hand day and night. But mainly Ali's activities consisted of gossiping with the hotel maids and playing games with Marie Louise, Coidovic's daughter, or—what seemed to please him even better—hanging around the stables with the grooms and stableboys. But this afternoon at Sans Souci, he was a whirlwind of activity. He immediately took charge of the house, even to the extent of telling Armes what to do.

Once he had set Armes to work with a broom, he disappeared for half an hour or more. On his return, he had several female slaves with him, whom he had recruited from the cane fields. These he armed with brooms, rags, mops, and dusters, threatening them with whipping if they failed to carry out his orders. His threats were unintelligible to them, but his pantomimes were as effective as words. When they were all busily working at the tasks he had set for them, he again left for Fabre's house, and soon had Madame Fabre and her brood running back and forth to the big house, their arms full of fruits, vegetables, squawking chickens, and fresh bread.

By late afternoon there was a semblance of order on the main floor. The clean, damp smell of washed masonry mingled with that of beeswax and lemon oil. Drawers had been opened, linen found and aired, rugs swept and beaten, floors polished, draperies shaken out, and beds made. Ali saw to it that a small bed was moved into the dressing room which adjoined Armes' bedroom. He would not allow any heavy-handed slave to arrange his bed or Armes' and insisted that the sheets be carefully smoothed just so and just as carefully tucked in. When this was finished to his satisfaction, he took a tour of the house, imperiously dismissed the slaves, shooing them down the back stairs, and returned to the drawing room to sink exhausted in an armchair. Armes was stretched out in another. However, Ali could not rest. He hopped up, darted across the room, carried back a footstool, placed it under Armes' long legs, and adjusted the louvres of the jalousies so the setting sun would not shine in his master's face. He noted that Armes was beginning to nod sleepily from his day of hard work and tiptoed out of the room.

Had Armes been awake, he would have heard a banging of pans and a clatter of utensils from the faraway kitchen, and smelled the smoke of burning charcoal. But he slept on until Ali came into the room with a tin bucket of warm water and started to wash his face. Then he awoke, smiled sleepily, and stretched in complete satisfaction, allowing Ali to finish the job and dry him with a towel. He stood up slowly, stretching again and yawning, and followed Ali's beckoning finger into the dining room.

Armes might well have been dreaming, for it was hard to believe the transformation that had taken place in that room while he had slept. The huge table top of mahogany had been polished until it shone like a dark mirror, and it now reflected a crystal bowl of roses in the center. Two tall silver candelabra shed a flickering light in the room. True, the candles were mismatched; some of them were hardly more than stubs. But they made a brave effect. The table was set for two with odds and ends of china—beautiful and delicate pieces of Sèvres which Ali had discovered with the crude peasant pottery of St. Domingue. The mismatched dishes mattered little, however, to Armes, whose attention was drawn to the steaming platter of chicken on the table, flanked by a bowl of hot yams and another of tiny black mushrooms, and to the buffet where another crystal bowl brimmed with a compote of pineapple and bananas, liberally sprinkled with fresh grated coconut.

Armes walked over to the table, dipped his finger in the chicken, and licked the rich gravy from his finger. He nodded his head approvingly.

"Surprisingly good cook, that overseer's wife," he said.

"She? Cook?" Ali drew his lips down in scorn. "That bloody wench, she cooks nothing fit to eat. You think she cooked this dinner?"

"Who else?"

"Ali! I did not want milord poisoned with her messes."

"And where did you learn to cook?"

Ali nodded his head wisely. "Ali learned many, many things on the ship with Captain Tait. Perhaps milord will soon find out how many wonderful things Ali knows. Perhaps Ali will surprise you. Ali knows many things"—he looked up at Armes —"many!"

"Well, thank God you learned something on that ship. From what Henry tells me of things that go on at the Couronne, you learned some things which you shouldn't have."

Ali's mouth closed to a narrow line. "Damn that Henry! Ali hates him. That big nigger is jealous of me. He wants to be your slave. Thinks you belong to him. He thinks because he brings that Justine, you like him. Bah! Here we have no Justine, but you have Ali. You belong to Ali, not to that stupid big black ox, Henry, nor that dirty yellow whore, Justine. Milord belongs to Ali."

Armes held up a warning finger. "Now hold on just a minute, young fellow. How do you figure this I belong to you stuff? Isn't it the other way around—don't you belong to me?"

Ali's hands waved the matter airily aside, but Armes was not to be put off. There was a strong tone of authority in his voice that forced Ali to drop his hands and listen as Armes continued.

"So far you and I have managed to get along pretty well, haven't we?"

Ali nodded, his chin drooping.

"Now then, listen to me, and don't get too big for your breeches. Henry has been a good friend to me. I like him and I trust him. He's intelligent, honest, and straight. There will be no trouble between you and Henry. You look up to him and respect him. And as for Justine, that's none of your goddamned business. When I want a woman, I'll take one, and I'm not coming to you to ask your permission either. Understand?"

Ali nodded again, but there were tears in his eyes this time.

"Because, my lad," Armes continued, "if you don't treat Henry right and forget about Justine, I'll sell you so goddamned fast you won't know where you are going."

"Milord, milord," Ali cried, and lifted up his tear-stained face to meet Armes' steady stare. "Oh, milord . . ." And he ran from the room.

Armes listened to the bare feet padding across the polished boards of the hall. He looked again at the table, the food, the candles fluttering in the breeze, the roses in the bowl. He sat down and began to eat, but he had no taste for the food, delicious as it was. Then he thought of the loving care which had prepared it as a surprise to him and lost his appetite completely. His conscience, so long forgotten, told him that he had been unkind and that he had needlessly hurt someone who cared for him. He tried to think he was only disciplining the boy, but he realized that his threat of selling Ali was small gratitude for what Ali had tried to do for him. It was not easy for Armes to admit he was wrong, but as he looked at the food in front of him, he knew he must make amends. He rose and walked out of the room, through the drawing room, and out onto the balcony.

In the darkness outside, Ali's white shirt and pantaloons appeared almost phosphorescent. The boy was crouched on the top step, his arms flung out, sobbing his heart out. Armes stood over him for a moment, then reached down and picked him up, carrying him in his arms back into the house. Ali continued sobbing as Armes carried him into the hall, pushed open the door of the bedroom with his foot, walked in and lay the boy down on the bed. Then he made a hurried trip to the dining room, returning with a handful of dishes. He placed these on the floor beside the bed and returned for the candelabra. The light showed Ali's face hidden in the pillow, his shoulders heaving. Armes slipped one hand under the boy's head and turned him over, then reached down and filled a large tin spoon with chicken and held it to Ali's mouth. Ali opened his eyes and his mouth at the same time. He looked up at Armes and nibbled at the chicken.

"Milord, don't sell Ali."

"Quiet, little fellow."

"Oh, milord, never, never, never sell Ali."

Armes' big hand on his shoulder reassured Ali. "I'll make you a promise, little fellow. I'll never sell you. You can depend on that. Now, let's do something about all this good food that you have prepared. Let's eat it before it gets cold and then, Ali, let's sleep. I'm so goddamned tired."

"And I'm so goddamned happy, milord."

They made short work of the chicken. The candle stubs were nearly burned out, so Armes extinguished them and opened the tall windows wide. A spot of moonlight reached onto the bed and touched Ali's dark curls on the pillow. The boy could not, Armes was sure, have dropped off to sleep so quickly, but his regular breathing indicated deep slumber. Armes shook him.

"Wake up, boy, and climb into your own bed."

There was no response. Armes shed his clothes in an untidy heap on the floor and reached down to lift Ali again and carry him to his own bed, but instead, Ali's arms encircled Armes' neck and drew him down. Armes did not resist. The arms were as warm and clinging as those of Topaze might have been, and their possessiveness was not unwelcome.

Slowly, very slowly, the spot of moonlight traveled from the big bed, glinting in its path on the smooth muscles of Armes shoulders making a dark shadow where Ali's head rested on his chest. The boy murmured in his contentment and Armes' fingers twined the dark curls. The curse of djinn, if curse it was, had apparently vanished. Armes was drowsily at peace.

11

JUST as the moonlight had ebbed from the room the night before, so, late the next morning, the sun forced its way in between the slatted jalousies to shine into Armes' eyes and awaken him. He opened his eyes, blinked in the strong light, then spent a few drowsy moments trying to orient himself to the reality of day and the strange surroundings. The events of the night before intruded on his memory and he tried, unsuccessfully, to feel even a momentary disgust for himself for having yielded. What the hell? What was done was done, and he blamed neither Ali nor himself—least of all himself. Not a few of his friends at Harvard had so indulged themselves, and although he had never joined them, it was probably because he had had Kitty and the little house in Cambridgeport. He yawned and stretched himself. Besides, Ali was his slave, and he could do with him as he wished. That made a difference—a big difference. Like Anastase Renaud who had brought his slave from New Orleans to school with him— Anastase was a hellion for the women, but he openly bragged that on those nights when he was unsuccessful, his Negro boy Polycarpe made a good substitute.

He turned over on his side to wake Ali, but Ali was nowhere to be seen, and only the rumpled pillow testified that he had been there. Armes wondered if Ali might have suffered some remorse, and if perhaps unwillingness to face him in the light of morning had made him flee. But Armes realized that all that had happened had been far more natural to Ali than it had to himself, and that Ali, far from feeling remorse, was probably exulting.

The aroma of boiling coffee, wafted along the hall and into the bedroom, provided a far better explanation of Ali's absence, which was immediately confirmed by his appearance in the doorway with a makeshift tray, laden with cups of coffee, bread, and fruit. Ali appeared very meek and subdued, and did not speak to Armes as he plumped the pillows behind Armes' back and settled the tray on his lap. Nor did Armes speak to him while they were eating, although he was rather curious as to why Ali had not dressed. When they had finished eating, Ali reached for the tray and in doing so, his hand,

91

with trembling fingers, rested for a moment tentatively on Armes' hand. Armes grinned up at him and winked, causing the boy to burst into a wild chant as he gathered up the tray and ran off with it to the kitchen. When he returned, dancing to his tuneless song, Armes was searching frantically.

"Where in hell are my breeches and shirt?" He looked at Ali. "And why in hell are you wandering around here bareassed? Get some clothes on and find mine for me."

"Your clothes, milord, will be ready for you in a few moments, and mine for me. After riding yesterday and especially after cleaning house, everything we had on was dirty and, milord, stank." He wrinkled up his nose. "Phew! So, I got up this morning early, while you were still asleep, and I washed them out. Now, they have all dried in the sun and I wait for an iron to heat. If milord will be patient, he will have his clothes."

Armes chased him out of the room and down the stairs to the kitchen where, sure enough, a charcoal iron was heating. The clothes had been sprinkled and were rolled into neat bundles. Ali tested the iron with a spit-moistened finger. The resultant hiss was evidently satisfactory, for he unrolled Armes' white breeches and spread them out on a long table which he had padded with sheets. Armes waited, leaning against the door. Ali looked up at him sideways.

"What does milord plan to do today,"

"Any one of a million things. Why?"

"Then may I make a suggestion to milord?"

Armes nodded.

"If Ali can find a piece of paper and something to write with, Ali wants to make a list of things we are going to need here at Ali's house. Milord, we have been robbed! Ali has found several boxes which have been broken open and everything taken out. One box must have contained silver, for Ali found one spoon in the bottom. There are no decent dishes, but several empty barrels in which I believe they were packed. We need many things, milord, if we are to live here. We need dishes, both for cooking and eating, silver for the table, linen for the beds, some new furniture—many things."

"I suppose taking inventory is another of the things Captain Tait taught you. He must have taught you a lot of things. Like last night. Did Captain Tait teach you or did you teach Captain Tait?"

Ali's face flushed but he pretended not to understand.

"Yes, milord, Captain Tait taught me to make what he

92

called the inventory. Each time we finish a voyage, Captain Tait have Ali take the inventory. That is everything we have, everything we lose or break, and what we need to buy for the next voyage. Now, I shall make the inventory for my home at Sans Souci."

Armes started to laugh. Not only did Ali own Armes himself, now he owned Sans Souci. "Your house?" he asked.

"Naturally, milord! You see—I am yours because you bought me and you own me. But, on the other hand, you are Ali's property just as much as Ali is yours. Ali owns milord. Tell me, milord, does everything I have belong to you?" He pointed to his own breeches, lying rolled up on the table. "My clothes?" He pointed to his body. "My body?"

"Guess you're right there," Armes admitted. "I bought the breeches you're going to iron and if I bought you, I bought your body, too."

"So," Ali continued, "if everything I have belongs to you, so does everything you have belong to me. These breeches of yours belong to Ali, so he irons them. And you, milord, you belong to me too."

"You're a little too fast for me, boy, but you seem to have got everything fixed to your own satisfaction. Well, go ahead, make the inventory. Who do you think robbed us?"

"That's easy," Ali said. "Who had the key?"

"The overseer."

"Then he's the one who robbed you."

"When he arrives, I'll try to find out how things stand. Can't accuse a man before I've even seen him. However, I don't think much of him. The place looks pretty bad. If we put it into production again, it's going to be a big job, but it used to make money and it looks like fertile land. I don't know a goddamned thing about running a plantation, but I think I've got brains enough to run it right and to my own satisfaction. I'd like to see it productive and prosperous again."

"And you've got Ali to help you, milord." Ali finished his ironing with a flourish and handed the freshly laundered shirt and breeches to Armes. He proceeded to press his own clothes.

"Today I get those same wenches back again and make them work more," he said as Armes turned to leave. "Lots still to be done here."

Armes nodded his assent and left, taking the little path that led through the shrubbery to Fabre's house. He noticed that some slight attempt had been made to clean up the surroundings. The clearing had been swept and picked up. He

93

rapped on the wooden frame of the open door and a man appeared from inside. He slouched against the door frame, eyeing Armes, and as Armes looked at him, he sensed something vaguely familiar about him. He was a mulatto, lighter in color than his wife, with black hair which waved in oily rings about his head and descended in long black streaks onto his cheeks. His features were finely chiseled and had once been handsome, but now they were blurred and softened by dissipation. Where his wife's face had been merely stupid, his was crafty.

Fabre peered at Armes suspiciously from large eyes with red-veined, yellowish whites. Although he was clean and decently dressed in white linen, there was something unkempt and soiled about his appearance. His uncleanliness was not on the outside—it seemed to seep through from some hidden spring inside the man. When he realized who Armes was, he greeted him effusively, with a proper display of obsequiousness, and invited him to come inside. But the dark interior of the house did not seem attractive and Armes motioned to a bench in the shade of a large mango tree and walked over and sat down. Fabre followed him.

They had scarcely settled themselves on the bench when Fabre started on a monotonous recitation of alibis which he carried on in a whining falsetto. He had had difficulties with the slaves; there had been a lack of rainfall; fires had been lit in the cane fields. It was a long, tiresome, and well-rehearsed recital of failures, which might have been plausible had not the man's manner put Armes on guard. The more Fabre attempted to explain, the more Armes was certain that the man was hiding something. Armes began to feel that Fabre was covering up not only for himself but for somebody else.

He questioned Fabre about the acreage. How much was under cultivation? What was the amount of cane raised last year? What did he expect this year? Even with Armes' meager knowledge he sensed the various discrepancies in the other's answers. He asked for an accounting of the livestock on the place—the number of oxen, mules, and donkeys. There were no horses, he found out, except the one that belonged to Fabre. Then he brought up the subject of the slaves.

"A poor lot, M'sieu Holbrook, a very poor lot." Fabre shrugged his shoulders and spread his hands wide in a gesture of helplessness. "What we have here now were left by the owner when he departed. The overseer that came before me did not buy any new ones, so that those which are left are getting old, and it is hard to get a decent day's work out of them, no matter how much I beat them. Lately they have been sullen and disobedient and the more I punish them, the worse they get. I've tried everything. I've had them whipped —in fact I've done it myself. I've strung them up by the thumbs and I've kept them in the stocks for days at a time. The goddamned nigger bastards! Lazy, thieving rascals, that's what they are! But the worst of them are gone—run up into the mountains where there are colonies of runaway slaves. Ten ran away last month."

"Thieving, did you say?" Armes remembered Ali's mention of the empty boxes in the house.

"Steal anything, they would." Fabre spat on the ground.

"Things are missing from the big house."

"Then they stole them." Fabre was quick to accuse.

"But how could they get in? The windows were all shuttered and the doors locked and only you had the key."

"Those bastards are like snakes, m'sieu, they can get in anywhere." He looked up at Armes calculatingly. "Do you know what is missing, M'sieu Holbrook?"

"No, but there are signs of thieving."

Fabre seemed relieved. He stood up, as though to dismiss the matter. "I'll be glad to show you around, M'sieu Holbrook. How about a glass of rum before we start?"

"Too early for drinking," Armes said, knowing from the reek of the other's breath that he did not regulate his drinking by the hours of the day. "But take me around and show me everything, Fabre."

They started off on foot. A little below the house which sat on the crest of a small hill, they came to a haphazard collection of wattled huts, poor ramshackle affairs of mud-daubed woven branches with thatched roofs. There was a center area of packed dirt with a muddy spring in one corner whose overflow had eaten a boggy course through the center, now clogged with refuse. The whole compound looked and smelled as if it were in the last stages of decay. Armes found courage to look into one of the hovels and retreated quickly. There was nothing inside but a pile of dirty grass in one corner, a few rags hanging from the walls, and a battered tin bucket. He took the freshly laundered handkerchief that Ali had so recently ironed and held it to his nose.

"What manner of animal lives here, and why must they be kept so near the big house? Are these pigsties?"

"We have no pigs, m'sieu. These are the slave quarters."

Armes spun around quickly and faced Fabre. He was hoping that he had misunderstood. "Repeat that, Fabre."

"Slave quarters, m'sieu."

"Surely you do not mean that this"—he waved his hand over the filth—"is where they live?"

"But of course! At least they sleep here. They eat over there." Fabre pointed to a larger thatched structure with open sides. "That is, they eat there night and morning, but of course at noon we carry their fodder to the fields. See! They are leaving with the food now."

Armes noticed two Negroes carrying a pole between their shoulders from which a large iron kettle was suspended.

"Tell them to stop."

Fabre spoke to the two slaves, and they shifted the kettle to the ground. Armes walked over to it and looked inside. He saw a gray, farinaceous mess—some sort of boiled grain with chunks of greasy fat in it. He stuck his finger in it to taste it, but the sliminess of it on his finger was too revolting. To have put it in his mouth would have made him vomit.

"You feed this mess to human beings?" His voice cracked with anger. "You expect men and women to work all day on sustenance like this? No wonder they are sullen. No wonder they flee to the hills. I would myself. Dump it out. Spill the whole rotten, stinking mess on the ground."

"But that is what slaves always eat—boiled millet."

"How often?"

"Every day, three times a day."

"Then from now on, here at this plantation, they will not eat it, not unless it is cooked better. They are to have a decent meal today. I don't care what you give them, but it must be real food. Kill a hundred chickens! Slaughter an ox! See to it that they are fed decent food, decently cooked. Something has got to be done. I cannot say what now, but I cannot have men and women who are entirely dependent on me eating this putrid slop and being punished for not working. These are orders, Fabre! Carry them out! Now I want to see all the slaves on this plantation. Summon them in from the fields. How long will it take?"

"I'll ring the bell, that will summon them. If we can get the lazy *cochons* started, it should not take more than a quarter of an hour for them to get here."

"Have them assemble in front of the steps to the big house. What language do they speak?"

96

"Creole."

"Would they understand my French?"

In reply Fabre merely shrugged his shoulders. "You can tell me what you want to say. I will translate."

Armes turned and left him, aware that he could not trust Fabre to translate for him. On the way back to the house he heard the plantation bell tolling. When he arrived, he told Ali to dismiss the female slaves that were working there, spruce himself up, and come out onto the balcony to stand beside him.

They had not long to wait. At first singly, then by twos and threes, and finally in large groups, the slaves came in from the fields with dragging steps, fearful of what this unusual summons might mean for them. Fabre, uninvited, came up on the balcony and stood besides Armes.

"Haven't counted them, M'sieu Holbrook, but I'd say they were all here."

From the mass of upturned faces below him, which he judged to be around some three hundred persons, ranging from toddlers to decrepit old men, Armes could distinguish nothing in the way of individuals, but as he scanned their faces more closely he noticed that there was not a smiling face in the assemblage. Abject misery and hopelessness, mingled with fear, were written on every face. He realized that they were a group of people totally without hope, to whom death would come as a welcome release from their sufferings. The older men and women were pitiful sights—lame, crippled, deformed, and blind, filthy with dirt, clad only in rags, with scarcely enough energy to stand up. Even the younger men and women, those who should have been strong and healthy, were so thin and emaciated that they appeared to have no strength. There wasn't a single article of clothing that was intact, and some of the slaves were even naked. Armes stared down at them. Now that he had assembled them and seen what they looked like, he was tongue-tied. It was hard for him to believe that they were his property.

As he looked at the faces staring blankly up at him, he began to pick out individual faces from the mass. In the second or third row, he noticed a young man, a head taller than those around him, with a face that seemed more intelligent than the rest. He pointed down at him and their eyes met.

"You!" Armes beckoned. "Come up here!"

The crowd parted to make way for the fellow, who advanced to the foot of the steps. He was clad only in a wisp of greasy rag held up by a thin rope of braided grass. Although tall and heavily boned, Armes could count his ribs. He did not seem quite as dirty as the rest, but his skin had the lackluster gray look of the others. He remained standing at the foot of the stairs.

"Come up here." Armes beckoned again.

"You going to whip me, master?"

"No, why should I? I want you to talk to these people for me."

Slowly the man ascended the steps, his dusty, splayed feet black against the white marble steps. As he reached the balcony, he stood facing Armes. The heavy musk from the slave's body was overpowering, but Armes took him by the shoulder and turned him around to face the group below. It was then that he noticed the hideous pattern of welts on the fellow's back. Some of the recent ones were unhealed and badly infected, with yellow pus seeping from them.

"What's your name?" Armes asked.

"*M'appelle Lazare.*"

"*Bien!* Can you understand me, Lazare?"

The man nodded his head in assent, but before Armes could speak, Fabre pushed forward.

"This is the worst buck on the plantation, m'sieu. He's a troublemaker. Always fighting. Needs a damn good hiding."

"Looks as though he's had it. Step back, Fabre. I'm handling this." Armes came up to the Negro and, much as he shrank from the fellow's nearness, he put his hand on his shoulder, not only to reassure him but the others.

"Hear me, Lazare! Do not be frightened. I am not going to harm you. Listen to what I say to you and then tell it to the people below in words they will understand."

"Yes, *patron.*"

Armes spoke slowly so that Lazare would understand.

"Tell them that I am the owner of this plantation and that I have just arrived. Tell them that from now on things are going to be changed here. Just as soon as I can manage it, these people are going to have decent places to live in, decent clothes to wear, and decent food to eat. The sick will be taken care of. There will be hours for work and hours for rest."

He waited for Lazare to repeat his words. The man took a step forward and spoke to the people below. They scarcely seemed to comprehend what he was saying. Armes could follow some of the Creole *patois,* but when Lazare started shouting at them, Armes knew he was speaking on his own.

"What are you telling them?" Armes asked. "I didn't say all that."

"I tell them, *patron,* that they must believe you. I tell them that you are a good man and you mean what you say. I tell them to hope because I know you will keep your word."

"Thank you. Now tell them that there will be no more whippings unless I, myself, order them. Nobody will ever be whipped again except on my orders, and then only when I have had a chance to investigate the case."

"These words from Lazare caused a brightening of faces. Armes noticed several smiling.

"Tell them also that I leave Sans Souci now to go into the city. I shall return in a few days. In the meantime, I appoint you *surveillant* of your people. You will take orders as usual from Monsieur Fabre, but you will report to me when I return. I charge you to keep order here while I am away. The dinner that was prepared for you today has been thrown away at my orders. You will, perforce, go hungry until nightfall, but then you will have real food. There will be no work done the rest of today or tomorrow. I want everyone to rest and clean their bodies in the river. We have a lot to do, Lazare, and it may take time, but the moment I return, we shall start."

Now Lazare's words were making sense to the people. A ray of hope had appeared in their lives. What started out as a feeble cheer grew in intensity. Armes waved in acknowledgment. Much to his surprise, Lazare fell to his knees before him and grabbed his hand, pressing it to his lips.

"We thank you, *patron,* but without you here to protect us, that man will punish us. As soon as you leave, he will beat me for having spoken—beat me as he has done many times before."

Armes pulled his hand away from Lazare's and faced Fabre.

"You have heard my orders, Fabre. No work on the plantation the rest of this day and tomorrow. A decent meal with meat for these people tonight and decent food until I return. I shall expect you to carry these orders out and shall hold you responsible. If anything happens to Lazare while I am away, I shall also hold you responsible, so guard him well and treat him well."

"Oui, oui, M'sieu Holbrook," Fabre agreed with oily servility.

"And you, Lazare, when I return, report to me. Do not wait to be bidden, but come here yourself and see me. Tell me if everything I have said today has been carried out. And one word more to these folks. Inform them that when I return I want to talk to each one of them in person."

"Merci, patron, merci."

"Go now, Lazare, and lead these folks back to their quarters. And you too, Fabre."

Armes and Ali waited on the balcony until all had left. As they passed, Armes accepted their pitiful greetings, the toothless smiles of the old women, the waving hands of the young ones, the grins of the young men, and the bows of the oldsters.

Armes and Ali stepped back into the house. Ali went to the desk in the bedroom and took up some pieces of paper to show to Armes, but Armes waved them away.

"Later, boy, later. We must leave. Get someone to saddle the horses, and let's get out of here. I cannot believe what I have seen. Those were people, Ali. People! Human beings! Did you see them?"

"I did, milord, and I thank Allah that I was not a slave like them."

"As well you might. Now run and get the horses ready. I'll lock up the house."

By the time Armes had closed all the shutters and locked the front door, Ali was waiting with the horses, and they galloped down the long avenue of palms onto the main road. Just as they turned onto the road, they could see that a carriage had halted under the shade of a group of palms. As they drew near it, Armes recognized the same gaudy equipage of Topaze which he had seen on the quay. She was in the carriage, leaning over the side, talking to a man in the road. It was Fabre. As Armes and Ali drew alongside, they slowed down in order to pass the carriage single file.

Topaze looked at Armes and smiled a slow, languorous smile. She leaned forward a little more, so that her bodice gave a better view of the perfection of her breasts. Her eyes fastened on him, and it was impossible to mistake the meaning of her glance. Then she spoke, and her voice, deep, low, and slightly husky, was as hypnotic as her eyes.

"You are Monsieur Holbrook, *oui?*" She allowed herself a smile to punctuate her question. "What a wicked brother I

100

have that he is so slow to introduce us. *Alors,* I must do it myself. I am Topaze, monsieur. Fernand"—she fluttered her hand in Fabre's direction—"is my brother." She leaned back against the cushions.

Armes stared at her, fascinated. The warm saffron of her skin was an invitation. The dark brown hair with glints of gold, the amber eyes, the curve of her lips, neck, and breasts all invited him. There were a million things he wished to say, but suddenly he was speechless. He could only manage a jerky bow of his head as he passed her. Ali followed him, surveying her boldly and calmly, appraising her carefully as he passed. He rose in his stirrups and deliberately spat into the carriage. Topaze half rose in her seat. With the slow, sinuous grace of a cat, she spat back at him, and for that brief moment, her lips curled in a mocking sneer that spoiled her beauty.

"Petite génisse!" She spat at him again. "Does the little heifer have eyes for the bull?"

"Let us say the bull has eyes only for the little heifer," Ali answered her, and trotted up beside Armes.

"A bitch!" Ali exclaimed.

Armes' eyes were glazed. He was looking straight ahead. He turned to look at Ali as though he had never seen him before.

"Undoubtedly a bitch, little fellow, but a most delightful one. Yes, a most delightful one!" He touched the whip to Tom and they galloped on in silence to Cap François.

12

ARMES had never been aware that he possessed any particular business ability before. He did not realize that he had inherited a certain amount of Yankee horse-trader acumen from his New England ancestors. Now his fingers itched to straighten out his affairs at Sans Souci. It was a challenge to him, and he surprised even himself with his energy. He awoke early at the Couronne and tumbled Ali out of bed to go in search of coffee and bread. When he had finished his breakfast, he went below and found Coidovic just entering his office. Armes went in with him and laid his cards on the table, explaining his lack of experience, his ignorance about

101

the management of a plantation and, most of all, his need for expert advice and practical help. He had a great deal of confidence in the portly, middle-aged Negro, who years ago had started with a coffeepot and two tin cups, and now owned the most important hostelry in St. Domingue, patronized exclusively by the white elite of the island.

Monsieur Coidovic turned out to be helpful. He liked Armes, and his advice was for Armes to borrow Henry for a week or even more and let Henry organize matters. For, as Coidovic explained, nobody knew more about affairs in St. Domingue than Henry Christophe. Henry's years as a stable boy, listening to the grooms and coachmen talk over the intimate secrets of the whites, and later his duties as attendant in the billiard room, where affairs of the colony were discussed as freely before him as though he were a piece of furniture, had all contributed to the vast fund of knowledge now stored in his head.

"*Mais oui,* Monsieur Holbrook," Coidovic said, nodding his head in judicious approval, "Henry is indeed your man. I'll gladly loan him to you. But this time you'll have to pay him. I said *him,* you understand, not me."

"Willingly, Monsieur Coidovic. I'll pay Henry, and I'll pay you with more than money—with my thanks."

"I have a special reason for asking," Coidovic replied. "You see, Henry is buying his own freedom and I am anxious to help him, although as soon as he pays me for himself and I give him his manumission, I intend to return his money to him in the form of a dowry for my daughter, Marie Louise."

"They are to be married?" Armes was surprised, as Henry had never mentioned his interest in the girl.

Coidovic laid a stubby finger against his full lips.

"Yes, but keep it a secret. Henry does not want it known until he becomes a free man. I offered to free him a long time ago, but he insisted on earning his freedom himself. He's saved the money, a sou here, a centime there, out of his tips, and now he has nearly reached the full amount. That's why I am anxious to help him."

Armes thought of the attractively plump little Marie Louise, who had played childish games with Ali. He had considered her little more than a child although she was now fifteen, a marriageable age in the Tropics. Then he thought of the tall young giant with the straight-cut features, and he knew that the marriage would be a success. They would be well mated.

"You will have a fine son-in-law, Monsieur Coidovic, and Henry will have a fine wife."

Coidovic acknowledged his thanks with a little bow. "You know, Monsieur Holbrook, Henry cares a lot about you, and it is very strange. You may not know it, seeing him around here, but he hates all whites. He hides it well, that Henry Christophe, but he hates them—all except you. He seems to worship you, Monsieur Holbrook. But do not take Henry's worship lightly. I would rather have Henry Christophe for a friend than an enemy. Henry's feeling for you is genuine, Monsieur Holbrook."

"And mine for him. *Au revoir,* Monsieur Coidovic. May I take Henry with me now?"

With Coidovic's ready assent, they left soon after, Armes striding ahead with Henry and Ali behind. Remembering Armes' warning, Ali was all graciousness to Henry now, and Henry treated the boy with the idle condescension one might give to a bumbling puppy at his heels. He teased Ali about his frantic efforts to keep up with the long-legged strides of two such giants as Armes and himself, and once, when Ali fell behind, he picked him up bodily and set him down a couple of paces ahead.

"Got to pump those legs of yours fast, boy, to keep up with your *patron* and Henry."

Armes turned and inquired of Henry where the best place would be to buy house furnishings—kitchen pots and pans, silver, draperies, sheets, candles, mirrors, pictures for the walls, and carpets for the floors, for Ali had listed all these things in his inventory. Henry recommended the Magasin Delacroix in the *Place* and Armes dispatched Ali off in that direction. But before the boy ran off, Armes warned him:

"Now look here! I know absolutely nothing about buying such things for a house, and I doubt very much if you do either. You claim you do, so go over to this place and look around. Pick out what you think we need at Sans Souci. Remember, I'm no millionaire, but I want the place to look right and I want it comfortable. Have them put everything to one side that you pick out and I'll come over and look at it later. If it looks good, I'll buy it. So now run along and get busy. Remember! Keep things simple—no gold furnishings, no red velvet, and no paintings of naked women."

"No naked women! No!" Ali made a hasty getaway, primed with the importance of his errand.

Armes and Henry walked on down to the street that

103

bordered the waterfront and into the office of Durham, Brown and Company, the English factors. Once inside Armes was greeted with a hushed solidarity that was far removed from the flamboyant atmosphere of the Tropics. The paneled walls of dark wood, the green baize-covered tables, and the rows of pen-scratching clerks reminded him of Mr. Frothingham's establishment in Boston. He engaged one of the partners in conversation and told him to draw on Mr. Frothingham in Boston for any bills that might come in, but the man advised him that he already had a credit of over ten thousand English pounds. Mr. Durham, for it turned out that it was he to whom Armes was talking, pointed out, with the same circumspection that Mr. Frothingham would have used, that such an amount should be sufficient not only for the present but for some time to come. Armes had little idea of the value of money, but he was aware that, considering Mr. Frothingham's usual caution, this amount must represent only a small part of his principal. Surely Mr. Frothingham would take no chances on Armes' spending it all. He made sure that Captain Tait's draft had been honored, and then was glad to quit the place; its somber austerity reminded him too much of what he had left behind.

Henry was waiting outside the door and together they walked along the waterfront, past the rows of ships with flags from many countries, until they reached a large banyan tree whose deep shade had invited others before them. There was a crude wooden bench beneath it. Armes motioned to Henry to sit, but Henry shook his head and remained standing.

"All right, all right!" Armes showed his impatience with Cap François' customs. "Stand up, damn it, if you must, but let's talk. We've got work to do, you and I. Did Monsieur Coidovic tell you that I am borrowing you?"

Henry shifted his feet in the dust and grinned. "I proposed it."

Armes feinted at him but Henry ducked. "Then where do we start? That place is in an unholy mess. Some fellow by the name of Fabre has been running it into the ground. And I think I know why." Armes looked at Henry for confirmation.

"You mean your little yellow Topaze?"

"You know that she is Fabre's sister?"

"*Mais oui.*"

"Why didn't you tell me?"

"Because, *mon ami,* I never interfere between a man and a
104

woman. I knew you would find out soon enough. If I had told you . . ." Henry shrugged his shoulders.

Armes understood. "Nevertheless, Henry, I'd be willing to bet my last sou that Fabre's been giving her a good share of the money from the plantation. Also many things are missing from the house."

Henry nodded his big head. "I told you she's been prowling around Cap François like a bitch in heat. She's not had a regular man in six months, and that Topaze spends money fast. Her stallion up in the hills takes plenty from her. She's probably broke and Fabre's tiding her over."

"You're probably right, Henry; and yet, you may be wrong. I've seen her twice, and if she's so anxious for a man, why hasn't she made a move toward me? Either time, if she had as much as crooked a little finger at me, I'd've been after her with my tongue hanging out of my mouth. But she has given me no encouragement."

"She's a wise one, that Topaze. She bides her time. But she has baited her trap. Soon she will spring it on you, so watch out. She knows that men do not pay too much for things that are easy to get. But enough of her—what about that worthless brother of hers?"

"I think we should get rid of him at once."

"I'll find someone else to take his place." Henry paced up and down in front of Armes. "I think I know the right person," he said after a moment. "He's a *blanc*—name of DuBois. I'd trust him as much as I'd trust any *blanc*. For many years he was manager of the Aubrey plantation until it was sold last year. I've always heard he was a good man —sober, intelligent, honest and, most important, he stands in good repute with the slaves."

"Then let us see him and see if we can arrange for him to come to Sans Souci."

"That I shall do this afternoon, and I am sure if we can get him, he will help us. He'll be able to get us started, TiArmes."

Armes looked up at Henry in surprise. "What did you call me just now, Henry?"

Henry looked around to see if they were observed and laid his huge hand gently on Armes' shoulder.

"Forgive me. It just slipped out. But that's how I think of you—'TiArmes.' "

"TiArmes? What does that mean?"

Henry looked up and down the street to make sure that

there was nobody in sight. He eased his huge frame down onto the bench and lowered his head to hide his embarrassment.

"Nothing bad, *mon ami!* Here in St. Domingue we use that expression as a sort of . . . I don't know how to say it—but we use it when we like a person very much. It's like saying '*petit*' for '*little*'—like calling you Little Armes, only it does not mean that I think of you as little. It means that you own a little corner of my heart."

Armes was really touched. That this rough brute of a man —this Henry Christophe of the Couronne stables—could even conceive of such a term of endearment, let alone express it, was a surprise to Armes.

"Thank you, Henry, it's the best compliment I ever had. I wonder if I deserve it."

Armes stood up and Henry with him to start back to the Couronne. On the way they met Ali, eyes glistening, feet dancing, white teeth shining, hands fluttering.

"Oh milord, what a home we shall have at Sans Souci! It will rival the palace of my father in Marrakech, and Ali will manage it all for you, milord!"

"Did you spend all of my money and more, too?" Armes asked.

"Much more, milord!" Ali danced around them in circles. "But not too much for milord's home and mine. Milord is a grand emir and he must live like one."

Henry gazed at him suspiciously, his brows puckering in a frown. He grabbed Ali's collar to keep him still.

"How much did you make on the deal for yourself, boy? What percentage comes back to you?"

The smile departed from Ali's face. His eyes grew dark and his mouth twisted into a vicious line. He slipped out of Henry's clutch and stood glaring up at him as belligerently as a bantam rooster facing a fighting cock. Armes had never seen more venom in a single glance.

"What do I want of money, you black baboon? Do you think that I am like you? Money? Bah! I spit on money. Ali has milord and milord has Ali and he has money so Ali has money, and we have a beautiful home in Sans Souci— far too good for stinking black trash like you. Do you think I would steal one centime from milord? Do you? Do you? Do you?" His fists beat a futile tattoo against Henry's chest.

Armes reached and grabbed Ali by the hair, pinioned his

106

arms, and held him close against him. Ali flung his arms around his master and suddenly started crying.

"Ali loves milord," he sobbed, "and milord knows Ali would not steal from him."

"Then stop your blubbering and apologize to Henry for hitting him."

"Make that black ox take back his filthy words first."

Armes looked at Henry, but no words were necessary. Henry roared, nearly bent double with laughter, and clapped a hand on the boy's shoulder, nearly felling him.

"Accept my apologies, *mon enfant*. It seems that I misjudged you, but it is a common custom around here. When a slave buys anything for his master he always manages to get a few centimes for himself in the deal. That you did not shows me you care for your *patron*. If I were your *patron*, however, I'd beat some sense into your head through your bottom."

"But you are not my *patron*, Henry, and milord will never beat me." Ali's evil mood passed as quickly as it had come. "You are clumsy and stupid, Henry Christophe, but I think you are a good friend to milord, so from now on I shall like you and not be jealous of milord's friendship for you."

They walked along the narrow street, finding shade from the blinding sun under the overhanging balconies with their purple masses of bougainvillea. Palm fronds etched delicate patterns against the clear turquoise of the sky. Scarlet hibiscus tumbled over garden walls, and the streets were a living arch of fiery flamboyants. As they neared the Couronne, Armes sent Ali ahead into the hotel. He wanted a word with Henry alone.

"Just a minute before we go in. What would you do, Henry, if you found a piece of rope in your bed, as I did at Sans Souci?"

Henry froze. Armes heard the quick intake of breath, saw the man's eyes roll and his skin turn ashen. When he spoke it was in a whisper.

"Was it a rope about this long?" He measured with his hands. "Green in color?"

"Yes."

"And was one end of it covered with blood?"

Armes nodded.

"And the other end with—" Henry hesitated—"with the *suc* of a man?"

Again Armes nodded.

"With red and white feathers on it?"

"Red on one end and white on the other."

"Then, TiArmes, I would send at once for the most powerful voodoo man on the island—the biggest *papaloi* in St. Domingue."

"Papaloi?"

"One skilled in voodoo—a voodoo priest."

"But why?"

"Because, TiArmes, that piece of rope is the powerful *ouanga* of Petro. That's why it is in the form of a green snake. Some woman has already put a charm on you. It's strong magic—*magie noire*. One end is covered with blood and that stands for woman and her monthly bleeding."

"And the other end, I suppose, represents man?"

"Vraiment."

"And being in my bed it means—?"

"That in spite of anything and everything you may do, unless you have the charm removed, the woman who put it there will be in that very same bed with you."

Armes laughed. "Look, Henry, do you really believe in that nonsense? It's just a piece of rope—it has no life, no power, no strength to accomplish anything. It's nothing."

"No, do not be so sure, TiArmes. There is power behind it which you *blancs* do not understand. See a *papaloi* and have him remove the curse of the *ouanga*."

"I have a pretty good idea of who put it there, Henry. Topaze did make the first move after all, so why should I get your *papaloi* to keep her away when I want her in that bed more than I've ever wanted anything?"

Henry shook his head sadly. He realized that there was nothing he could say that might change Armes' mind. However, there was one hope—he might divert him.

"Justine has missed you, TiArmes. She told me there is not another man in St. Domingue, black, yellow, or white, to compare with you."

"No, Henry, not Justine today! Already I have tired of her, for I know all her little tricks. Did you not mention another girl who lives in the same house?"

"Yes—Marianne."

"Then fetch her, Henry. Let us make her as happy as we did Justine."

"But she is darker than Justine, TiArmes. She has no white blood."

108

"And we are in St. Domingue, Henry, where there is twice as much black blood as white."

"I'll fetch her, TiArmes. But I warn you. You're going to be plumb tuckered out come evening. Plumb tuckered out!"

13

HENRY'S week at Sans Souci stretched out into a month, and each day that he remained at the plantation increased Armes' admiration for the huge Negro and his endless capacity for work. He had an ability to get things organized down to the smallest detail and then to carry them out with an impatience that brooked no delay. Things happened as if by magic the moment Henry took control. At first Henry had been more than skeptical about accepting Lazare as a lieutenant, and although Armes knew nothing about the fellow to recommend him, he felt that Henry should give him a trial. This Henry did, and after a few days admitted that Armes was right and he was wrong. Decent food, humane treatment, and the delegation of some authority changed the emaciated wretch into a willing, devoted worker. What he lacked in training and education, he compensated for by intelligence and Henry found him an able assistant. He, in turn, although he respected Henry, reserved all his devotion for Armes.

Armes discovered that Ali was equally efficient inside the house as Henry was outside. Gradually the neglected plantation showed signs of coming to life, and the house achieved a new look of importance. No longer was it engulfed in a tropical jungle, for Ali had preempted the services of a dozen slaves from under Henry's nose, who chopped away with their machetes at the creeping mass of vegetation, then pruned and coaxed what was left into a semblance of order. Within, polished mahogany floors mirrored the gleaming highlights of gilded mirrors and shining silver. In the evenings, limpid pools of candlelight gleamed on the dark floors and heightened the rich glow of brocades and furniture. The stark rooms became livable, and the neglected house became a home. Armes, through Henry again, purchased a competent cook in the Cap, although Ali continued to supervise the menus. Dinners at night were for three—Armes, Ali, and Henry. With his usual acumen, Henry accommodated himself to the complicated array of silver knives and forks and to the fact that he was no longer treated as a slave but as an equal. He slept in one of the big rooms on the main floor, although at first he had felt that both he and Ali should occupy the small rooms on the ground floor. But Armes did not want to be alone on the entire second floor at night and he had, as Ali reminded him, promised the boy that he need not sleep in the damp cells below. So, with Henry only a few rooms away and Ali still sharing his room, Armes was content.

Outside, the fields which were Henry's special province began to show signs of regular and careful cultivation. The crazy jumble of slave quarters was being rebuilt, and every few days witnessed the firing of one of the vermin-infested huts and its replacement by a snug masonry *cabane*. Work was commenced on two long dormitories, one for males and one for females, and a big new building for the common mess and for weekly dances. It was Armes' intention, seconded by Henry, eventually to sort the slaves into family units, using the dormitories for an overflow of single men and women until such time as proper matings could be achieved.

The slaves themselves were losing their gray, hangdog appearance as their flesh filled out and their spirits rose. They became willing workers as they saw their living conditions bettered. Now there was singing and dancing in the evening in the slave quarters, accompanied by the throb of drums. When they met Armes they smiled at him and addressed him as *bon patron*.

Fabre had at first protested over being dismissed, then threatened, then pleaded, but in the end he made a skulking exit with his mulatto brood, and DuBois and his jolly fat wife were installed in the overseer's cottage which, after a week, took on the well-ordered appearance of a cottage in Brittany rather than a tropical home.

Henry appeared on the balcony one morning after breakfast with a sheaf of papers which he handed to Armes. Armes took them to examine them but discovered that each piece of paper was blank. He questioned Henry as to their purpose.

"I do not write, TiArmes," Henry replied. "That is for you to do."

"But what do you want me to write?"

"I wish that on this one plantation, the only one in St.

110

Domingue where Henry Christophe has any authority, we might have a code of laws."

"Why on earth do we need a code of laws?"

"Because, TiArmes"—Henry's smooth brow wrinkled into furrows from deep concentration—"this Sans Souci is like a little kingdom, a country all by itself. Here you have, all told, four hundred and eighty-three subjects, and you are their king. In some ways you have more power than any king. You say to this man, 'Work', and he works until you tell him to stop. You say to another man, 'Get this woman with child,' and he must obey you. You can pat a man on the head if he pleases you or have him flogged if he disobeys you. You can even kill him if it so pleases you. You are a monarch here, TiArmes." Henry waited a moment before continuing. "I know you want to govern your people intelligently, but how can you do that if they do not know what is right and what is wrong?"

Armes considered the matter. Henry was right, as usual. No wrong was a wrong until it had been so established. They pulled their chairs up to a table and together they filled several sheets of foolscap with words, regulating the life of the slaves—their hours of work; their holidays; their times of labor; their rights, and their obligations. Armes was amazed at Henry's precise and orderly thinking and his grasp of the fine points of equity. When it was finished it was a fair constitution. It protected both Armes and the slaves, and it wasn't any harsher on the subjects than on the master. They had duties to each other, and they were interdependent. Both were welded together into one cooperative whole. There were not only rules and regulations for the present but plans for the future. There were provisions for the continued construction of decent housing, rules for mating and for the establishment of families, and provisions for sickness and old age. Their duties were definitely outlined—duties to Armes as the *patron;* to DuBois as the overseer; to Lazare as the foreman; to Ali as the head of the house; and even to Henry, who occupied a semi-official position as adviser.

When they had finished and Armes had read it aloud, Henry nodded his head slowly in approval.

"We should give ourselves real titles, TiArmes. A title means something. It makes a man stand out and be respected. I think my greatest ambition is to have a title, TiArmes. Imagine how nice it would sound to be the Marquis Henry Christophe, or even Vicomte Henry Christophe. And King

Henry Christophe would not sound too bad. But here, you will have to be king, and Monsieur DuBois could be your duke."

"And Ali?" Armes smiled to himself, trying to picture Henry as a marquis.

"That little devil can be the Lord High Chamberlain."

"And what about Henry?"

Henry hid a shamed smile. "Forget what I said about being a marquis, TiArmes. Henry is nothing but a slave, and probably that's all he ever will be, yet there are times that I forget I am a slave. I seem to feel some sort of power within me. I know that I am different from the rest of these blacks. I could govern them, TiArmes, and govern them well. I am sure I could take over your plantation and make it prosper and produce. Then I would take that produce and sell it for a high price, invest it, and make it produce still more. I would get more work out of your slaves than even the good DuBois and still keep them happy."

"Yes, I believe you could, Henry. You have a good head on your shoulders."

Henry shook the head in question. His thick fingers scratched the close, wiry skullcap of hair. Then he spread his hands before him in a gesture of defeat.

"But my head is black," he said.

"You know, Henry"—Armes stood up and walked to the balcony railing, as a horseman turned through the gateposts— "I've come to think that black and white is going to mean very little here in St. Domingue someday. I've seen some pretty rotten examples of white men and some fine men like you and Coidovic who are black. After all, the color of a man's skin does not denote the capacity of his brain . . ." He ran down the steps to meet the visitor as the man dismounted in the gravel drive.

"René!" he cried, and despite his willingness to part from the Vicomte that day on the ship, it now seemed good to see him. Indeed it was! It had been a long time since he had last seen him, and René brought the white world back to Armes. He had not realized how his world had changed color. He turned around for Henry, but Henry had disappeared.

René looked around at the trimmed and garnished lawns, the gleaming white lime on the house, and the new slave cabins extending in a block at the back.

"Mon Dieu, Armes, you've come into a fortune."

"Hardly, but it does look a lot better than it did a few weeks ago."

"A few weeks ago! Wasn't it always like this?"

"Far from it—but that's another story. Now come inside and let me give you a drink. It will be good to talk with you."

Inside the house it was darkly cool, with only a dim light coming through the closed jalousies. A little breeze rustled the pendants of the chandeliers, producing a faint tinkling music. Armes clapped his hands and, almost by magic, Ali appeared, his soft slippers making no noise on the glossy floors. Ali had now adopted Moorish clothes, made under his supervision by a slave seamstress. A snowy white jellaba of thin white cotton trailed to the floor, and his black curls were hidden under a turban of white muslin.

René gazed at him with astonishment and ill-concealed desire. His eyes passed over the exotic clothes and rested on the boy's face, then lingered there.

"Mon brave, you're living like some Eastern potentate, with turbaned Moors to wait on you. Where did you ever find such a slave, and tell me, where do you keep your harem?"

"One Moorish boy does not make a harem, René." Armes was becoming annoyed at René's frank appraisal of Ali and all that it implied. "This is Ali, a Moorish prince who is masquerading as a houseman—or should I say my Lord Chamberlain." He turned to Ali. "Some wine for the Vicomte de St. Gabriel."

"Quite a boy." René's eyes followed Ali out of the room. His tongue encircled his lips and he opened his mouth to speak, but Armes interrupted him.

"And your good wife, the Vicomtesse?"

René shrugged. "She is still indisposed."

Ali glided back in, his red slippers peeping out from beneath his robe. He poured the wine and served it, placed the decanter on a little table, and disappeared from view, though Armes felt he was not far away. A slight motion behind the portieres justified his suspicions. He reminded himself to speak to Ali about the evil of eavesdropping.

"It's been a long time since we saw each other." René sipped his wine.

"Altogether too long," Armes agreed. "But I've been busy, René. Getting this place going has meant a lot of work."

"Then it's time you had a change, *mon brave.* Come over to my place. I'm inviting some of the leading planters of the

113

Cap for next Tuesday. Come and meet them. Men only," he grinned, "so don't tempt them by bringing your harem." His voice underlined the last word.

"Next Tuesday?" Armes decided to ignore the innuendo.

"In the afternoon, to remain for dinner. I'm planning a very special form of entertainment for you and my guests. *Différent! Amusant! Extraordinaire!* You will enjoy it."

"Then I shall come. It is time I got away from work and became acquainted with my neighbors. I shall be glad to see you, meet your friends, and pay my respects to your wife, whom I have never had the pleasure of meeting."

René paused for a moment, and set his wineglass carefully down on the table.

"I doubt if you ever will, Armes."

"Why not? A moment ago you were speaking of Moors and a harem. Do you subscribe to the belief that women should never be seen unless heavily veiled? Surely you cannot mistrust me so greatly as to hesitate to introduce me to your wife." Armes remembered the one glimpse he had had of her on board ship, and realized that perhaps René was altogether wise in not having them meet.

René shook his head. "You do not understand. It is not I who make the prohibition. It is she herself, and I must admit she has very good reason, but that is her business. Let us forget about her. I try damn hard to do so, but I always remember that if it were not for her, my head would be looking for the rest of my body in France, or else I would be a penniless hanger-on at a stuffy little German court." He stood up, gathered his gloves and his big straw hat from the table. Ali opened the portieres. René turned toward the boy and reappraised him carefully.

"Nice boy you've got there, Armes. I'd like to buy him. . . . Sell him to me?"

Ali stood stiffly, not moving. Only his eyelids fluttered under his white turban. Then he bowed low to René. When he spoke his words were scarcely audible.

"Ali is not for sale, Monsieur le Vicomte."

As he straightened up, René slashed at him with his gloves. Ali stood still, a red welt darkening on his cheek. René's eyes flashed with anger.

"Your slave forgets himself, Armes. He had the audacity to address me without my having spoken to him. I request that you give him twenty lashes after I leave."

Armes was provoked with Ali, but his anger toward René was greater. He tried to control it as he said, "You are mistaken, René. Ali is not my slave."

"No?"

"No! He is well-born and I consider him my equal. Therefore he has the right to address you. I am sure he meant no offense."

René regarded Ali again.

"None was taken," he mumbled, "but no goddamned nigger is going to speak to me and get away with it."

"Of that I am sure, Monsieur le Vicomte." Ali did not bow this time.

Armes walked with René to the door. "Until Tuesday, Armes?"

René proceeded slowly down the curving steps.

"Until Tuesday."

Armes waited for René to mount his horse, waved to him, and then reentered the house. Ali was still standing in the hall, but his grin faded when he saw Armes' serious expression.

"When are you going to learn to keep your goddamned mouth closed?"

"When to speak gains me nothing, milord. Today it gained me my freedom. Today I learned that I am no longer your slave. I am well-born and you consider me your equal." His grin returned, showing the even row of white teeth against the moist lips. With a sweeping bow, he made obeisance to Armes.

It was difficult to be cross with Ali; he had a way of changing one's anger to amusement. Armes made a dive to clutch the neck of the white jellaba, but Ali slipped out of his hands. He ran down the hall, but when he did not hear Armes pursuing him he halted and turned back. Although Armes' bulk was spread against the light of the doorway, Ali could see that he was smiling. He knew he was forgiven. He shuffled across the polished floor toward Armes, drew himself up pompously, puffed out his cheeks, lowered his voice to its deepest octave, and started to declaim in some outlandish gibberish.

"Now what?" Armes laughed at the absurd pantomime.

"Henry!" Ali answered. "He's down reading your laws to the slaves. He looks down at the paper and pretends to read

115

off the words while all the time the big baboon can't tell one word from the other."

"But he knows what they are, Ali. He knows because he really wrote them himself."

14

ARMES decided that he would arrive at the St. Gabriel plantation in far more style and elegance than he had previously adopted in St. Domingue. The prime reason for his decision was that Henry had discovered a fine coach in the carriage house at Sans Souci, which had been carefully preserved by a voluminous wrapping of protective cloths. These, when removed, had revealed the coach in all its varnished and gold-leafed splendor. As it was in excellent condition, Henry had purchased four white mules, which, with the red and silver harnesses and the painted panels of the coach, gave the equipage a grandeur that would have done credit to an ambassador. It was far too splendid for daily use, and Armes had been awaiting some opportunity to try it out. The visit to St. Gabriel seemed to be an excellent excuse. Armes designated Lazare as coachman and chose two youths as footmen, his choice influenced by the size of the liveries found with the coach. The former coachman must have been a large man but not as large as Lazare, for several inches of blueblack skin showed below the gold-braided sleeves, though when Lazare was mounted on the box it was not apparent.

As it was somewhat less than five miles, over fairly good roads, they did not leave until mid-afternoon. Armes insisted on going alone despite Ali's protests that it was not seemly for a man of his station to appear without a personal servant. In spite of his newly declared freedom, Ali was loath to relinquish any part of his attendance on Armes. One minute the boy would be very much the young Moorish prince, graciously and condescendingly conferring his royal favors on Armes, and the next he would be polishing Armes' boots or performing some other menial task.

This time, however, he forgot his princely prerogatives and pleaded with Armes to be taken along, but Armes was adamant in refusing him. He was a little apprehensive of the opinion his neighbors might form of him were Ali to accompany him, for he was well aware that René had understood immediately. His reasons, of course, were not explained to Ali, but Armes mollified the boy by granting him permission to ride as far as the gates with him, where Ali bade him a tearful farewell.

"You'd think I was going for a month." Armes cupped his hand under the boy's chin and raised it. "By your Prophet and your Allah, I promise to be back in a few hours, oh ready shedder of tears."

"But something might happen to milord and Ali would not be there to take care of you." The bronze fingers hesitated on the handle of the door.

"Nothing will happen and I'll be back after dinner. Now, how about making up some of your special sandwiches and we'll have a bite together on the balcony before going to bed —just you and I together, and I'll tell you all about the party."

Ali was mollified by the prospect of having Armes to himself and jumped down from the coach to stand by the gates. The coach went on and Armes waved back as they turned the corner. Ali was still there.

It was a pleasant ride, climbing upward into the mauve mountains and down into the green valleys. The road was a white path through brilliant fields of waving cane, which gave way to the glossy green of coffee leaves as they climbed higher. Armes passed the Granville plantation and remembered the invitation of young Edouard Granville, given him at the Couronne on the day he made the mistake of wearing the *affranchi* suit. The Granville house sat well back from the road behind a towering avenue of palms, gleaming pinkly in the strong sun. It was a far more pretentious house than Sans Souci and, as Armes understood, a richer one.

He decided, now that he was away from the daily life of Sans Souci, that he would get out more, see more people, have more social life. He had been staying at home too much, relying almost entirely on Henry, Ali, and Lazare for company. He must seek more intellectual companions or he, himself, would sink to a slave mentality. If Granville were at René's today, he would remind him of his invitation, and perhaps he would make other acquaintances today. Surely there was more to do in St. Domingue than working in the fields, and already Sans Souci was fit for entertaining.

As the coach rolled on, he passed other imposing estates, each with its ornate wrought-iron gates, its avenue of royal

117

palms and its big house, showing white or pink or pistachio in the midst of lush, tropical gardens. But the beauty of all these houses did little to prepare him for the almost regal magnificence of René's home. He thought of the staid red-brick houses of Beacon Hill back in Boston, which so determinedly understated the large fortunes they represented. There was certainly no understatement about René's house. It shrieked its opulence. Terraces of close-clipped lawns connected by staircases of whitened stone—each terrace a veritable hanging garden—led up to the mansion. The coach had to circle back and forth in a series of ascending hairpin turns before it deposited him at the door of the house. Now he was glad he had used the coach, even though its previously admired magnificence appeared rather shabby alongside the other turnouts drawn around the graveled drive. But to have arrived by horseback would have been even more embarrassing in the face of so much magnificence. Slaves in blue and white livery met him, helped him alight, and ushered him up the wide stone steps into the house through massive twin mahogany doors.

Within there was a crush of people. There were men everywhere, but, as far as Armes could see, no women. He remained for a moment just inside the doorway, to let his eyes become accustomed to the cool darkness after the blaze of light outside. While he stood there he heard his name announced by the Negro majordomo at the door.

"Monsieur Armes Holbrook of Sans Souci Plantation."

No sooner had his name echoed down the length of the long hall than René was at his side. It was the same René he had known on shipboard, only a sleeker, more polished René. His eyes were brighter, his hair glistened with bluer highlights, his sallow cheeks glowed, and there certainly was no lack of warmth in his welcome.

"Armes, *mon ami.*" René embraced him. "How good to see you again."

Armes extricated himself gently from the embrace. Yes, it was good to see René again, now that the enforced intimacy of those days on shipboard was a thing of the past. Armes returned the greeting with equal warmth.

René grabbed his arm as they passed down the hall.

"The Moorish boy?" he whispered.

"You told me not to bring him."

"It is just as well." René winked. "Your little secret is safe

118

with me, *mon ami,* but it would be safer if you would permit him to visit me for a few days, *hein?"*

Armes was saved the embarrassment of a refusal by their encounter with a gentleman, who stopped before them.

"Monsieur Nevers may I introduce Monsieur Holbrook of Sans Souci?" René was once again the host.

"Enchanté, Monsieur Holbrook."

And then followed a steady stream of introductions.

"Monsieur de Mailly." The man bowed to Armes.

"Monsieur Coislin, Monsieur Holbrook."

"Monsieur Granville, Monsieur Holbrook."

"Ah, my neighbor from Sans Souci. Enchanted, Monsieur Holbrook." He fingered Armes' coat sleeve and smiled. "A most delightful shade of light blue, monsieur. We shall certainly not mistake you for an *affranchi* this time, no?"

They were all there, or so it seemed—the elite of the Plain du Nord, the elite of Cap François, and that meant the elite of all St. Domingue, for the northern province of the island far outshone the southern in wealth and prosperity. How well the fanciful name of Armes' plantation fitted the whole gathering. *Sans Souci!* Without care! Without anxiety! Without trouble! Surely if there were any one group of people in the whole world totally without care, it was the planters of St. Domingue. There were no difficult problems, nothing for them to worry about, except perhaps one very small black cloud of little importance. To be sure, things were not going too well with the slaves. But things never did go well with the slaves unless the whites ruled with an iron hand, and lately they might have been a little careless. It had to be remedied. There had to be a little more firmness. Of course theirs was the superior power, theirs the wealth and education and culture. But, despite their power, the *blancs* were beginning to realize that the blacks really controlled St. Domingue, and controlled it ten to one through the overwhelming mass of black humanity that was now beginning to smolder with hidden fires as it slowly became aware of its own strength and importance.

Yes, there had been mutterings—low, underground mutterings—which presaged the eruption of a volcano of hatred, but they had been only mutterings. They were not of sufficient importance to consider seriously. Of course, in Mother France, on the other side of the Atlantic, a voice had arisen through the Reign of Terror to cry *Liberté, Egalité, Fraternité.* Liberty? Equality? Fraternity? Ah, the words had a beautiful sound, but surely the words did not apply to St. Domingue. Liberty for the slaves? Then who would do the work on the plantations? Equality for the slaves? Imagine considering a sweaty stinking nigger as one's equal! Fraternity? *Quelle absurdité!* How could one fraternize with a field hand or even with one's own coachman? There could be no equality between black and white, no fraternity between slave and master, no liberty—not when a man's gambling debts could be paid by merely handing a slave over to his debtor.

But the free men of color—the damned hybrid *affranchi* bastards—and now even some of the blacks were watching and learning, biding their time. They had heard how Mother France had thrown off the yoke of the aristocrats and accomplished it with unspeakable bloodshed and horror. If such a thing could happen in France it might well happen in St. Domingue. Not all of the blacks were stupid work animals. There was a renegade slave up in the hills named Bouckmann, the same of whom Topaze was said to be enamored. There was another called Toussaint, and yet a third, an ugly, ill-formed Negro with the strength of a gorilla and the cunning of a fox—Jean Jacques Dessalines. And then there was that Henry Christophe of the Hotel Couronne to whom more and more of the blacks around Cap François looked for advice and counsel. These men had begun to think, and thinking was dangerous for a slave.

The whites had talked about it between afternoons at billiards and evenings at the opera. They had discussed it before their mulatto mistresses and over elaborate repasts before their Negro butlers and footmen. And the whites were unanimous in their agreement. Severe measures must be taken immediately, to forestall the appearance of even the slightest superiority of black over white. The brutes must never realize their own power. Consequently every insubordination, no matter how inconsequential, must be taken care of speedily and harshly. An impudent word or even a sullen look merited swift retribution. The black bastards must know their place and keep it. On this one plan of action, the *blancs* were united.

Here today at St. Gabriel were the men who had dictated that policy. Here, gathered at René's house, were those very men of power who commanded and expected immediate obedience. Nothing could arise to challenge their power—that must never be challenged for an instant. Otherwise, disaster

120

would come quickly. But today, they had forgotten that little black cloud. Why remember it?

As Armes passed from room to room with René, he became more and more impressed with him, his home, and his friends. With René—to whom the easy grace of the Court of Versailles came so naturally! With his home—these large spacious rooms, beautifully furnished and beautifully kept, with a gleaming patina of wealth over everything from the sparkling girandoles to the parquetry floors. With René's friends—those who had transplanted the brittle life of France with all its affectations of gentility to this tropical island where it had flourished more than it ever had in Paris!

One could not escape the blue-and-white liveried slaves, however. There was always one at one's elbow with a silver tray of cooled wines in tall-stemmed glasses. How noiselessly the blue-and-white liveries moved in and out of the hum of cultivated voices, the musically modulated laughter, and the sibilant whispers. How easily they dodged the proffered jeweled snuff boxes, avoided the fluttering of lace-edged handkerchiefs, and kept out of the way of the movement of ivory and tortoiseshell fans. Armes tried to picture his own huge hand wielding a fan. He smiled to himself at the absurdity of the image, and yet these flashing toys looked not out of place in the hands of René's friends.

René abandoned Armes to greet some new arrivals, leaving him with a group who were chuckling over the fact that so-and-so's wife had just discovered that her mulatto rival had a far more splendid diamond *parure* than she herself possessed. Armes listened attentively, laughing with the rest at so-and-so's discomfiture when he was forced to buy another equally expensive, set of diamonds for his fat wife. But no sooner had the delightful anecdote ended than René appeared again, this time head and shoulders above the sea of faces. René, it appeared, had climbed on a chair in the center of the salon. He clapped his hands for silence. Everyone turned in his direction, and the murmur of conversation slowly died down. When he had the attention of all in the room, he started to speak.

"My friends and neighbors," he began. "Welcome to my home. I have invited you this afternoon for a dual purpose. First, because I wanted to meet you and to know all of you as I already know a few. This was most important to me. I desire to know all my neighbors in St. Domingue. Then, having gathered you all together for a purely selfish purpose of

121

my own, I wanted to afford you some entertainment and I felt that it should be something unusual to repay you for coming here."

"Bravo, René," someone cried and waved a handkerchief. "Did you bring Chloe out from the Cap to dance for us?"

René smiled and shook his head. "No. Perhaps you would have preferred Chloe to the entertainment I have arranged for you, for certainly her dancing is inspiring, as I can well attest. However, you are all men of the world and are accustomed to the finest in entertainment. You have attended the balls at Versailles, ballets at Fontainebleau and *fêtes champêtres* at Trianon. What could I offer you that you have not seen before? That was my problem, and it could not be solved by a yellow wench dancing for you even in the most transparent of draperies, for I imagine that most of you have seen the fair Chloe without her draperies."

He waited for the answering laughter to die down.

"But"—he turned to a young man near him—"my friend Louis de LaSalle of Marly Plantation gave me an excellent idea."

"I?" The man whom René had addressed looked puzzled.

"Yes, you, Louis. Recently Louis had some slight trouble on his plantation and it was necessary to punish several of his slaves. The impetuous Louis killed them. Ah, Louis, that was most unprofitable. No sooner had you spitted them on your sword than they died quickly and far too easily. *Hélas!* What a waste of entertainment!"

"But I had to kill them," LaSalle said in self-justification.

"However, *mon cher* Louis, were you not just a bit selfish about it?" René continued. "No, do not misunderstand me. I have really no serious fault to find with you. Every man is master of his own slaves and he may dispose of them as he sees fit, but did you, Louis, take full advantage of your opportunity? Was not your form of punishment just a little too easy? Did it accomplish the purpose you desired? Did it put fear into the rebellious black hearts of other slaves who might cherish ideas of insubordination in their thick heads? No, it did not! Neither did it offer any particularly interesting form of entertainment."

There was an uneasy stir among René's audience. Armes sensed a tenseness—an expectancy.

"And so, *mes amis,*" René continued after a short and smiling pause, "let me say that I have been faced with the same problem as our friend Louis. Only the day before yesterday my overseer came to me and told me that two of my slaves had refused to obey his orders. I had the men put in chains. Then some of the other slaves had the audacity to protest that my treatment was unfair, and that it was the overseer who was to blame and not the slaves. They wished to dispute with me. I permit nobody to dispute with me in regard to my slaves, least of all my slaves themselves. So, it was necessary for me to put ten of them in chains."

He held up the fingers of both hands.

"Ten, messieurs. Ten men! Ten! As I thought about it that number carried me back to an afternoon at the Petit Trianon when her late Majesty and the Comte de Fersen entertained us on the lawn before the Châlet. I was inspired. So come, let us adjourn to the terrace on the north side of the house, which I have purposely kept from your view, and I shall show you how that magical number of ten inspired me to offer you the most unusual, the most amusing, and the most exciting form of entertainment you have ever witnessed. But it will be more than mere entertainment, messieurs. That number of ten will never be forgotten in St. Domingue. You are about to witness an episode in history today. I guarantee that from this day on, no slave will ever dispute with his master again. Messieurs, be so kind as to follow me."

Not until the liveried slaves began to pull back the damask draperies from the tall French windows did Armes realize why the room had seemed so dark. They unlocked the doors and flung them open. One by one René's friends followed him out onto the grassy terrace beyond the windows. Armes accompanied them. The slave who held the door open for him to pass through seemed to be making a clattering sound with the bronze latch. Armes noticed that the fellow's hands were trembling. He looked up past the starched whiteness of the elaborate stock around the slave's neck and saw that his face was ashen, his lips drawn tight, and his eyes smoldering. Armes passed by the man and out onto the terrace.

15

A zephyr-like breeze fanned the north terrace which was shielded from the sun by the mansion house. The long grassy terrace stretched out, a veritable *tapis vert* of close-cropped lawn, bordered with a balustrade of white stone. Somewhere at the end of the terrace a fountain splashed musically, and the air was heavy with the cloying scent of tuberoses. Armes, who was one of the last to leave the salon, now found himself up in the front line of guests, all of whom were standing behind a broad rose-colored silken ribbon which stretched from the house to a small statue of Antinoüs that stood on the parapet. René and René alone stood on the other side of the dividing ribbon. But no, René was not alone, Armes realized to his horror. There were ten other men beside him. Ten other men!

Quickly he shut his eyes to blot out the sight, but nothing could erase the unspeakable horror that the glimpse of those ten men had already engendered in him. At first he had not noticed them, but once having seen them he could see nothing else, neither the smiling René, the expectant faces behind him, the smooth green velvet of the lawns, nor the distant purple mountains. Only the tortured faces of ten men appeared, for only their heads showed above the closely clipped lawn. Ten heads, with soil closely packed around them, and the green sod artfully replaced as though it had never been removed. Ten heads, with wide-open eyes that were filled with terror and dread! Ten heads, their mouths gagged with tightly drawn cloths! Ten heads, ten suffering humans buried to their chins, immovable, mute, and doomed.

Armes now saw that they were arranged in an orderly sequence, mathematically and equally spaced. There were four in the back row, three in the second, two in the third and one, the apex of the triangle, in lonely isolation in front. Ten men! Then . . . Suddenly it all became terribly clear to Armes, even before he saw the heavy, polished mahogany balls lying in a row on the grass at René's feet. Ten men! Ten pins! It was the ancient game of bowls, which the empty-headed Marie Antoinette and her Swedish paramour the Comte de Fersen had once played in the artificial dingle of the Petit Trianon. And here, under the bright blue sky of St. Domingue, was another greensward; here were the balls and there were the "pins." Armes was not the only one who gasped. He saw surprise and consternation on the faces of some of the guests. But, most of them were laughing. The muscles of Armes' stomach quivered with a nausea of fear and disgust, a cold sweat broke out on his hands, and his whole body trembled, but, horrified as he was, he could not

124

take his eyes from the eyes of the ten men before him. It seemed that each stared directly at him.

"You dog, René!" It was LaSalle, doubled over with laughter. "Damn you for a very dog. I nominate you the cleverest man in all St. Domingue."

René acknowledged the compliment with a languid wave of his hand.

"Now why couldn't I have thought of this?" LaSalle pretended a chagrin which was nevertheless genuine. "What a sport! How much better than spitting the bastards to hell by an easy road."

"Bravo, René," someone shouted. "Who gets the first ball?"

"I'm the champion at bowls of St. Domingue," a voice from behind Armes was shouting. "I demand . . ."

"Nonsense!" There was an edge of anger to the second voice. "I beat you the last time, de Brissac."

"Messieurs." René's voice was quietly assertive. "I know you all desire to try your luck, but unfortunately we shall have to take turns, because my tenpins are not of very durable material. Shall we draw lots for two teams of four men each? I've come prepared. See!" He held a silver bowl high over his head. "It's filled with coins—one for each of you—and most of them are copper coins, but among them are eight gold ones. I'll pass among you myself, as I cannot entrust this duty to any slave. Reach in and take your pick. Those who are fortunate enough to hold the gold coins will be the players. Then, after they have enjoyed their game, you can all participate, provided, of course, there still remains something to aim at."

He held the silver bowl high over his head and, as he passed among them, eager fingers dipped into it. When it came to Armes, he hesitated, but feeling the eyes of the crowd on him, he plunged his hand into the bowl and drew out a coin. He held it hidden in his hand for a moment, dreading to look at it. Then, not wishing to become conspicuous, he opened his fingers cautiously until he could see the dull gleam of copper. Relieved, he held it up to display it to the others. But Armes was the only one relieved to have drawn the copper coin. The others cursed them and dashed them to the ground, grinding them into the grass with their heels. Suddenly someone cried out and held up a gold coin for all to see. It took the others only a few minutes to complete the drawing and, when the bowl was empty, the eight

125

holders of the gold coins, at René's invitation, stepped to the other side of the ribbon.

"Fifty louis d'or for your gold coin," someone called to young Granville.

"A hundred," another bid.

"Not for sale, *mes amis*."

"And you, LeMaitre, you'll have bad luck at the game because you've been lucky in love," a disgruntled man behind Armes shouted.

LeMaitre, a loose-lipped, gangling youth, blushed as he tested the weight of one of the balls in his hand.

"At last she found a man and she appreciates him," he called back.

Armes noticed the green flies crawling on the tortured black faces as René patiently gestured for silence.

"Lay your bets, messieurs. Bet on your favorites at whatever odds you desire. As for me, I shall wager that Granville takes number three man the first time."

"Taken!"

"Twenty louis that LeMaitre gets number one."

"Forty on Laurent to hit number four."

"And . . . ten that Tancrède will hit two with one ball."

The betting ceased as Louis de LaSalle picked up one of the balls, tested its weight in his hands, then took his position. He raised his arm slowly, sighted the first man carefully, brought his arm down with a quick force, and released the ball. It sped along the grass straight and true, but whether some pebble deflected its course or whether it was poorly aimed, it merely followed a grassy path between the heads. Nothing else! The heads were still intact. Armes' eyes had followed the ball on its course. As the ball neared the man in the apex of the fatal triangle, he had found his gaze drawn to that terrified pair of eyes which were watching the swift course of the ball. The eyes didn't close. They saw it coming toward them, they saw its deflection, and for one swift second they reflected relief. Then the haunting look of terror returned.

"Another try, Louis?"

"Damn it, no! He's had his turn and missed. It's mine now."

Tancrède Nesle took up another ball and sighted it fully. He was a far stronger man than LaSalle, and this time the ball rolled with greater force and reached its mark. It crashed into the face of the left-hand man in the second row. There was a spurt of blood from one of his eyes. Half of one cheek was laid open, showing the bleeding gums and broken teeth. The blow had dislodged the gag from the slave's mouth, and his screams spewed forth in a bloody froth. The ball rolled on with diminished force.

"Shut the bastard up, LeMaitre!"

One by one the remaining six men stepped up, sighted their mark, and aimed their ball. In nearly every instance they scored a direct hit. Armes could no longer look at the carnage which littered the green grass. One of the heads had burst like an overripe tomato, spilling its pulp of brains on the ground. All were now bleeding from repulsive wounds. Some were mercifully dead, their skulls cracked like eggs. One of the four wretches in the back row had managed to loosen his gag and was howling with an unspeakable panic that made Armes' flesh creep.

Eight other men, eager volunteers, ran to retrieve the balls, and a trembling slave boy with fear-crazed eyes wiped them clean. Once again there was a sighting of targets and again the balls followed a deadly path over the grass. Now the shrieking of the man who had loosened his gag was stilled. Another head had completely disappeared. The eyes of the man in the middle of the last row were still open, gazing at the oncoming balls. There was another hit, still another, and yet another. The eyes continued to watch them from the battered face.

One of the bowlers, his hand raised in the air, ready to release the ball, brought his arm down, but a wild scream from the opened windows startled him, and the ball fell to the ground.

"Stop, messieurs, for the love of God!"

All eyes turned to the woman in the doorway, even those of the head in the back row.

"Stop, René! Stop, messieurs! I forbid you to continue this ghastly game."

Armes noticed that the woman was dressed in white, and that her face was shrouded by a white scarf.

"René, have you lost your senses?" she screamed. "Gentlemen, are you men?"

René pushed through the crowd, which was now strangely silent.

"Athenée, go into the house." He turned to the men. "My wife, gentlemen, the Vicomtesse de St. Gabriel. Allow me to apologize for her. She forgets her role of hostess."

"I do not forget, messieurs, because I am not your hostess." She stepped out of the door. "Although this is my home I am

127

not your hostess, as I have been held a prisoner in my room until I managed to pick the lock with a hairpin and escape. Yes, this is my home and these unfortunate creatures are, or rather were, my slaves. Now, with your permission, I shall assume the role of hostess and beg you to stop. Please go to your homes at once and forget that you have indulged in this cruel sport. May God forgive us all, for we have all sinned against Him."

René advanced to stand beside her. He took her hand, raised it to his lips, and kissed it—a strange gesture which she mutely accepted. Then slowly, even gently, he led her across the terrace to where his friends were grouped. She followed meekly. Neither spoke. They halted within a few feet of the guests. Both were so near Armes that he could have put out his hand and touched them. René bowed to his guests.

"*Mes amis,* you have never had the pleasure of meeting my wife before. As a matter of fact, you have never seen her before, not even when she lived in St. Domingue before I married her. I think it time that you were presented to her and she to you. Gentlemen, my wife!"

He inclined his head toward her in a mocking salute, and at the same time, his hand reached for the thin white veil which covered her face. There was a sound of ripping cloth as it parted. Suddenly she stood before them without the protection of her mask. Armes stared at her. Now he understood. Now so many things which had seemed strange and mysterious suddenly resolved themselves in his thoughts. Athenée de St. Gabriel stood before him and, despite her clothes, she seemed naked. One side of her face, the side he had seen that night on the boat, was beautiful. God! How beautiful she was! But the other side of her face was splotched by a violet birthmark from eye to chin—a blotch of purple that stained the pure perfection of her cheek like wine spilled on a white damask cloth.

She bowed her head, turned slowly, and walked back through the open window. As her silent footsteps carried her into the house, a hush fell on the assemblage. One by one the men turned and walked away, until only Armes remained with René. He could not explain what held him there. Certainly it was not any feeling of friendship for the man beside him. Rather, perhaps, it was that he was loath to forsake the spot where he had seen this strange woman, for he now realized that the glimpse he had had of her on the ship had been excluded from his thoughts because he knew he could never have her. At that moment he knew that he wanted her more than he had ever wanted any woman. Her beauty was so perfect that even the disfiguring birthmark did not mar it for him. Suddenly he realized why he had allowed Topaze to dominate his desires, for he had tried only to substitute her for this unattainable Athenée. No other woman could ever really satisfy him, for truly he had not wanted either Justine nor Topaze since he and Ali had come to Sans Souci. Yes, he might enjoy the perfection of Topaze's body, but he knew he really wanted Athenée.

Damn him! What was wrong with him? Why must he pant after every woman he saw? Why must he tire so quickly of them, once he had satisfied himself with them? But this woman, this Athenée, he would never tire of. How he knew this and was so sure of it, he could not tell, but he realized that there were infinite resources within her to satisfy him and hold him. Yet he was certain that she was unobtainable. So, would he waste his life yearning after her? No—if he couldn't have her he would have Topaze. He would have her even if he had to go into the Cap and break down the door of her rotting mansion. Perhaps in her tawny skin he could forget this white woman who he now realized had haunted him since he first saw her. His need at this moment was great. Damn it! The ancient Romans were right. Their gladiatorial contests and the ruthless shedding of blood in the arena were a powerful aphrodisiac. Never had he wanted a woman so before.

René advanced a hesitant step toward him, a babble of apologies on his lips. Armes deliberately turned his back on him and walked away, oblivious to the fact that he was walking toward the shambles of ten men—ten strong healthy young Negroes. Ten men who had felt their muscles ache from days of labor in the cane fields—ten men who had perhaps found a brief surcease from the pain of living in the arms of someone lying beside them in a wretched hut. He was not aware that he was among them until his foot slipped on the bloodied grass and he nearly fell.

Armes did not know why he stopped to look down on them. Possibly it was some morbid effort to alleviate his own frustrated desires that compelled him to regard them. He stopped beside the crushed head of the first man, walked between the next two. His boots were crimson from the grass, and a nausea churned in his stomach. Lifting his eyes from the broken skulls and spattered brains at his feet, he scanned

129

the row of heads in the back. One head returned his gaze with living eyes above the bleeding pulp of a face. Although there was a dying despair in them, as Armes continued to look their expression changed to mute pleading. He walked over to the head, squatted down on his knees, and put his hand tenderly on the wiry black head. It came away slippery with the warm stickiness of blood. His fingers found the knot in the tight rawhide thong at the back of the head, untied it, and pulled the gag from the man's mouth. He had strength enough to suck in a long draught of air.

"Can you hold on?" Armes asked.

The man was unable to speak, but he made a slight motion of the head.

"Trust me! Keep breathing and I'll go for help. Don't give up! I'll be back soon," Armes promised. He ran back to where René was still standing. He fumbled in his pocket for his purse, pulled it out, and took out a number of gold pieces. He reached for René's hand and placed them in his palm, noting with grim satisfaction that his fingers had bloodied René's hand.

"I'm buying your slave," he said.

René did not answer, but looked numbly at the coins in his hand.

Armes ran around the house as fast as he could to where his coach was standing alone in the driveway. Lazare and the two footmen were crouched beside the wheels, their faces livid with fear.

"You"—he pointed to one of the footmen—"go and get as many of the St. Gabriel slaves as you can find, and you"—he grabbed the shoulder of the second footman and pulled him up—"find where they keep their spades. Get them and come back quickly. Run! There is no time to lose if we want to save that poor devil's life."

They sped away, but Lazare remained.

"Don't let them do that to me, *patron*." His teeth were chattering.

"Never fear, boy, I'm no monster."

With Armes to protect him, Lazare snapped into action. He ducked under the coach and unstrapped a small spade, fastened there to extricate the coach from mud or sand. Armes snatched it from his hand and raced back to the terrace with Lazare behind him. The man was still alive. Armes dug frantically. The Negro seemed to sense that rescue was at hand

130

and closed his eyes. Armes could see that an artery in his temple was still pulsating. By this time a dozen slaves had arrived, headed by the two footmen, who stripped off their coats and shirts and started digging. The dirt flew fast, although Armes cautioned them to work slowly when they neared the body. Finally the man's naked body, encrusted with dirt, was freed, and they lifted him from the pit. A bottle of brandy appeared from somewhere and Armes dribbled it through his lips. The fellow opened his eyes and saw that he was free. Armes ran through the open window into the salon, clutched one of the long damask draperies, wrenched it loose, and ran back. The slaves laid the man on it, wrapped its silken folds around him, and carried him to Armes' coach, then gently eased him through the door and onto the satin cushions.

As the coach started down the drive, Armes saw René appear around the corner of the now deserted house from which the guests had departed and the slaves had fled. He stood there, silent but defiant, his shoulders thrown back, his head high. When he saw Armes looking at him, he bowed low, formal and courtly, as though all that had passed had been as nothing. But Armes did not acknowledge the gesture.

A low moan came from the recumbent form on the seat across from him. He bent his head to hear the mumbled words.

"I am Pompee, m'sieu. If I live, I shall serve you well." He closed his eyes. Again he had lost consciousness.

It was useless for Armes to sort out his thoughts and make any sense from the jumble that occupied his mind. How could he be in love with Athenée after only two brief glimpses? And, if he were in love with Athenée, why did he desire Topaze? Why had he defied his own class and color to rescue this black wretch who meant nothing to him? What was this strange land of St. Domingue doing to him? It was twisting him into a different manner of person entirely. He was not sure that he wanted to be that kind of person, but he was aware that it was a better sort than he had been before. He leaned over and reached his hand down under the folds of the damask, running it over the dirty skin of the slave until it rested over the man's heart. It was still beating and Armes was glad. Saving this man's life meant something to him—he didn't know just what, but it seemed important. And loving this cold white woman seemed important, too. But neither lessened his lecherous itch for the tawny body of Topaze.

131

16

POMPEE did not regain consciousness during the trip back to Sans Souci, and as the coach rattled and swayed over the road, Armes had an opportunity to study the Negro's face. From what little that was not battered into a swollen, bloody mass, he could see that it was a fine face, a handsome face, even a noble face. Even his short association with the blacks had taught him that they could not all be lumped together into the one category of *black*. This man was not one of the squat, bandy-legged, big-lipped, and low-browed blacks of the common herd. There was something about him that lifted him out of the ranks of the ordinary. He had a well-shaped, somewhat aquiline nose which suggested either Moorish or Egyptian blood. The cheekbones were high, the forehead wide, and the ears delicately shaped. This Pompee was a tall man, powerfully built, his chest thickly armored with muscle. From what little he knew of Negroes, he imagined the man to be a Mandingo or a Hausa—those Northern tribes whose blood was more Hamitic than Negro. That he was now skeleton-thin was probably due to the fact that he had been ill-nourished, if not starved, during his imprisonment. Armes guessed his age to be around twenty-five.

Twice during the trip Armes felt certain that Pompee had died. The first time he managed to detect a feeble pulse, but the second time he stopped the coach. A few drops from the brandy bottle revived the fluttering heartbeat and they moved on. During the jolting progress, Armes reflected on the man before him. He not only studied his physique but his strange condition. Here was a human being who, through no fault of his own, had been nearly murdered for a witless and foolish sport, indulged in by witless and foolish men. His sympathies were entirely with the man Pompee and yet, Armes knew that if he were to continue to live in St. Domingue, as he fully intended to do, he could not demonstrate his sympathy again in such an overt manner. After all, he was a white man, and he could not openly offend his own kind by taking sides with the blacks. Fortunately there could be no possible censure of his actions at René's today. He had made no move to stop the slaughter—that had come from Athenée. There must have been others among René's guests who did not approve of his actions. Certainly all had turned from him and walked away, but that had obviously been because of René's treatment of Athenée.

The intrusion of her name into his thoughts drew his attention from the wounded man. Now at least he understood so many things which had hitherto been a mystery. He understood why Athenée's parents had left St. Domingue. He knew why she had not appeared on board ship and possibly why René felt toward her as he did. Or . . . did he really understand? Surely the tragedy of the birthmark could not be entirely the cause for René's revulsion toward her. Such sublime beauty as one side of her face presented must compensate for the other; must be indicative of a charm of personality that might cause one to overlook the defect and completely forget it. Ah! That one glimpse of her he had had on board ship! How it had lingered in his memory until he realized that he had always been in love with her. Yet, with this realization, the overpowering physical desire that blotted out the image of Athenée returned. Instead it evoked a fantasy of curved, moist red lips; of honey-colored breasts with circles of bronze nipples; of eyes fringed with sooty lashes. His sentimentalized moonlight vision of Athenée was completely obliterated by the hot sunlight image of Topaze.

Damn! If he couldn't have Athenée, at least he could have the mulatto wench who anxiously sold herself to the highest bidder. He would be the highest bidder even if it took all the money he had to buy her. In her he could forget Athenée. Topaze! He stretched his legs out straight before him to ease the constriction of his tight trousers. Damn! Were it not for the suffering cargo on the opposite seat, he would tell the coachman to drive straight to the Cap and storm the house that sheltered her, beat down the doors, and carry her to that upstairs room behind the closed shutters. He would tear off her clothes and he would . . .

A moan from the dying man and the lighted flambeaux at the gates of Sans Souci brought his thoughts back from his voluptuous fantasy to the present reality. Ali and a slave were awaiting him at the gates. After all the alien faces he had seen, it was comforting to see Ali again, but Armes could not understand how Ali happened to be there, nor how, when the boy jumped up onto the step of the coach, he seemed to know all about what had happened.

133

"I have prepared one of the servants' rooms on the ground floor for the sick man," he said.

"But how did you know I had a sick man with me?"

"About an hour ago, a Negro came to the house. He told me that you were bringing a slave back with you and that the man was sick, maybe dying. He asked me to prepare a place for him and I did."

Armes found it difficult to believe, but now he remembered that all the way along the road he had heard the constant throb of voodoo drums high up in the mountains and he knew that the news must have preceded him. Others had told him about the mysterious telegraphic messages of the drums and how they carried news from one end of the island to the other more quickly than men on horseback. He hadn't believed it then—now he was convinced.

"Who was the slave that brought the message?"

"I do not know, milord. He is an old man, very kind and patient—a gentle soul, well dressed, and he seems more educated than most slaves."

Armes was to see this old man as soon as they arrived at the house. He was awaiting them. Short, gray-haired, and stooped with the weight of years, he advanced to meet them. He spoke in perfect French rather than in the Creole patois.

"I am Toussaint, coachman at the Breda Plantation." He bowed respectfully to Armes. "As I have the reputation of being somewhat of a physician, I have come to attend the sick man in your coach."

"Can you help him?" Armes asked. "I have a particular desire that the man should live."

"I'll do what I can, monsieur."

Several slaves lifted Pompee gently down from the coach and carried him into the ground-floor room. Ali had spread sheets on the bed and lighted a fire in a charcoal brazier to dispel the dampness. Water was already steaming in a pan; there was a pile of clean, torn linen on the table, and a multitude of candles provided a bright light. The slaves laid Pompee carefully down on the bed. Toussaint examined him, felt of his pulse, and laid his ear gently on his chest. He looked up at Armes, and his eyes brimmed with tears.

"And yet another, monsieur," he sighed. "Another sacrifice. But I thank you for your kindness and through me all the blacks thank you. I fear there is very little I can do. The man seems too far gone for my simple herbs and remedies." He stood up in helpless resignation.

One of the slaves standing in the doorway spoke rapidly to Toussaint. Armes did not understand the words, which seemed to be in an African dialect. Toussaint shook his head, but the man continued, becoming vehement in his insistence.

"What is he saying?" Armes demanded.

"He says the man can be saved," Toussaint answered. "I must hurry. If I may borrow a horse, there is a faint chance that the man might live."

"A horse?"

"Yes, another horse. I must go to fetch a certain man and I will need a horse for him to return on. It is only a chance —the man may die before we return."

"I do not understand, but you may take a horse." He turned to Ali. "Have them saddle Lalla." Armes was determined that the man should live.

"My horse, milord?"

"This man Toussaint will treat Lalla well." He turned to Toussaint with a question in his eyes.

"Yes, monsieur, as a coachman I love horses."

Ali left for the stables, gathering up the skirts of his jellaba around his knees, his heelless slippers falling off as he sped down the drive.

Toussaint dampened a cloth with the warm water and sponged off Pompee's face. As he was working, he kept shaking his head from side to side. Finally he looked up at Armes doubtfully.

"I am about to do something, monsieur, which I cannot explain. I have always refused to have any dealings with voodoo because I am a Christian and I do not believe in it, and yet I cannot entirely disbelieve in it because I have seen what voodoo is able to do. You know voodoo, monsieur?"

"Naturally I have heard about it. One does not stay in St. Domingue long without hearing of its mumbo-jumbo."

"It is the ancient religion of the Negroes." Toussaint wet the cloth again and sponged the soil from Pompee's body. "They brought it here with them from Africa. Many claim that there is great power in it, but I do not understand it, practice it, or approve of it. Your slave told me that this man here is a man of voodoo. His name is Pompee and he is a famous *papaloi*."

"I have heard the word before."

"A *papaloi* is a voodoo priest. It happens that this Pompee is the leading *papaloi* of St. Domingue—a man of powerful

135

influence among the blacks. He has accomplished many miracles in the past, but now he is helpless to work for himself. I go to seek another *papaloi* from my home plantation—a man who has studied for some years with Pompee. I trust you do not disapprove of what I do."

"No, I do not disapprove, although I have no faith in it. Save the man if you can, but do not ask me to witness the affair. I've had enough for today. Here's Ali with the horses. I'll have someone stay with Pompee while you are gone."

"Then take this." Toussaint rummaged in the little goatskin bag he carried and pushed a small bottle, half filled with some dark liquid, into Armes' hand. "Have them give him a few drops of this. It may help him."

Armes turned the bottle over to one of the house slaves—the same man who had spoken with Toussaint—and instructed him to sit beside Pompee's bed. He heard the spatter of gravel outside as Toussaint left, then he and Ali together walked out of the house and around to the front steps.

"I'm tired." Armes stopped at the bottom step and rested his arms on the balustrade. "Not only tired but disgusted. I've half a mind to chuck the whole thing, this damned plantation, this damned island, and return to a normal way of life in Boston. I'm fed up with all this mystery, this voodoo, this torture of men, and this whole crazy topsy-turvy place where too many things happen in too short a time. I'm sick of blacks and I'm sick of whites and I don't know what I am myself, for I fear I'm thinking more black than white. Shall I give it all up, Ali?"

"That is for milord to say. As for Ali, it matters only that he is with milord."

"Yes, I'm tempted, boy, but I'll be damned if I will. I'm going to see it through."

"Yes, milord!" Ali's voice came softly through the scented darkness. He slid his arm around Armes' waist and helped him up the stairs, taking them one at a time, slowly. "You'll soon feel better, milord. I have a hot bath waiting for you with bergamot in the water, as we do in my country. We have no proper *hammam* here, but I've done the best I can to make our bathroom into a *hammam*. I'm going to give you a real Moroccan bath. Wait and see. When I have finished you will have forgotten all these ugly things. Then, when you are in bed, propped up with pillows and the candles lit in our room, Ali will bring the sandwiches he made and the

136

hot chocolate. We will eat and we will talk and you can stretch your long legs on the cool sheets and grow drowsy. Then Ali will blow out the candles and milord will sleep."

And sleep Armes did. After the aromatic steaming water and the soothing manipulations of Ali's practiced hands, the welcoming kiss of the linen sheets, the sandwiches and the chocolate, he dropped off to sleep with Ali beside him. Sometime in the night Armes half awoke to hear the sound of muffled drums in the room below. There seemed to be a subdued cadenced chanting which rose and fell with the beat of the drums. The shrill cry of a rooster was cut off quickly on a high note and a thick, pungent aroma of leaves burning drifted in through the opened windows. Again he slept. When he awoke the sun was striping the floor in bars of white light through the nearly closed jalousies. Ali entered, hesitating for a moment at the door to see if Armes were awake. The boy was speechless; fright had driven any words from his mouth. He ran to the bed and threw himself down, creeping up into the protection of Armes' arms. He was trembling and Armes tried to calm him.

"What's the matter with you, boy? You look as though you've seen a ghost."

Ali was incapable of answering. He could only point to the door. Armes followed the direction of his shaking finger to the Negro who stood in the doorway. He was tall and straight and vaguely familiar with his finely cut features and his air of nobility. He advanced slowly across the room and knelt beside the bed. Armes was able to recognize the features of the dying man of the night before. But now, except for a slight puffiness of the face, some purple blotches and an ugly scar from ear to chin which looked nearly healed, there was no hint of the dying man of the night before. This man appeared to be in good health. True, he might have suffered an accident, such as a fall from a horse, but his wounds were only superficial. The chattering of Ali's teeth was contagious. Armes found difficulty in forming his words.

"You are the man I brought with me last night?"

"Yes, I am Pompee."

"But you were dying."

Pompee shook his head and smiled, although it seemed to be a painful effort.

"The gods desire that I live and serve you, *patron*. I heed their command and shall take joy in it. You need never doubt my faithfulness, *patron*."

17

ARMES lost no time in riding into the Cap and presenting himself at the Villa Topaze, but it was a futile storming of an empty castle. Mam'selle Topaze, so the ill-visaged slave informed him, was not at home and indeed, from the abandoned appearance of the villa, Armes had no reason to doubt him, for he appeared to be the only servant in the house. In response to questioning he would only shake his head and reiterate that he did not know where Mam'selle Topaze was, nor where she could be reached, nor where a note could be addressed to her. Armes even tried to bribe him with money, to no avail. Nor did further inquiries in the Cap elicit any information. Even her precious brother and his mulatto brood had disappeared. Henry was certain, however, that she was up in the mountain hideout of her lover, the renegade slave Bouckmann.

There was nothing for Armes to do but return to Sans Souci and attempt to put both Athenée and Topaze out of his mind, if such a superhuman task were possible. To accomplish this there was only one recourse—work. With work, the sun-filled days at Sans Souci ran into weeks and the weeks into one month and then another. Armes began to find in his little kingdom, as Henry had described it, the fulfillment of many of his ambitions. He, as king, tried to rule his subjects with a degree of benign discipline, and they in turn reciprocated by increasing the yield of his land for him. DuBois turned out to be an excellent overseer, ably seconded by Pompee, whose devotion to Armes and skill with the slaves and the land equaled that of Ali in the big house. His life became well-ordered and was made up of interesting and constructive work, but finally Armes was surfeited with both work and order. Armes' whole world had become concentrated in the confines of Sans Souci but it was no longer enough for him. Henry made frequent visits and Armes enjoyed the big Negro's company; he was grateful to Pompee; and he appreciated Ali, but he found that his world was becoming increasingly black. He attempted to widen it by contacts with his neighbors. He called on the Granvilles and the de Brissacs, but did not feel at home in the artificial formality of their lives. Their brittle conversations which ignored the realities of life in St. Domingue bored him as much as his lonely life at Sans Souci.

René appeared one day at Sans Souci, abjectly suing for forgiveness and, as the man seemed truly chastened, Armes decided there could be no harm in retaining the appearance of friendship, particularly as it might afford him an opportunity to see Athenée again. As a result of René's visit, Armes invited the Vicomte and his wife to dinner. Much to his surprise they both accepted, although Athenée once more relied on the protection of her veil. Then, the ice having been broken, Armes was invited to St. Gabriel, and they drifted into the habit of weekly dinners. Little by little, Athenée lost her frigidity and came to talk naturally with Armes. Some state of neutrality had been set up between her and René and they seemed to be more compatible, at least when Armes was present, although it was common knowledge that René kept a succession of mulatto mistresses in his establishment in the Cap. At any rate, Armes was willing to put up with René in order to enjoy those few contacts with Athenée. The mere fact of her being under his roof, gracing his table, relieved the overwhelming black and masculine atmosphere of Sans Souci.

Armes was lost without the companionship of women. He had made several experiments with the slave wenches on the plantation, all of which were unsatisfactory, as they were all too coarse and bestial to provide anything more than a mechanical release of his pent-up energies. In vain he tried to relieve the situation as much as possible by constant application to hard work but, even though his muscles ached from the unaccustomed strain, he possessed a need which neither the slave wenches nor Ali could meet. Finally, in desperation, he had ridden into Cap François and returned to Justine and Marianne. Then, at Henry's suggestion, he had knocked on a certain red door in a narrow street near the *Place* where, his senses titillated by a series of *tableaux* which were produced there, he found momentary easement in sheer quantity of diversions. After these visits, he returned to Sans Souci physically satiated but mentally as lonely as before. Henry had suggested importing one of the mulatto wenches from town and setting her up at Sans Souci, but after looking them all over, Armes found none that appealed to him sufficiently to share his existence with. He even considered sending to Cambridge and having Kitty make

139

the long journey to St. Domingue, but he knew that to do so would entail her bringing her, or rather their, child with her, and he did not feel in a paternal mood. Certainly not with the prospect of eventually having Topaze.

Thus he continued to tire himself daily in the fields, yield to Ali's scented baths, and relax under the soothing manipulations of the boy's hands. In this way he managed to sleep nights, but his dreams made him restless. Whenever he awoke in the night, he heard Ali's questioning voice, "Milord, are you all right?" Then he would sleepily affirm his well-being and go back to sleep. Thus his life went on.

Late one afternoon, as he was returning from a particularly exhausting day, spent in clearing a section of land for additional planting, during which he had stripped to the waist and worked side by side with the slaves the more thoroughly to submerge his unspoken longings, he saw Ali riding across the fields to meet him. Ali's air of urgency and the fact that he had quitted the house heralded something unusual. Ali was standing in his stirrups, his white jellaba floating out behind him, and as he approached Armes, Armes could see an expression of anger and defeat on the boy's face. He was breathless when he arrived. He wheeled Lalla around and trotted beside Armes.

He swallowed hard once or twice before he could speak and then the words came in a torrent.

"Milord, milord, what shall we do? That woman's here."

"That woman?" Armes asked in surprise. "What woman?"

"That Topaze, the sister of Fabre."

"Topaze?" Armes no longer felt tired. "She is here, at the house? What does she want?"

"You, milord. She waits for you. But do not go, milord, do not go. She is not good for you. Stay away from her. Let me go back and say that you are not here. Oh, let me, milord."

Armes felt the hot blood creeping up his neck and spreading over his face. Something started to pound inside him and he knew it must be his heart beating, although it had never sounded like that before. Ali and all of Sans Souci disappeared, and he could only see the shuttered windows of the decrepit villa in the Cap and once again, as it had so many times before, his imagination crept between the slatted jalousies to the woman who was inside—to Topaze.

"Why should I send the lady away? Perhaps she has business with me." His words were purposely abrupt, for he had a strange new desire to hurt the boy—to hurt and humiliate him. The spurs on his boots which he had never used before dug deep into Tom's sleek sides and the horse reared and bolted, leaving Ali behind.

Armes did not slacken speed until he reached the house and saw Topaze's gaudy carriage in the drive. He tossed the reins to a slave and leaped up the front steps two at a time. Ali was only a moment behind him. Inside the hall, Armes hesitated a moment before entering the salon. He caught a quick glimpse of himself in the mirror and saw the sweaty streaks of dirt on his chest and shoulders and the grimy, once-white breeches which clung to him damply. The red earth of St. Domingue stained his hands and his clumsy boots were encrusted with it. To hell with it! If she could welcome the embraces of a nigger slave in the mountains, she would not object to a little honest white sweat in a drawing room. He couldn't wait. He strode into the room.

She was sitting on a wide couch at the far end of the room just beyond the golden fingers of sunlight which striped the floor. Her dress was some sort of golden tissue with woven stripes of pale green—colors which emphasized the clear amber of her skin and the glowing emerald of her eyes. A fan of ivory lace traced slow circles before her face, hiding her eyes for a moment as he entered, then revealing them so that they might invite him, beckon to him, devour him. She did not rise, speak, or even smile, but merely continued to wave the delicate lacy arc before her face. He heard the clatter of his boots on the polished floor as he ran across the room to stand before her, but once there, he discovered that he was mute. There were no words that he could say. Her eyes had spoken to him and his to hers, and words seemed useless. Their glances had met and locked together. For a long moment they held each other transfixed, then her eyes shifted to something behind him. He turned quickly and saw Ali standing in the door.

He waved his hand in dismissal, but Ali hesitated.

"Go!" Armes had difficulty in shaping the single word. Ali did not move.

"Fi!" She lowered her fan and stuck out her tongue at Ali. "It seems your *petit poulet* does not intend to go."

Armes turned his back on Topaze and advanced a step toward Ali with clenched fists. For a second Ali's imploring eyes met Armes' unflinching ones, then he turned and ran. Armes waited until he had gone, then turned to Topaze.

141

She moved one small foot, trimly shod in amber satin, out from under the lacy froth of her petticoats. The little golden cord that fastened it had become untied. Slowly her eyes inventoried the utter male hugeness of him, then she lifted her foot an inch or so from the floor. Only then did she speak to him, and her voice had lost the harshness of the moment before. It became low and musical, liquid smooth.

"My poor little shoe, M'sieu Armes! Look, it has become untied. Would you please be so kind?"

He knelt before her to tie the shoe, lifting it in one of his work-stained hands while the other fumbled with the knot. But before he had a chance to tie it, she slid forward from the chair onto the floor beside him, her arms wrapped around his neck, her lips pressed close to his. Whether by accident or design, the pins that held her hair released their hold and, as she drew her lips away from his so that he could look at her, the coif of hair slowly untwisted and cascaded down her back. Once again her voracious lips fastened on his, her arms pulled him even closer, her hands made bold explorations and their two bodies slumped together to the floor.

"Armes," she whispered, "Armes, your very name I love as I adore you. Arms are the instruments that men do battle with. Let me discover what arms you carry, Armes. Can they conquer a woman, Armes? Oh, let me know those arms. Let me feel their power, Armes, for your arms must conquer me."

He half rose, supporting his weight on one elbow, and looked down into her face, contorted now with an animality which only enhanced its strange beauty. He possessed no words to say to her. He repeated her name over and over again and each time he said it, it took on a new meaning for him. Whether his inflection made the word tender or demanding, he felt her pressing closer to him. He felt her fingers grip his hair; he felt them probe the hardness of the muscles in his back; he felt them creep around his body to lose themselves in the thick pelt of his chest, then down until those same questing fingers discovered and fumbled at the sturdy buttons of his one garment. His own hands touched warmth of tender flesh under gossamer silk but their impatience could not cope with tiny buttons and ruthlessly ripped away the thin silk and the froth of laces. Now the moist lips pressed against his own with new power and he felt the tumescent strength of his own flesh, rising to take proud possession of her as she yielded to the surge of his

142

necessity—yielded and met it. Somewhere, as though it were an echo from another world, he heard a sob and then the sound of the big double mahogany doors banging together, but no outside noise could penetrate his mind now.

His eyes, which were closed, opened and stared down into hers. He sought and lost himself in those luminous wide green pools which mirrored his own face. He saw himself swimming far down in their depths which were like liquid fire on his skin. Deeper and deeper he plunged, swimming in a steady rhythm. There was no bottom to be reached but yet he went down, deeper, deeper, deeper, until he gasped for breath and fought for air against the inexorable force that possessed him. His lungs were bursting. He must fill them or die. Just one breath! Yet he must go on, deeper and deeper, to quench the fire that was consuming him. Now the very core of his being was eaten away by the merciless holocaust, and his wracked body could no longer contain the pressure. Some vital nerve within him snapped and his entire cosmos spurted forth in one shattering cataclysmic explosion that left him lying spent and broken, gasping on the shore of that green pool, seeking a coolness on the smoldering ashes of his charred body.

Slowly he returned to reality. He gathered up the broken shards of his sundered body and laboriously reshaped them piece by piece until he could muster enough strength to turn his head and see Topaze on the floor beside him. Her hand caught in the mat of hair on his chest and she carefully twined one dark tendril around her finger. Her inconsequential words shattered the silence.

"*Hélas!* You have ruined my gown, Armes, and it was such an expensive gown. I bought it especially for you and it was the first time I ever wore it." She kicked the tumbled pile of yellow stuff with her foot. "Poor Topaze." She pouted prettily. "How can she return to Cap François without a gown?"

Armes reached for the sodden grimy white pantaloons on the floor beside them and pulled them on. He stood up, reached down his hand to her, and lifted her up.

"And must you return to Cap François?" he whispered close to her ear.

"Must I?"

"Not as long as I am here."

They clung together. Armes did not know how long they had been there when he heard the doors open. His back was toward them. Suddenly Topaze stiffened in his arms. Her hand disengaged itself from his neck and reached back, fumbling for something on the table behind her. He felt her tenseness as she grabbed something, saw the rising arc of her arm, and caught the colorful glint of the little Meissen shepherdess as she threw it. There was a crash of shattered porcelain and Ali's cry of pain.

"*Cochon!*" she screamed. "Get out, you little *pisse-froid*, you dirty little Arab, you *petit poulet*. Oh, get out, get out, get out and leave us alone."

The door closed. Armes picked her up in his arms and carried her across the room, kicked the door open with his bare foot and carried her across the hall to his bedroom. Ali was flung down on the bed, curled up in a little heap of woe. Armes regarded him for a second, then reached his foot up to find lodgment in the small of Ali's back. He pushed and the force of his push sent Ali sprawling onto the floor.

"Out!" Armes' one word had a finality that brought Ali to his feet and sent him scurrying from the room.

Armes laid Topaze down in the same spot which Ali had vacated. She did not relinquish him but pulled him down beside her.

"Him you will not need anymore—" her head inclined toward the doorway—"now that you have Topaze."

"Him I shall not need now that I have Topaze," Armes echoed.

18

ARMES returned to reality the next morning from an hour or so of fitful slumber to find Topaze's moist lips pressed against his own, as they had been most of the night. The heat of the night and the fecundity of the Tropics possessed the room, and it reeked of sweat and seminal odors. A close damp smell crept in from the garden—a smell of things that had grown, died, rotted, and grown again. Myriad noises kept up a *sotto voce* accompaniment to his thoughts—noises of the primeval struggle of life itself, conception, birth, growth, death, and decay. Running through this theme was the throbbing cadence of the distant drums in the mountains as they spelled out the message into the first streaks of dawn that the white master of Sans Souci was bedded with the mulatto Topaze, mistress of the maroon Bouckmann.

The wan light crept timidly through the thickly interlaced branches of mango and avocado, forced its way with feeble tentacles through the mat of bougainvillea on the balcony, and weakly pried open the slender slats of the jalousies to rest in silver ribbons on the sinuous form of Topaze beside him. The pressure of her lips, still insistent in her sleep, made it difficult for him to breathe; the hard points of her breasts forced themselves into his now unwilling flesh. It had been impossible to satisfy her and now, in his waking, he was surfeited, drained of energy, an unwilling victim of the flesh that rested so hot and moist against him. Sickened with heat, his mind fled, seeking coolness. He remembered Boston on a winter's evening with the yellow candlelight of Mount Vernon Street houses gilding the snow; cold water dipped from a mint-fringed spring; and the feel of icy sheets that had not been warmed with a longhandled brass pan. Anything! Anything but this hot, musky entanglement of sweaty arms and slippery legs which now smothered him. Anything but the heat of those lips upon his.

He heaved himself from the bed, lurched drunkenly across the floor, and gained the dim solitude of the bathroom, where he slipped into the marble tub. With the cool caress of the water, a semblance of rationality returned to his thoughts. He was able to think a little more clearly, and to breathe without the cloying odor of musk in his nostrils. When he had finished and returned to the bedroom, he was humming softly to himself some half-remembered song which he and fellow students had sung in another life on the banks of the Charles.

Topaze still lay on the bed, stupefied in sleep. When Armes walked over and looked down at her in the welter of sweat-stained linen, tongues of desire began to flick at his newly gained composure. He shook his head and reached over to pull up a sheet, hiding the amber flesh before he left the room.

He encountered no sign of life in the hall. It was deserted and so was the salon, except for the Meissen shepherdess which was now only a scattering of porcelain chips on the floor. He listened and absorbed the unaccustomed silence of the house. Always before there had been a quiet stirring when he got up—some of the slave wenches would be wax-

145

ing the floors with oversized slippers of folded rags; others dusting, sweeping, or polishing. But this morning the entire household was devoid of movement. Surprised, he walked into the dining room. Here the table presented an unbroken expanse of polished mahogany, and lacked the two carefully set places which he and Ali had always occupied. He progressed on through the silent house, meeting nobody, and when he reached the stairs that led to the ground floor he grasped the iron railing and descended them, not knowing whether he was angry, unhappy, or merely hungry.

One of the largest rooms on the ground floor had been allotted to Pompee. Armes had never entered it since the night he had brought Pompee home and now, although the door was closed, he suspected that Ali might be inside, for a close friendship had developed between Ali and Pompee. Armes knew that Pompee was already out in the fields, for he was always the first one up on the plantation, so the closed door betokened some other occupancy. He stood for a moment in hesitation before the door, then, without knocking, pushed it open. Inside a murky half-light was filtered through the green leaves of the vines and the shadow of the overhanging balcony. As he had supposed, Ali was there alone. He was sitting motionless on a straight chair, his hands folded in resignation in his lap, his head bowed. He was still dressed in the same clothes as the afternoon before, but the white turban had become uncoiled, releasing the long curls of his hair. Ali did not look up as he entered although Armes could tell by the stiffening of the muscles in Ali's neck that he was aware of his presence. Armes walked over to the chair, laid his hand on the boy's shoulder, and waited. Ali's thin frame trembled under the pressure of Armes' fingers, but he did not speak.

"I wish I could make you understand, little fellow." Armes groped for words. "It isn't that I don't care about you anymore, it's just . . ."

"That you love that woman upstairs." Ali's voice was hoarse.

"Yes, I guess you are right, Ali, I think I do love her, but I am not sure. I've never quite known anything like this feeling before. Even now, a few moments after I've left her, I want to return to her. I resent these few minutes I am spending with you because they keep me away from her. And yet as much as I want to be with her, I do not want to go back to her. I want to be out in the fields, working with

146

Pompee, talking with DuBois." He drew up a chair beside the silent figure and sat down.

Waiting for Ali to speak, he looked around the room. On the far side of the chamber, across from the open window, a crude shelf was covered with a white cloth. In the exact center, he saw a tall cross, made of some dark polished wood, with a crudely carved snake, painted a bright green, pendant upon it. Several candles were stuck in the necks of wine bottles, and on the white cloth a number of objects that looked like dark round stones made a symmetrical pattern. Leaning against the wall were two cheaply framed, highly colored lithographs of Catholic saints whom Armes did not recognize, and in front of them were several covered pottery jars. Directly in front of the cross was a china plate holding a conical mound of yellow corn meal which had an egg precisely balanced on its peak. Armes conjectured that as Pompee was a voodoo *papaloi*, this must be the altar of his sect. Surely it was innocuous enough, even though the carved snake was surprisingly lifelike.

He reached over and lifted Ali's chin with his hand.

"I'm sorry, little fellow. I never should have allowed you to care so much about me. Surely you must have known that I couldn't reciprocate your feeling. I was cruel to you last night, and I do not want to be cruel again. All I can say is that Topaze is here to stay, at least for a while. I know that is going to make a big difference to you. Believe me, I do not want to hurt you, after all that has passed between us. Let's talk the matter over, huh?"

"Yes, milord, we talk."

"All right, then. That's more like it. Now! Do you want to stay here, even with Topaze in the house?"

Ali nodded assent.

"Because if you don't, I'll arrange to send you back to Africa. There are ships leaving Cap François which stop at Mazagan or some other Moroccan port. I'll pay your passage back and give you enough so you can get to Marrakech and your father's home."

Ali did not answer. Armes prompted him.

"How about that?"

Ali shook his head. "It has been a long time since I left my father's home. I have nearly forgotten the language that I spoke there. My place is with milord. You need me now more than ever before to protect you. May I stay, milord?"

"Yes." Armes' answer came slowly. "Yes, you may stay,

147

but under one condition. As long as Topaze is here, you must treat her with respect and you must not show your jealousy. Do you understand?"

"What milord desires is difficult, but it shall be done."

"And no more sulking."

"No, milord."

"And you'll be happy."

"No, milord."

"But if you stay you will not cause any trouble."

"Ali will stay and he will not cause any trouble. He will be as a shadow."

"You'll see that breakfast is served every morning when I get up, that the house is always clean, and that things go on as smoothly now as they did before? You will superintend the house, plan the meals, and serve them to Topaze and me?"

"Yes, milord, but one question."

"Ask it."

"Where shall Ali sleep if he can no longer share milord's bed?"

"There are four bedrooms on the floor above. Choose any one you want for your own."

"Then milord continues to sleep with her?"

"It is natural for a man to sleep with a woman."

"Yes, milord."

"So . . . now that we understand each other, we shall shake hands." Armes reached over and took Ali's limp hand in his own. Ali allowed him to shake it solemnly, then raised Armes' hand and brushed it across his cheek.

"We have made an agreement, milord. I'll conduct myself properly toward your Topaze. I shall treat her with respect, even though I hate her. You did not make me promise not to hate her, and I always shall for the awful things she is doing to you. Someday you will come to me and you will say that Ali was right and then, once more, Sans Souci will be our home."

Armes smiled at him and stood up. "You're an incurable sentimentalist, little fellow, and it's true, I do need you. Why, boy, if it were not for you and Pompee, I couldn't run Sans Souci. I depend on you both."

"Thank you, monsieur." A deeper voice spoke from the doorway. Armes turned. Pompee was standing in the doorway. Armes beckoned to him to come in.

"Ali and I have solved our little problem, Pompee."

"Have you?" Pompee asked. "Are you sure?"

Armes laughed. "Quite."

Pompee crossed the room, genuflected briefly before the altar, then rose and lighted one of the candles. He made the Christian sign of the cross, turned, and faced Armes.

"I am a voodoo *papaloi*," he said, looking directly at Armes. "Here I serve my god, Damballah, the great green serpent of Dahomey. My god is a tender god and a good god. There is nothing evil in Damballah Weydo nor in his wife, Ayda Weydo. You who are a Christian know our god Damballah, for he was your Saint Patrick. Nor is our Erzuli a wicked goddess; it is she whom you know as the mother of your Holy Jesus. We have other gods, too. Papa Legba stands guard at the door of heaven like your Saint Peter. Then there is Agwe of the sea, Baron Samedi of death, Papa Zaca of the fields, and Ogoun Feraille of war. They are all Rada gods. They are my gods—the ancient gods of Dahomey."

He walked to the other end of the altar and lighted another candle.

"My gods are good gods. But there are other gods which are evil—Petro gods who are wicked gods. May I speak more, *patron?*"

"Yes, speak, Pompee, but quickly, for I am hungry."

Ali paused a moment in the doorway before he slipped out of the room.

"There will be breakfast for two in a few moments, milord —breakfast for you and . . . her."

Pompee questioned Armes with his eyes.

"What did you want to tell me, Pompee?"

"I am your slave, M'sieu Armes. You bought me, but that does not make me your slave. You saved my life, and that does. You came to a dying man and laid your white hand gently on his head. That is what makes me your slave, not the money you paid for me to St. Gabriel. No matter if you free me, I shall always be your slave. As a slave whom you purchased, I have no right to speak to you, but as a slave who has given himself to you, I feel that I have that right, and I shall speak."

"Certainly, Pompee."

"You will not be offended?" Pompee fingered a small stone amulet which he wore around his neck.

Armes shook his head.

"Then let me tell you that that woman whom you have upstairs is a woman known all through St. Domingue as a
149

worshiper of the evil Petro gods. That is bad, M'sieu Armes. Bad for you and bad for all of us. I do not know how she managed it, but she has bewitched you. She has used *magie noire* on you. Let me cure you. Here"—he picked up one of the small covered jars—"and here"—he picked up another. "These two jars which we call *govis* contain the *loas*—the spirits—of Attiso and his wife Aizan. They are Rada gods and their purpose is to protect good people against the black magic of Petro. Say the word and I will take off the covers, release the *loas*, and cure you. Say the word, M'sieu Armes."

Armes did not answer. He turned slowly and walked toward the door, then hesitated and returned. He reached for one of the *govis* and Pompee placed it carefully in Armes' hand. He examined it closely. It was a very ordinary-looking jar, of unglazed peasant pottery with a tight fitting cover. He handed it back to Pompee.

"You may be right, Pompee. It can well be black magic, but not the kind you mean. It's a black magic composed of red lips, honey-colored skin, firm round breasts, and the musky smell of a woman. If it's that kind of black magic, nothing you might have in that little jar could cure it. Besides, I do not know if I want to be cured."

He left the room and bounded up the stairs. There was a rattle of silver in the dining room where Ali was supervising the setting of the table. The door to Armes' bedroom was still closed. He flung it open and entered. Once again the close, musky smell enveloped him. Topaze was still sleeping, and he walked over and awakened her with a kiss. She stretched slowly with a sinuous, cat-like grace, then reached up and pushed his lips away.

"Topaze is sleepy," she said.

"Then sleep, my dear." He turned to leave the room.

"But Armes . . . ?"

"Yes."

"We must get ready to go to Cap François."

"Whatever for?"

"Did you not forget, *mon Hercule?* Today you must buy Topaze a new dress to take the place of the one you tore last night. And there is a pair of diamond earbobs which poor Topaze had to let the pawnbroker have. Now she needs them." She smiled and placed the tip of her finger against his lips.

"To Cap François then, as soon as you are ready."

Her hands clasped behind the nape of his neck and drew him down to her.

"Mon cher, you are so big, so strong, and you make love with such power, how can poor Topaze refuse you? If you insist that we go to the Cap, we must go, *hein?"*

"That, my dear"—he stretched out beside her—"is what is known as twisting a man around your little finger, *hein?"*

19

DURING the weeks that followed, the former peaceful harmony of Sans Souci was shattered by the continuous and piercing screaming of Topaze. Only while Armes was in the house did her conduct approach any form of docility. Then she would woo him with flattery and even abase herself to wait upon him. She was, however, supremely confident of her power over him. She well knew that the soft touch of her fingers sent an electric shock through him; she was aware that her lips robbed him of all reason; and that her body was a never-ending temptation to him. Topaze was very wise in the ways of men. She knew how to take full advantage of her power over them.

While she remained at Sans Souci, the Villa Topaze in the Cap was closed. The caretaker informed all callers that Mam'selle Topaze was away, but although the front door remained closed, the back door opened frequently to receive drayloads of furniture and valuable stuffs which Topaze purchased and Armes paid for. Several times a week she insisted that he accompany her into the Cap, and their destination was always the most expensive shops. Her taste ran to the more gaudy and gilded Louis Quinze pieces which had been dumped from France on the less fortunate St. Domingue. The furniture was followed by bolts of damask, rolls of Aubusson carpets, barrels of Sèvres china, crystal chandeliers, and ormolu clocks—anything that was costly and showy. These heavy pieces all went to the Villa Topaze, while the armoires at Sans Souci were bursting with gowns, and a Buhl casket in Armes' bedroom was overflowing with jewels. Fortunately for Armes, her taste was not too discriminating. Fake jewels delighted her as much as real ones—as a matter of fact, she liked them even better, for they were much larger and flashier.

The house usually quieted down in the evening when Armes came in from the fields, but as soon as he left in the morning with Pompee all hell broke loose. Topaze lolled in the big bed in Armes' room and screamed without interruption. Nothing satisfied her. Nothing was ever done the way she wished. Every five minutes she countermanded her commands of five minutes before until she had set the whole house into a state of nervous tension. The more furore she caused, the better she enjoyed it. When she could think of no other mischief to perpetrate, she would deliberately break something, then berate all the servants in turn for having broken it. She especially loved to inflict punishment herself, and every servant in the house bore the marks of her vindictive pinchings.

Ali, naturally, was the special object of her vituperations, although she had never quite dared to touch him. He was ever mindful of his pledge to Armes and attempted to serve her well. Regardless of her accusations he never answered her back, but would stand silently before her while she tongue-lashed him with vile abuse. His very unwillingness to clash with her made her even more vindictive. She was quite aware of the strong bond which had previously existed between Armes and Ali and for this reason alone, she was determined to humiliate him. Whenever he came into her presence, she reviled him. If he stayed away, she called him back merely as an excuse to abuse him. She was determined to break his spirit, even as she had cowed all the other household servants, but he alone seemed unafraid of the vitriol of her tongue.

Daily she would toss from side to side in the huge bed in a frenzy of petulance until the clock neared noon. Then she would slowly compose herself into the person she felt Armes expected her to be. The littered bed with its rumpled sheets would be forsaken and she would strip off her nightclothes, douse herself with perfume—she hated water like a cat— apply her elaborate *maquillage* with care, and then dress herself, and be ready to receive him when he returned to the big house for the midday meal. While he was with her, she cloyed the air with her honeyed words, spoke most graciously to the slaves, and tried to conduct herself as much *à la marquise* as she knew how. Then, each day when they retired for their siesta after lunch, she strengthened her hold on

152

Armes and drew him deeper and deeper into the velvet trap she had prepared for him.

One afternoon, as Armes was dressing after a longer than usual midday *divertissement* with Topaze—it could hardly have been called rest—he heard the clatter of gravel in the drive below. Company was rare these days at Sans Souci, and his curiosity caused him to pull up the jalousies. He shielded his eyes from the glare of white sunshine that streamed into the room through the opened window. He could barely see the top of a head through the balcony railing, but even that slight glimpse of the wool-crowned pate told him it was Henry, for no other man in St. Domingue was as tall as Henry Christophe. Armes ran to the edge of the balcony. He was right—it was Henry.

"Henry, Henry Christophe," he called out, and the welcome in his voice and his pleasure at seeing Henry was apparent to Topaze. Her catlike jealousy was immediately aroused.

"Who is it?" she whispered, as she followed him out onto the balcony, dragging a froth of gauze behind her.

"*Mon ami*, Henry Christophe from the Couronne." Armes raced back into the room, hastily drawing on his clothes.

Topaze flounced in behind him.

"That nigger!" Her voice was contemptuous. "That black ape from the Couronne! You'll not see him here, Armes. I forbid it. Tell him to go back to the Cap. He is not welcome here." The negligee fell to the floor and she stretched her arms out to embrace him.

He ignored her as he continued to dress.

"Armes, come to me," she commanded.

He slipped his arms into the sleeves of his shirt and tucked the tails into his breeches.

"Armes, I demand . . ."

"Shut up and dress yourself." The tone of his voice warned her that she had overstepped the limits of his patience. "Henry has ridden far to see me and I will see him. We will not discuss the matter further."

She walked penitently across the floor and sat down cross-legged on the bed, flashing her most enticing smile.

"Then you will not do that one little thing for Topaze?"

"No!"

She held out her arms to him again, confident that he would not resist their appeal.

"You do not love Topaze?"

"Oh, for heaven's sake, yes. Haven't I proved it to you often enough—just a half hour ago, in fact? But just because I love you, I am not going to stop seeing my friends."

"I think you are getting a little tired of Topaze, no?"

"Of course not."

"Then come kiss me, Armes, and let us forget about that *gros nègre*. Topaze will make you forget him."

He looked at her but did not answer her. For the first time since the night she arrived, he felt a revulsion for her too well-known flesh. The mascara on one of her eyes was streaked and there was a smudge on her cheek. Her hair was in disarray and she looked unkempt and dirty. His slight shudder was apparent. When he walked to the door, he could feel her eyes on him, and he turned and saw that they were narrow slits of hatred. Anxious to be quit of her he walked out, slamming the door behind him, and went out onto the balcony in front. Henry was awaiting him on the steps.

"TiArmes." Henry spread his huge arms and greeted Armes with resounding slaps on the back—slaps which surely would have felled a man of lesser proportions. "*Mon ami*, it is good to see you, and I wish I could see you for a better reason than that for which I come today."

"Bad news, Henry? Since when have you ever been the bearer of bad news? Just seeing you is the best news I could ask for."

Henry shook his head slowly. "Perhaps it is not so bad after all. Perhaps I am too much concerned, but something is wrong. Tell me, have you noticed anything unusual here at Sans Souci—anything different in your daily routine?"

"Well, yes." Armes grinned broadly and winked at Henry.

"I don't mean your little *amie*, Topaze." Henry grinned back. "I mean have you seen any evidence of unrest among your slaves?"

Armes considered for a moment, then shook his head. Since Pompee had come to Sans Souci, everything had run smoothly, like a well-oiled machine. The story of Pompee's torture and subsequent release by Armes had sped throughout the island, and everywhere that Armes went, he was greeted with respect, deference, and even affection by the blacks. Here on his own plantation there was complete harmony. The blacks worked well, and in turn they were treated well. Several new slaves had been purchased—powerful, muscular field hands whom DuBois had handpicked from the barracoons and whom Pompee had indoctrinated. They too respected Armes.

"But yes, Henry." Armes recalled a number of incidents. "But it's so insignificant that it hardly seems worth mentioning."

"And that is, TiArmes?"

"Several times during the past weeks one or two of the slaves would be missing at evening roll call, but they always returned later—at least they always reported for work in the morning—so Pompee did not punish them. We have no objections to our men attending a *bamboche* at some neighboring plantation."

"This man Pompee, do you trust him?" Henry asked.

Armes smiled. "As I trust you, Henry."

Henry nodded slowly in well-considered agreement. He had made it his business to find out about Pompee and the exalted position he maintained in the voodoo hierarchy. "Pompee's a good man."

"I know it, Henry."

"And he is a Rada *papaloi*. . . ."

"Come, come, Henry! You have not ridden all the way from the Cap in the heat of the day to tell me that Pompee is a Rada *papaloi*. Out with it, man. What's on your mind?" Armes drew Henry up the stairs into the shade of the balcony and motioned to a chair.

Henry sat down gingerly, for the chair was rather fragile in appearance. First he told Armes about the execution of the mulattoes Ogé and Chavannes some time ago in the Cap. Naturally Armes had heard about it, but he did not know all the details and Henry filled those in. Jacques Ogé, the brilliant *affranchi,* had gone as a delegate to the National Convention in Paris and had returned to St. Domingue, filled with the revolutionary spirit which was sweeping France. He had converted the young mulatto poet, Chavannes, and together they had built up a considerable following among the *hommes de couleur* of the colony. The *blancs* had arrested them, dragged them to the Cap, and executed them by breaking them on the wheel in the Place des Armes. All blacks and mulattoes were compelled by law to witness the execution. First Ogé and then Chavannes was led to the executioner's platform. Henry had heard the crunch of broken bones under the iron rods. He had seen the two men die in horrible agonies, while the *blancs* made a holiday of the execution. He had been one of the blacks who watched silently and sullenly with the

155

realization that the two men would not have died had it not been for the black blood in their veins that threatened the white supremacy of the colony.

Ogé and Chavannes had died like heroes, and their black blood had made them martyrs to the slaves.

Henry had not watched alone. Toussaint had stood on one side of him and Jean Jacques Dessalines on the other. Together these three slaves had sensed the first faint stirrings of revolt; the first questioning impulse in the minds of the blacks; the first wondering if freedom might not be theirs. They were thinking that that often-mouthed phrase which rang so loudly in Paris—*Liberté, Egalité, Fraternité*—might possibly apply in St. Domingue. If there could be equality between peasant and duke, was there not a possibility of equality between white and black? If the peasants of France who had been little more than slaves could now enjoy liberty, why not the slaves of St. Domingue? And surely if the common men of France could band together in fraternity, so could the blacks of this island.

From that day on, Henry explained to Armes, there had been an attempt at organization among the slaves. Each plantation had secretly elected a head man, some slave who through natural ability or education was able to command the respect of others. These in turn reported to the leaders of higher rank such as Toussaint, Dessalines, and—Henry admitted—himself.

"You are a *blanc*, TiArmes, but you are my good friend. There has never been any such a thing as color between you and me. I never think of you as a white man or a black man, only as my friend. Am I right, TiArmes? I must know, because I am telling you many things, dangerous things, and you are the only white man in all St. Domingue who knows them. *Par Damballah*, TiArmes, can I trust you?"

Armes realized that this was serious. He was aware of Henry's friendship for him, but for a Negro to confide such matters in a white was beyond even friendship. He appreciated Henry's confidence in him, but wondered if he deserved it. He did not reply at once.

"Yes, you can trust me to keep your secrets, Henry Christophe. I shall respect your confidence, but let me warn you. I shall not be a party to anything that will harm the whites. Just as I rescued Pompee from white cruelty, so would I try to rescue a white man from black savagery."

156

Henry reached for Armes' hand, pressed it tightly, and released it.

"I have come to warn you, TiArmes. Do not be offended at what I shall say. Remember the rope you once found in your bed?"

Armes nodded.

"It was a Petro *ouanga*. Black magic! Evil!"

"So you told me."

"Then be careful, TiArmes. But that is not all. May I speak of Topaze? She is here, yes?"

"Yes, Henry, Topaze is here, and I love her very much." Henry shook his head slowly from side to side.

"Are you sure?"

Armes hesitated but Henry did not wait for his answer.

"I hope you don't, TiArmes. She is a devotee of Petro. For a long time she has been under the influence of Bouckmann, the Petro *bocor*. He is a maroon, an escaped slave who lives in the mountains. It is said that Bouckmann is a *loup-garou*, a werewolf who has sold himself to the wicked gods of Petro. It is also common gossip that your Topaze is a *baka*, an evil spirit that helps him."

Armes laughed and clapped Henry on the back.

"Henry, Henry, Henry! Are you losing your mind? What is all this talk of *loups-garous*, *bakas*, and *bocors*? You never believed in them before and I know you don't now. Furthermore, you know damned well I don't."

"Then, TiArmes, it's time you did." Henry became even more serious. "But I didn't come to Sans Souci to talk about werewolves, although that is bad enough. I believe Bouckmann and Topaze are fleecing you. Your life even may be in danger. My reason for coming is to warn you and also to deliver a message from Toussaint. He says we need you and he says you are the only *blanc* we can trust. Dessalines does not agree, but Toussaint's word is more powerful than his. Toussaint saw what you did for Pompee and he trusts you. He wants to see you." Henry's voice sank to a whisper. "Terrible things are about to happen and soon. It is not as Toussaint and I want them, nor even as that *brute* Dessalines wants them. But they are going to happen, anyway."

"*Merci beaucoup*, Henry. I'm glad we are friends. I would not want you for an enemy. You are a powerful man."

Henry smiled and rolled his sleeve back, then slowly doubled up his arm, causing the huge muscles to ripple under the ebon skin.

"Yes, Henry, you are strong, but I did not mean that kind of strength. You have a brain. But . . . tell me more."

"Well, this Bouckmann has much power among the blacks. For weeks he has been visiting all the plantations secretly at night. Men from distant plantations have been coming to visit him. He has been talking to the slaves and he has much influence with those of the Petro faith. He is preaching revolution. Revolution now! Kill every white man, woman and child in St. Domingue, burn the plantations, fire the cane fields, destroy the cities and villages. He wants to wipe out every trace of white civilization and turn St. Domingue into a little Africa with the blacks living once again as savages."

"Well, isn't that what your friend Dessalines wants, too?"

Henry shook his head. "Jean Jacques is not my friend, TiArmes. True, we work together for the freedom of the blacks, but Jean Jacques' aim is not the same as mine or Bouckmann's. Yes, Jean Jacques says to kill all the whites, but he wants the blacks to take the place of the whites. Jean Jacques does not want to be a petty African chief, living in a hut in the forest. He wants a general's uniform with many pretty medals and a palace filled with women to sleep with. He would kill the whites but preserve their way of life for the blacks. So, he opposes Bouckmann."

"And Toussaint?" Armes could not picture the gentle old Toussaint in such bloodthirsty plottings.

"Toussaint wants liberty as much as we do, but he advises getting it slowly and carefully, without killing. He says we must organize first. We must have a revolution by treating with the whites, sending them back to France, and taking their wealth."

"And what does Henry Christophe say?" Armes sought the answer in Henry's eyes.

"I am somewhere between the two of them, TiArmes. I agree with Jean Jacques that we must gain power."

"How?"

"By taking advantage of our superiority of numbers. There are hundreds of blacks to every white in St. Domingue. Let us unite! We can form an army in the mountains. We can drill and become soldiers. We can have discipline and order. Then, when we have the power, we can negotiate with the whites. I do not want to kill them nor ship them back to France, because we shall need them. They have the education and they know how to do things. We do not. We are ignorant and in order to become educated it will require another generation. In the meantime we keep the whites and let them work for us."

Armes heard a door close softly inside the house, but from where he was sitting he could not see into the hall. The soft click of the latch bothered him, although he could not understand why. He considered Henry's words in his mind and then spoke aloud.

"Toussaint through words, Dessalines through slaughter, and Henry through power. I think you have the right solution, Henry. I am not French, I am an American, and we had a revolution before France even thought of one. My sympathies are always with the underdog. I can remember when I was at school . . . but never mind that. I'm for you, Henry, and I hope you win. No needless slaughter of the whites, but the rights of man for the blacks and the two living together peacefully. Is that it?"

Henry smiled showing an even row of teeth.

"Then if I can help, let me know," Armes added.

"You can." Henry's smile faded. "We are in great danger. Neither Toussaint's plan nor Dessalines' nor mine can succeed. This Bouckmann has another plan of his own. He wants to kill and kill now. In that Dessalines agrees with him, but Bouckmann wants to destroy everything, and in that neither Jean Jacques nor Toussaint nor I agree. Tonight, TiArmes, Bouckmann has called a secret meeting—a Petro *conclave*—somewhere on the plain behind the St. Gabriel plantation. Jean Jacques, Toussaint, and I are not invited, but we must go, because the future of St. Domingue may be decided tonight. So, TiArmes, we need your brains. Toussaint wants you to go with us and so do I and so does even Dessalines would he but admit it. Will you go with us tonight?"

"Where?" Armes asked.

"I do not know yet but will you go?"

"Me? A white?"

Henry linked his arm in Armes'. "Tonight, TiArmes, you will be black, as black as I am. Tonight you will be a Negro."

"Even voodoo cannot change a man from white to black."

"But Toussaint can, provided it does not rain, for rain would be awfully bad for the black man you will be tonight."

For the second time, Armes heard a door close. This time the door was slammed, and it was one of the doors in the back of the house. He walked to the corner and looked down the broad sweep of the balcony, but saw nothing. When he returned, Henry was pointing. Armes shielded his eyes from the sun and followed the direction of Henry's finger. He caught a glimpse of a horse galloping into a clump of trees far down the side of the drive. The rider was a woman and the woman looked like Topaze. Yes, it was Topaze. She was indulging in one of her piques and intended to punish Armes. Because she could not have her own way about Henry, she was going to make Armes sick with worry about her absence. But she would return. That he knew, if for nothing else than her dresses and her chest of jewels. He shrugged his shoulders and rang for a slave. He would turn the tables and let her worry about his return, for when she got back, he would not be there. He stepped into the hall and pulled the bellcord.

"Saddle my horse, boy, and tell Ali that I shall be gone some time. He is not to worry about me. Tell him and tell Pompee that I am with Henry Christophe."

20

IT WAS a long distance to the Breda Plantation if one went by road, Henry told Armes, but much shorter by a trail over the mountains. Despite its distance, Henry said, the Breda Plantation joined St. Gabriel far back where the mountains leveled out onto the great Plain du Nord. Where plain and mountains met was a place of sinister repute—the Bois Caïman or Forest of the Alligators. It was a famous Petro meeting ground and Henry suspected that it was there that the meeting would take place.

Armes had never seen a more peaceful country than that which unrolled before him during the ride. He kept one eye on Henry's broad back ahead of him as the trail was narrow and winding, but he took advantage of the occasional openings among the trees to see the panoramic vistas of St. Domingue that spread out before him. They had to ride slowly, as the path was either a steep ascent or a precipitous descent. At times the density of the foliage blotted out the sun, often the trail was scarcely distinguishable. A hushed cathedral quiet possessed the forests. Underneath, the soft velvety compost muffled the hoofbeats of their horses. Overhead the towering branches of mahogany, ironwood, and ceiba trees arched together to soaring Gothic heights. Brilliant streaks of jade lightning flashed through the leaves as swarms of parrakeets beat the air with their wings. Green, yellow, and chartreuse orchids cascaded down the branches and thick lianas hung in living screens.

Occasionally they passed a clearing where the forest thinned out on the crest of a hill. A thatched-roof *caille*, a few banana trees, and some clucking hens bespoke the efforts of a freed, or possibly an escaped slave to live by his own labor. Husband and wife might be seen together, grubbing in the rich soil with clumsy mattocks or hacking away a few more feet of tillable land from the dense forest. More often, however, the man would be seen sleeping in the shade, while a woman stood shading her eyes in the doorway, with a cluster of naked babies around her.

At one point on the trail, it was crossed by another, this one evidently more traveled, for Armes could see rude cart trails on it. Where the two crossed—a *carrefour* as it was called—a tall pole had been erected and from the top of it a recently killed black goat dangled from a rope around its horns. All *carrefours* were sacred places, and many had a small altar to some local *loa*.

Henry stopped his horse and pointed to the goat.

"A Petro sign, TiArmes." He rode up to the pole and examined the carcass. "Killed today, too! It's a powerful magic when anything as valuable as a goat is sacrificed. Usually a couple of cocks are enough. But let us be glad of one thing—it's a goat with horns."

Armes stopped beside him and looked up at the dead animal swaying in the breeze.

"Don't all goats have horns? What's so unusual about that?"

"Sometimes the goats they sacrifice at Petro rites do not have horns. It's an expression, *mon ami*—'the goat without horns'—in other words, a man. Some of our ancestors enjoyed man meat, but they were more delicate in their speech than they were in their appetites. They didn't like to go around saying they were having a man for supper, so they said they were having a goat without horns."

"But you are speaking of Africa, Henry. Cannibalism does not exist today in St. Domingue."

"Oh no? Of course it does. It happens around here, though more often down Port-au-Prince way. There are more mulattoes in the South. They hate the whites and therefore they do not want to be Catholics. But they hate the blacks even more, so they do not want to follow the black man's

161

Rada rites which came from Africa. So they follow the Petro rites which came from Cuba, and Petro believers sacrifice the goat without horns and then eat it. They believe that a man strengthens himself by eating portions of another man; the brains of a man makes the eater wise; the heart and liver make him brave; and the testicles, if they are big ones, make a weak man potent."

Armes was revolted.

"That's stupid, Henry. Just ignorance! These people are going backward and not forward."

"*Certainement*! And that's what we have to fight against, Toussaint and Jean Jacques and myself and you, if you will help us. These blacks are an ignorant people, and why not? Most of them had little civilization in Africa, and they were torn away from what little they had. They were brought over here against their will, kicked and cursed and worked to death. They have had no time nor opportunity to assimilate your civilization. Therefore they are what they are. They may be ignorant, TiArmes, but they are not stupid. They need a strong hand over them." Henry raised his right hand and regarded it. The fingers were long, spatulate, and powerful. Thick veins stood out on the back of his hand. He turned it over—the palm was pink and heavily callused. "Like this," he added.

"Do you think that hand could rule St. Domingue, Henry?"

"It could goddam rule it or kill it, TiArmes."

They turned onto the wider cart path which descended to a well-traveled road. As they left the forests of the mountains behind them for the rippling cane fields of the plain, they came into a more populous area. At frequent intervals they passed sugar mills with oxen forever plodding in circles to turn the giant grinding wheels. They were passing people on the road now, men on horseback, men on *bourriques,* men on cane-laden carts, and women walking in the white dust. Henry pointed to a huge white house down the road.

"That's the Breda Plantation where Toussaint lives."

They turned off before they reached the big house and followed a path which wound around to the back of the house between two fields of cane. As they neared the slave quarters, which Armes thought the finest he had seen in St. Domingue, Henry motioned for him to stop. He pointed to a thicket of poinsettia shrubs which still bore clusters of

162

ragged scarlet blossoms on branches that were taller than a man.

"Stay behind there, TiArmes! I'll ride on to see where Toussaint is. Keep out of sight and I'll be back soon. Be patient, *mon ami!*"

Armes heard him ride away. He returned in a few moments.

"We'll leave our horses here. Toussaint is in his house and it's nearby. All the other slaves are out in the fields, but Toussaint's the coachman here so he's not working."

Toussaint was waiting for them in the door of his *cabane*. It was a snug little house of whitewashed stucco with a steep thatched roof. It even boasted glazed windows, proof of the esteem that Toussaint enjoyed at Breda. Once they had entered, the old man closed the door and bolted it from the inside. Armes saw that there was another man in the cabin, who did not rise as they entered. His only recognition of their presence was a casual lifting of his hand toward Henry and a flash of hatred in his eyes as he looked at Armes. Armes saw his eyes only for a second before the man lowered his head immediately.

Toussaint welcomed them by pouring a glass of *clairin,* the fiery native white rum, for each of them. The other Negro refused a glass, and as they sat down at the table he pushed his chair back.

Toussaint stretched out his hand to Armes and Armes clasped it warmly.

"We have met before," Toussaint said softly, and Armes remembered the old man who had come to his house the night he brought Pompee home. Although he had paid little attention to him that night, he now regarded him closely. Under the wisps of white hair which fringed his head, there was a broad intelligent forehead. Sweeping bushy brows, also white, shaded large eyes, kindly and benevolent. The mouth was wide and Negroid. Altogether it was an ugly face, but beautiful in its very ugliness—so patient, so godlike, that Armes felt he was in the presence of a great and benign power.

"And this"—Toussaint motioned to the other man—"is Jean Jacques Dessalines."

Armes extended his hand across the table, but the other man made no move, not even to lift his eyes.

Toussaint smiled nervously, embarrassed at the other's

163

boorishness. "You'll have to excuse Jean Jacques," he apologized. "He doesn't like you."

"But why?" Armes' hand was still extended. "I've never harmed him, have I?"

Dessalines raised his head for an instant, avoiding Armes' eyes. "No!" The syllable exploded from his lips.

"Then why?"

Henry answered for him. "Because this Jean Jacques hates all men whose skin is white. He has made a vow never to look a white man in the face. Oh, he is a wicked man, our Jean Jacques." In an attempt to lighten the situation, Henry leaned across the table and thumped the other playfully on his barrel chest. "I repeat, he's a wicked man, but he's honest. Come, Jean Jacques, draw up your chair to the table. TiArmes is my friend. Forget, as I have done, that he is white." Henry started to laugh and Dessalines darted a malevolent look at him.

"Ho, ho!" Henry bellowed. "TiArmes won't be white much longer, anyway. Pretty soon he's going to be blacker than you, Jean Jacques and, man, that sure is black, because you're the blackest goddam black I've ever seen."

"And proud of it! If I was one of these pretty little yellow *masisis* who call themselves men, I'd slit my throat." Dessalines hitched his chair up to the table and rested his elbows defiantly on it.

Armes could see him better now. He knew himself for a big man and he conceded that Henry was even bigger, but he had never seen such brute power in any man as he now saw in Jean Jacques Dessalines. The man was not tall, but he was shaped like a gorilla. His wide shoulders supported a thick, bull-like neck, and above it was a face whose features were those of a man, but so jumbled together that it appeared like a mass of black clay which had fallen from the sculptor's pedestal to the floor and been stepped on. Thick purple lips curved under an enormous wide-nostriled, misshapen nose. Small eyes, sunken under overhanging brows, flashed brilliant black pupils from yellowish whites. The forehead was low and receded to a cap of wiry hair that reached nearly down to the eyebrows.

Dessalines' huge paw reached for the glass he had previously declined. He drained it and motioned to Toussaint to refill it. Then, head lowered so he would not have to look at Armes, he spat out his words.

"You are a friend of Henry's, *blanc*. And Toussaint says

164

you are a good man. I doubt it. No *blanc* ever lived that was good. You are as bad as the rest of them. But Toussaint says he wants you and this *gros nègre* Henry thinks you are somewhere between Jesus Christ and Damballah, so it's two to one. You're here, so drink your goddamn drink, *blanc,* and after you've drunk it, I'll drink mine, because I'll not drink with any *blanc,* not even your cursed white god if he came down to earth. But tonight we have a truce. Tonight I will not slit your white gullet, though maybe the next time I see you, I will. We'll let it go at that, *blanc."*

Armes drank, and a moment later Dessalines drained his glass. He looked at the bit of crystal so dwarfed in his hand and then flung it to the floor with an oath. In an instant his manner changed. He lost his surliness and reached his hand halfway across the table toward Armes.

"If I go halfway now, M'sieu Blanc, will you go the other half?"

Armes stretched out his hand until their fingers nearly touched. Then Dessalines snatched his hand away and laughed.

"Did you think I would touch a white hand, *blanc?"* It seemed to clear some of the venom from him, however, and when he spoke again it was seemingly without hatred. "Now, let's get down to business."

They talked. Dessalines was the best informed. He told them in detail about the movement that Bouckmann was heading and explained how the slaves of each plantation had elected certain delegates to represent them. These had been meeting at various out-of-the-way places in the mountains. All this had been going on for some time. However, many of the so-called delegates had dropped out. Some were afraid of the *bocor* Bouckmann, and others were disgusted with his fanatic Petro religion. But for everyone that dropped out, he made two new converts, so his following had grown.

Now the weeks of talking were over. Action was imminent. Tonight, there was to be a big meeting—the biggest and perhaps the final meeting. Every province was to be represented from Jérémie to the Cap du Nord. Bouckmann had promised a big display of Petro magic, for tonight was to be the night of decision.

"And we know," Toussaint's gentle voice interrupted Dessalines, "that tonight's decision may set us back a hundred years in our fight for freedom."

"Tonight's decision may ruin St. Domingue," Dessalines grunted.

"Tonight's decision may strip St. Domingue of all her wealth," Henry agreed thoughtfully. "After tonight there may be nothing left but a blazing hell."

"But what can we do?" Armes asked.

"Maybe nothing, maybe much!" Toussaint nodded his head wisely. "First we must find out what is going to happen. We do not even know where the meeting is going to be. But the drums will tell us as soon as it gets dark."

"Then when we find out what can we do?" Armes persisted.

"Who knows?" Dessalines muttered. He stood up and banged his huge hand on the table so that the glasses jumped. "I do not give one goddamn if all the whites are killed. I do not care, I tell you. But I'll be damned if I'll let them destroy St. Domingue. They cannot burn and destroy. There'll be nothing left for me."

"You are right, Jean Jacques." Henry forced him back into the chair. "Although Toussaint and I do not agree about killing the whites."

"Then save them, you *stupides,* you white-ass kissers. Save them if you can and let them string Bouckmann up by his balls for all I care. He's a worse menace than the whites. But I'll not save one of them, not even you," he said, pointing to Armes. "No, not even you! But come! This man is white, and if you insist we take him with us, what are we going to do?"

Toussaint walked to an unlighted charcoal brazier in the corner of the room. He removed some of the charcoal and put it in a wooden mortar and ground it fine. Then he rummaged on a shelf over his head and found a small earthen jar. Opened, it gave forth a strong, spicy aroma. With a wooden spoon he scooped out some of the sticky substance and added it to the pulverized charcoal. A few strokes of the pestle mixed it. He hesitated for a moment, added a few drops of some black viscous fluid which flowed slowly, like tar, from the bottle, and then stirred the mixture again. He dipped an experimental finger in the concoction and walked over to where Armes was sitting. His finger touched Armes' face lightly and traced a black streak across his forehead. Henry came closer and looked at the color.

"Too black!" he said. "He'll look like an iron kettle."

"Blacker than I am," Jean Jacques laughed. "Add a little cochineal, it'll make him redder."

Again Toussaint rummaged on the shelf and found another jar. He sprinkled some of the ruby powder in the mortar and mixed again.

"That's better," Henry exclaimed as Toussaint proved the mixture on Armes' cheek.

"Take off your shirt, *blanc*," Dessalines commanded. "They're going to make you pretty goddamned black."

Toussaint and Henry worked on Armes, although Dessalines refused to touch him. When they had finished, Toussaint wound a soiled red rag around Armes' head to hide his hair. He produced a worn and patched pair of cotton pantaloons, a decrepit pair of run-down boots, and a torn shirt.

"Now you can dress, M'sieu Armes."

Armes stripped off his clothes. His white legs were a striking contrast to his ebony torso. Dessalines laughed as Armes stood there naked.

"Goddamndest-looking mulatto, I ever saw—his black blood and his white blood are evenly divided. But he must have some black blood in him after all," Dessalines snickered, "because he's hung like a black man—no little puny white worm like most *blancs*."

For Henry's sake, Armes had restrained his anger toward Dessalines. Once more he held back his rising choler and slipped into the ragged clothing. It was clean and freshly laundered with the smell of sunshine in it.

Henry started to laugh along with Dessalines.

"Un gros nègre!" he bellowed.

"A goddamned *gros nègre!*" Dessalines echoed him, "and tonight his name is Etalon, because if any white man ever deserved to be called a stallion, this one does."

Toussaint opened the door of a crude cupboard on the wall and handed Armes a piece of broken mirror. He looked at himself or rather at the reflection in the mirror, since he could not believe that the face really belonged to him. A Negro stared back at him—a Negro with fine mulatto features. He placed the mirror on the table and saw that Dessalines was staring at him. For the first time, Dessalines lifted his head and their eyes met. Armes saw that the grotesque face was almost smiling, and he stretched out his hand to Jean Jacques.

Dessalines shook his head. "No, Etalon, I'll not shake

hands with you, not even now. Under that black paint you're still white. You've got a white heart, and a white brain. That's why I hate you. It'll take more than a little charcoal to make me like you. But I'll say this—you're a goddamned fine-looking nigger, even if your belly is as white as a pig's."

He blew out the candle.

"Come on, men, let's get started."

21

THE tropic night descended upon them suddenly. There was a flash of vivid colors in the sky—a kaleidoscopic shifting of orange, cerise, green, and heliotrope—then all faded to a sapphire which in turn changed to amethyst and finally, when the scrubbed tin plate of the moon rose, to an emerald black. A soft whir of bats' wings fanned the air as Toussaint opened the door. The drums had started. The sound extended from nowhere to everywhere, down from the mountains, up from the plains and back again. The night became alive with the primitive drums of Africa, a booming, throbbing, pulsating vitality that even to Armes' untrained ears carried a message of destiny. Toussaint stood in the doorway and listened. He turned and beckoned to Dessalines who joined him, then to Henry, and together the three men pondered the message of the drums.

"The St. Gabriel plantation," Toussaint spelled out the words slowly. "It's the St. Gabriel plantation for sure, but where, Henry, where on the plantation is the meeting to be held?"

Henry listened even more attentively, nodding his head in rhythm to the drums. He started to speak, then stopped, listening a moment longer. "The Bois Caïman! Am I right?"

They listened again.

"It's the Bois Caïman all right. That's exactly where it is." Dessalines spoke with authority. "Listen to the *maman* drum. I know who's playing that—it's Moun Rouge from the Brissac plantation. Nobody else can beat a drum like that bastard. 'Bois Caïman' they say, 'Bois Caïman, Bois Caïman'."

Toussaint put his fingers to his lips. He slipped inside the cabin, whispered to Armes, and they emerged. Henry pointed

168

in the direction of the poinsettia thicket where they had left their horses and Dessalines nodded in understanding. He mumbled to Henry in a strange language and Henry reached for Armes' hand to guide him through the darkness.

"Toussaint and Jean Jacques will meet us at the thicket," he whispered. Henry seemed to be able to see in the dark, for he guided Armes directly to the horses. As Armes' eyes became accustomed to the darkness, he could see the forms of two men approaching on horseback, and when the moon slipped out from under a cloud, he saw that they were Toussaint and Dessalines. The four of them started out together —their horses' hooves making no noise on the thick grass.

The drums kept calling them. At times they seemed to be near at hand, then they receded only to return, but the longer they rode the nearer the drums became until the sound of them made the air quiver. It was an insistent, unbearable noise which stretched Armes' nerves while it beat upon his eardrums with a relentless tom-tom-tom-tiddy-on-tom like a great heartbeat that never stopped. In it, Armes found an answer to many questions and yet discovered the answer to none. Even his untrained ear began to understand the wordless booming. It translated itself into a message of blood and hate and uncontrolled power, and at the same time throbbed a message of rampant carnality. It did things to him. It birthed strange desires, uncontrollable fantasies, deceitful lusts, and a strange rare tenderness. Topaze's face materialized before him out of the blackness, but her face was not alone. All the other women he had ever known were there, blended together into one aphrodisiac phantasmagoria.

The four men rode on, in and out of the blackness of the trees which cast leafy black shadows on their black faces. Armes caught a glimpse of black hands in the moonlight and suddenly realized that they were his own. As he studied their appearance, he began to feel like a Negro, and he realized that he was now thinking like one. The message of the drums came through to him with a distinct clarity. They spoke to him, and he longed to do all the things they suggested. He wanted to feel warm black flesh in his fingers and satisfy his needs crudely and primitively with a ruthless savage power. But with that desire for soft black flesh to caress, he found he needed other flesh—white flesh to bruise and hurt, to kill and mangle.

And still the drums exploded like invisible fireworks into the night.

They emerged from the forest, out onto a trail, then up the trail a distance until they reached the *carrefour*, the same crossroads he had passed earlier that afternoon. The lifeless body of the goat still hung from the pole, but now crude lights flickered around it—tiny flames sprouting from shallow bowls of oil.

"We were right." Dessalines tried to keep his voice muted, but in the overwhelming noise of the drums he had to raise it to a shout.

"Oui, the Bois Caïman!"

"It's near here!"

"Mais oui!"

"Then we had better leave the horses."

"Certainement! We'll go by foot."

Toussaint found a secluded place in the forest and they tied the horses securely to a tall tree. As they walked to the *carrefour*, Toussaint broke a branch from a shrub and called their attention to the way it pointed. They started down the road together, keeping in the shadow of the trees. They were but four undistinguished men—three Negro slaves and a white man, walking together that night, casting four moon-etched shadows on the ground. Who could prophesy on that fateful night that three of those black shadows would lengthen into those of a lieutenant-governor, an emperor, and a king of St. Domingue?

After a short distance down the road, they could see a light blazing through the trees. Toussaint motioned for them to stop behind the broad leaves of a clump of shrubs.

He held a warning finger to his lips. "Now we must proceed with caution. Remember Bouckmann does not want us here. He has tried to keep this meeting a secret from all three of us. We are well-known, so pull your hats down over your eyes and shade your faces, and you, m'sieu, if anyone asks who you are tell them that you are Antoine or Jean Marie or Albert from Sans Souci."

"No, he's Etalon from Sans Souci," Dessalines said. "Now, shut up and let's go. Even though we're all black except him"—he jerked his thumb at Armes—"that goddamned Bouckmann would kill us all on sight. *Allez!*"

They walked down the road, keeping in the shadows as much as possible, until it broadened out into a large clearing. A huge bonfire blazed in the center, so large that they could

170

feel its heat many yards away, although the men and women seated around it seemed oblivious to either the fire or the scorching heat. The drums were louder now, and Armes saw the whole battery of them on the far side of the blaze. The fitful flames stained the sweat-drenched bodies of the drummers vermilion, and the rise and fall of their arms and hands was so swiftly repeated, Armes could hardly see the drummers themselves. They seemed like some hundred-handed primitive god, pounding with mechanical arms, guided by one brain. In the background black palms etched their ragged fronds against the emerald sky. The moon shone with a white brilliance and the soaring fire vomited volcanoes of sparks as more and more branches were piled up on it. Henry grabbed Armes' hand and guided him into the shadow of some low-lying bushes on the outer perimeter of the seated audience. He squatted down and pulled Armes down beside him.

The pulsing rhythm of the drums increased as an old woman rose slowly to her feet beside the fire. Her anile body with its pendulous withered breasts started to sway with the drums, and suddenly she rent the pulsating darkness with a ululating shriek. As if it were a prearranged signal, all the others took up the chant. It was meaningless to Armes—a jargon of strange words in a tuneless, heavily accented recitative. Henry started to sing along with the others, Dessalines joined in, and at length Toussaint. In order not to appear conspicuous, Armes opened and closed his mouth in rhythm. Here and there throughout the seated assemblage, men and women leaped to their feet, shaking, shivering, and twisting their bodies in hysterical abandon. The searing flames cast weird shadows on the sweaty black torsos, powerful arms, broad chests, and contorted faces of the men, and on the pointed breasts, shining bellies and undulating hips of the women. Gradually and without any seeming direction, the spectators all rose and formed a weaving, swaying line, each one with his hands on the hips of the man or woman ahead of him and, as the tempo of the drums increased, the chant became more melodious, more fraught with meaning.

Now it pleaded, now it cajoled, now it demanded, but the swaying line of bodies kept perfect time to each change of tempo. As the shrieks grew louder, the line started to move, step by step in slow procession around the fire. Another circle formed around the first, treading the same direction, then a third. A fourth line started to form, and the men near Armes rose, shook their bodies, clasped the hips of the one nearest them, and joined in the quivering march. Armes found himself between Henry and Dessalines—Henry behind him and Dessalines in front. Dessalines was apparently unconcerned that white hands were gripping him.

As the line started to move, Armes glanced back at Henry, and then stared at him in shocked amazement. Instead of the familiar Henry Armes saw only a stranger—a shrieking savage, stripped of his shirt, his head thrown back, his eyes closed, and his throat quivering with the strain of the chant. He felt Henry's hands grip his flanks and sensed the uncontrollable frenzy in the man's fingers, then realized that his own hands were clutching Dessalines in the same feverish clutch. Through some complicated process of weaving in and out, they found themselves in the third line, then gradually in the second, and after a matter of minutes they were a part of the innermost line that circled the fire. The heat struck them with such force as almost to blister their bodies. Armes' shirt had been torn off, and he felt the flash of fire on his shoulders and back. It was a relief when they passed out of the orbit of the fire into the coolness beyond the drums. Now the line halted periodically, the dancers marking time, then proceeded again in spasmodic jerks. Ahead Armes saw something on the ground. It was that something which caused the line to stop, stare, and then pass on. Step by step he came nearer until he could see what it was. He stopped. His hands slipped from Jean Jacques' hips but Dessalines reached behind him and grabbed Armes' hands and placed them back.

"You can do nothing, Etalon," Dessalines snarled. "Do nothing! Say nothing! One move and you'll be there too with both of us along with you."

Armes looked more closely at the object on the ground. He saw a writhing, tormented, human form, spread-eagled, each arm and leg bound with rawhide thongs to heavy stakes. It was the stark naked body of a white man, or possibly an extremely light-skinned mulatto. The head was swathed in cloths and rolled from side to side in agony, but even the thick cloths could not muffle the horrified shrieks. Armes could not distinguish the face, but the nude body was that of a young man, almost a boy, with slender arms and legs, smooth and hairless except for the one black island of pubic hair. Armes felt Henry prodding his back and he danced on with the line, passing the prisoner, and then, through the

172

same complicated weaving process, they found themselves once more in the line that was on the outside.

Fresh drummers, called up as replacements, added new vigor to the drums. Now their rhythm was stronger, more elemental—a primitive message that the drums were spelling out. Their rhythm became sexual, erotic, orgiastic, a bestial, compelling command. The chanting was hushed. Armes glanced at the faces nearest him. Their eyes were closed to narrow slits, their heavy nostrils pulsated, their lips were slack, drooling with saliva. He saw a Negro near him reach for a woman, pull her violently to him, rip her single garment from her and cover her body with his. Another giant buck grabbed an adolescent youth by the shoulders and forced the boy to his knees in front of him, his hands gripping the boy's hair, compelling him by brute strength to yield to his demands. Garments were stripped from ebon bodies, lips sought other lips, while the drums kept up the rhythm of Petro—the rhythm of the body, the steady rhythm of generation. It climbed to such a pitch that Armes knew his eardrums were about to split, then, having achieved this crashing crescendo, it stopped abruptly. With its cessation, men and women ground their bodies together, shrieking and groaning in mass ecstasy, until the tense bodies grew limp, lips became unlocked, and arms hung helpless. Followed a vast, all-pervading quietness in which nobody moved. The desire of the drums had spent itself. Passion had fled with satiation.

In the oppressive stillness, a procession of *hunsis*—minor priestesses—dressed in white, wound sinuously in single file from the shadows of the trees. The metronomic tapping of a single small drum only heightened the silence. Following them, a Negro dressed in a spangled scarlet loincloth strode out into the firelight, stiff-legged, with measured steps. His head was turbaned with multicolored cloths which were coiled together into a high conical headdress from which cock feathers sprung.

It was evident that he was in a state of hysteria bordering on trance, as he advanced to the center of the open space near the fire where the prisoner was still straining at his bonds. He shook the gourd rattle over the bound youth and started to talk. It was a language which Armes did not understand, but he realized that Henry, Dessalines, and Toussaint comprehended the strange words. Armes did not need to understand them. He could tell from the fanatical pitch of the voice, the haranguing gestures, and the bitter enunciation that the speech was a hellish diatribe against the whites. With increased fury the man shouted on and on, walking back and forth in front of the fire and stopping at intervals to point an accusing finger at the pitiful object on the ground. His scathing denunciations made the prisoner the scapegoat for all the whites. Almost without Armes' becoming aware of the noise, the drums started again. At first it was scarcely more than a whisper—the mere rubbing of a palm across the taut goatskin, but slowly the tempo increased. The scarlet-girt figure disappeared, swallowed up in the darkness.

Armes ventured a whisper to Henry.

"The man in red, who is he?"

"Bouckmann," Henry answered.

Out of the shadows the man materialized with two enormous black cocks, one in each hand. He started to dance, holding the pitiful flapping creatures by their necks. His movements were stately and ceremonious, and it was evident that he was a priest, offering a sacrifice to some strange god. His slow steps brought him ever nearer the figure of the captive, and when he was only a few steps away, he flung one of the cocks into the air. It had life enough to flutter its wings a little, hovered in the air for a second, then landed on the prisoner's chest with both wings outstretched. A shout of approbation came from the crowd. Bouckmann tore off the other bird's head with his teeth, held the headless body over his mouth, and drank the streaming blood. With vicious hands, he tore the bird to pieces and scattered the bloody feathers on the body. His hands now free, he raised them above his head, commanding silence. Even the drums stopped.

Kneeling beside the pinioned body, he straightened the elongated throat of the rooster and aligned it so that it made a black path along the boy's throat. He carefully spread the wings of the cock more symmetrically until the black feathers made a heraldic design against the pale skin.

Bouckmann rose slowly, turned, and walked toward the fire. He reached his hand into the flames and drew from them a machete which glowed a dull red. Grasping it with both hands he held it aloft and stepped back to the prisoner. Then he lowered it slowly, only to bring it back up into the air and swing it, with all the force of his powerful muscles, down across the throat of the black cock and that of the pale-skinned youth.

A spontaneous shriek of joy came from the blackness of

the trees, and a woman leaped out into the firelight. She was nude, and her skin glowed red amber in the light of the flames. Armes gasped as he recognized her. It was Topaze. How well he knew every curve of her body, the swelling of her breasts, the little hollow of her throat, the smooth polished feel of her skin. Henry's heavy arm encircled his shoulders and held him motionless as he struggled to rise, although he did not know what impulse directed his movement. Imprisoned by Henry's arm, he gazed at Topaze with disbelief and sadness in his eyes.

She reached down and took the severed head in her hands, holding it at arm's length over her head, so that the blood streamed down over her uplifted face. Lowering it, she began to dance, holding the head close to her, gnawing at the flesh, and stripping it off with her teeth. As the drums increased in volume, her dance grew wilder. A young buck arose from the group near the fire and she motioned to him to come closer. He danced over to her, but she eluded him with sinuous motions, holding the mutilated head between them. Then she stopped, her body quivering. Inch by inch he came closer, shedding his one garment as he neared her, his body vibrating in sensuous mimicry, until, with an animal roar, he reached her, grabbed the head from her hands, and flung it into the fire. Arms outstretched, she cursed it viciously, spat after it, and, while the vituperations flowed from her lips, Bouckmann reached down, severed the thongs that held the body to the ground, picked it up, and flung it into the arms of the Negro who was standing before Topaze, his legs spread wide apart, his whole body braced firmly on the soles of his feet. He stared at the body and offered it to Topaze, who tore at it with her teeth and raked the chest with her fingernails. Then, with a mighty heave, the man threw it into the fire. His eyes narrowed to mere slits, he grabbed Topaze, pressed her to him, bore her to the ground, and consummated the dance, his body heaving in rhythm to the drums until, exhausted, he sagged on top of her. The drums stopped and Bouckmann spread his arms over the two recumbent forms.

This time Bouckmann spoke with no impassioned oratory. He spoke in Creole, which Armes could understand.

"Mes amis!" The crowd looked up at him. "Our ancient sacrifice is over. We have destroyed the white man and he is gone. Petro gods have consumed him with fire, and from his blood you have seen a new man conceived. This new man is you"—he pointed to the upturned faces—"and you,

and you, and you." His voice rose high. "Yes, all of you are new men, conceived from the blood of a white man. You have been torn from the womb of slavery and born again to freedom. The past is dead and now you are free. Free! As you and your fathers were free in Guinea. You are free to become hunters again. You are free to have your compounds in the mountains and your villages in the plains. Strip yourselves of the false ways of the white man. Free Africans you were and free Africans you now are. Use that freedom and use it now. Become hunters. You have the power of death in your hands! You have the power of fire in your hands! Just as your fathers destroyed the villages of their enemies, destroy the whites. Send them to death and consume them with fire as you have seen me do tonight, and from their blood and ashes a new race will arise. A race of free Africans! Go! Go now!" His voice broke on the last high note.

Men and women struggled toward him, but he waved them away. "Go! Kill! Burn! Rape! Pillage! Destroy!"

A voice rang out from the pressing throng.

"To the plantations!"

"To the plantations!" Bouckmann echoed.

"Mon dieu!" Henry gasped, "it's happened."

Toussaint turned toward them. His face was ashen.

"Did you hear? He said, 'To the plantations!' You know what that means. The nearest ones are my own and St. Gabriel. We must warn them. With horses we can get ahead of the mob. I go to Breda. I love my master and mistress."

St. Gabriel made Armes think of Athenée. Strange that he should think of her after seeing Topaze only a few moments ago. But now his connection with Topaze was over. The Petro spell she had cast over him had been broken by Petro magic. The thought of her body was repulsive to him now. He thought only of Athenée. He turned to Henry.

"Come with me, *mon ami.* Toussaint goes to warn Breda."

"And you?" Henry asked.

"To warn St. Gabriel."

Henry looked around. Dessalines had disappeared. Henry shook his head. "No, TiArmes, I will not lift a finger to save that miserable Vicomte."

"But his wife," Armes pleaded.

"Yes, she has endured enough hell living with him. Let us warn her. Come, TiArmes, we have no time to lose." Henry pushed Armes through the bushes. Armes ventured a quick look behind. The fire was dying down, but he could

176

see that the Negroes were drinking gourd after gourd full of fiery *clairin*. Some were still engrossed with the women, but most were possessed by a greater lust. The lust of the flesh would soon be forgotten in the lust for murder.

The bushes seemed to part miraculously before Henry, and they reached the horses in time to see Toussaint gallop away. Armes fumbled for the stirrup, but Henry sent him into the saddle with a mighty heave. The lights around the slaughtered goat had already died out when they came to the *carrefour*, where they turned off and started on the trail to St. Gabriel.

22

THE drums had started again with a quickened restless tempo, and their frantic beating followed Armes and Henry down over the trail. That which had been so quiet and peaceful the afternoon before was now fraught with menacing shadows which seemed to dance in the moonlight to the accompaniment of the distant drums. Not far behind them they could hear shouts and occasional snatches of song. Several hundred slaves were behind—all sex-maddened, blood-maddened, and besotted with clairin, lusting for the unlicensed freedom and unbridled power which Bouckmann had promised them.

"Fools," Henry muttered between the galloping hoofbeats of his horse, "stupid fools to destroy wealth. Idiots, to burn the Breda sugar. It's money they're turning into flames— money which we need now more than ever."

Armes was aware of a dull, reddish glare in the sky behind them. "You think it's Breda? Do you think Toussaint got there in time?"

"Who knows? But ride faster if you want to get to St. Gabriel before them. Damn this trail!" Henry's horse stumbled and nearly fell. They had to halt and rest their horses before starting the next steep ascent. Both Armes and Henry were breathing as hard as their mounts. "Can you make it, TiArmes?" Henry called over his shoulder as he started up among the boulders of the hillside.

Armes didn't answer. He knew that every hill that lay ahead of them would slow down the oncoming slaves more than it would their horses. When they finally reached the

177

crest of the last hill, they could see the St. Gabriel mansion below them, white in the moonlight. Here the trail became wider and they were able to make better time. Henry cut off from the trail, galloped through a field of young maize, then through the deserted street of tumbledown slave quarters. He waited for Armes to catch up with him.

"Here you are, *mon ami*." He swallowed the air in great gulps. "I've brought you here as I promised you, but I'll not say a word or raise a hand to save that spawn of hell, the Vicomte. Do what you can for his lady. I'm riding on to Sans Souci and I'll meet you there. Before the night is over, this mob"—he waved his hand behind him—"will be at the gates of Sans Souci. Maybe Henry Christophe can find the words that will save it for you. I hope so. If I cannot, I shall take your Ali and Pompee with me to the Cap."

"Thank you, Henry. Yes, go! Save Ali whatever you do. I have much to make up to him. Save Pompee and if God is willing, save Sans Souci."

The darkness swallowed up the blackness of Henry. Armes rode on to the big house. Lights burned in only two rooms on the upper floor. Without waiting to dismount, Armes rode around the terrace and up the marble steps to the front door. The nervous feet of his horse made a ringing tattoo on the marble as he reached over and lifted the heavy knocker, letting it fall again and again and again. Its echoes resounded throughout the house.

"René, René," he screamed with bursting lungs. "Open up! It's Armes."

The moments he waited seemed years, for he could hear the shouts of the mob coming nearer. Finally he saw a light descending the stairs, shining through the glass panes on either side of the door. A face—that of René's—was pressed against the glass and then suddenly withdrawn. Armes kept up an incessant clatter with the heavy knocker until the door opened a crack. The moonlight glinted on the pistol barrel that protruded.

"Get away, you black bastard! Get away before I shoot you."

"It's Armes, René! Armes Holbrook! Don't shoot! Open quick! For the love of God, believe me!"

René must have recognized his voice, for he flung open the door.

"Good God, man, what's happened to you? You're as black as a nigger. Why? What's up?"

178

"Don't waste time asking questions. Get your wife and come with me. We may be safe at Sans Souci under Henry Christophe's protection. There's a mob of bloodthirsty drunken slaves due here any minute. They are out for murder."

A white arm reached up and grabbed the candle from René's hand. Athenée came out onto the terrace. She lifted the candle to Armes' face.

"Is it really you, Monsieur Holbrook?"

"Yes, but hurry, we have no time to lose. Do not bother even to dress. Time is too precious."

She turned to René. "I knew something was wrong tonight. I knew it when all the slaves ran away after dinner. There's not a single one left on the place. What is it, Armes?"

"Stop asking questions. Come!" He reached down and lifted her up on his horse. "Follow us, René! Come!"

The shouts of the slaves were now in the rear of the house and coming nearer as he turned his horse's head and descended the steps. René still stood in the doorway. Armes called back to him.

"Hide, René, if you're not going with us."

"I'll not let a bunch of niggers scare me." René tightened the belt of his breeches and spread his feet wide in the doorway. He brandished his gun in both hands. "Take Athenée! I'll stay here. I'm armed. I'm not afraid of the stinking bastards."

"Leave the horse," Athenée cried. "We can't get away now. We can hide. I know a place."

Armes jumped down and reached up for her. She was clad only in a flimsy nightgown. His hands felt the smoothness of her flesh under the thin cambric, and for a moment his mind lingered on it. White skin after a surfeit of amber skin! Rose-pink and white after honey and ivory!

He gave Tom a resounding slap which sent him trotting off into the night.

"Where? Where can we hide?"

"The cracked fountain in the wall!" She pointed to a low marble wall that ran around the edge of the terrace. "It hasn't been used in years and there's a wooden cover over the basin. I used to play there when I was a child."

She pulled him over to the big marble basin, which was supported on the curved tails of dolphins. The heavy wooden cover of thick planking seemed bolted in place as Armes tried to move it, but with a mighty heave, he forced it

179

up. Athenée jumped inside, and he followed her. By kneeling, he was able to move the cover back with his shoulders. There was sufficient room inside for both of them, but it was necessary for them to lie side by side, the lengths of their bodies touching, their cheeks pressed together. Armes could feel the trembling of her body. A ray of pale moonlight entered through the crack in the marble. "At least we'll have some air," Armes thought. Then he found that he could see through the crack, although his vision was limited to the steps of the big house and the lower part of the door. He could see René's bare feet planted resolutely on the threshold.

There was a crash of glass and a shout which increased a hundredfold as the slaves wheeled en masse onto the terrace. More windows crashed. Then a pistol shot rang out, clear and decisive. Armes saw one of René's feet move backward. The black legs of the slaves retreated from the door. Somebody jumped up on the wooden planking over Armes' head and he could hear the soft upholstered pad of bare feet on the boards above him.

The narrow slit in the marble only served to confuse Armes' picture of what happened immediately afterward. He could hear the frenzied shouts of the Negroes and then René's words.

"Back, you dogs! Off my property! I'll have you beaten to a pulp tomorrow. What do you think you are, you black *poltrons*? Go! Run! Get away from here."

The mob became strangely silent. They were far too accustomed to white authority to fully realize that now they were hundreds against this one lone man. Armes could not see the gun in René's hands, but he knew it was there. Another crash of glass sounded and René's gun spoke a second time. A scream followed, and Armes realized that René must have killed a man. Then there was silence, punctuated by the stamping of the bare feet on the planking above.

"I'll kill the first man that takes a step," René said with authority. "Now disperse. St. Gabriel slaves, get back to your quarters. Others, back to your own plantations. You?" René was evidently pointing. "Are you one of my slaves?"

"Yes, m'sieu." The answer from long habit was meekly respectful.

"Then fifty lashes for you in the morning!"

"No!" A mighty chorus shrieked that one word. "No! No! No!" Above the shouts a voice rose high and clear. "Do not be afraid, men, his pistols are not loaded."

180

There was a ring of metal against stone and Armes could see the steely brightness of a machete bounce up the steps, then another, followed by a deluge of steel. The night rang with the reverberation of metal on marble. Then he saw René's knees buckle under him and his body slump to the floor, hesitate for a minute, and pitch headlong down the steps. Before it reached the bottom of the steps, the slaves were upon it, covering it like bluebottle flies on carrion, hacking at it, stabbing, cutting, screaming, shouting. They tore the body limb from limb and waved bloody arms and legs in the cold moonlight and the flickering torchlight. A weird howling turned into a wild chant of victory and shuffling feet on the marble terrace kept time to the ghoulish cadence. A burst of brilliant light shone through the crack in their fountain tomb, and Armes realized that the house was blazing.

He reached for Athenée in the cramped confines and drew her closer to him. Their only defense was an inch of planking over their heads. The shuffling feet above them departed and the only sound left was the receding wailing of the slaves and the crackling of the flames. The heat was becoming almost unbearable, but they did not dare to move. Armes knew that with their limited supply of air and the suffocating heat they would soon smother. Only some desperate gamble could save them. Using his back for leverage, he moved the heavy cover until about an inch of fiery brilliance shone through. With his back braced against the cover, ready to move it in an instant, he whispered to her.

"Quick, Athenée, when I move this over, take one quick look and see if there is anyone about. I think the heat has driven them all a distance away."

She shifted her position until she could see through the opening. There was nothing silhouetted against the burst of orange light from the big house. The terrace stretched empty at either side. Down on the terrace below, she thought she saw forms moving. Yes, she could see them now, dancing a wild saturnalia as they watched the fire.

Armes let the cover down again, but the stifling air choked them, for they had let smoke in as well as heat. He removed one of his boots, wriggling like a contortionist, and propped open the lid at the back. They had only one chance in ten thousand to escape alive. He drew Athenée down to him, and he could feel her relax in his arms. Their faces were so close together that her eyelashes brushed his cheek. With the message of the Petro drums still ringing in his brain, he forced his lips hard against hers. It was their first kiss and it might well be their last. He felt her shrink from him at first, but to his surprise she returned his kiss and clung tightly to him. Words were unnecessary. Each understood the other.

He took his lips away from hers.

"I wish Henry were here," he said, thinking aloud. "He said he admired the *blancs* because of their brains. Surely we should be able to outwit this bunch of drunken savages." He became quiet, concentrating on the situation they were in. "There might be a way, Athenée, but it's only a gamble."

"Anything is better than staying here."

"Then listen! Every primitive emotion they possess is raised to the breaking point tonight. They are half-crazed with sex, raw rum, African superstition, and murder. By now they cannot even believe what they see. There's just one thing left. Do as Henry said. Pit our brains against their ignorance."

Athenée understood. "You mean prey on their superstitions?"

"That's it. Now listen! For all they know, you were in the house, sleeping, when it was fired. They did not see you come out. They can well imagine you are dead. You're all dressed in white and the nightgown is filmy enough to be a shroud."

"I'm beginning to see. Go on, Armes."

"I'm going to move this cover far enough back so you can crawl out. Flatten your body along the edge of the planks and let's pray to God that nobody notices you until you are completely out. Then I want you to stand up slowly. Raise your hands up over your head, wave your arms so that the light will filter through those thin sleeves. Then talk to them—you know Creole?"

Her whispered "yes" was faint.

"Then yell! Scream like a demon out of hell. And tell them this. 'I'm Ayda of the Rada gods and I curse you, oh men of Petro. Listen to me, followers of the false gods. I, Ayda, wife of Damballah Weydo, curse you.' Then talk on. Think of all the terrible things you have ever heard and heap on curse after curse. It's only a gamble, Athenée, and I hesitate to make you take the chance, but if I am not mistaken, those superstitious savages will turn tail and run."

"I'll do it." She had stopped trembling, and he felt her muscles stiffen in resolution.

"Can you forgive me for exposing you to this danger?"

"Is it any less than the danger we are in now? No. It's our only chance."

Once again Armes applied his back to the heavy planking. This time he moved it forward enough for Athenée's head to slip through, then her shoulders. She leaned back on the wooden lid and drew her body out. The coping of the terrace wall hid her from the mob below. Armes could see only her feet, but he stretched out one hand and curled it reassuringly around her ankle. Then he felt her move and he knew that she was kneeling, then standing. She stood erect for a second, and he could picture in his mind the effect she made—the windswept folds of her nightgown swirling around her, her long hair blowing in the breeze, her arms uplifted against the red background of the flames.

He heard her shriek, and then male gasps of surprise and fear from the under-terrace. She started to speak, and the slurred Creole words came out in a torrent.

"Slaves of St. Domingue," she cried. "False worshipers of the Petro gods. Behold Ayda who is speaking to you now. I tell you to be gone. I put the curse of all the Rada gods on you, the most horrible *ouanga* the world has ever known. Go and go at once, or I shall turn you all into serpents—crawling green serpents—so that Damballah can make you worship him. Oh my husband, Great Lord Damballah Weydo, I call on you. Change these evil Petro worshipers into snakes. Lower them to their bellies and make them crawl in the dust. Change their evil words into hisses. Take away their words and let them dart out their tongues dumbly. Punish them, Damballah! Use your great power on them! Damballah! Damballah! Damballah!"

Armes' grip on her ankle tightened.

"Wonderful! What's happening?"

She did not answer him but continued her diatribe.

"You, Antoine!" She seemed to be speaking directly to someone. "You are a St. Gabriel slave. Go to your quarters, Antoine, while you can still walk on your legs, for if you do not go now, the curses of Ayda and Damballah are upon you and you will crawl on your belly the rest of your life."

There was a deep silence, punctuated only by the crackling embers. Armes heard a rush of movement, and the sound of something being dragged across the terrace. For several minutes Athenée did not move. Then she knelt and placed her face close to Armes.

183

"You can come out now. They have gone. I think they will not stop running until they have put miles between us. But oh, Armes, I am afraid."

"But if they have gone, there's nothing to fear."

"It's not that. Something very strange just happened—so strange that it frightens me. I recognized one of the slaves below. He is a groom here. When I pointed to him and told him I'd turn him into a snake, he fell onto the terrace and started to wriggle along on his belly, his tongue darting out of his mouth in quick little movements. They had to drag him away because he could not walk. I invoked Damballah against him, and see what happened. Oh, Armes, what awful power did I use? I'm afraid."

He extricated himself from the basin of the fountain, leaped over the edge, and lifted her down to the terrace.

"The only thing we have to fear now is being roasted alive. Let's get out of this inferno." He picked her up, astonished at her lightness, and ran down the steps to the terrace below. The high banking shielded them momentarily from the heat. Other steps led to a still lower terrace, and these he took two at a time. A cluster of banana trees made a circle of shadow from the light of the fire, and he laid her down on the ground. It was cooler here and the air was free from smoke.

"It's a long way to Sans Souci, Athenée. I don't know how we shall make it. You are barefooted and I have but one shoe."

She stood up and put her hands in his.

"With you, Armes, I think I'd willingly go barefooted to the end of the world. But it won't be necessary. I've had some little taste for gardening lately. In the summerhouse there"—she pointed to a latticed gazebo—"I have shoes which I use for gardening. Aprons, too! But"—she smiled—"I'm afraid my shoes will not fit you."

Once more he lifted her in his arms and carried her down to the summerhouse.

"Little by little you are getting to be a white man again," she said as she rubbed her hand against his chest, "and I am getting black—see!" She held up her hand.

"Closer," he whispered in her ear. "I cannot hear."

She moved her lips closer to his face. He ducked his head suddenly and kissed her hand. She snatched it away.

"I hated the kiss you gave me when we were hiding in the fountain." She spoke each word distinctly, "But I returned

184

it, because I feared I might never have a chance to kiss you again, and I wanted to very badly because, Armes Holbrook, it happens that I love you. I had hoped that your kiss might be different from René's, but it was the same— a kiss hot with passion but devoid of love. Please believe me, I shall never let you kiss me again, nor shall I kiss you. Do you understand that and will you remember?"

He refused to take her words seriously. "You say you love me, Athenée. And what is love without a few kisses, and what are kisses unless they are warmed with passion? What other kind of kisses are there? Give me time and I can convince you. Because . . . it also happens that I love you."

She shook her head in denial.

"I doubt very much if you know what the word 'love' means. There is much more to it than you think. But this is no place to discuss it. We had best be on our way."

23

A PALE green streak of light, which foretold the coming dawn, appeared in the sky when Armes and Athenée stumbled down the last long hill that bordered Sans Souci. It had been a night of endless miles over primitive paths and through dense woods. How they had achieved it, they themselves never quite realized. Despite Armes' strength, he had reached the point of exhaustion hours before. Only some indomitable force of will kept him going, lifting Athenée over the difficult spots, supporting her when the going was smoother, and forever holding back branches for her to pass under. He knew that they must reach Sans Souci before daybreak and the full light drew attention to his sweat-streaked masquerade.

The brilliant red glow in the skies had increased throughout the night as plantation after plantation, cane fields, sugar refineries, and coffee bushes were fired. Twice they had come near other plantations, only to find them ringed with black bodies that glistened like carved obsidian in the dancing light of the flames. They had hidden in thickets until they could make their escape. Once, pursuing a fairly well-marked trail, they had heard voices approach. There was no place to hide. Armes flung Athenée to the ground, unmindful of her protests, pulled her nightgown up over her face, and clamped his body over hers. As the reeling blacks approached, he lifted his head and grinned foolishly into the light of their blazing torch, fearful that they would decide to await his consummation and then demand their separate turns, but they only grinned back at him and passed on with obscene gestures and ribald words. He had been grateful for the dye on his face, and although it had worn thin, the shadows had not revealed hi.n as a white man—just another black, rutting in the road. But, after the marauders had passed, it was difficult for him to revert to his white self. Willingly he would have remained there, his black body pressed against Athenée's white skin, despite her struggles, but her violen. protests prevailed, and he conquered himself sufficiently to quit her and lift her to her feet. He was glad she did not become angry and reprimand him for his lapse into the brutality which had not completely left him since the orgy of the dance.

Strangely enough, as they limped along Athenée seemed to gather strength as Armes tired. His unshod foot was cut and bleeding from rocks and fields of stubble, and at times he found himself leaning on her, letting her support him. Their roles became reversed, and at times she was almost carrying him.

The crest of the last hill showed them the white walls of Sans Souci, rose-tinted by the first fingers of dawn. But . . . it stood! Thank God it stood! It was not burning, and there was no chanting ring of drunken dancing blacks around it. Its detached serenity beckoned them over that last weary mile, although each step seemed impossible—a picking up of one foot and a placing down of the other, Armes and Athenée arrived at long last. They trudged by the shuttered slave cabins unnoticed except for a child, squatting to relieve herself by one of the houses, and finally dragged themselves around to the steps to the big house.

A dark form moved in the shadows of the balcony and came to the head of the stairs. It was Henry, with Pompee behind him. Together they reached down and caught Armes just as he was about to fall and then, as unceremoniously as though he were a bundle of sugarcane, Henry threw him over his shoulder and carried him up the steps, down the hall and into the bedroom, and there gently lowered him onto the bed.

"I'll not light a candle, TiArmes. It will soon be full daylight and it is better that we sit in the dark now. God knows

186

how much longer we shall be able to sit here. Can you talk, TiArmes?"

Armes raised himself up on one elbow and Athenée slipped a pillow under his head.

"Lie down here, madame." Henry pointed to the other half of the bed. "Rest yourself there while we talk, if TiArmes is able to talk."

Armes groaned. "I'll talk, but first have Ali bring us some brandy and cool water. We both need it."

"I'll get the brandy, milord." Pompee started from the room.

A wave of Armes' hand stopped him. "No, let Ali get it. He knows where it is." He looked around the room, then called as loudly as he could, "Ali!"

Henry walked over and drew up a chair beside the bed.

"Pompee'll get the brandy just now, TiArmes." His usually booming voice was strangely quiet and soothing, and his big hand restrained Armes gently.

Pompee returned in a moment and poured two glasses. He handed one to Athenée. "Take it, madame, it'll make you feel better, and you, milord, you'd better take two."

Armes drank and sank back on the pillow, grateful for the warm glow of the brandy in his stomach. He glanced over at Athenée, sitting on the bed beside him. He was glad he could see only the perfect side of her face, the profile like an antique cameo. Her beauty made him want to touch her— to grasp her hand. His grimy hand sought hers, but she only patted it with detached sympathy and moved her own hand away.

"Listen to these men, Armes. I do not know who they are, but this one thing is most apparent: they are friends of yours even though they are not white."

Henry bowed without rising. "Perhaps it is because we are Negroes, madame, that we are friends of TiArmes. It's been no night for introductions, but I take it you are the Vicomtesse St. Gabriel."

She nodded in assent.

"And I am Henry Christophe and this is Pompee. We are both friends of TiArmes."

"And Ali? Where is he? Why isn't he here? Why don't you call him?" Armes questioned petulantly.

"He's away just now, TiArmes. I'll explain in good time." Henry's voice was gravely soothing. "There are many things to talk about now. It is important and we have no time to lose."

"I'm listening, Henry."

"First, TiArmes, this plantation of Sans Souci no longer belongs to you."

"Then whose is it?"

"As far as the world of St. Domingue knows, it has become mine. You sold it to me. But as far as you and I are concerned it's just as much yours as it ever was. All during the night, whenever bands of marauding slaves came here, I told them it was mine and defied them to touch a match to it. They listened to me because I am Henry Christophe and they know me for a *gros nègre*—a goddamned *gros nègre* that they fear. That is why Sans Souci is the only plantation standing within miles of the Cap. Pompee backed me up, and although they were Petro men, they respect him as a Rada priest. So, we have been unmolested. The house stands; most of the slaves are in their cabins; the fields have not been burned; the cattle have not been stolen. That is why I must tell you this first, because at any moment more slaves may come and I shall tell them the same story, so you must keep hidden. If they see you they will not believe me."

Armes turned toward Henry, although the effort caused him pain. He sank back again on the pillow.

"As far as I am concerned, Henry, you can have the cursed place. All I want now is to get the hell out of St. Domingue and take Athenée and Ali with me."

"I can understand that, TiArmes, but I do not think wou will leave St. Domingue. You told me once that you would help me. Aren't you going to keep that promise? I need you now, TiArmes."

"Good God, Henry! You ask me to stay here after tonight?"

"Because of tonight."

"Oh hell, Henry! I can't think now. I want Athenée to be comfortable. Call Ali and have him take her to the big room down the hall. Have him heat a warm bath. Then let her sleep. When Ali has finished, have him come here to me. He knows how to take care of me. After a half an hour in my bath, and his massage, I'll be a new person. I've many things to explain to Ali, and much to make up to him for the sorrow I've caused him."

Pompee walked slowly across the room with a heavy tread and opened the jalousies wide. The fresh breeze zephyred in and blew out the guttering candle. Armes blinked in the unexpected light. Pompee slowly retraced his steps as if he had a dreaded duty to perform and stood at the foot of the bed, framed by the tall posts, his face in shadow. Slowly he raised his arms as though to call down some sort of benediction. His lips moved but no words came. Then he lowered his hands and laid them tenderly on Armes' bloodied feet.

"Even my gods are powerless to make this difficult task easier for me." The big fellow was crying—his shoulders heaved and tears coursed down his cheeks. "I have bad news for you, milord. I wish I could spare you and tell it to you gently, but bad news can never be gentle. It is harsh and bitter, and such must be my words to you. Milord"—he lingered over the word—"Ali is dead."

Armes jackknifed up, beating the counterpane with frenzied hands.

"Ali, Ali, come here!" He waited. There was no sound of running feet. His hands, seeking some action, no matter how trivial, reached up and clutched at the netting around the bed, pulled it down, and ripped it to shreds. "Ali, come here! Ali."

"Ali is dead, milord."

"Dead? How can he be dead? He was here yesterday. What sort of a trick are you playing on me?"

"It is no trick, TiArmes." Henry's big hands, now gentle, removed the shreds of netting from Armes' fingers. "Your boy is dead."

"But you, Henry! I told you to protect him. It was the last thing I asked of you. You let those crazy goddamned niggers kill my boy." He sank back on the pillow. "Oh, poor little fellow."

Henry's head sank down on his chest. He gazed at the floor with unseeing eyes.

"No, milord," Pompee spoke for Henry, "Henry did not let them kill him any more than you did. You were both powerless to protect him."

"Powerless? What do you mean? Surely if I had known . . ."

"You saw him die, milord, and neither you nor Henry could help him."

Armes' eyes stared at the ceiling. Now it was Athenée's hand, warm with consolation, that sought his.

"Your friend Topaze killed Ali." Pompee beat his hands against the mahogany foot rail of the bed.

Armes stared in disbelief. "That mulatto bitch! Tonight I

189

saw her for what she was. I saw her dance before Bouck-mann's fire. I saw her take that Negro buck into her and knowing her as I do, I know how much she enjoyed the enormity of that black stallion. I saw her filthy hands take the head of the white boy they killed . . ." He looked up at Pompee with an agonized question in his eyes. "Oh, my God, Pompee! Henry!" Again he saw the slim nude body, staked to the ground. He knew now without being told.

He jumped up from the bed. "Henry, Pompee! Help me! I'll kill them, murder them, kill them! Oh little Ali, why did I hurt you for that goddamned bitch whose whole rotten body was not worth your little finger? Let me at them! I'll tear them apart as they did my boy." His screams echoed up and down the hall, and they had difficulty in restraining him from running out of the room.

"Quiet, TiArmes, lie down, do." Henry, with Pompee's help, maneuvered him gently back onto the bed. "It won't do any good. Not a goddamned bit of good. Your little fellow's not suffering anymore." Henry held Armes down on the bed. "I liked him, too, TiArmes."

"I loved him," Pompee added. "He was devoted to you."

Armes' struggles ceased, and he burst into a wild fit of un-controlled weeping. Athenée motioned for Henry to sit down, and Pompee took up his position again at the foot of the bed. She inclined her head toward Armes. "It's better this way," she whispered. "Let him exhaust his emotions by crying, then there will be a calm."

His sobs subsided gradually. He stared at Pompee.

"Tell me all. Don't leave anything out."

With bowed head, Pompee began. "Soon after you left, milord, Topaze came out to the stables and ordered a horse saddled."

"No, it was before we left," Henry interrupted. "TiArmes and I saw her down the drive, starting to cut across the fields."

"Well, she was gone about an hour. Then she came back, flounced into the house, ordered the maids to pack all her clothes, and called for a cart. When this was brought around, she had the house slaves load her trunks into the cart and sent Michel, the stableman, to the Cap. She told him to put the trunks and things in her house. She gathered up her jewel box and started for the door. Just then Ali came in. He tried to stop her and grabbed the jewel box out of her hands. He said they were yours and she had no right to them."

"Poor little fellow! He was always trying to protect me."

The pressure of Athenée's hand calmed him, and she motioned to Pompee to proceed.

"I was not here—these facts I heard from the servants. It seems that they must have had a pretty violent quarrel. One of the house slaves ran out to the fields to fetch me. When I got to the house Ali had her by the hair and was slapping her so smartly I could hear it before I came into the house. She was clawing, scratching, and biting. I separated them. She was so fighting mad, she left without taking the jewel casket." He pointed to the corner. "It's still there."

"A lot of fake jewels." Armes shook his head. "Fake jewels that probably cost Ali his life."

"But Ali didn't know that," Henry exclaimed. "He thought they were valuable."

"Yes, he used to try them on when Topaze was not in her room."

Pompee went on with his story. "She ran out of the house, sent Michel on his way, got on her horse again, and galloped down the drive. Ali started to straighten things up. See! There's his broom still in the corner. I stayed and talked with him for a while, trying to quiet him down. She really didn't hurt him any except for a few scratches on his face. Then when everything seemed to be normal again, I went back to the fields, but I became nervous. I knew strange things were happening. I knew Bouckmann was calling a Petro meeting that night, and I felt sure that Topaze planned to be there with him, but of course I didn't know he planned a revolt. Topaze always played the winning side. She was willing to leave you and cast her lot with Bouckmann, for she thought that by now you would be dead and he would be the most important man in St. Domingue."

"That's why she didn't want me to see you, Henry," Armes said. "She was afraid you might have heard of Bouckmann's plans and came to warn me."

Henry nodded in agreement.

"About an hour later," Pompee continued, "the *loa* of Papa Zaca came to me and told me to return to the house. Papa Zaca is the god of the fields, you know. So I came back to the house, and no sooner had I arrived than two men came running up the driveway. They were slaves from some other plantation. I did not know them."

Pompee reached over for the bottle of brandy and poured

himself a finger. He drank it slowly before he started to speak again.

"Ali came out on the steps to meet them just as I came around the corner. They asked to speak to Ali and when he told them who he was, they told him that you had fallen from your horse up in the mountains and that the black who was with you had sent them to Sans Souci for Ali, as he did not dare to leave M'sieu Holbrook alone. They said you were badly hurt and needed medicine. Ali ran into the house and tore up linen for bandages and took your small medicine chest. He called a groom and had Lalla saddled. That's the last I saw of him, milord, as he rode down the drive."

Armes glanced up quickly.

"You've been calling me 'milord,' Pompee. That's Ali's name for me."

"From now on, with your permission, I shall call you 'milord' in memory of him."

"Thank you, Pompee, it is well that we should remember the little fellow. Such love and loyalty as he had for me is seldom seen."

"Yes, Ali was good. The best." Henry's eyes were brimming with moisture. "Go on, Pompee, tell him the rest."

"Well, I came back to the house and went down to my room. Something told me that things were not right and I regretted that I had not gone instead of Ali, but according to the men, your instructions were for Ali to come. However, I knew if you had been hurt, the best way I could help you was to ask my gods to help you. I opened the *govi* which contains the *loa* of Papa Zaca, because he was the one who came to me in the fields. But the *loa* of Baron Samedi, who is one of the Guede death family, pushed old Papa Zaca aside. When Baron Samedi had possessed me, I was able to leave my body and ride along with Ali and the men. They left the road and started up a trail into the mountains. A short way up the trail several other men joined them. They pulled Ali from his horse and beat him until he was unconscious, then tied him back on the horse and started across the mountain. Through the *loa* of Baron Samedi, I followed them until they came to a clearing the other side of the mountains. Bouckmann was there and Topaze was with him. They stripped Ali of his clothes, tied a cloth around his head, and staked him to the ground. Before Bouckmann tied the cloth over his head, he poured something down Ali's throat. I think it was a drug to keep him quiet. Anyway, I'm sure he didn't

192

know anything all the afternoon. Then the *loa* left me, and try as I could, I could not become possessed again, not by Baron Samedi or by any of the other gods. The Petro influence where Ali was was too strong."

Henry looked over to Armes.

"I guess we know the rest."

Armes sank back on the pillow, and Athenée got up from the bed and tiptoed from the room.

"I leave him to you . . . messieurs." She hesitated over the title. "Undress him, wash him, and put him to bed. Then stay and protect him, will you?"

"We will, madame," they answered in unison.

Pompee came around to the head of the bed.

"The power of the *ouanga* that Topaze placed on your bed is gone," he said. "Even without your permission, I broke it. You are free of her."

Armes' eyes did not move from the whiteness of the ceiling which his fancy was painting with vivid colors. Once more he saw the thin-limbed adolescent body staked to the ground. Again he saw it glow in the firelight, accented by the one black patch of hair. He watched Bouckmann pull the glowing red machete from the blaze with his bare hands, and his eyes followed its swift descent. He shrank from the obscene kisses that Topaze's teeth tore from Ali's lifeless lips while the Negro youth made his way toward her. He followed Ali's smooth, slim body as it was heaved into the flames, and then watched Topaze arch her body to meet the thrusts of the black stallion who covered her.

"Ali!" It was an insane shriek of mingled grief and horror.

Henry and Pompee gently removed the stained slave garments, and Pompee brought a bowl of warm water. Under his ministrations, Armes slowly emerged as a white man again, but from the heat of his body Pompee knew that his master was sick. Armes slept, and in the delirium of his fevered sleep, he relived the horrors of that night. In his ravings he called out names. "Ali, Topaze, Athenée." Always with the latter name, his tortured mind seemed to achieve momentary peace, then the whirling squirrel cage of his thoughts would start once more and the awful cycle of fantasy would begin all over again. Black hands, black bellies, black breasts! All pressed and wove themselves together in a savage dance around a streaming fire from whose mounting flames, phoenix-like, the severed head of Ali rose to watch with blind eyes the bestial mating of Topaze and her black stud.

24

ARMES' fever tortured his mind and racked his body for eight days. For as many days the rebellion of the slaves under the leadership of Bouckmann lasted. During those eight days, anarchy reigned in St. Domingue. Some two hundred of the great mansions of the Plain du Nord and the country surrounding Cap François had become smoldering piles of rubble. Sugar, coffee, and indigo were burned. Refineries were gutted. Those whites who had managed to flee the countryside and seek sanctuary in the Cap were thankful to be alive, but thousands had been surprised in their homes and their bodies consumed in the funeral pyres of their houses or left to swell and rot in the tropic sun.

The army of slaves had marched on, clad in tattered remnants of their masters' finery, constantly swelling in numbers day by day until their march brought them to the very gates of Cap François. For eight days they caroused in a debauched revel, and during that time they gave vent to a savage retaliation for the sadistic treatment the whites had imposed upon them. Their veneer of civilization was gone and they had become savages again. Whites were captured, hacked to pieces, cooked, and eaten. White women were ruthlessly raped by a hundred black men standing in line to await their turn. Revenge tasted sweet to the blacks.

The bloody froth of revolution spread down through the hills and valleys, but it stopped at the gates of Cap François. The city was prepared for them. As the ragtag Negro army had swelled in numbers, the white population of the Cap grew in proportion, from white refugees who managed to creep into the city from outlying plantations. Each had his own vivid story to tell of escape, hiding, flight, and safe arrival. There were soldiers of France in the Cap—disciplined men under trained leadership—and they, together with the willing white volunteers, stopped the black tide at the very gates of the city and then pursued it back into the hills. They captured the braggart Bouckmann, and all the power of his Petro gods could not prevent the French from chopping off his head. As a warning, they impaled it on a pole in the Place des Armes, where it grinned a horrible warning to the house slaves of the city.

The French had stopped the rebellion, but their leaders knew it had been accomplished by a very narrow margin. Only because the blacks lacked leadership had they been defeated. But leaders were arising in the Negro ranks. Toussaint, who had not yet become the world's greatest Negro general, was busy helping his master and mistress over the tortuous miles from Breda to the Cap, walking by night and hiding by day. When they were safe in the city, Toussaint left them and devoted his energies to his own people. Henry Christophe, who little dreamed that the ermine-edged mantle of kingship was one day to be clasped around his shoulders, stood guard at Sans Souci, but his talents for organization were operating in a hundred different directions. Jean Jacques Dessalines, not yet feeling the cumbersome weight of an imperial crown on his wiry pate, was able to drill his ignorant soldiers by day while he embraced his new mistress Topaze at night. True to her nature, Topaze had deserted the defunct cause of Bouckmann and hitched her fortunes to the rising star of Dessalines.

Practically all of the slaves in Cap François had remained faithful to their masters—a few, like Toussaint, from love, but the majority through fear. Many of the blacks, however, had been slain within the city walls in a senseless and brutish retaliation for the rapine and pillage outside. The mulattoes, as usual, did not know which side they were on. They hated the blacks who, in turn, detested them, but they also hated the whites, whom they envied, as much as the whites disliked them. In either camp their light-brown skins were only tolerated, until continual snubbing from the whites eventually drove them, albeit unwillingly, to the side of the Negroes. Although they were never liked nor trusted by the blacks, they managed by means of their superior education and ability to reach positions of prominence among them. The *affranchis* figured, and wisely too, that if the whites remained in control of St. Domingue, they would continue to be snubbed, whereas with the blacks in control, they stood a chance of rising to power in whatever government might be formed.

King Louis the Sixteenth of France—that obese repairer of clocks—finally lost his stupid head to Madame Guillotine and revolution reigned in Mother France as it did in the colony.

The untrained idealists who tried vainly to govern France failed completely to establish order in St. Domingue.

Chaos, however, can often be salutary, as it dredges up great leaders from the debris of revolution. Just as the little Corsican corporal, Napoleon, emerged as the leader of France, so did the ex-slave Toussaint rise to prominence in St. Domingue. Having assured the safety of his beloved master and mistress, he fled the Cap and appeared in the Negro encampment in the Plain du Nord. His keen mind, his innate ability, and his comprehensive grasp of any situation won him the support of the Negroes. They were looking for a leader and Toussaint appealed to their intellect, for although they were crude, unlettered, and uneducated, they were, nevertheless, men of brains and reason. Neither the color of their skin nor the years of oppression had dimmed their native intelligence. Bouckmann had inflamed them through hate and bestiality. Now Toussaint inspired them through knowledge. Bouckmann had cried "Murder, kill, rape, burn, pillage, show no mercy." Touissant said quietly but authoritatively, "Build, organize, arm, obey!"

Although Toussaint was a Negro, he was first a Frenchman. He loved France with a deep though undeserved loyalty. As a Negro he hated slavery, but as a Frenchman he loved order and authority. His decision was a difficult one for him to make. Should he place his affections with the white planters who constituted authority and who had made life hell for the blacks, or should he strive with the blacks to obtain equality for them with the whites? He decided on the latter course. The blacks rallied around him and elected him general.

As General Toussaint of the Black Army of St. Domingue, he sent representatives to the Cap, to sue for peace, and he guaranteed a peaceful return of the rebellious Negroes to the plantations—as free men, however, not as slaves. By that time they were quite willing to go almost anywhere. Their supplies were already exhausted and they had had a bellyful of mangoes. The once fertile lands of St. Domingue were charred and black; there was nothing to eat but the wild fruit of the hills, and a steady diet of mangoes becomes tiresome even to a black belly.

Toussaint's emissaries returned and flung the letters that the general had so carefully written down on the table in front of him. There was no government left in Cap Francois to deal with. Nobody could say a decisive word. Nobody could be trusted. Regretfully Toussaint tore the letters up. He had tried. He wanted peace, but now he did not know where to find it. His outstretched hand of friendship had been ignored.

True, he was now a general, but he was still in a quandary. He was in command of an army which had no place to go, nothing to eat, and no way of replenishing its arms. They had sacked and and burned all the houses and there was nothing left for them to steal. Bouckmann's followers now realized too late how wrong their leader had been. They had no desire to revert to naked savages in grass huts, once having tasted civilization. How much better it would have been to have saved the resources of the country and now have the rich plentitude of the Plain to support them. Alas! It was too late to remedy the situation.

Toussaint, burying his deep loyalty to France, forsook his beloved mother country and crossed the mountains to Santo Domingo, the Spanish part of the island. At least, if nothing more, there was a plentiful supply of mangoes growing there. Once arrived, he half-heartedly offered his men to the Spanish captain general. Although this worthy hardly knew what to do with a starving army, he accepted them graciously, and as France was at war with Spain, he sent them back to St. Domingue, outfitted in Spanish uniforms, carrying Spanish guns with Spanish lead and bullet molds, to conquer as much of French St. Domingue as possible for the Spanish crown.

It worked out exactly as Toussaint had planned. Now, thanks to the stupidity of Spain, he had a well-equipped army with adequate supplies and guns and ammunition for every man. Back over the mountains he marched again, but this time he came as a conqueror.

The seeds of rebellion which Bouckmann had scattered had been carried by the tropical winds and had taken root even in the southernmost parts of the island—Port-au-Prince, Aux Cayes, Jacmel, and Jérémie. Here and there, bands of slaves stole off into the hills and raided the surrounding country. Houses continued to be burned, whites killed, and towns sacked. All of St. Domingue from north to south became an armed camp, sharply cleaved by the color of a man's skin—black—any shade of black from pale *café au lait* to the prune-black of Africa—on one side, white on the other. It was no longer a question of ideals, aims, or desires, but a division according to race. Only in the cities of Cap François and Port-au-Prince, still white strongholds, were the blacks sub-

197

servient. Throughout the vast stretches of the mountains and the once fertile plains, the conquering color was black.

There was one exception—one small island of peace that remained in St. Domingue—the plantation of Sans Souci. Here life went on as usual or nearly so. No longer were there nearly half a thousand slaves in the fields, but there were still a goodly number, as many of them had elected to stay on through loyalty to Henry Christophe or love for Armes. Now they were no longer slaves but free men working for stated wages. There were fewer servants in the house, but those who remained stayed on through desire rather than compulsion. A crudely carved green snake, the symbol of Damballah, hung from one of the iron gates; a gaudily painted heart-shaped plaque, the sign of Ayda, hung from the other. They were potent talismans, for they protected the plantation and its inmates. The black world of St. Domingue regarded Sans Souci as Henry Christophe's plantation. That the big house still sheltered whites was none of their business, for Henry Christophe was a *gros nègre* to be respected, and the voodoo *papaloi* Pompee also lived there.

Henry Christophe had lately become an important man in St. Domingue. He was in constant communication with Toussaint, and Toussaint relied far more on Henry than on any other man in the colony. It was Henry who, on dark nights, met little bands that came from all over St. Domingue and distributed arms to them. It was Henry who arranged for boats, laden with what produce they could scrape together, to steal out of isolated coastal harbors at night and head for Jamaica, Cuba, or even far off New Orleans to sell their sugar, coffee, indigo, and fruit in exchange for guns and powder. With Toussaint leading his army under the scarlet and gold banners of Spain; with Jean Jacques already a general along with him, sporting wide gold epaulettes and a voluptuous mistress called Topaze, all those who remained in the north of St. Domingue looked to Henry for leadership. Let the south adore the handsome mulatto General Pétion! The north had their *gros nègre* Henry Christophe.

For weeks, ever since the Bouckmann rebellion, Henry had been patiently investigating. He questioned every stranger that came from the direction of the Cap, and one day he finally got his answer—the answer that sent him back to the city of Cap François, still securely held by the French. Not that he could ride into the city openly. The French sentries allowed no strange Negroes inside, and Henry knew that if he

198

were discovered he faced not merely death but retaliatory torture. Henry, however, knew the Cap as well as he knew the lines of his own pink palm, and he thumbed his nose at the French.

When night came, he slipped in through an unguarded breach in the city walls. His huge figure cast a gigantically grotesque shadow on the moonlit streets leading to the Couronne, but when he arrived there, he found the hotel in ruins. Well, he had expected that! It had belonged to a Negro, so the French had fired it in a petty gesture of revenge. Henry's former life lay before him in ashes—all that he had known and loved and cared for. But not quite all. There was a little left of the stable in back of the charred walls of the hotel. The bright moonlight showed that somebody had stopped up the holes in the walls and tried to mend what little of the roof remained.

Henry halted in the deep shadow of a crumbled doorway and scanned the narrow street. It was as deserted as he had prayed to the white gods and the black gods that it would be. Inching along in the shadows, he reached the end, then ducked low and scuttled across the open space before the ruined stable until he reached the doorway, which was covered with a heavy piece of sacking. With a pause to collect his breath, he prayed again, not knowing what he might find inside, but hoping. Still in the shadow of the doorway, he lifted the heavy cloth. Nothing but pale moonlight creeping through a cobwebbed window illuminated the darkness inside, but the sound of someone breathing—the deep regular breathing of slumber—came from a pallet in the corner. He slipped a knife from the inside of his boot and advanced through the white strip of moonlight over to the darkness of the pallet. He stood poised above the unseen sleeper, then he knelt down and his hand, guided only by the sound of breathing, groped until it found a throat. His fingers tightened enough to wake the sleeper, then clutched tighter. The sleeper lay still.

"Quiet!" Henry cautioned. "One move, one scream, and you'll die."

Hands grasped his wrists and dug sharp nails into his skin until he was forced to relax some of his pressure.

"Henry Christophe." The words came with difficulty, but the voice was warm and feminine. "You take your big hands off my throat. You're choking me! What do you mean stealing in here in the middle of the night with me asleep and

199

only in my shift? If you have any idea that you're going to do what I think you want to do, Henry Christophe, I'll slap that black face of yours. Do you hear? Now get away from me!" She brushed Henry's now limp hand away and sat up. "The very idea, you big ape."

Henry gathered her up in his arms. "Oh, Marie Louise. Thank *le bon Dieu* that you are safe. I've looked all over for you. I've asked everyone for news of you. And Monsieur Coidovic?"

"They killed him." Her voice caught with a sob. "Killed him when they burned the Couronne. But I got away. I hid with the Brown family, the Americans who own the big warehouse. You remember them; they once lived at the Couronne. Then when they left for Baltimore a week ago, I had no place to go, so I came back here. No one has harmed me. Nobody has noticed a fifteen-year-old girl who hides during the day and steals out at night. Oh, Henry! I'm so glad you're here." She nestled down in his powerful arms.

He drew her closer to him and pressed his lips gently against her smooth forehead. "Marie Louise, I've always loved you, and I had hoped that someday I could marry you. Your father was willing and I was waiting for you to grow up, but now, let's not wait any longer."

His hand crept down under the ragged blanket to discover her nakedness and encountered the hard nipples of her breasts. He sensed that she wanted him as much as he wanted her, for she was tense in his arms, but when he removed his fingers to fumble with the buttons of his breeches, she pushed at his chest, beating on it with clenched fists.

"Then, Henry Christophe, if you want to marry me, you act decent. I may be only fifteen, but if you think for one moment that you are going to crawl in bed with me and do to me what I once caught you doing to Jeanne Marie upstairs, you're mistaken."

"Oh, Marie Louise, I wasn't thinking of that," he lied bravely. The smoothness of her skin against his callused palms had excited him, and he restrained himself with difficulty. But he wanted Marie Louise for more than just tonight. "Wasn't thinking of that at all," he repeated. "Just loving you to show you how glad I am to see you."

"Then take your hand off my tits. I know what men think about and you most of all, Henry Christophe. Now you leave me alone and get up on your feet and turn around and face the other way. I'm not taking any chances. Now! Where are you?"

"Standing here, Marie Louise." Henry's voice was strangely meek, considering the ramrod bulge in his breeches.

"And is your back turned?"

"Mais oui, ma chérie."

"Then I'm going to get dressed and you're going to take me with you. I don't care where. But tomorrow you are going to find a priest and I'm going to marry you. Do you hear that, Henry Christophe? I'm going to marry you because I love you, you great big black ox."

Henry chuckled in the darkness, his immediate needs almost forgotten. "I sure do hear you, Marie Louise."

"And why do I love a big ape like you?"

"I don't know, Marie Louise."

"Because you're strong and tall and handsome, Henry Christophe, and from what I have heard you have something that makes women love you. At any rate, every wench in the Couronne always bragged about it for days afterward when you made love to her. So, if it's true, I want it for my own. Is it true, Henry Christophe?"

"I never had any complaints, Marie Louise, so I guess it's true."

"Well, that isn't the only reason. I know too that you are good and kind and gentle, and that those big hands of yours can be warm and loving. Those are the reasons why I am going to marry you tomorrow. Besides, I've always worshiped you."

Henry reached out through the darkness and found her hand. "Then come on, *ma petite,* hurry up." He paused a moment, letting his hand slip up her arm. "But let's get one thing straight. You're a bossy little wench, but don't forget, Henry Christophe is a *gros nègre* and he's going to wear the pants in this family."

"Why of course, Henry, of course." She giggled, moving his hand from her arm down into the neck of her dress.

He tried to force her back onto the pallet, but she resisted him silently.

"Why of course, Henry, you'll wear the pants. They certainly wouldn't fit me very well." Her fingers were fumbling now. "Shame on you, Henry Christophe, going around with your pants unbuttoned. You'll lose them. Then who'll be wearing the pants?"

He pulled her closer, his body rigid under the tantalizing

201

motion of her hand. Her other arm drew his head down to hers, and her kisses burned his lips. Suddenly he shuddered, drew in a long breath of air, and sagged in her arms, his knees almost buckling under him. It was she who was strong and held him in her arms.

"What happened, Henry, what happened? Are you hurt? Oh, Henry, what did I do to you?"

His fingers untied the neckerchief from around his throat and he handed it to her.

"Wipe your hands," he whispered hoarsely. "Nothing happened to me that doesn't happen sometimes to every man. You'll learn about men, Marie Louise. Sometimes the weakest woman can be stronger than the biggest man. I've got a lot to teach you and you've got a lot to learn. I'm all right now. We've wasted too much time." He picked her up in his arms, ducked under the sacking, and looked up and down the street. It was deserted.

Once outside, he set her down carefully on the rounded cobbles.

"Hurry, *ma petite*. We have a long way to go, you and I. Our path leads through the city walls and then over a longer road that goes to Sans Souci."

"To Sans Souci and M'sieu Armes? Will I be welcome?"

He nodded. He envisioned the plantation as he had left it earlier that evening, but if he could have looked into the future, he would have seen another Sans Souci. The plantation house would be gone and in its place would be a palace, the most regal and the most magnificent in all the New World. He would have seen the light of a thousand candles blazing from its long windows, and he would have entered and seen Queen Marie Louise of Haiti, sitting on a throne with a diadem of jewels in her hair. He would have seen every head bowed before her but his own. Yet Henry Christophe was nothing but a poor, uneducated slave. How could he envisage a gold crown on the head of this little black girl beside him whose grasping fingers had so recently pleasured him?

All he wanted now was to find a priest or even a *père savanne* so that they might be married and he could become the giver of pleasure as well as she.

"Hurry, *ma chérie!*"

25

HENRY Christophe and Marie Louise Coidovic were married at Sans Souci the next week. Henry had wanted it to be the day after he brought Marie Louise back to the plantation, but Athenée would not permit it. Marie Louise must have a real wedding, she insisted, and that would necessitate a wedding gown and a priest—and not a black *père savanne*, a bush priest such as Henry would have found. After searching for two days, Henry located a white priest and persuaded him, by threatening him with a machete, to come to Sans Souci and perform the ceremony. The man had never married two blacks before and he deemed it almost a sacrilege, but Henry's machete was persuasive and the man came. Henry was black, but Henry was an important man.

Armes, still convalescing from his fever, sat pillow-propped in an armchair, his face thin and showing the ravages of his sickness. Athenée, partially veiled, as always, stood beside Marie Louise, and Pompee stood beside Henry. From his vantage point in the big chair, Armes looked at the four people standing near him and realized how his own life and, perhaps even more important, his viewpoint had changed since he arrived in St. Domingue. Now these Negroes were his friends, nay, even more than that, they were his family—the only family he had ever had. Henry was the elder brother he had always wanted. He knew Henry's faults —he was egotistical, ruthless, sometimes cruel, often bull-headed and obstinate—but he appreciated the good that was in Henry. Henry was loyal, staunch, and dependable—a true elder brother.

And there was Pompee, now so different from the miserable, emaciated wretch Armes had dug out of the earth at St. Gabriel. How could he ever have foreseen that the dying man on the seat of the coach opposite him that night could possibly have turned into the handsome, soft-spoken, serious young fellow that Pompee now was. He was Armes' younger brother, and a brother to be proud of, for Armes well knew that there was not enough money in St. Domingue, no, not in all the world, to buy such deep loyalty and love as that which Pompee had for him. Today Pompee's face was suffused with a quiet joy. The close skullcap of tightly curled black hair was molded to the fine shape of his head. His high cheekbones caught purple highlights which glanced to the straight, well-formed nose and the full lips. His tobacco-brown skin glowed with youth and vitality. His breeches were crisply white, his blue coat shining with brass buttons, his boots a mirror-black, all so different from the soil-encrusted slave Armes had purchased from René.

Henry stood beside Pompee, gazing down fondly at his little Marie Louise. Henry Christophe was a free man now, and it showed in the very way he planted his feet on the floor. Henry was tall and straight, broad of shoulder and narrow of hip. His fine face was so filled with love for the dainty Marie Louise, he actually simpered. Armes was not deceived by the fatuous look on Henry's face. He knew that behind those dark eyes, momentous plans were brewing—plans for St. Domingue as well as for Henry himself and his bride. Henry smiled down at her, possessively and tenderly, and Armes saw her return the look.

"Let not her smallness deceive you, my friend," Armes thought, "for, little as she is, she has a mind of her own, and she is bound to rule you."

Marie Louise was tiny and delicately made. Her skin was a soft brown, her hair wavy and black. Her face was charmingly oval, still adolescent, but there was a firm straight line to her lips which presaged domination, pleasant or unpleasant as it might be for her husband. Today she was wearing white—a shimmering damask which Armes recognized as one of the Sans Souci tablecloths, hastily but stylishly turned into a wedding gown under the direction of Athenée.

And Athenée herself? Ah, she was an enigma. Since she had been under Armes' roof, he had scarcely seen her. True, she had paid a daily visit to his room, each time bringing something for his comfort or pleasure—a bowl of sliced oranges with freshly grated coconut; a platter of juicy mangoes with golden ripe *figs,* as bananas were called in St. Domingue, or a vase of flowers which she had picked for him. Always veiled, she would sit beside his bed and read or talk with him about such inconsequential subjects as the weather or household matters, then she would offer some very good excuse for leaving. As much as he wanted to talk with her about his feelings, he did not opportune her to remain, nor force his conversation upon her. He could not forget kissing her in the close confines of the fountain, nor

204

could he forget the soft fullness of her lips with their eager pressure against his. Unwillingly he accepted the present situation, for something in her manner deterred him from speaking his thoughts. Never anything but the perfect half of her face was ever revealed to him, and he reveled in that chaste beauty which had always remained in his memory from that moonlit night at sea. He had only a dim memory of the purple stain which had appeared the afternoon René tore the veil away.

Athenée had taken over Ali's duties as head of the household, and she ran it even more efficiently than he had done. All the servants were devoted to her and ran to do her bidding. Between her and Pompee a quiet understanding and interdependence had grown up. Pompee had never forgotten her plea for mercy for the slaves on the terrace and she, in turn, was grateful for his constant vigil while Armes had been sick.

Armes' thoughts returned to the room and the people before him. The priest adjusted his grimy cassock and began the words of the marriage ceremony. He mumbled on—meaningless words in a thick Gascon dialect, interspersed with even thicker Latin as Henry Christophe and Marie Louise knelt before him.

"These few words," Armes thought, "these poor inarticulate words, mumbled by a man with egg on his dirty cassock, are already working a miracle. They are uniting a man and a woman—making them one. But . . . these words! Are they so necessary? Do they increase Henry's love for Marie Louise or hers for him? Can these words preserve that love and make it secure? Will they guarantee that Henry will never seek other lips to kiss or that Marie Louise will not tire of Henry's too strenuous lovemaking?"

His questions found no answer even in his own mind as the priest droned on. A fly came and settled on Henry's forehead and Henry, forgetting the seriousness of the occasion, cursed aloud and waved the fly away. Marie Louise nudged him and Henry became properly humble again, but Armes could see that the big fellow was getting restless and that his drum-tight breeches were about to split. Finally, when it seemed the priest would go on forever, he came to a stop like a clock which had run down. Henry stood there looking at his bride awkwardly. His big hands clasped and unclasped themselves at his side and he shifted his weight from one foot to another. Marie Louise was in full command of the situation, however. She grabbed one of Henry's hands and placed it around her waist.

"Kiss me, Henry, we're married now."

Henry grinned shamefacedly. Kisses to him were something that took place in private, preferably in the dark, certainly not in broad daylight before a roomful of people. He leaned down, pecked her on the end of the nose, and continued to grin.

Athenée walked over to him, her face lifted expectantly, but he merely stared down at her.

"Henry Christophe!" She smiled up at him, wagging her finger at him. "Are you going to bend that stiff neck of yours and kiss me or must I get a chair and climb up on it in order to kiss you?"

Henry swallowed hard. His eyes rolled back to show the yellowed whites and his hands trembled.

"But I . . . madame . . . I . . . I am black, madame, and you are white. You are the Vicomtesse de St. Gabriel. I couldn't kiss a white woman."

"Couldn't, Henry?" Athenée took a step nearer to him. "Of course you 'couldn't' a year ago. I understand that. But that was a year ago. Today you not only can but may. We are here together, you and Marie Louise, Pompee, Armes, and I. We all live under the same roof. We eat the same food at the same table. Your life has become a part of my life and mine of yours. Why? Because we all love you, Henry Christophe, and I think you love us. Therefore I say that today, you most certainly may kiss me, just as you would have kissed your sister had she been here to stand up with you and Marie Louise. For, except for the color of my skin, am I so different from a sister you might have had?"

Henry could only mumble an almost inaudible "no."

"Or perhaps"—and now her voice sank to a whisper so low that only Henry could hear—"it is because you know what is under my veil that you do not wish to kiss me. Is that the reason, Henry Christophe?"

He dropped to his knees in front of her and crushed the folds of her skirt in his hands.

"Oh no, madame! No, no, no! You who are so good and kind and so wonderful in all ways. No, madame, never that."

Marie Louise reached down and grabbed Henry by his coat collar.

"Get up! For heaven's sake, kiss madame on the cheek and stop kneeling there like an ox hit over the head with a cleaver." Marie Louise turned to Athenée. "Forgive him, madame. He's always been like this where white women were concerned."

Henry brushed Athenée awkwardly on the cheek. She turned to Pompee.

"You were my slave once, Pompee, and I suppose I thought no more about you than the *bourrique* which carried our produce to market. But you are a slave no longer." She touched his cheek lightly with her lips. "Come! Let us all join together in the wedding feast of Henry Christophe and Marie Louise. Your arm, Pompee, and yours, Armes." She waited for him to extricate himself from the pillows. "Now you, Father, will you lead the procession to the dining room? Then you, Henry and Marie Louise, you follow him, and we three shall bring up the rear. We have champagne to toast the bride and groom and best wishes to offer them for a long and happy life."

"To say nothing of many little Henrys and just as many little Marie Louises," Armes added.

They walked into the dining room together and sat down at the big table, glittering with crystal and silver, resplendent with white damask and tall white tapers.

It was a happy time, this wedding of Henry Christophe and Marie Louise, a day that none of them present would ever forget. The talk drifted from the wedding to the outside world—to Toussaint, now General Toussaint L'Ouverture of the Spanish armies of Santo Domingo.

"We shall hear from Toussaint soon," Henry said.

"But isn't he in Santo Domingo with the army of Spain?" Athenée asked.

Henry watched the bubbles in his glass of champagne, sipped it, and made a wry face as the bubbles bounded up into his wide nostrils.

"Toussaint has captured nearly all of St. Domingue, that is, all except this territory around Cap François and the far south. Even now he is on his way here to take the Cap, and his army swells in number each mile that he advances. It is the largest army ever assembled in the Antilles. Yes, Toussaint comes to capture Cap François, but he does not come at the head of a Spanish army, even though his soldiers wear Spanish uniforms and carry Spanish muskets. He comes as head of an army of the men of St. Domingue. It is his army and he comes to ally it with the army of France, to make it the army of France in St. Domingue. He holds nearly all of

207

St. Domingue in his hands, and he alone will prepare the terms."

"You seem to be well-informed." Armes leaned across the table to Henry. "Perhaps you know what those terms are."

"I should, I helped him write them. Freedom for every man in St. Domingue. Freedom from black fear of white and from white fear of black. That is the aim of Toussaint. I may not agree with him entirely, but I'm willing to go along with him for the present. Even Jean Jacques is willing . . . for the present."

"Toussaint is a great man." Pompee bowed his head.

"Toussaint is a kind man." Marie Louise looked at Henry.

"Toussaint is an intelligent man," Armes added.

"And now Toussaint is a man of power," Henry climaxed. "But do not forget Jean Jacques Dessalines. He too is a man of power, though Toussaint manages to hold him in check."

Toussaint indeed was powerful. That very night the city of Cap François fell to the army of General Toussaint L'Ouverture; fell without a shot being fired; fell without a single fatality, black or white. Couriers came riding out to Sans Souci during the night, but their arrival was so quiet Armes did not awaken until there was a knock on his door.

"Milord, I must awaken you." It was Pompee's voice.

Armes stirred, shook the sleep from his head, and blinked in the candlelight as the door opened.

"Milord, Henry Christophe would have a word with you," Pompee said.

"But, good God, man! This is Henry Christophe's wedding night. Doesn't he know what to do on this night of all nights without routing me out of bed? Tell him to get a pot of lard from the kitchen if he can't accomplish anything. It'll make it easier."

"The advice is good, TiArmes." Henry strode into the room. "But Henry knows more about such things than you do. Goose grease is better than lard—more slippery—and I was already prepared."

The light of Pompee's candle shone full on Henry, making his high black riding boots glisten. Henry held up a hand to silence Armes' laughter.

"Marie Louise will never forgive me for quitting her on this night. Even now you can hear her squalling. Listen!"

And Armes did hear her.

"Henry Christophe! You come back here. Do you hear me? Come back here!"

"But now Henry Christophe wears the pants." He flicked his hands at the tight trousers of white broadcloth. "And the coat, too." He brushed an imaginary speck from the heavy gold embroidery of the blue coat. "And these." He pointed to the stiff gold epaulettes on his shoulder. "And this." He held out the half-moon hat with the white plume.

Armes raised himself up on the pillows.

"Why, Henry, you look exactly like a . . ."

"A general, would you say, TiArmes? And you would be right. Tonight a messenger arrived from Toussaint with this." He unrolled a parchment heavy with seals and ribbons and handed it to Armes. "My commission as a general in the Army of St. Domingue. I leave to join Toussaint. The Cap belongs to him now. He holds all of St. Domingue."

"On your wedding night, Henry?"

"I've already done my duty, twice over. I'm ready to leave even if Marie Louise isn't ready to have me go."

"But these clothes?" Armes regarded the resplendent Henry.

"Sent me by the same messenger from Toussaint."

"Then God ride with you, Henry Christophe, but first, come over here."

Henry strode across the room, the silver spurs on his boots ringing on the floor. He leaned down over the bed and took Armes' proffered hand.

"That's a strong hand, Henry Christophe." Armes nodded his head thoughtfully. "And that's what you said St. Domingue needs. So use that strong hand well, *mon frère*."

Henry regarded his hand for a moment, clenched his fingers tightly together, then opened them and let his hand drop to his side.

"I shall call you 'my brother' too, TiArmes, so *au revoir, mon frère*. I leave Marie Louise with you and the Vicomtesse and Pompee. Take good care of her, and I shall be looking out for you all, even though I am away. You are now under the protection of General Henry Christophe of the Army of St. Domingue. *Au revoir*, TiArmes. I guess we're the first two brothers in the world to have different skins." He walked to the door. "And, TiArmes," he called back, "see if you can't do something about that goddamned caterwauling from my wife. Go down and spank her if she doesn't stop. And, while you're spanking her, tell her that Henry loves her, but that he loves St. Domingue almost as much as he loves her.

This is the moment I have been waiting for. It's my first step, and I wonder where it will lead me."

"It can't lead any higher than being a general, can it?"

"Perhaps not, but being a general on my first day in the army is something, what?"

Henry waved at Armes and left the room, and Armes heard his spurs clatter on the polished boards of the hall. Then they stopped and he heard Henry return. He popped his head in the door and winked at Armes.

"I leave a little legacy for you, TiArmes. With Topaze gone and Ali no longer here, I'm thinking you're going to be needing something just as soon as you get up and about. I don't think you're going to be getting it from the Vicomtesse, either. That kind has to have a wedding band on her finger, just like my Marie Louise. Remember that new little cabin at the far end of the street in the quarters?"

Armes nodded.

"Well, when you get up and about, better visit it. You'll find an old friend of yours there. Justine! She came a-running from the Cap and I kind of needed her around until I got married, so I told her to stay. Found she came in goddamned handy, and so will you. Told her to be expecting you in a few days when you got to feeling better. Won't need any goose grease there, TiArmes."

Before Armes had a chance to answer, Henry was gone. Armes heard the crunch of gravel as he mounted his horse, then the hoofbeats down the drive. After that it was quiet except for the booming of distant drums in the mountains and the sobs of Marie Louise coming through the closed door of her room. Then the sobs quieted down, but the drums continued throughout the night, telling every black peasant in his thatched *caille* that General Henry Christophe was joining General Toussaint L'Ouverture in Cap François.

As always the drums beat their rhythm into Armes' brain and germinated desire. The empty space beside him intensified his loneliness, for he could not reach out his hand and touch warm willing flesh. His sickness had left him weak, but he felt his strength returning with the insistent drumbeats. Slowly he sat up, swung his feet over the side of the bed, and searched with them for his slippers. With these on, he stood up and gathered his robe about him. The house was dark, but he needed no candle to find his way out onto the balcony, and once outside there was a remnant of a moon to guide him. With halting steps he went around the house and down

210

the street of the quarters to the last whitewashed cabin. It took several raps on the door to waken the sleeper, but the door opened and Armes stepped inside, into the warm arms of Justine. The rhythm of the drums took on a real meaning for him in the darkness of her cabin.

26

NOWHERE on earth does habit forge such strong chains as it does in the Tropics. The temperate climes with their four changes of season afford a man no time to settle into too deep a rut. The vagaries of climate force him to change his way of life whether he wills it or not. No sooner does he get used to sitting by a winter fire than suddenly it becomes summer, and he swings in a hammock between the trees and rejoices in the heat of a July evening. But when autumn comes around again and a smoky haze floats over the hills, he is forced again to seek the indoors and establish once more a new pattern, even though it be only for a season.

But in the Tropics, one day follows another with the monotony of uniformity. Day after brilliant day the sun shines with an incandescent fierceness and hot, black night follows amethyst evening without variation. Thus man finds himself doing the same things endlessly, always in the same manner, until the deepening channel of habit becomes smoothly polished and he is content to remain comfortably within it.

In like fashion, the days passed at Sans Souci, broken only by minor events that scarcely ruffled the even tenor of existence. As Armes daily regained strength, he grew more and more adjusted to the day-to-day pattern of tropic existence, until he grew to accept the life almost without boredom. Each day he rose early in the morning, awakened either by Pompee's voice or the cool light of dawn, strained greenly through the flickering vine leaves of the balcony. Followed a leisurely bath in water scented by pungent herbs, which removed the sweat of his night's slumber. After dressing with the help of Hippolyte, one of the servants he was training to be his valet, he appeared for breakfast, clean-shaven and crisp in cool white linen.

The circle of polished mahogany in the dining room was

always set for four—for Armes, Athenée, Marie Louise, and Pompee. On frequent occasions, a fifth place was set for Henry, who returned to Sans Souci whenever his increasing military duties at the Cap allowed him. Breakfast was a leisurely meal, for Pompee had already started the men to work in the fields, and the four of them would sit at table, dawdling over interminable cups of coffee. Their talk touched lightly on the unimportant events of the day that had passed and on the day that was ahead of them—little happenings of their peaceful island in the midst of St. Domingue's turmoil.

The little Negro girl who had been Marie Louise Coidovic, under Athenée's expert tutelage was now assuming the graces of a duchess, not through affectation but through her own innate sense of good breeding and her unconscious imitation of the Vicomtesse. She no longer had any taste for the primitive colors of Africa, and her gowns had become as restrained and well-chosen as Athenée's. The soft slurred Creole was slowly changing into perfect French, and she checked her lapses back into the peasant patois with fluttering annoyance.

Pompee, the smooth polished darkness of his skin strikingly set off by his white starched linen, lavished devotion on the other three, but particularly on Armes. Pompee's air of serious maturity belied his youth. Although he smiled often, he laughed but seldom. Often while sitting at table, he would be worlds away from his companions as he silently conversed with the *loas* of his voodoo gods.

As for Athenée, she had gradually and with reluctance discarded the veils which she had always worn and appeared before them as she was—cool, serene, and lovely from one side; her beauty marred by the purple wine stain on the other. But as the human eye and the human mind quickly adjust to anything outside the accepted norm, those few who loved her soon forgot their initial revulsion. They looked only at her eyes, and in their violet depths they all but forgot the disfigured cheek beneath. Armes had—entirely. Daily contact with her had erased it from his mind.

Armes was leaner since his illness. The tropic sun had tanned his face and arms to a deep sienna, and now he could well have been mistaken for one of the *café-au-lait affranchis*. In truth, his color was deeper than many of them. The ready smile which had always played on his features was more reluctant to show itself these days, and the lines around his mouth were beginning to deepen. The carefree college youth

212

was being transformed into a man. He still laughed with Pompee, played little jokes on Marie Louise, and treated Athenée with all the deference he would have shown a sister, although his heart ached for greater intimacy. He envisioned a relationship in which they shared small secrets; coined little words that had a special meaning to them alone; stole glances that spoke of shared moments; and experienced the deep contentment of complete satisfaction in each other's arms. So often it would be on the tip of his tongue to speak of these things, but Athenée was always on her guard, tender and charming but cool and impersonal. She was all friendly solicitude and helpfulness, but intimacy stopped there.

When breakfast was finished, she would leave her position behind the tall silver coffee urn and Marie Louise would follow. They might walk together through the gardens, filling their arms with damask roses, or seek the seclusion of Athenée's apartments at the rear of the house, not to appear again until midday. After they had left, Pompee would push his chair back from the table and depart for the fields. More and more the management of the plantation was falling into Pompee's capable hands. The sweat and labor of the fields no longer appealed to Armes, and he was happy to delegate the major responsibilities to Pompee.

Between Henry and Pompee, they managed Sans Souci well. DuBois and his wife had left. Open-minded as the Frenchman had been, he felt he would lose caste in the white community by working for Henry, who was now the ostensible owner of the plantation. DuBois was not the only one who had left. Many of the former slaves had gone, most of whom had been the undesirables. The worthless, the malcontents, and the lazy had drifted off, some seeking a precarious independence in the mountains and others joining the army. In their places, attracted by the fair wages which Henry had offered and the added inducement that they would not be working for a *blanc*, a group of willing workers had assembled at Sans Souci. Most of them were ambitious men who, through family ties or a love of the land, did not care for the more adventurous life of the army.

The old slave quarters was growing into a village. New houses were being built and streets being laid out. In the center of the little town, Pompee and the men had erected a large *houmfort* where Pompee presided over voodoo rites. It was a simple structure, merely a huge high-pitched thatched roof supported on posts with a floor of pounded

213

dirt. Adjoining it was the small building which housed the altar and which contained a special room, dedicated to Erzuli, complete with bed and embroidered covers. Directly across from it, Armes had had a place cleared for the eventual erection of a Christian church. This was also under the supervision of Pompee, for to him the crucified Jesus was merely a white Damballah, and the pink and white virgin in her blue robes represented the light-skinned goddess Erzuli. In fact, little by little, Pompee was adapting much of the Christian ritual into his own voodoo services, intermingling the two so that it was difficult to tell where one left off and the other began.

The Negroes at Sans Souci did not resent Armes. As a white, he had seemed a person superior to them, but they were beginning to lose their awe of whites. They were not quite sure of his position at Sans Souci, since he exercised very little direct authority. He had no desire to give the lie to the story that Henry owned the plantation, for the general belief in Henry's ownership insured safety for all. His residence there was tolerated on the grounds that he was General Christophe's friend—a fact that was supported by the times he and Henry rode together through the fields.

There was always plenty of work to be done until the big bell at the plantation rang at noon. Then it was time for the midday meal and the long afternoon *somme,* for Henry had decided that if the whites could sleep in the afternoon, so could the Negroes. Once again the four at the big house appeared at table, and once more the inconsequential conversation was resumed. Athenée nursed the sick, welcomed new arrivals with christening clothes, saw that sanitation and cleanliness were observed throughout the little town, and conducted herself, albeit with considerably more tenderness and understainding, in the same manner as other French women had done on other big plantations. Marie Louise, her apt pupil, took a more active part in the instruction of the village women. She taught them how to cook better food and keep cleaner houses. With her experience in mending sheets and pillowcases at the Couronne, she was able to instruct them in sewing. These activities were their topics of conversation throughout the meals.

After dinner came the *somme.* Armes and Pompee retired to their rooms, separated by thick walls from those of Marie Louise and Athenée. Pompee no longer slept in the damp basement, although he still kept the room there for his

214

private devotions at his voodoo altar. During Armes' illness he had occupied the little room adjoining Armes' and at Armes' suggestion, he continued to occupy it. Armes and Pompee remained in their rooms until the whole house had settled down to its afternoon slumber, and its quiet was unbroken by so much as the tiptoeing of a servant through the halls. It was then that Armes and Pompee quietly opened the door of Armes' room—so quietly that no telltale latch click would betray them—and walked silently down the empty hall, out onto the balcony, and down the horseshoe stairs in front. Here they separated, each with the unspoken understanding of where the other was going.

Pompee, cognizant of the part Ali had played in Armes' life, made no secret to Armes of the fact that he preferred sleeping with one of his several *hunsis*—youths he had chosen because of their good looks to be his acolytes at voodoo ceremonies. Such was the custom for a voodoo *papaloi* in Africa, and it was equally acceptable in St. Domingue. One of the *hunsi* boys was always waiting for Pompee in the little house beside the voodoo *houmfort*, and they slept together in Erzuli's bed during the hours of the *somme*.

Armes understood. As for himself, he paid a daily visit to the little white cabin where Justine was now permanently installed. It was a physical act which was necessary to his well-being—something which his body demanded daily—but it was purely mechanical, merely a draining off of his desire. At times he tired of Justine, but he always returned the next day, although on occasion Pompee had hinted that he could supply another of his *hunsis*, if Armes were inclined. Several of them, he implied, had expressed a desire to know a white man. But Armes was not interested. The period with Ali had been a strange and unnatural interlude which Armes now realized had been occasioned merely by their proximity and the lack of a suitable woman at Sans Souci. Ali had been convenient and useful and Armes often wondered if he had not cared far more for Ali than he did for Justine. He did not regret the interlude. But he had no desire to return to such practices—at least not while Justine or another like her was at hand. She served a purpose, as had Ali, but she served only a part of it. Armes wanted something more than the quick explosion he found in a trained prostitute's embraces. He wanted love and love meant Athenée. But he was content to bide his time. In the meantime, Justine served his needs.

After the hot hours of the afternoon *somme,* the plantation would come to life and there would be a few more hours of work in the fields. Armes and Pompee would meet with a meaningful glance which told of how they had spent the afternoon, have their horses saddled and ride about the plantation, checking on the work accomplished that day while the sinking sun had lost its power to scorch.

At seven, the big bell sounded and the field hands started joyfully back to their quarters. With the swift descent of the tropical night, the house servants would light candles, protected by big glass hurricane shields, all through the house, and after a dinner that was more formal than their midday meal, they would retire to the salon, where Athenée would play the pianoforte or teach Marie Louise to play. Perhaps there would be more talk as the two women bent their heads over needlepoint or embroidered the panel of a new gown. On other nights they would all move out onto the broad balcony to enjoy the coolness of the evening. Far up in the mountains the drums would begin and as the night progressed, so did their insistent rhythm, coming from points far distant and near at hand.

Pompee often left them in the evening to preside, along with his corps of *hunsis,* at voodoo rites in other towns and villages, and on those occasions he rarely appeared until breakfast the next morning. On those evenings, Armes was left alone with the two women. When the hands of the clock right-angled at nine, Marie Louise would begin to yawn, patting her mouth prettily as she had seen Athenée do, then the two women would gather up their crewels, slip their needles into their tapestries, and bid Armes good night. He would linger a few moments, perhaps walk to the head of the balcony stairs, drink in the rose-scented air from the garden below, and listen to the drums, trying to determine from which plantation they came. The drums had never lost their aphrodisiac effect on him and often their insistent rhythm, particularly with Athenée so lately near him, would stimulate him beyond the point of control and he would steal off, through the perfumed darkness, to rap for the second time that day on the door of Justine's cabin. It would open and he would find the quick consolation of her professional lips. On other nights, too sleepy to make the second trip to the cabin, he would merely retire to his huge canopied bed with its voluminous draperies of white netting.

Such was the daily pattern of life at Sans Souci, broken

216

only by visits from Henry. When he arrived he would come dashing up to the house, resplendent in his general's uniform, swing Marie Louise off her feet with a fierce embrace, and disperse his gold-braided aides-de-camp to the village to find entertainment. Sometimes if Marie Louise begged him hard enough, he would remain all night, and then the talk would be of St. Domingue and politics. On those occasions the drums did not bother Armes and he would be content to sit and talk with Henry, for Henry always brought news and there would be much to discuss.

Henry had early developèd a bitter hatred for the little Corsican corporal, that Napoleon Bonaparte who had crawled to the top of the heap of slain bodies that the Revolution had provided and was now casting a threatening shadow over all of France. Fortunately, for the present at least, Napoleon was far too busy consolidating his position in France to pay much attention to faraway St. Domingue. Toussaint was competent to direct the colony, for it was still a French possession. Toussaint had conquered the Spanish armies of Santo Domingo after having been a part of them. He had repulsed the greedy English who had eyed the colony suspiciously from Jamaica while France was recovering from her self-inflicted wounds. Now Toussaint was governor general of St. Domingue for life, duly elected by the inhabitants, white, black, and mulatto. But, he was only governor general, duly constituted by France. He was loyal to the mother country. Not all of Toussaint's advisers approved of his loyalty. Certainly not Dessalines! But he was keeping quiet, trying hard to forget he had been a black slave to a black master while he designed ever gaudier uniforms and hung even more lavish glass jewels on his mistress, Topaze.

Henry Christophe was also a general, along with the mulatto Pétion and a score of others. St. Domingue was rich in black generals in ornate uniforms, most of whom wished St. Domingue for themselves, but Henry kept them in line and managed to keep them loyal to Toussaint, although he himself did not approve of Toussaint's blind passivity. But Henry knew that St. Domingue could not stand on its own feet just now, and his hatred of Napoleon was engendered by fear of what the Corsican might do. Henry knew that Napoleon had not forgotten the once rich colony of St. Domingue. He neither forgot nor forgave, but since a few livres had started to trickle back to France, Napoleon was content to let Toussaint govern. Henry knew it would not be for long.

Henry was waiting. But while he waited he nursed his hatred for Napoleon.

One afternoon, after the big house had come to life from the daily *somme*, and Armes and Pompee had returned from the sweaty embraces of Justine and the particular *hunsi* of the day, Henry Christophe arrived at Sans Souci without the usual retinue of aides. He greeted Armes warmly, bowed formally to Athenée, and hurriedly escorted Marie Louise down the hall to their room and bolted the door. When he reappeared a few hours later he waved aside the invitation to dinner and took only a moment to say good-bye to Armes, who was sitting on the balcony.

"I must get back to the Cap," he called from his horse. "There's hell to pay there. A message just arrived from France that Napoleon has been made first consul, and it's rumored that he is going to send his own governor general to St. Domingue." He was gone before Armes had a chance to answer.

That night the drums disturbed Armes, but their message was not blood-warming. Instead it seemed to be a dire warning of some great disaster to come. He tried to read the meaning of their frenetic throbbing, but never since the night that he had accompanied Henry, Toussaint, and Dessalines had the meaning of their reverberations been entirely clear to him. The ladies had retired and he was alone on the balcony with no desire to sleep or to revisit Justine. If Pompee had been there, he could have interpreted the drums' message for him, but Pompee was away. With nervous steps, timed to the rhythm of the drums, he paced the balcony, watching the weaving lights of fireflies in the garden below. At length, tired of the endless pacing, he went to his room, but the thought of Henry, who had been in the house so recently behind a closed door with Marie Louise, filled his thoughts with disturbing images. Henry possessed something which was denied to Armes, and something which Armes longed desperately to have. It was a longing which could not be assuaged by Justine's embraces. It was the soul-searing loneliness of a man without a woman.

He quitted his room and walked aimlessly into the big salon. The candles guttered in the chandelier and the girandoles; the armchairs yawned silently; the ticking of the ormolu clock beat on his brain like a hammer. Suddenly he knew he could stand this terrible isolation no longer. He must have someone to talk to. Who? He ran across the room and tugged at the embroidered bell cord which hung beside the door. The long, bullioned tassel felt heavy in his hands and its metal threads scratched him, but l.e was rewarded by the jangle of a bell on the floor below and then by the shuffling sounds of footsteps on the stairs. The boy Hippolyte entered the room, and bobbed his head in a cursory obeisance to Armes.

"Are you ready to go to bed, M'sieu Armes?"

Armes hesitated. Perhaps that would be the thing to do. But no! He found sufficient courage to say the words he had been speaking to himself in his thoughts for so long.

"Later. Go now to the room of the Vicomtesse. Knock on her door. If she answers, ask her if she would join me for a few moments on the balcony." The boy shuffled away, and Armes walked outside.

In a few moments she came down the hall and out onto the balcony. Armes rose and pointed to a chair, and as she sat down, she arranged the folds of her stiff taffeta *robe de chambre* about her.

"Are you ill, Armes?" she asked, a little line creasing her forehead.

He denied it with a shake of his head.

"Oh, I am so glad." The line disappeared. "When Hippolyte came and said you wanted to see me, I feared perhaps the fever had returned."

"No, Athenée, I've had no relapse. I am well and yes, I am happy after a fashion. Our life here together has been pleasant—yes?"

"Yes, Armes, it has been most pleasant, and that now makes it all the more difficult for me to say something which I have been dreading to say."

He looked down at her in surprise.

"You have something to say to me, Athenée?"

She sighed. "Something which I do not wish to say, but as we are alone here, this seems to be as good a time as any to say it. Please believe me, it is not something I want to say."

"But on the other hand. I have something which I really do want to say."

"Then say it, Armes. After all, what you have to say must be the most important, because you asked me to come here."

He walked over to the balustrade and looked down in the garden, then turned suddenly. His words came quickly, vibrating with hopefulness.

"Will you marry me, Athenée?"

"No, Armes, I shall not," she answered without hesitation. She rose from her chair to stand beside him. Again the moonlight touched her face as it had that night aboard ship. Armes slipped his arm around her, his hands feeling the uncorseted warmth of her flesh under the fabric.

"Why don't you want to marry me, Athenée?"

She turned toward him, letting his arm slip away from her.

"There are many reasons, Armes. Once I married a man with the full realization that he was marrying me through ambition, not for love. I endured that marriage. I put up with his graceless pawings, his obscene perversions, the tortures of his little whips, and his vile tempers. Perhaps it would have made that marriage easier if I could have felt but one small spark of love for him or one atom of desire for his body. I could feel neither, so I endured the lonely days and suffered through the hellish nights."

"But that is over, Athenée."

"Yes, it is over, and I thank God. I try never to think of René, because if I do, I might think of him with some regret, since possibly I might have tried harder to understand his warped mind and thus made things easier for us both. But, as you say, it is over."

"Then marry me!" This time Armes drew her to him and kissed her. To his surprise, she accepted his kiss and even returned it. Then she pushed him away, very gently but firmly.

"I said one man married me through ambition. I could not let another man marry me through pity." Her voice trembled and she reached for the bit of cambric in her sleeve to wipe her eyes.

"Who said anything about pity? I asked you to marry me because I love you."

She shook her head sadly. "You love me, Armes? Oh, how much I wish you did, but even if you did, I would not marry you because . . ." She turned her face away from him. "I love you too much. Yes, I must tell you that, and then I pray you will forget it. I love you so deeply, so thoroughly, so finally that it is all my life. But you do not love me, Armes."

"Why do you say that? Are you God that you know my feelings for you?"

"Because I know men, *mon cher*. You are indeed a lazy lot, you men. You do not seek love. You wait for it to come to you. Topaze came here to you, and you thought you loved her. Now I have come and you have become so accustomed to me that you think you love me, whereas you really care no more for me than the colored girl who lives in the cabin in the quarters. Look around you. Look at St. Domingue. Every mulatto that you see is a living proof of what I say. Mere propinquity breeds what you men delight in calling love. Frenchmen on plantations all over this island have found their sort of love in the arms of the nearest Negro wench—such love as you find daily down in that little white cabin. I am handy, Armes, and you have become accustomed to seeing me around. My presence has become as comfortable as an old shoe. But that does not mean you love me. Perhaps you want me. Yes, I'll agree to that, but if you have any real feeling for me it is only pity. Because of this!" She lifted her head and pointed to her face.

"Oh, how wrong you are, Athenée."

"Wrong? Oh, no! And don't think I am jealous of your pretty Justine—you see, I even know her name. No, Armes, even if I knew you loved me as much as I love you, I would not marry you. Here, when we are together with only Marie Louise and Pompee and the house servants, you do not think of my appearance. But we cannot always stay here, hidden from the world. Some day we must leave; go out into the world; mix with people again. Have you ever thought of that?"

"No, and why should I think of it when it would be a perfectly normal thing to do? We shall not remain hidden at Sans Souci all our lives."

"For you, yes, it would be normal, and for any other woman too, but not for me. Oh, Armes, I can see the other women looking at me, appraising me, and then looking at you with a pitying sidelong glance. I can even hear what they would be saying. 'What a tragedy! Poor Mr. Holbrook! He's such a handsome man to be saddled with that poor woman.' Then my heart would break inside me and I would die a thousand deaths. Once again I would have to seek seclusion and hide myself from the world, as I have always hidden myself. You would soon begin to hate me for a stupid, neurotic, and foolish woman, while I would still be adoring you."

He walked to the head of the stairs and peered out into the darkness.

"That would never happen." His voice was full of assurance. "Never!"

"No, indeed, it never shall." Her words were as positive as his. "And now, having told you that I love you, I cannot stay here any longer. I am leaving Sans Souci, Armes. That is what I had to tell you."

"But where are you going?"

"Back to France. I will not rejoin my parents, but seek sanctuary in some obscure little village where the peasants will accept the tragedy of my poor face. I do not know where I shall go, except that it must be away from St. Domingue . . . and you." She slid down into the chair and bowed her head in her hands.

Suddenly he turned from his contemplation of the garden and stumbled toward her. He crumpled at her feet, his tall body arched toward her, his hands groping for her, his head seeking consolation in her lap.

"Athenée, Athenée, Athenée! Don't leave me. Let us stay here as we've been staying. I'll never mention love to you again, if you'll just stay. Don't leave me, I beg of you." He felt the stiff taffeta of her robe against his cheeks and under it the warmth of her flesh. His kiss burned through the fabric, his tears wet the cloth, and there was a lump in his throat which he found impossible to swallow. What would life be like without Athenée—he a white man drowned in a sea of black faces, with only a long procession of Justines to comfort him? He wanted to stay in St. Domingue, but how could he if she were not with him?

Her fingers gently twined among the thick black curls on his head.

"It is a difficult thing for a woman to see a man weep, Armes, for men do not weep easily. That is a woman's privilege, but I shall not resort to tears, for now, in truth, I realize that you do love me. Surely a man would not weep from pity alone. And although your love for me may not be as all-encompassing as mine for you, I believe that there is real love for me in your heart. I glory in it, but even your love for me will not persuade me to marry you, although it may well convince me to remain with you."

"Oh, Athenée!" He did not try to suppress his sobs now. The movement of his head had caused her robe to separate and now his lips touched her flesh. Her hands which had touched his hair so lightly now clenched tightly.

"No, Armes, I shall not marry you. I will not tie you to me, but leave you free to leave me when you wish. So do not ask me again . . . ever. And yet, *mon bien-aimé,* I will

222

love you more than anyone ever loved you before. Shall we let it go at that?"

He raised his head and looked at her, joy chasing surprise from his eyes.

"You mean . . . ?"

"I mean that I shall not leave you until the time comes that you wish me to go or that I feel it would be better for you if I left. Come, beloved." She stood up, and the feather touch of her hands lifted him beside her. "If we love each other tonight why think about tomorrow?"

As he kissed her mouth, the drums began to throb wildly. Their message was no longer filled with fear but with love. He was a man and she was a woman and the night was black and rich with fecund tropical heat. The drums spoke to him and he rose to meet their message. This time he did not need to seek Justine. With his arm around Athenée, they walked into the hall. The candles had become floating wicks in pools of molten wax. He blew them out, one by one, as they traversed the darkness of the hall. Strange wraiths appeared at the door of his room. He thought he could see Ali's flashing smile and catch the odor of Topaze's tawny flesh. Then the wraiths vanished as they passed through the door, closing it behind them.

His lips sought hers again and his eager hands undid the taffeta ribbons of her *robe de chambre* before he lifted it from her shoulders and let it billow to the floor. Into its collapsing pile, he kicked his thin slippers and then loosened his belt. His trousers fell to the floor and he stepped out of them as he bore her to the bed in his arms and placed her in the spot of moonlight that whitened the sheets. He lowered himself beside her until their lips were close.

"After tonight, the little white cabin will be empty," he whispered to her. "I shall give it to Pompee to house his *hunsis.*"

The drums continued to answer each other from mountain to mountain with a primitive rhythm that timed Armes' love-making. Then, one by one, as the dawn approached, the drums became quiet. The night was still and so was Armes, who slept, his dark head pillowed on Athenée's breast, his hands mute and motionless against the pallor of her skin.

27

IN THE weeks that followed, with the inspiration of Athenée's love, a bright new meaning motivated Armes' life. No longer was he content to drift from day to day in that narrow indolent groove that habit had so comfortably worn smooth for him. Now, in a burst of activity, he found the days not long enough to accomplish all the things he wanted to do. His overwhelming desire was to make Sans Souci the embodiment of all his dreams—a place of perfection—the very center and circumference of his world. By so doing, he realized, he could keep Athenée forever at his side. As he would never be able to convince her to go into the larger world outside, he must make the little world of Sans Souci large enough and interesting enough to hold her and satisfy him. It was the world of Sans Souci or nothing.

But . . . and so much hinged on that word! He must make sure that all his efforts would not be in vain. It was impossible to build and create and expand if one felt that eventually it might all be destroyed. For the first time he realized how absolutely he and everything that he possessed in St. Domingue depended on Henry Christophe and the dangerously thin thread of Henry's power and protection. Henry was popular, yes—at the moment. He was Toussaint's general of the North as Dessalines and Pétion were generals of the West and South. But a generalship in the Army of St. Domingue was not a position of any great permanence. Generals had a way of disappearing just as quickly as they appeared. The man of the hour was merely that—the man of the *hour*. Tomorrow he might be dead or forgotten.

Armes realized that his entire happiness with Athenée depended on establishing their world at Sans Souci. Sans Souci, in turn, depended on Henry Christophe and Henry Christophe depended on . . . what? That was the important question. It was entirely up to Armes to make sure that he was building on a firm foundation, and that firm foundation must be a responsible government in St. Domingue and, of necessity, one in which Henry Christophe would occupy a place of prominence. Perhaps Henry could accomplish this

224

alone, but he could accomplish it more quickly and better with Armes' help.

Armes knew Henry—his capabilities and his limitations. He admired and respected him, even loved him with that deep love which one man can feel for another—a love which is far greater than a man can feel for a woman, for it is a love without passion. Being devoid of passion, it is not subject to whims or vagaries. It is built on mutual respect, mutual admiration, and mutual assistance. Armes realized that Henry needed him and that he could help Henry. He had learned more at Harvard than how to conjugate Latin verbs. Let Henry have the benefit of his education. The decision made, he acted upon it immediately—in fact, that very morning.

Tom and Lalla were saddled and brought around to the foot of the front steps while Armes bade a lingering *au revoir* to Athenée. He would willingly have taken her with him, but he knew she would refuse to go, so Pompee was to accompany him. Armes regarded the horses below and for a fleeting moment saw a flowing white *jellaba* and a flashing white smile. He could never look at Lalla, who had found her way back to Sans Souci the night that Ali was slain, without seeing the laughing boy who had once ridden her. Now Pompee rode Lalla. Pompee was just as devoted and loyal as Ali, but in a different way. Unlike Ali, who had been jealous and possessive, feminine and capricious, Pompee made no claims on Armes. Ali was a chapter in Armes' life which he found difficult to close. His thoughts were on the boy as he mounted Tom.

"Can't seem to get the little fellow out of my mind, Pompee." As always when Armes spoke of Ali, his voice choked in his throat.

"I talked with Ali last night, milord, and Ali sent a message to you."

Tom started and carried Armes a few yards down the drive. Suddenly Armes wheeled Tom around. The full import of Pompee's words had not penetrated his consciousness immediately.

"You what . . . ?"

"I talked with Ali last night."

"But Ali is dead."

"To you, yes, milord, but we who are versed in voodoo have a way of talking with those who pass through the gate of Papa Legba."

225

"I don't believe it."

Pompee smiled and shook his head sadly.

"I do not ask you to believe it, milord. Wait! Someday you will realize the power of voodoo. But even if you do do not believe in it now, believe in Pompee, for he would never lie to you."

Armes rode on but drew up his horse again. This time he hesitated a moment before speaking. "But if Ali did speak to you, what did the little fellow say?"

"That he had a very important message for you, milord, which he must give to you himself."

"Ali would have been jealous of you, Pompee, yet I know you are not jealous of him nor his memory. Therefore I have to believe you. I would like to hear Ali's message. May I?"

"When the time comes, milord. Then I shall let you know."

They rode on through the brilliant morning light. What had once been only a narrow, rutted path to Cap François was now gradually becoming a wide, well-traveled road. Henry, his aides, his couriers, and his messengers had widened it. The little village that had sprung up from the old slave quarters at Sans Souci was rapidly gaining size and importance. It even had a name. The peasants called it Milot. The name had puzzled Armes at first, and he had asked Pompee about it.

"Milot? Milord!" Pompee had smiled. "You see, Ali really named the village. It was he who first called you milord. Then after he died I used the same name in memory of him. The peasants heard me call you that, and they began to call the place where they live *la ville de Milord*. But our peasants are a lazy lot when it comes to words and they couldn't pronounce the English word very well, so they changed it to Milot, which better fits their Creole tongues."

Armes was pleased. He had thought of raising some sort of a memorial to Ali, something that would perpetuate the boy's memory. Now he had a village that Pompee said Ali had named—inadvertently to be sure—where Ali's memory and his sacrifice might be enshrined. In a church, perhaps! Yes, that was it, a church! But could it be a church? As far as Armes knew, he himself had been Ali's only god, but he presumed that Ali was nominally Mohammedan. Yet was a Mohammedan very different from a Christian? Jehovah and Allah were the same God, simply interpreted a little differently by Jesus and Mohammed. Then why not a church for

226

Ali? It need not necessarily take the outward form of a Christian church, even though it would be dedicated to the Christian religion. As Armes thought about it, he saw pictures in his mind of the domed mosques of Islam. That was it! It would take the form of a church that looked like a mosque out of remembrance to Ali, but it would be dedicated to the gentle white prophet who had been crucified on a cross even as Ali had been crucified on the ground.

Armes decided to ask Henry's opinion.

But when he and Pompee arrived at the Cap and were ushered into the white and gold salon of some planter's town house which now served as Henry's headquarters, Henry's exuberant welcome left no room for questions about churches. But Armes did not forget his idea. In time the church was built, and even today visitors to the little town of Milot can see the domed church—a silent memorial to a boy of Morocco who came many miles from his home beneath the snow-covered Atlas to redden the earth of Haiti with his blood.

This was a day when Henry was overflowing with healthy animal vitality and abounding good spirits. He grinned widely at Armes from the head of a long table, around which were seated a number of full-blooded Negroes and a few mulattoes. Henry presided proudly in all his splendor, but he paled into sartorial insignificance beside the fantastically resplendent uniforms of the others. Henry's tight white trousers and dark blue coat were lost in the multicolored blaze of scarlet, emerald, purple, and orange. Armes estimated that there was enough gold braid around that one table to bedeck all the generals of all the armies of the world. From Henry's white-toothed grin, Armes knew that the big fellow was happy about something. He looked up and winked at Armes, pushing the papers on the table before him aside with impatience. His long fingers bundled others together into an untidy roll and shoved them into the hands of a slender mulatto who sat beside him. He waved the people out the door and, once they were gone, held out his hands to Armes.

"Mon frère," he cried. "Such a surprise, and am I glad to see you here! How is my Marie Louise and your Vicomtesse?" Without waiting for an answer he jumped up from the table and ran to intercept Armes, threw his arms around him, and practically smothered him. "Just this afternoon I was coming to Sans Souci. Now we can ride back together. I have news for you, *mais oui,* such news!"

Armes extricated himself from the clutter of medals on Henry's chest and rubbed his scratched face. He had the feeling that if he were to touch a match to Henry, he would explode in a skyrocket blaze of glory.

"It must be good news."

"Wait till you hear! Today I am not only a general but a governor. Yes, today I am the governor of the Département du Nord, the richest province in St. Domingue. Toussaint has made me governor of all the blacks and whites in this province. I, Henry Christophe, former stableboy at the Couronne, am now a governor."

Armes retreated a step and bowed in mock obeisance.

"Your Excellency. Is that how I must address you now?"

Henry's gay mood departed and his smile turned into a worried frown.

"My Excellency! You mean my Stupidity! What do I, an ex-slave, know about being a governor? Oh TiArmes, teach me! Tell me what to do and how to do it. Teach me how to eat with a fork and not gobble my food; teach me to dress like a governor and not like those dressed-up monkeys you saw here; teach me how to talk with another man when he addresses me as 'your Excellency'. Oh, TiArmes, there is so much to learn and so little time in which to learn it. I want to be a real governor, not some nigger son-of-a-bitch dressed up in fancy clothes."

"You'll be a governor, Henry, a real one."

"But not one like Jean Jacques! Dessalines is a clever man in battle and a great soldier, but as a governor . . . *mon Dieu!* He has eyes only for that mulatto trollop, and when he is not sleeping with her, he's dressing up in fancy uniforms and, believe it or not, the goddamned gorilla is learning to dance. Picture him dancing! What does he care what happens in his province? Does it matter to him that weeds choke the cane fields, that the wheels of the sugar mills are rusting, and that the coffee drops from the trees?"

"From what I know of Dessalines, I doubt that it does."

"Jean Jacques doesn't give one good goddamn just as long as he fills his belly with food, shoots two or three whites every day, minces to the scrape of fiddles, and rides his filly Topaze all night." Henry paced the length of the table and back. "I want to be a real governor, TiArmes. To hell with the wenches, the uniforms, and all the other folderol."

"Look, Henry! You'll be a real governor because I'm going to help you be one."

228

"How, TiArmes?"

"In any way and every way I can."

They walked back to the table and sat down. Armes tidied up the disorderly pile of papers, sorted them, and stacked them. When he had finished, Henry reached over and picked up a letter from the top of the pile.

"What does that one say, TiArmes?" he asked.

Armes took the paper and read the spidery handwriting.

"It is a letter from the widow Beaumont. She requests the return of her town house." Armes looked around him. "By the way, isn't this the Beaumont house?"

"Damn her for a meddling bitch and damn her miserable hovel." Henry leaned across the table. "TiArmes, you know I cannot read or write."

Armes nodded.

"And now I do not have time to learn."

Armes agreed. "No, Henry, you do not have time, and it places you in a difficult position. Words on paper can be the most important things on earth. Words can affect a man's whole future or the future of the country he governs. I'll help you all I can, but I cannot always be with you. You must have somebody you can trust, because if anyone should read words to you and deliberately change them, even one word, it could be disastrous. Do you know of anyone?"

"By God, yes, TiArmes. Outside of you and my wife and the Vicomtesse and your Pompee there is only one I can trust, and that's my little friend Valentin. Valentin Vastey! You know him, TiArmes, he's one of my aides-de-camp."

"The little mulatto?"

"The same. I saved his life once." Henry reached for the bell cord and pulled it. "And he's never forgotten."

"But he's a mulatto, Henry. Are you sure you can trust him?"

"Almost as much as I can you, TiArmes."

The door opened and a dapper young man appeared. His light skin shone, his black hair was carefully oiled to remove the curl, and he seemed to have been poured into his immaculate white uniform.

"You rang, your Excellency?" he asked.

"Come over here and sit down, Valentin my boy." Henry's toe pushed out one of the chairs on the opposite side of the table. "This is Monsieur Holbrook of Sans Souci. You have met him before, *n'est-ce pas?*"

"*Enchanté,* Monsieur Holbrook." Vastey extended a deli-

229

cate brown hand with elaborately manicured nails before he sat down.

The tip of Henry's tongue showed red against his lips as he looked from one to the other. Then he brought his fist down on the table.

"I'm a governor now, Valentin. You know that, but you don't know that I'm going to be a goddamned good governor, thanks to you and TiArmes. When anything comes up that is particularly important, you send for TiArmes, then the three of us will sit down and discuss it between us. In that way, we'll arrive at the right decision. From now on, Valentin, you're going to be my secretary. That's all, you can go now."

Vastey got up to leave, but Armes laid a restraining hand on his shoulder. "No, Monsieur Vastey, that is not all. Let us accomplish one thing before you leave." He picked up the letter they had been discussing before and handed it to Henry. "What about the widow Beaumont?"

"To hell with that old white bitch! I said when anything important comes up." He threw the letter on the floor.

Armes retrieved the letter and put it back in Henry's hand.

"But this *is* important, Henry. It's important to her, and therefore you must make it important to yourself. Remember she is one of the people you govern. She has come to you as governor, and it lies in your power right now to make her a friend or an enemy. This is her house, right?"

"Right!"

"Then, Henry, if you want to be a good governor, you must do the right thing. It is only right that she have her own house back."

Henry handed the letter to Vastey.

"Give her back her goddamned house. We'll find some other place to go."

Armes laughed at Henry's sputtering.

"Now. Henry, you've done the right thing. I don't know who the widow Beaumont is, but I can assure you that you will have made a friend. From now on every time your name is mentioned in the worthy lady's presence, she will praise you, and all her friends will hear about your benevolence. That's being a good governor, Henry." Armes reached into an inside pocket and drew out a piece of paper from his wallet. He removed the pile of papers from before Henry and laid the single piece of paper on the table.

Henry stared at the words on the paper.

"What in hell is that?" he growled.

230

Vastey reached over and took it, held it up, and read it. His eyes opened wide in surprise and he looked at Armes in astonishment.

"Well, what is it, what is it?" Henry said impatiently.

"That, your Excellency," Vastey said with a tremble in his voice, "is a draft for ten thousand English pounds, drawn to the order of General Henry Christophe on the firm of Durham, Brown and Company of Cap François and London, and signed by Monsieur Armes Holbrook.

Henry grabbed the paper from Vastey's limp hand and looked at it blankly.

"But why, TiArmes, and what for?" The draft floated from his hand to the table. To hide the tears in his eyes, he blew his nose hard on a silk kerchief.

Armes pushed back his chair and stood up. He took the check and replaced it in Henry's hand.

"When I drew that draft I did not know what purpose it could be used for except to help you. But now I see. You are governor of St. Domingue now, Henry, and you must live like one. This"—he pointed to the draft—"will build you a new home the like of which has never been seen in Cap François. The Negroes will come and look at it and they will say, 'This belongs to our governor, Henry Christophe. He is a *gros nègre* to live in a house like that.' Then the whites will come and they will say, 'He is a powerful man, that Henry Christophe.' You will enjoy your new home because you will know that it was not built through the sweat and suffering of your fellow men but through the friendship which I have for you. Take it, Henry, and start work on your new home tomorrow, and if that is not enough, there will be more."

Henry's eyes were fastened on the piece of paper.

"Some day, TiArmes, I shall try to repay you."

"You can do it now, Henry. When Vastey"—he nodded to the young lieutenant—"chooses an architect for your new house, tell him that I too have need of an architect—the best in St. Domingue. I have decided to build a church."

"You getting religion, TiArmes?"

"No, but I want a church."

"Then you shall have one." Henry rose slowly from the table. His downcast eyes crept up to meet Armes' and he grinned, then started to laugh. Great guffaws tumbled out of his mouth.

"Now you can see, TiArmes, how stupid I really am. Here

231

I was telling you all this great news about my being made governor and you knew it all the time. Otherwise you wouldn't have brought that."

"Yes, Henry, Pompee heard the news when we arrived at the Cap this morning, and I wanted to make you a little present to celebrate your good fortune."

They started to walk out of the room together. Henry's playful slap on Armes' back would have felled almost any other man.

"Goddam, TiArmes, Governor Henry Christophe's got the finest brother in the world." His voice sank to a hoarse whisper. "And it's not the money, TiArmes. Remember how you offered me your hand the first day we met?"

"We've come a long way since then, Henry."

"And we've got a long way to go, TiArmes, and oh, *mon frère,* we've got so little time."

28

THE cities of St. Domingue were dancing a frenzied riga-doon on the crumbling edges of their own graves. Laws, government, morals, and customs were all so impermanent that license prevailed, and it was enough to live frantically for the day, because tomorrow might never come. A feverish, hectic gaiety pervaded the entire colony, and Cap François had become the pace setter for the island, adopting every fantastic innovation. Once its wickedness had been a matter of lovely octoroon mistresses sequestered in charming little flower-covered villas, but now the city was a welter of jerry-built wine shops, night-blooming cabarets which vied with each other in staging lewd orgies, and waterfront whore-houses whose painted *dominicaines* were as willing to slit a throat as they were to spread their legs. All of these establishments were well-patronized, and some even boasted a long line of loose-lipped males waiting for admission.

Although the cities were living on borrowed time, the country was quieter. After a long day's work in the fields, the peasants were willing to trudge home, eat their mess of beans and rice, and crawl into bed. Saturday nights were the exception, however, for Sunday was a day of rest, and even a black buck with aching muscles could not resist the blood-warming message of the drums. It was on Saturday nights that the voodoo *houmfort* in the little village of Milot blazed with light and Pompee presided over the *vévés*—those mystical symbols of the voodoo gods, drawn on the *houmfort* floor with white corn meal as an invitation to the *loas* of the gods to enter into the human forms of their worshipers. Sometimes, on these Saturday nights, the *loa* would ride Pompee too strongly, and he would return to his room at Sans Souci in utter exhaustion. On some nights he did not return at all, sharing the bed of Erzuli with one of his *hunsis*.

On this particular Saturday evening, Pompee had canceled the voodoo meeting and called the people of the neighboring villages together for a *bamboche*—a country dance—at the *houmfort* in Milot. He said the time was not propitious for a voodoo *assemblée* because the gods were silent and for this reason he had substituted a purely social affair for the religious meeting.

Henry and Marie Louise were together in the Cap, supervising details of the new house, and Armes and Athenée were alone at Sans Souci. Pompee had invited them to the dance, but they knew that their presence would put a damper on the festivities and, in truth, they preferred to be alone. They had dismissed all the house servants, dined *à deux*, and then sought the cool evening breezes of the balcony, where they sat in deep basket chairs, hardly able to see each other except as patches of dim white in the darkness. A love such as theirs demanded neither conversation nor amusement. Sufficient for their contentment was the knowledge that they were together, within speaking distance of each other, near enough for the light touch of a hand or a simple caress.

Below, in the garden, fireflies made a living tracery of light in the emerald darkness, weaving a tapestry of miniature comets across the jasmine-scented air. The sound of drums and music floated across the fields from Milot and the lights of the *houmfort* flickered through the palms. Both of them rejoiced in the distant sounds of revelry, happy that the others were enjoying themselves. The dance, they knew, would go on for hours. *Clairin* and *tafia*—the powerful native drinks—would increase the tempo of the drums and the drums in turn would heat African blood until the dancers, their desires approaching consummation, would steal away into the shadowy palms, two by two, for a drum-paced finale to the evening. As the night advanced the *houmfort* would be deserted, but the drums would keep on until the pale light of dawn appeared in the sky to awaken the sleepers and send them back to their proper habitations.

Armes broke the comfortable silence not so much to make conversation as to hear the sound of his own voice.

"Marie Louise looked very lovely at the reception for Henry's officers this afternoon."

Athenée's voice emerged from the shadows.

"And what did she wear?"

"Oh, something yellow, I think. Looked very well on her."

The quiet vibrated with Athenée's laugh.

"You men! We poor women spend hours picking out a gown and other hours on our *toilette,* all of it for just one reason. . . ."

"To impress other women?"

"No! To impress you men! Then you say 'something yellow,' and that's all it means to you. Well that 'something yellow' was a dress that Marie Louise and I spent hours planning. It was of finest India muslin and, believe it or not, it was copied directly from a picture of one that Pauline Bonaparte wore at a reception at the Tuileries. All except the embroidery, that is, because the detail was so tiny in the picture that we couldn't copy it. But I drew a charming design of wheat and Marie Louise had it embroidered in silver. So —that's your 'something yellow'!"

"It *was* a pretty dress, though, and Marie Louise has style."

Athenée laughed again.

"Armes, I do believe if I were to appear in my shift, you would say I had style."

"And so you would, my dear, for I can imagine nothing lovelier than *those* in a shift." He reached out through the darkness to touch her breasts. "They say that Pauline has the most beautiful breasts in France. . . ."

"Who says so? The young officers of Napoleon's army? Well, they should know, for it's common gossip that she entertains a different one every night. By this time, the army must be running out of officers. And furthermore, it's said that she's . . ."

"A woman whose dresses are worth copying. Oh, you women! You're all alike. Now that Marie Louise has copied Pauline's dress, half the female population in the Cap will be rushing to the dressmaker tomorrow to copy hers. Then the *marchandes* will see it and copy it in calico and display it before the peasants, who will copy it in denim. Finally we shall see Pauline's dress tramping up and down the country

234

roads. Even the Jezebels of the waterfront . . ." He paused to listen. "Did you hear something, Athenée?" Using his hands for leverage he leaped out of the chair and ran to the balustrade, trying to pierce the wall of darkness.

A strange noise in the night! Since the time of the Bouckmann uprising, any strange noise might mean death. Armes listened and another sound caused him to cup his ear in his hand and lean over the railing. All at once he wished that Henry were at Sans Souci. Henry was a protecting shield.

"I hear it too." Athenée stood up.

As the sound grew more distinct it resolved itself into the crunch of footsteps running on the graveled drive. Armes dashed back into the hall, reaching for his pistol which hung on the wall beside the door. He motioned to Athenée to go into the house. Instead she took her place beside him at the top of the steps.

"My place is here, Armes, with you."

The running footsteps drew nearer. Even when they approached the bottom of the staircase, Armes could not identify the runner, whose black face was a part of the darkness. He aimed his pistol at the while blur of a man's shirt.

"Stop, and tell me who you are!" he called.

"Pompee." The familiar name quieted their fears. "Milord, I must speak with you at once."

He bounded up the stairs onto the balcony, panting. Armes put his hand out and felt the dampness of Pompee's shirt.

"You've been running, man. You're all tired out."

Athenée went into the house and fumbled with a tinder box. They could hear the sound of flint striking steel, then a tiny circle of light spread from the candlewick and painted a larger circle on the polished floor. Armes motioned for Pompee to go inside. Once inside, he closed and bolted the tall doors.

Pompee wordlessly refused the chair in the salon which Athenée pushed toward him. He was unable to talk and remained standing in the doorway, drinking in the air with long, thirsty gulps. With an effort, he turned and spoke to Armes.

"Come," he panted, "you and Madame. Let us go below to my altar."

Armes crossed the floor with rapid strides to stand in front of him. His hands reached out for Pompee's shoulders as though to shake the words out of him. "For the love of God, Pompee, what is it? Have you good news or bad? Is there another uprising? Has Henry been assassinated? Tell us, quick."

Pompee reassuringly removed Armes' hand from his shoulder. "It's none of those things, milord, nothing bad. I'm sure of that. It's Ali . . ."

"Ali?" Athenée gasped. "You mean Armes' boy, Ali, who was killed?"

"I think I know what he means, my dear." Armes' relief showed in the expression of his face. "Pompee has spoken to me about it. It seems he has had some sort of spiritual communication with Ali from time to time." He looked to Pompee for confirmation.

"Yes, it might be that, milord, or it might not. I do not know exactly what 'spiritual communication' means. But Ali does speak to me and tonight in the dancing he spoke again, and he commanded so strongly I lost no time in getting here, for I knew it was important. So, come!" He picked up the ornate gilt candelabrum, lit the dozen candles, and motioned for them to precede him. "Let us go below."

They walked in single file down the stairs. A musty smell, which seemed to be compounded of damp leaves and wet plaster, greeted them from Pompee's room. It was cooler down there, but the skin on Armes' back did not shiver from the cold. The room seemed filled with an eerie strangeness. They waited, standing, while Pompee placed the heavy candlestick at the end of a rough altar, then with a taper, fired by the candles, lit several oil lamps—twisted wicks floating in small bowls of oil. This accomplished, he extinguished the candles, leaving the room almost in darkness, lighted only by the blue pinpoints of light from the flickering wicks.

"I shall have to leave you," Pompee said to them both. "I do not know how long I shall be gone or where I shall go, but I shall not be with you. Please remain here until I return. If you should need me at any time, call my name loudly, but do not do it unless it is absolutely necessary. Above all, do not be afraid. There is nothing to fear."

Athenée settled herself on one of the crude peasant chairs. "Why should we be afraid, Pompee?"

"There is no reason, madame. Except, perhaps, that this may be a new experience for you, and sometimes we are all afraid of the unknown. Sit, milord." He pointed to another chair, half hidden in the dim light.

He stripped the sweat-sodden shirt from his shoulders and flung it in the corner. The feeble flames burnished the muscles of his back as he knelt and raised trembling hands in prayer. The words were an unintelligible gibberish to both Armes and Athenée. They were not Creole words, but tumbled from Pompee's mouth in a thick, guttural, African torrent. When the prayer, if prayer it was, had finished, Pompee touched his head three times to the floor, then turned to them and made the Christian sign of the cross. He arose, took a faience bowl filled with white corn meal from the altar, and knelt once more. The flour dribbled slowly through his fingers, forming the intricate *vévé* of Damballah—the ophidian design sacred to his godhead. Pompee painted the design with infinite care and as it grew under his careful fingers, it became a minor work of art with its two twisting serpents amid a convolution of scrolls and symbols. Completed to his satisfaction, he stood up, reached for a bottle of wine, filled his cheeks, and sprayed it over the *vévé*, invoking the *loa* of Damballah in a soft chant. The singing ceased and he tore some green leaves from a branch, placed them in a small iron pot, and lighted them, blowing out the flame and allowing them only to smolder until the room filled with the thick aromatic smoke which wreathed around the tiny flames of the lamps. Both Armes and Athenée started to cough as the acrid smoke stung their nostrils, and as they continued to breathe it they became light-headed.

Pompee uncovered one of the crude, earthenware bowls on the altar with a reverent gesture and placed it on the floor, then squatted with it in front of the *vévé*, drawing the bowl of smoking incense between his knees, beside the opened *govi* which contained the *loa* of the god. One of his hands reached over to the cot and pulled off a thick woolen blanket which he spread over his head, enveloping himself, the burning leaves, and the sacred jar.

The room became strangely quiet, and yet the silence itself screamed at them. The distant sound of the *bamboche* drums reverberated in their ears. The shrouded figure on the floor now occupied their attention and, as they looked, it seemed to melt and flatten to the floor, like a waxen image which had been placed too near the fire. Where a moment before it had had the outlines of a human figure, it had now lost both height and breadth, sinking ever lower until it seemed almost level with the floor. There was no movement under the blanket and Armes now believed Pompee's words when he said he was going to leave them. Apparently he had gone, but no—the blanket started to move, almost imperceptibly at first, then gradually the motion became more and more apparent.

Armes tried to collect his thoughts through the strange dizziness that possessed him and strained his eyes through the smoky darkness. Was it a hand that appeared from under the edge of the blanket or a snake's head that rose and fell with sinuous grace? He could not be sure, but whatever it was writhed in time to some unheard rhythm. He tried hard to convince himself that it was one of Pompee's hands, but not until an arm emerged from under the blanket could he be sure. After the arm, Pompee himself slowly appeared, but not as a man. His body, entirely naked now, was human in every detail, but despite the obvious human anatomy, it had taken on the boneless sinuosity of a snake.

Athenée shrank closer to Armes, as the body that had been Pompee's writhed along the floor, sliding along effortlessly on its belly. The head was erect but the eyes were sightless, merely narrow slits of obsidian brilliance in the contorted blackness of the face. A pointed tongue darted in and out of the mouth—a thin red thread of life—as the body glided over the floor, and a hissing noise came from the lips. The *vévé* which had been so carefully drawn was entirely obliterated by the writhings. Then slowly, as a serpent might seek hiding in a crack of the wall, the body disappeared again under the folds of the blanket. In truth Pompee had departed. The familiar friend had gone, entirely changed into this weird serpent which had crawled in the dust of the floor.

Armes reached for Athenée's hand and found it cold, damp, and unresponsive. Her breathing was quick and labored and he realized, somewhere in the clouded consciousness which remained to him, that he too was under a peculiar spell—some mental hypnosis which he accepted compliantly and almost with gratitude. He felt enlarged, uplifted, free. The walls of the room receded, and although he still held Athenée's hand, he seemed to be miles away from her.

The figure under the blanket appeared to rise, and they could hear a hissing, spitting sound coming from under the folds of the cloth. It sounded like a string of wet firecrackers which merely spit and spluttered but did not explode. So quic'ly, that he was entirely unprepared for it, Armes heard a voice.

"Milord," the voice said, "thank you for coming." There was a little laugh and then a low chuckle.

Athenée's fingers tightened in the palm of Armes' hand.

"It is Ali's voice," he whispered to her. "I'd know it anywhere, but listen, Athenée, listen well, for this is the strange part. The voice is speaking English. We always spoke English together."

"I do not understand English," she replied. His hand cautioned her to be still.

"Neither does Pompee," he answered.

"Oh, milord," the voice said, and now there was an urgent, breathless quality to the lilting voice which mixed joy with sorrow. "I have so wanted to talk with you. I have only a little time, and there is so much I want to say. Are you listening to Ali, milord?"

"Yes, Ali, I am listening. There is much I want to say to you, too."

"I know it all, milord. You do not have to tell me because I know what you know, but I do have to tell you, as you cannot know all the things I know now. I speak of danger, milord, for you and the Vicomtesse, but I shall call her Athenée because she loves you as much as I do."

To Armes it did not seem that he was looking at a shapeless mass of blanket, and in truth he was not. Ali stood before him, his face transcendently bright, glowing with an inner light of its own, in his white *jellaba,* his red fez with the black tassel, his pointed Moorish slippers. Armes spoke to him and not to the blanketed mass.

"Did you say danger, Ali? Where?"

"Not now, milord, but someday soon. You will know when it comes, for I shall warn you. But you must start to prepare for that danger, milord. If you prepare, you will be saved."

"Is the danger for both Athenée and myself?"

"No. Many thousands of people will die, both black and white, but more whites than blacks. I cannot save them all, milord, but I can save you two. Listen carefully, milord! If you ever had any doubts of my love for you, doubt no more, for nobody ever loved anybody as much as I loved you. If you knew how difficult it was to come back to you, you would understand my love for you. Are you listening, milord?"

"I listen, little fellow."

"You know the mountain back of Sans Souci? The one they call the Bishop's Hat—*le Bonnet à l'Evêque?*"

"Yes, Ali, I know it. It's the highest mountain around here."

"There you will be safe."

"On the mountain?"

"Yes, but hear me well. Within the next month, you and Pompee ride up the mountain. Go as far to the top as you can. You will find a little level place there. It is a quiet little valley with green grass and trees and a little stream. You will know when you arrive by the waterfall. Remember."

"The waterfall, yes."

"There you and Pompee must build a house—a peasant's *caille* with thatched roof. Build it well, for it is cold on the mountain at night. Then furnish it. Take things from Sans Souci, but take care to let no one see you take them, because nobody must know about this but ourselves and Pompee and the good Henry and his wife. I do see somebody else there— a black boy—but he cannot speak to me and I do not know who he is, but he can be trusted."

"And after the house is built and furnished?" Armes asked.

"You must take food up there. Have Pompee plow the ground and plant things there—*figs* and mangoes and chick-peas and yams. Plaint maize and vegetables. It must be ready for you at a moment's notice when the time comes and I give you the word. Do you understand, milord?"

"Yes, we shall start work soon."

"You will not wait more than a month?"

"No."

The voice sank lower and became choked with sobs.

"I must leave you now, milord, and oh, how I hate to go, because I love you so much. I could be happy here, could I but feel your arms around me. Yet I go knowing that you are in good hands. Athenée loves you. So do Pompee and Henry Christophe, as much as he can love anyone."

"One question, little fellow," Armes begged. "What about Henry Christophe?"

"That big ape, my old enemy?" A little laugh came through the sobs. "You can trust Henry. He is on his way up and he will keep going up until he reaches far above you, milord. And he will take you with him, milord, because he needs you. But the higher Henry goes, the greater distance he has to fall, and big Henry will fall a long way. Do not doubt his friendship, milord, yet warn him. Tell Henry this from me. Tell him to avoid the mountain that will save you, for that very mountain will see Henry's death."

Armes sat silently, pondering Ali's words.

Ali's voice was becoming weaker. "Before I go, milord, will you do me one favor?"

"Anything you ask, little fellow."

240

"Stretch out your hand, milord."

Armes lifted his right hand and extended it. It might have been his imagination, but for one fleeting instant, he could feel somehting warm and moist on the back of his hand—something that felt like the impress of living lips and the quick flick of a tongue. Then the room became merely the room on the ground floor of Sans Souci—a dimly lit room filled with smoke. For long moments there was complete silence. Neither Armes nor Athenée moved, fearing to break some spell, but the mass under the blanket stirred and then Pompee stood up, clutching the blanket around his nakedness. Once more it was the familiar Pompee.

Armes rushed to support him, for he saw that the man was dazed and wavered on his feet. He clung to Armes, until he regained his strength and had full control of himself.

"Damballah Weydo rode me hard tonight, milord. Did you get the message from Ali?"

"You do not know what he said?" Athenée came up to stand on the other side of Pompee.

"How could I hear it when I was not here? I told you I would be leaving you."

"Then who did speak, Pompee?" Armes pressed the question.

"My breath spoke the words, milord, and my lips formed them, but the words themselves were not mine. Your Ali spoke them through Damballah Weydo. And now, milord, if Ali gave you permission to repeat those words, tell me what he said, because it must be very important. I have never been seized so thoroughly before."

Armes repeated Ali's words for Pompee's and Athenée's benefit. When he had finished, Pompee nodded knowingly.

"And now do you believe, milord?"

"It's incredible, but I must believe," Armes said in English.

"I do not understand you, milord. What language are you speaking?"

"English, Pompee. Forgive me, but I did not realize you do not speak English. But to answer your question, yes, I do believe now."

29

NEVER before in the history of St. Domingue had so many stonecutters, masons, carpenters, plasterers, and painters been recruited from the inhabitants of the colony. If a man had ever slapped stone on mortar, sawed a log, or hammered a nail, his services were immediately impressed by the governor of the Département du Nord. It mattered not if he lived in St. Marc, Port-au-Prince, Hinche, Gonaïves or Port-de-Paix, he had only time to kiss his wife good-bye before the soldiers marched him off to Cap François to work on the governor's mansion. He was paying good solid money in wages and plenty of it, but no matter how much they hurried, Henry groaned in impatience as the walls of the palace rose all too slowly above the city. At times Henry himself stripped off his blue coat with the gold braid and started slapping mortar in his haste to see the building completed. There was always so much to do and so little time to do it. He was not content merely to drive himself. Everyone else must join in the effort. Couldn't those stupid niggers understand that even if the house was being built for Henry, it was being built for them too—a symbol of how they had risen and what heights they had now attained?

The feverish activity extended even to Sans Souci, where Athenée and Marie Louise burned double the number of wax candles as they selected draperies and upholsteries from samples of brocade sent from France or pored over pictures of the latest styles in Directoire furniture. No sooner would they decide on a chair or bed or table than Henry would rip the page from the book of designs, dispatch it to some local cabinetmaker to copy, and then badger the poor man if it was not completed the next day. There was so much to do and so little time in which to do it!

Imperceptibly though it seemed, the walls did rise, course by course. The tall mahogany trees were sawed into boards and cured in the sun for floors and paneling. The carvers and the gilders and the decorators arrived and finally, in a matter of months which had seemed like years to Henry, the palace was on its way to being finished. Half of St. Domingue came to stare at it in awe. This was the home of General

Henry Christophe. Despite their jealousy, the blacks were proud of it; the whites resented it, although some of them hoped they might be invited to attend functions there; and the mulattoes sneered at it and speculated on how soon they might be able to take it over for themselves.

Toussaint L'Ouverture, the ex-coachman of the Breda Plantation, had been a bitter pill for the *affranchis* and the *blancs* to swallow, but Toussaint was a retiring man and they rarely saw or heard much of him. Grudgingly, they gave him credit for keeping the blacks in check and making it safe for a white man to walk the streets of Cap François. Toussaint was one thing, but this upstart Henry Christophe was another! Many of the whites remembered when they had either patted him on the head or kicked his behind when he was a stable boy at the Couronne, and some remembered and trembled at things they might have said in front of him while he was a waiter at the same hotel. Now this same erstwhile black slave was their governor, and they would go—provided they were invited—to the immense white palace that had risen on the hill to bow before him and his black wife. But they would sneer at them afterward.

There was nothing retiring about Henry Christophe. His influence was felt everywhere, for Henry was everywhere at all times, poking his nose into everybody's business. But, as the widow Beaumont so often remarked to all her friends, "General Christophe is a man of his word. He may be blacker than the ace of spades, but he is a fine man." And the widow Beaumont was a woman to be believed. Had she not, after just one letter, received her house back from the general? Apparently it paid to be a friend to Henry Christophe. The whites decided to make tentative advances to the *gros nègre*, and were surprised when Henry met them halfway. They were quite unaware that he detested them even more than they did him.

Henry had insisted that the entire household of Sans Souci be transferred to the new palace when it was completed. Marie Louise was his wife and Armes, Athenée, and Pompee were his family. All the family that he had! By God, he was going to keep his family together. He gave his orders and in these days when Henry commanded he most certainly expected to be obeyed. Athenée, however, thanked Henry prettily but refused to go, and in this decision Armes upheld her. On this one point he was adamant. He would come to the Cap daily if Henry wished, and would be on hand to confer with Henry whenever he was needed, but he would not take up residence at the palace and leave Athenée alone at Sans Souci, nor would she, under any circumstances, move to the Cap and live in the white and gold apartment Henry was planning for her in the Palace.

Accustomed to being obeyed, Henry stormed, blustered, and finally threatened. He would, he assured Armes, be double goddamned if he would leave Athenée at Sans Souci. Whatever honors he had achieved must be shared by those he loved. He'd see to it that every knee in St. Domingue bowed before her. He'd throw any man or woman into prison who dared look askance at her poor face. He . . . !

Then Athenée stepped in and quietly straightened the matter out, for she had a way with Henry that even Marie Louise did not possess. There were few people in St. Domingue who did not quail before the wrath of Henry Christophe, and Athenèe was one of them. She cornered him one evening on the balcony at Sans Souci, slipped her arm through his, and within five minutes, she had brought Henry around to her way of thinking so easily and so convincingly that Henry felt it had been his own idea all along that she and Armes remain at Sans Souci. For, as Athenée had pointed out to him, it behooved the governor of the Northern Province to have two homes—a plantation in the country as well as a palace in the town. He and Marie Louise would naturally be in charge of the Cap François palace, therefore it seemed only logical that she and Armes remain at San Souci so that everything might be prepared for Henry and Marie Louise whenever they arrived at a moment's notice.

"Why, Henry," she said, squeezing his arm under the blue broadcloth, "just think how much nicer it will be to have Armes and me here to greet you when you tire of affairs of state and want to come home here for a rest." Henry patted her hand with his big one and was pleased to believe that it had been his idea all along.

Athenée herself was inwardly pleased at the change that had taken place in St. Domingue. Her position under the old regime would have been untenable. As a widow, she could not have lived openly with another man. What a rich subject that would have been for gossip among the plantation wives! But now things were different; everything had been turned upside down. The social strata of St. Domingue had been completely reversed. Although the *blancs* clung desperately to the tattered remnants of their social supremacy, they

244

were fighting a losing battle with their former butlers, coachmen, and scullery maids, who had suddenly become the elite. This new social order was all too busy with its new importance to bother about what a former Vicomtesse might be doing. If she wanted to live with a man without marrying him, who cared? Precious few of the resplendent generals and their ladies had ever been married—the most they had ever done was to "jump the stick" in a primitive Dahomean ceremony brought over from Africa.

For the first time in her life, Athenée was beginning to know what real happiness was. Most of the time she sought refuge behind her veil, even when she and Armes were alone. It had become such a part of her, she explained, that she felt better with it. It had shielded her for so long, let it, she begged him, shield her a little longer. He agreed. He was willing to agree to anything that would make her happy, for with her Armes had found peace himself. True, it was a peace which balanced itself precariously on the brink of impermanence, but nothing in St. Domingue was permanent. Never think of the morrow! Let each day take care of itself.

After months of labor, Henry's palace was finally completed. Never before had such a house been seen in Cap François. Despite its almost barbaric exuberance, it did not offend, for it seemed to harmonize with the natural flamboyance of the Tropics. It occupied the crest of a hill a little behind and above the city and commanded a view of the blue sea from the front and a vista of purple mountains in back. A shadowy portico of pillar-supported arches shaded the rooms along the front and caught the cool breezes from the ocean. Inside the house glowed with the tapestries, paintings, and rugs which Henry had imported from France. Most of the furniture was the work of local craftsmen who had copied well, and if their handiwork lacked some of the delicacy and grace of the French originals, the complete effect was most pleasant.

Armes had attended Henry's first reception in the new palace and had admired the self-possession and poise of the giant African as he stood at the end of the long salon, looking far more distinguished in his plain blue coat and tight white breeches than all the other Negro generals of St. Domingue in the fanciful uniforms they designed for themselves. Marie Louise, as the governor's lady, was beside him —a little stouter than before, but with a quiet smile for

245

white, mulatto, or black, whoever bowed before her. Some of the white knees creaked stiffly as they made the required genuflection; some of the blacks were clumsy and awkward; and most of the mulattoes were sneering, but they all paid homage to Henry and Marie Louise. All of them remembered the barefooted Henry of the Couronne with the stink of the stable clinging to his torn shirt and ragged pants. Only a very few realized that he now stood where he was because he deserved it.

For the mulattoes it was a far more bitter pill to swallow than for the whites, for they had always felt that they had been born to rule. Unlike their slave mothers, they had been born free, so they argued that the amalgam of blood in their veins which placed them in both camps made them the logical ones to hold the reins of government. Nevertheless they were relieved that Henry Christophe was governor-general of the Province of the North rather than that damned Dessalines. Jean Jacques ruthlessly murdered every white man who appeared in his province, and as Jean Jacques considered mulattoes white, they too were hunted down. Both whites and mulattoes had much to be grateful for in Henry Christophe, although neither would ever acknowledge it.

Armes had been' as busy at home with the process of building as Henry was at the Cap. His own little village of Milot was growing fast. The foundations of the church which Henry's architects had designed were already laid and work was beginning on the walls. The design had turned out to be exactly what Armes had in mind. The sketch showed a round dome, rising like the bubble of a mosque from a circular base. It was a strange Islamic structure, unlike anything else in St. Domingue. Overseeing these building operations, combined with almost daily trips to the Cap for conferences with Henry, had kept Armes far too occupied to be over-mindful of the strange advice which had come to him through Pompee the night Ali had spoken to him.

After the initial shock of the strange interview had worn off, Armes was inclined to scoff at the whole performance as something concocted entirely by his imagination. But, on second thought, there was too much in it that was difficult, nay impossible, to explain. He knew that Pompee did not speak a single word of English, and he was forced to discount the possibility that there could have been someone else hiding under the blanket who spoke English. To be sure, the light in the room had been dim and there'd been a blue thickness of smoke from the bowl of smoldering leaves. Pompee might, by some sleight of hand, have hidden some-one else under the blanket. But why should he? He had nothing to gain from it. The message conveyed no advantage to Pompee. It all added up to one incontrovertible fact—the voice that spoke to him had been Ali's. It was not a voice similar to Ali's, nor a voice that imitated Ali's. It *was* Ali's, in pitch, timbre, and inflection. The voice itself had recon-structed Ali, and now when Armes thought about it, he was sure that he had seen the boy himself and talked with him. Therefore it behooved him to take Ali's advice, for, after all, it was a simple thing to do and involved only a little work and no danger.

The hot tropical summer had passed and a degree of cool-ness arrived with January. The change in temperature caused a resurgence of ambition in Armes and filled him with a desire to do something different. Ali's words recurred to him with increasing regularity until he confided in Pompee his desire to ride to the top of the towering Bishop's Hat. Al-though Pompee had remained strangely quiet on the subject, Armes could tell that the man was pleased with his recog-nition of the strange command.

"I'm going with you," Athenée had insisted when they informed her of their plans. They both said that it was far too difficult a trip for her, but they failed to convince her of the wisdom of remaining behind. She reminded Armes that Ali's warning included her equally with him and then added, "I go out so little, *mon cher*. There are few places that I really want to go, but we shall make a picnic of our little expedition and there on the top of the mountain with only you and Pompee, I shall be free and happy." They were at length convinced.

The next morning they got up early, breakfasted, saddled the horses, and were all ready to depart while the dewy chill of the night still lingered over the fields. Their ascent began almost at once. A trail of sorts led them up the mountain, at times so narrow that it was almost hidden in the gloom of thick vegetation where the trees arched together to form an impenetrable roof. Pompee went ahead with his machete, hacking off low-lying branches and thick ropes of lianas, but often the jungle growth was so dense that they were forced to lie flat on their horses, and even then branches and vines slapped at them viciously. Once or twice they saw vivid green snakes in the branches of the trees, and each time

247

Pompee halted his horse and made a reverential bow. Armes even caught himself looking at the green serpents with reverence and smiled inwardly. He, Armes Holbrook of Boston, Bachelor of Arts of Harvard College, bowing before a green snake in the jungles of St. Domingue! How Mr. Frothingham would laugh! He, Armes Holbrook, following the broad back of a kinky-haired African up a mountain because a mumbo-jumbo of words and the heady smoke of burning leaves had hypnotized him into believing he had heard a dead slave boy speaking to him! Truly, looking at the cold facts, it was ridiculous. Then why in the hell was he doing it? He already knew the answer. He believed that Ali had spoken to him through Pompee, and he also realized that the green snake, sacred to Damballah, although it was only a symbol, represented a far deeper mysticism than he would ever be able to understand. It was something so ancient and so wise it was beyond his comprehension. That, therefore, was the reason why he was here now, climbing the precipitous slope of the Bishop's Hat, looking for something, he did not know what.

As they advanced, the vegetation became thicker. Grotesque tree trunks writhed in weird convolutions, seeking a way to the upper sunshine. Ropes of vines hung in pendulous festoons between the nightmarish trunks. The light, filtered through the leaves, took on an aqueous green tint, and they appeared to be swimming in some fantastic ocean depth. Still they climbed the slope. From time to time they stopped to rest the horses and, as they ascended higher, the vegetation thinned out. The trees became straighter, and although Armes was unfamiliar with their leaves, he took them to be hardwoods. They were passing from the Tropics to the Temperate Zone.

After considerable climbing, Pompee caught the sound of running water and they headed their horses in its direction. They discovered a little stream that leaped down from huge granite boulders, glimmered over mossy pebbles, and then lost itself in a bank of dew-pearled ferns. Pompee splashed his horse into the stream and let Lalla pick her way uphill through the water. She tested each step delicately, but it was easier riding through the stream than through the woods. After about half an hour, they arrived at a small cataract, twice the height of a man, where a sheet of translucent water curtained an overhanging rock and sprayed the bankside ferns with a rainbow of mist. Beneath the cascade there was a large pool, shimmering over white pebbles.

Here they halted, and Pompee, who was in the lead, spoke but one word. "Waterfall!" A burst of sunlight coming over the lip of the cataract guided him to a steep rise. Armes and Athenée followed, and when the three of them were together at the top, they halted.

"This is it." Pompee's voice was exultant. His was not the voice of discovery, but that of rediscovery, although Armes was certain that Pompee had never been on the spot before. As they followed the sweep of his hand, both Armes and Athenée recognized that he had spoken the truth. Whatever it was that Ali had envisioned, this indeed was it.

A little green valley, perhaps some five acres in extent, nestled under the towering granite peak of le Bonnet à l'Evêque in back. In front a slight rise, crowned with trees, cupped the valley. At one point this dipped to the valley floor for a hundred feet or so to give a vista of flashing sea in the distance, of the diamond-studded Atlantic glistening in the sunlight far, far below. The grass in the valley was rich and green. The little stream wandered peacefully through the field before it plunged over the rocks on its precipitous descent. All about them the air flashed with iridescent blue sparks of butterflies, and the grass was studded with vari-colored wildflowers such as Armes had never seen before.

"Yes, Pompee, this is it," Armes agreed. "Have you ever been here before?"

Pompee shook his head. He seemed lost in thought. After long consideration, he pointed to a little rise by the stream. "There is where we shall build the house."

"And who shall build it?" Armes asked.

"You and I, milord. It is not difficult to erect a *caille*. From what Ali said, this place must be kept a secret. We shall come here, whenever we can spare the time. Here we will build a peasant's hut, a typical *caille*. It will appear that some ex-slave has run away and chosen this spot, should anyone see it. Our *caille* will not be elaborate, but it will be comfortable."

Athenée rode ahead, over to the spot that Pompee had designated, and looked out over the treetops to the distant ocean. She dismounted slowly, lifting her heavy skirt as she walked down to the brook. There she knelt and drank deep of the clear cool water. As she returned to Armes and Pompee, she did not bother to refasten her veil.

"Yes, Armes, let us build our *caille* here, and let us live here forever. Oh, I am so happy here! So free, so joyous, so triumphant! There is nothing evil here—just the sun and the trees and the warm, green grass. Do let us build our house here." She laid her hand lightly on Armes' knee and looked up at him, freed from her veil and unabashed. "Oh, my dear, my very dear, how I wish our house were built today and we never had to return to the other world below."

Armes removed his wide-brimmed hat and ran his hand through the black tendrils of his hair that had curled tight with moisture.

"Damned if I do not think you are right, Athenée. Here we could live and forget the whole world, even though it's right at our doorstep." He stretched out his arm toward the blue sea. "I don't know what Ali meant when he told us to come here. . . ."

"But after you see this, you cannot doubt him."

"No, I cannot doubt him, darling, nor can I doubt you either, Pompee." He jumped off his horse and joined Athenée on the ground. "Come, Pompee." He waited for the other to dismount. "Come, we'll eat our first meal at Sans Souci, for this is the real *Sans Souci*—the place without care."

Athenée took his arm. "I'm about to contradict you, beloved." Her eyes were dancing. "Let Sans Souci be Sans Souci, for, in truth, there is neither care nor worry there anymore. But let me name this place, for I feel that it is my own. May I?"

"Name it anything you please." Armes smiled indulgently and leaned over to kiss her.

"Then I shall call it Mon Repos. I know that here I can find rest from all the troubles of the world."

"Mon Repos it shall be and there it shall be." He pointed to the spot that Pompee had chosen. "Whether we ever come here to live or not, we shall build Pompee's *caille* there. But, my goodness Athena, where is your much vaunted wisdom? Do you not know that a man gets hungry? What have you packed away in those *paniers?*"

They undid the baskets from the saddles and Athenée spread a linen cloth on the grass. Pompee struck flint to steel and lighted a fire, kindling it with dry grass, and feeding it with sticks which he gathered from the edge of the forest. Soon there was a pot of coffee boiling, and Athenée piled slices of white bread and pink ham on broad green leaves. They had *bon appetit* there in the sparkling air and they ate

250

and were satisfied. After eating, Pompee quenched the fire and announced that he would make a tour of inspection of the little valley.

Although the sun was bright and warm, here on the mountain height, the air was cool. They did not need the shade of a tree. Armes stretched sleepily, threw himself down on the grass, and rolled his coat into a pillow for Athenée. She sank back on it, contentedly nibbling a blade of grass. He moved closer to her, pillowed his head in her lap, and closed his eyes to shut out the turquoise brilliance of the sky.

"Athenée." He hesitated a moment after her name. "Just once more I want to ask . . ."

Her fingers pressed against his lips.

"You promised never to speak of that again."

"How did you know I was going to speak of . . ."

"Marriage? Yes, I knew it because I know you so well I know your thoughts before you speak them. Do not, I beg of you, spoil these perfect moments. We have today, Armes, and who knows, perhaps we shall have tomorrow and tomorrow and tomorrow. Isn't that enough?"

"Enough for any man." His hand sought hers. The grasses swayed over them and the sun warmed them. The little brook provided a rhythmic, lilting tune and the white clouds high above them blanketed them with swansdown. Starry flowers were crushed beneath their heads, and the warm vitality of the earth flowed into them. While the golden minutes sped by, a blue-winged butterfly fluttered through the air and hovered over them, but soon found the opened petals of a scarlet flower more interesting. He balanced on its lip and curled his long tongue deep down into the throat of the blossom as he sought the hidden nectar inside. The breeze moved the flower in a metronomnic rhythm as his tongue discovered the sweetness inside, then, surfeited, he flew away, drunk with ecstasy.

Armes turned onto his back and watched the castle-building clouds pile up against the granite summit. Suddenly he jerked to his feet and looked at where the horses were tethered. He counted them—one, two, three! Pompee had gone off on foot but, nevertheless, Armes heard the hoof-beats of a horse, dislodging the stones of the brook. Athenée heard the noise too and sat up, leaning against his firmly planted legs for protection while they tensely awaited the arrival of the unseen horseman. In a short moment, they saw him, ascending by the lip of the waterfall.

"Good God! It's Henry!" Armes waved to him.

Henry galloped over the field, and before his horse had stopped he was on the ground, rushing toward them.

"TiArmes, TiArmes," he called, "we've had bad news! So bad that I followed you here, and a hell of a climb it was. What in hell are you doing in this godforsaken place, and why weren't you at Sans Souci when I needed you?"

Arms held up his hand. "One question at a time, *mon général*. You speak of bad news. What news could be so bad that you would climb the Bishop's Hat?"

"Bad enough for me to climb a devil's hat, let alone a bishop's. Armes, the biggest army France has ever sent overseas is on its way to St. Domingue. Eight-six ships of war, the finest France ever built, with twenty-two thousand French soldiers, the pick of the Grand Army of France, are on their way here. All for our poor little St. Domingue! Napoleon wants St. Domingue, TiArmes. All of it and all of us! He'll never rest until he gets it back for the *blancs*. Then we'll be slaves again."

"This news, Henry, where did it come from?"

"From the captain of the *Pride of Bristol* who landed in Cap François this morning. France and England are at peace now, and he came directly from Le Havre. The French fleet had started before he left. It's true! I know that goddamned Corsican had his greedy eyes on St. Domingue."

Armes called out for Pompee, who heard his voice and came running across the valley.

"We're leaving, Pompee. I must go to the Cap with Henry. The French are coming to take the island. All hell's about to break loose."

Henry left them as they were gathering up the implements of the picnic. He walked over to the break in the rise to look down over the mass of treetops to the ocean below. As he came back and mounted his horse, his brow was creased in thought.

"If I had a fortress up there, TiArmes"—he pointed to the granite peak of le Bonnet which thrust its bald head into the sky—"the French would never take St. Domingue. There, TiArmes, is where I would like to build the strongest citadel in the world, then goddamn the mouth-fornicating French if they ever set foot on St. Domingue."

Armes followed the direction of Henry's hand. The bold top of the Bishop's Hat stood out dark against the sky. Suddenly it became forbidding and menacing—a black and evil shadow. Ali's words returned to Armes. "The Bishop's Hat will see the death of Henry Christophe."

"You and your dreams, Henry." He tried to laugh. "No man could ever build a fortress here. It would be impossible."

Henry fitted his foot into the stirrup and mounted his horse. He reached the edge of the valley before them and halted, glanced over his shoulder, and waited for Armes to come abreast of him.

"Impossible, did you say, TiArmes? Nothing is impossible to Henry Christophe. It may be difficult, but not impossible."

They descended the mountain in single file. The black shadow of the peak enveloped them as they descended, but up in the little valley the sun still shone. The blue butterfly returned to the spot where the grass had been matted down by two bodies. All the flowers in that spot had been crushed, so he flew away. No other flower offered the surfeit of nectar he had found in that one red bloom.

30

ARMES returned with Henry to Cap François and remained there by his side during a week of anxious waiting. Each day and far into the night, he sat at a round of conferences which Henry insisted that he attend. Although he was the only white man at the meetings, he found that he was gradually being accepted by the Negro leaders and that his words carried weight. A motley crew surrounded Henry—there was the mayor of Cap François, Telemaque; the elegantly perfumed young General Rigaud who lisped his words with an affected Parisian accent; a collection of gaudy colonels; even an admiral of the nonexistent St. Domingue fleet; and, as always, the faithful Valentin Vastey. In spite of their extreme vanity and their flair for the unusual and opulent in uniforms, the fact remained that they were intelligent men with an instinctive knowledge of war, inherited from their African ancestors. Having won their freedom from white domination they were loath to put their necks back into the noose of slavery.

The city of Cap François now numbered only about two thousand whites in its variegated population. These were remnants of the former wealthy planters, a collection of bourgeois shopkeepers and tradesmen, and a few English and Americans. The latter, in their own exclusive colony, kept aloof from politics but the white French, en masse, were jubilant over the rumors that a French fleet was already on its way. To be sure, they were only rumors, but each new ship, arriving from France or England, had news—whether it was true or false—of the impending invasion. Henry questioned each incoming captain and from the maze of conflicting stories, he and Armes were able to sift out a few facts which seemed to have some creditable basis. The fleet was surely on its way; it was an enormous fleet and carried over twenty thousand soldiers; and it was under the command of General Leclerc, that brilliant young officer whose career so closely paralleled Henry's own. Leclerc had started out as a private and had quickly attached himself to the tail of Napoleon's comet. In short order, he had become a captain, then a general and now, through marriage to the amorous Pauline, Napoleon's sister, he was the brother-in-law of the first consul. Although Leclerc was, like Henry, a very young man, his generalship, like that of Henry, was founded on his innate intelligence and his ability to command. Not only did the rumors say that he was in command of the expeditionary force, but furthermore that Napoleon had appointed him governor-general of St. Domingue in order that Pauline, who was his favorite sister, might receive all the honors pertaining to that almost viceregal position. That meant that Leclerc would replace Toussaint, and that would not be good for the blacks. Toussaint's election and reign had been a fair one; the new appointment reeked of political treachery and, far worse, a return to slavery.

Armes sat for endless hours in the lofty council charmber of Henry's new palace on the hill. When he tired of listening to the pompous verbiage which never arrived at any definite conclusion, his eyes meandered along the carved intricacies of the paneling, followed the sweep of brocaded draperies, and counted the flashing prisms of the chandeliers, but they always returned to rest on the face of Henry Christophe. It had changed during these last few days. Youth was still present in the satin skin that stretched so smoothly over his cheeks, but lines were beginning to appear—lines of worry, frustration, and determination. Armes wondered if they might not also be lines of cruelty. Well, they could be, for Henry had learned to scowl and bang his hand on the table —impatient with all others and scornful of their opinions, convinced that he alone was right and knew the only solution. He had become curt and short-tempered. When some of his council became too eloquent and soared too loftily in rhetoric, Henry shut them off abruptly and commanded them to sit down. But he always listened to Armes and usually adopted his advice.

All the heated arguments, however, led absolutely nowhere. The paltry army that Henry commanded in the North was no match for twenty thousand French soldiers. They were trained veterans of Napoleon's far-flung campaigns—professional soldiers who had never met defeat. All that Henry could muster to oppose them was the company of his own personal guard—his hand-picked Dahomeys—plus a thousand or more St. Domingue blacks who were poorly armed, mostly undisciplined, and far more familiar with a machete than with a musket. They could not last five minutes in pitched battle with the French. So the arguments led nowhere and the answer was always the same. There was nothing they could do to defend the Cap.

Napoleon had known all this and he had reckoned on the weakness of the blacks, but there was an unknown factor which the great Napoleon, for all his wisdom and his military genius, had not taken into account. That was courage, and in particular the courage of these same blacks in St. Domingue. Any man will fight for his life, his family, and his home. Some men will fight for their country and their monarch, but Henry Christophe and his men were fighting for more than their lives or their country. Only a short time before they had been slaves, toiling under the lash of white overseers, working from sunup till sundown with only a meager plate of boiled millet in their stomachs. Henry Christophe and his men were fighting for freedom. Better death than slavery again!

Regardless of what Napoleon or Leclerc might say or do, regardless of the promises they might make and the lofty sentiments they might utter, Henry and every black in St. Domingue knew that slavery was the ultimate goal of the French. They desired a return to the former prosperity of the colony, when all the livres fell into the pockets of the plantation owners, leaving nothing for the slaves but a handful of rags to clutch about their nakedness. Better death than slavery again! A man could die only once and every man must die sometime, but as a slave a man died every night and was reborn in hell every morning.

255

These deep reserves of courage were what Napoleon had not counted on. These men were defending their souls. This courage, this indomitable will for freedom, had become concentrated in two men—Henry Christophe of the North and Jean Jacques Dessalines of the West. Toussaint L'Ouverture? Yes, of course Toussaint had courage, but Toussaint was tired. Toussaint was black, but Toussaint was French. Henry was black and so was Dessalines. They were men of St. Domingue and to hell with France! To hell with the first consul! To hell with his poppycock General Leclerc!

They met, those two black generals, Henry Christophe and Jean Jacques, one night halfway between Cap François and St. Marc, Dessalines' city. Armes did not accompany Henry that night. He was not invited. Henry knew that Dessalines would not talk in front of Armes. Any white man was anathema to Dessalines. His hatred of them was so great that he killed them on sight.

Between them, Henry and Jean Jacques reached an agreement that night. They had purposely not conferred with Toussaint, giving as an excuse that he was too far away in Hinche, a little town near the Dominican border. But the truth was that they did not want Toussaint. They could act better alone—Toussaint was too French and Napoleon's suave ambassador with his glib tongue could talk the loyal Toussaint into anything.

Armes spent the night of the conference between Henry and Jean Jacques at Sans Souci with Athenée, but rode back to the Cap at daybreak, arriving from the east just as Henry rode in from the west. Henry's blue general's coat was dark with sweat, his breeches were torn, and he had ripped off his linen stock, but there was a grin on his big face as he welcomed Armes. He flung the reins to a waiting boy, dashed up the steps of the palace, and beckoned to Armes to follow.

Marie Louise had been waiting all night, pacing the floor of her suite, and when she heard Henry's voice, she ran down the stairs to meet him. He kissed her quickly, pushed her aside almost roughly, mumbled one word, "coffee," to a footman, and all but dragged Armes bodily into the council chamber.

"I'm calling a meeting at once, TiArmes. But before they come, I must talk with you. I've spent the night arguing with Jean Jacques and we're agreed that we are going to resist Leclerc." Henry delivered his words like an ultimatum.

"But how can you resist him, *mon frère?* We've all agreed it can't be done."

"By fighting him!" Henry's voice cracked like a pistol shot. "Listen!" His eyes appraised Armes as though he had never seen him before. "I'm trusting you, *mon frère* with something nobody knows but Jean Jacques and myself. I'm going to take drastic steps. I'm going to make bitter enemies of all the whites, most of the mulattoes, and probably as many blacks, in Cap François. I'm not asking you if I'm right or wrong and nothing you can say will make any difference but, TiArmes"—his voice sank to a hoarse whisper—"if you do say I am right and if you think so in your heart, I shall feel better. Do not deceive me, TiArmes. Tell me the truth and I pray God that you will say that I am right."

"I'll tell you the truth, Henry, and if I think you're right, I'll say so, but if I think you're wrong, I'll waste no words in telling you."

"Then, TiArmes, here it is. Rather than let Leclerc occupy the city, I'm going to burn Cap François to the ground. He'll find nothing here but a heap of smoldering ruins. There'll be not as much as a *fig* for either him or his high-class whore Pauline or his whole goddamned army to eat. And that isn't all! I'm going to burn every field, every house, every tree, every living thing for miles around the city."

"Good God, Henry, no!"

"No? Why not? The French will take Cap François in spite of all that we can do. We cannot defend it for more than a few hours. What chance would my men have against twenty thousand French soldiers? But we can leave Cap François and hide in the mountains, and there one of my men will be better than twenty Frenchmen. So why should we let them have this city with all its facilities for feeding and keeping an army to fight against us? Do you still say no, TiArmes?"

Armes' thoughts raced wildly through his mind for one dreadful second. He looked at the familiar paneling, the rich brocades, and the sparkling crystals that he had been seeing all the past week.

"But this, Henry, your home?"

"And what is this, TiArmes? We built it, you and I, and we can build another, but if I am a slave again, we will never build another one. Think, *mon frère*—you are no longer white, no longer an American. To the French you are tarred with the same brush as I am, and they will thirst for the renegade white man's blood even more than they do for mine. You and I are brothers, TiArmes, and you are as black as I am in their eyes. All of St. Domingue knows of our relationship and every man that hates me hates you too. Think, TiArmes, for God's sake, think."

Henry slumped down in the big gilded chair. His nervous hands plucked at the tear in his breeches; his huge head rested in tired desperation on his chest. Armes could see a thick vein pulsating in the dark column of his neck. After a few seconds he lifted his head slowly as though it were a ponderous weight and looked at Armes through half-closed eyes.

"Your answer, *mon frère?*"

"I have considered it and considered it carefully." Armes could feel his words being forced through his throat by the pounding of his heart. "You are right. Burn the Cap, and may God be with us."

The door opened and a liveried footman entered. Despite his satin-clad elegance, his gangling adolescence appeared better suited for the cane fields than a palace, and the silver tray and coffeepot which he carried looked strangely out of place in his overgrown hands. Henry disdained the delicate Sèvres cup and grabbed the silver pot with one hand circled around the spout and the other on the handle. He drained it in huge gulps, then banged the coffeepot back onto the tray with such force that the ebony handle came off in his hand. He looked at it scornfully and flung it away from him, then stood up and walked over to pick it up, brought it back, and tried clumsily to refit it to the pot. "It can be mended," he mumbled half apologetically to himself, and then turned to Armes.

"Thank you, TiArmes, thank you for agreeing with me."

"So . . . we burn the Cap, Henry?"

"But not until they arrive. First they must see the Cap, if only from the deck of their goddamned ships. They must see her houses, her stores, the ships tied at her wharves, and above all the black general's palace on the hill. They must see the green palms and the flowers. But they can only glimpse it from their ships. When they land they will find only ashes. So be it."

His head sank to his chest again. Armes thought the man was going to collapse from fatigue. He walked over to the chair and tried to lift Henry to his feet, but even Armes' superb strength could not budge the huge bulk of Henry Christophe.

"You must get some rest, Henry, you've been riding all night."

Henry sat up straight in his chair. "Rest? How can I? There is so much to do and so little time to do it in. Listen, TiArmes! First I am sending my company of Dahomeys to Sans Souci today with orders to defend the place. I cannot go myself, there is too much to do here, but you go. Take Marie Louise with you. Tell her to pack all her jewels, the gold plate, anything that is small and valuable, but not more than enough to fill the coach. I'll not have it said that Henry Christophe saved his own valuables while he burned the rest of the Cap. Quarter my officers on the ground floor of Sans Souci. Let the men find lodging in Milot. Have them build a series of fortifications around the house and tell them to mount cannons in the back. We'll burn Cap François, TiArmes, but we'll defend Sans Souci—it's a natural fortress."

"You give the orders, Henry. I'll see that they are carried out."

"And the *caille* that Pompee is building on Le Bonnet?

"I don't know. He has been cutting timber for it, but he has not finished it yet."

"Then tell him to hurry, for we may all be lice in the Bishop's bonnet before very long."

The footman had stood motionless and forgotten in the corner during their conversation. Entirely oblivious of where he was, he was standing there, eyes half closed, miles away in some fantasy of his own imagining while his pocketed hand manipulated himself slowly under the sleek satin of his breeches. Henry noticed the boy and his preoccupation for the first time. His state was all too obvious, for there was no hiding the rigid bulge in his trousers.

"Now there's a nigger for you, TiArmes! See where his hand is! See what he's doing. Leave the bastards alone for a minute and that's the only thing they think about. St. Domingue is about to fall into the hands of the French! The Negroes are about to be enslaved again! Cap François is about to be burned! And what does that half-witted horny *brute* do? I ask you, what does he do? Not a goddamned thing but stand there and jerk off in his pants. Sometimes I wonder if it's all worth it. Why am I killing myself for a bunch of lazy, ignorant niggers? What do they want out of

259

life? Nothing, but to stand in the corner and come off in their pants."

He stopped his wild ranting and his voice softened. Instead of scolding the boy, he leaned over toward Armes.

"But they're like children, TiArmes. The poor *brutes* have never had anything, never hoped for anything, never needed anything except a woman to sleep with, enough food to fill their poor starved bellies, and some warm sunshine on their naked backs. Damn them, I love them, and I'm going to make them want something more. I'm going to civilize them. I'm going to force them to take their place in the world. I'm going to make them proud of themselves even if I have to kill every goddamned one of them and myself to do it."

The boy realized that they were talking about him and he ducked his head shamefacedly. His overgrown hand came out of his pocket and hung limply at his side. With an abashed glance at Henry, he shuffled across the floor, picked up the tray, and slipped out of the room. Henry allowed him to go without censure and when the door was closed behind him, he sank back in his chair. Armes sipped his coffee while Henry's head again slumped onto his chest in utter exhaustion. Quietly Armes replaced his cup, stood up, and tiptoed to the door. As he reached for the big bronze handle, however, Henry lifted his head.

"Hurry back from Sans Souci, TiArmes. Hurry back! I need you. My hands are not big enough, my eyes are not keen enough, and my brain *pas kapab*." Henry smiled as he lapsed into Creole.

Armes answered from the door.

"My hands are pretty big, Henry, and I'll keep my eyes open and perhaps my brain *kapab*."

"Sometimes," Henry groaned, "I feel a heavy weight on my shoulders as if I were holding up the world. I see so much to do and so little time to do it all."

"I'm leaving, Henry. I'll get Marie Louise and take her to Sans Souci and return as soon as I can." He closed the door behind him.

In his impatience, Henry ripped the gilt buttons from his coat, the quicker to shed himself of it, undid the buckle of his belt, and slumped forward in the chair, his head and arms on the table.

"Je vois tout et tout voit per moi dans l'universe."

Henry Christophe slept, alone in the vast gilded council chamber he had built for himself.

31

THE BLARE of trumpets and the rattle of drums shattered the late afternoon somnolence of Sans Souci. It was an unexpected sound—so unusual that Athenée laid down her needlework and ran out onto the balcony. Much to her amazement, she saw the road leading up to the house alive with serried ranks of soldiers—the First Dahomey Regiment of General Henry Christophe. The sun gleamed on their scarlet uniforms and the white plumes of their shakos, on their gold braid and polished cuirasses. Ahead of them, with cavalry outriders, lumbered the cumbersome gilt coach which Henry had ordered from Lisbon and in it, Athenée could see a weeping Marie Louise with Armes beside her. At least Marie Louise appeared to be weeping, for she kept dabbing at her eyes with a handkerchief.

Athenée adjusted her veil and went down the staircase to greet them, curious as to the military fanfare, the state coach, and the weeping Marie Louise. The coach swept up to the steps, scattering a hail of gravel upon them before it stopped and a footman jumped down to open the door. The little folding ladder of steps clattered down and Armes leaped out to assist Marie Louise, who immediately melted into Athenée's arms. Her eyes questioned Armes over the lemon-colored tips of Marie Louise's bonnet plumes, and he motioned for her to lead the girl up into the house. But Marie Louise was not one to dissolve in tears for very long. She straightened up, wiped her eyes, and glared at the world in general.

"Damn that Henry Christophe!" She stamped her little satin shoe petulantly on the bottom step. "First he builds a palace for me, and then just as I get used to living in it, he tells me he is going to burn it down. Oh, what a husband I have! Instead of another woman, he's in love with St. Domingue. St. Domingue! That's all I hear. The idiot even forgets that he has a wife." She halted on the top step and spun around. "Oh, do be careful, you clumsy men," she screamed at the soldiers who were unloading the coach. "My very best crystal goblets are in that box. And be careful of that one, too"—she pointed to a brassbound trunk—

"that's my silver coffee service, and there's my gold-plated epergne, and those are my dresses and my bonnets and my shoes and my jewels and Henry's uniforms and that's all we have left and, oh, Athenée, what am I going to do? Henry is burning our house at Cap François."

Athenée regarded her in bewilderment, but Armes led Marie Louise gently up the stairs, settled her in one of the chairs on the balcony where she could supervise the unloading of the coach, and clapped his hands for a servant to bring her a cooling drink. Then he turned to Athenée and explained the situation. She betrayed no look of surprise.

"I'm really proud of Henry," she said.

"And I guess I'm proud of him, too," Marie Louise sniffled, "because I do love him. But, Athenée it was such a lovely house, and he says he's going to burn it, and you know Henry. If he says he'll do it, he will."

"You'll have another just as lovely some day," Athenée reassured her, "and although Sans Souci cannot compare with your palace in the Cap, you know you are welcome here. Yours and Henry's room are waiting for you, and this *is* your home, you know."

Marie Louise smiled up at her gratefully. "Best of all, we'll be together again, Athenée. Oh, how I've missed you. The Frenchwomen who came to see me at the Cap looked down their white noses at me, the mulatto women looked down their yellow noses, and the Negro women didn't even look down their black noses, they just stared at the floor. Yes, it's good to be back home at Sans Souci, and I don't care if Henry does burn down the palace, I don't, I don't, I don't!"

Armes nodded at Athenée. "That's Henry's wife speaking now."

"But what are we going to do about the soldiers, Armes?" She indicated the long line of men which extended down the driveway.

Armes ran down the steps and spoke to a young captain. They discussed Henry's orders, pointed to various strategic points on the terrain, and scanned the hills behind the house. A group of officers dismounted to join them and they all huddled together, planning the defenses of Sans Souci. Two of the officers produced surveying instruments; another set up a folding table in the shade of the balcony and tacked a sheet of white paper to it. In a short time, military headquarters had been established under the broad balcony.

Squads of soldiers disappeared into the shrubbery only to reappear, shorn of their glittering finery, in ragged cotton pantaloons, their brilliant uniforms carefully folded and placed in neat bundles on the ground. Small companies were counted off to march in the direction of Milot; others produced shovels and mattocks. Oxen appeared down the long, palm-shaded drive, leisurely dragging heavy cannon. Down in the village there was the sound of axe blows as trees were being felled. Armes marveled at the perfect organization responsible for all this—Henry's acumen and foresight—and he began to admire and appreciate Henry even more.

By evening, when Armes, with Pompee for escort, was ready to return to Cap François, Sans Souci was well on its way to becoming a fortified camp. Lights from cooking fires glowed in a broad circle around it. Earthworks were beginning to take form in a wide circumference around the house. Oxen had dragged the cannon to strategic points up on the mountain where pinpoints of light twinkled in the darkness. Guards were posted by the gate that led into the main road, and Pompee and Armes were stopped for the password of the day before they were permitted to leave. Armes had no difficulty in remembering it—it was his own name—and even the corporal at the gate smiled when Armes laughed and responded with "TiArmes."

After he had bid *bonne nuit* to the corporal, whom he remembered as one of his own former slaves, Armes turned in his saddle to look back. The lights of the big house shone through the palm trees and he felt he could leave with the sure knowledge that Athenée and Marie Louise were safely protected by Henry's Dahomeys. Safe! Once again it had become a very important word in St. Domingue.

By now Tom and Lalla knew the road to Cap François as well as their riders. They trotted along through the cooling night.

"How are things going up on the Bishop's Hat?" Armes said to Pompee's black shadow.

"Slowly, milord, slowly. With you away I have been working alone. The trees are felled to frame the *caille*, but I shall need help to raise them. Then it will be a simple task, once the fame is finished."

"As soon as I get a moment, I'll come and we'll do it together."

"I've been thinking about that, milord, and I don't think I shall need you."

"But, man! You just said you can't do it alone."

"I shall have help."

Armes expressed surprise. "You told me nobody must know about this."

"Nobody shall."

"I can't follow you, Pompee."

"Forgive me if I seem to be speaking in riddles, milord. I do not mean to. Do you by any chance remember TiTonTon, the slave boy who came to us from the St. Gabriel plantation?"

Armes tried to remember the name. "TiTonTon? You mean the young lad who cannot speak?"

". . . Because St. Gabriel had the poor boy's tongue cut out." For the first time Armes heard bitterness in Pompee's voice. "That's the boy! He's become one of my *hunsis,* and he is a true disciple of the *mystères* of voodoo. I would like to take TiTonTon up there because I am as anxious about his safety as you are about Madame's. He won't be able to tell anyone where we are going or where we are after we get there. Big and strong and husky as he is, he'll be able to help me. As a matter of fact, I'd like to leave him up there."

"Can you trust him?"

"He is one of my *hunsis,* milord. My favorite! There is a strong bond between us. Need I say more?"

Armes understood.

"And besides," Pompee contiued, "he adores Madame because she nursed him after the Vicomte had tortured him. Furthermore, he is devoted to you because you gave him a home after St. Gabriel was burned. He can neither speak nor write, so there is no way he could give information even under questioning."

"If you want him, Pompee, it's all right with me," Armes agreed warmly.

"I'll give him a mule and a plow and let him cultivate the meadow. He can plant crops there, raise food, chickens and pigs. Nobody'll know he's up there and if someone should stumble across him, what can he say? Nothing! They'll assume it's his own place."

"You think of everything, Pompee."

"Where you are concerned, milord, I try to. "

They rode on in silence to where the road forded a little river and stopped there to water the horses. A white moon was rising over the ragged palm fronds, which made a black lace border against the star-studded emerald velvet of the

264

sky. There was no sound but the ripple of the water over the stones and the distant sound of drums far up in the mountains. Pompee pulled Lalla's head up from the water with a quick jerk, placed his fingers to his lips to assure Armes' silence, and turned his head in the direction of the drums. Even Armes' untrained ears could catch a new urgency in their beat. Pompee listened attentively, his fingers repeating the drumbeats on the saddle.

"What is it, Pompee?" Armes moved Tom a step or two nearer.

"The French are already here, milord." Pompee again cautioned silence and listened. He translated slowly between intervals of drumbeats. "They passed the headland of Fort Liberté this morning and are now off the cliffs of Caracol. They will be in Cap François by morning. The sister of Napoleon is on the flagship with her handsome young husband, the General·Leclerc." He shook his head in bewildered sorrow. "This is the last night in a long time that the blacks of St. Domingue can go to bed in peace, milord."

They whipped up their horses and galloped along the road to the Cap. When they arrived, they found a feverish excitement in the town. Late as it was, the houses of the *blancs* were ablaze with lights. Orchestras were playing in the villas and dancing figures were silhouetted against the tall windows. Down in the center of the town, wine shops were wide open and guitars and maracas from the rough dives of the waterfront competed with the scrape of fiddles from the houses of the elite. A drunken drab stumbled up a dark alley with three men at her heels panting after her like dogs slavering after a bitch in heat. Watching them, a group of sailors, arms entwined, split the night with a boisterous sea chantey. Over all the city, the moon beat down, painting the buildings with silver, touching the rotting swill in the gutters, painting elongated black shadows of palm trees on the white walls. Cap François, all unknowing, danced on her deathbed. Never again would she be as dissolute, as degenerate, and as beautiful.

The big double doors of the opera house swung open as they passed, and the candles of the foyer shone out over the cobbles. A long line of varnished carriages moved slowly along the street to meet the home-going audience. Jewels sparkled on black arms, on copper-colored arms, on *café-au-lait* arms, and on breasts the color of cream, of milk, and of snow. A chorus of cheerful *bonne nuits, au revoirs,* and *à tout à l'heures* rang out as Armes and Pompee passed the theater crowd.

The streets leading up the hill to the palace were quieter, but when they arrived, they found the palace quite as frantic with activity as the town below. The soldiers at the entrance presented arms as they passed through and the footmen, standing on each side of the big mahogany doors that guarded the council room, bowed. One of them, however, motioned for Armes to wait, but he brushed aside the man's hand and, without waiting to be announced, pushed open the doors and walked in.

Henry was alone, slumped over the council table. His face lighted up as he saw Armes and Pompee enter, and he spread his hands before him in a helpless gesture.

"You have heard?" he asked.

"Pompee read the message of the drums on the way from Sans Souci."

"The drums tell the truth. The French are here."

"Here? Now? At Cap François?"

"Even now the lights of their ships can be seen in the harbor." Henry pointed to a brassbound telescope lying on the table beside his hand.

Armes grabbed the glass and walked to the tall windows that gave access to the terrace. Yes! They were here. The bobbing lights of the ships made pinpricks of light out on the ocean.

"Will they land tonight? What do you think?"

Henry shook his head. "I do not think so. Fort Picolet could defend the city for at least one night. They have orders to fire on any ship which enters the harbor unless I give permission. But remember, TiArmes, the French are not at war with us. Supposedly they come in peace, and Leclerc arrives as governor-general of St. Domingue. He does not want to show his hand this early. But, TiArmes," Henry laughed, "ask yourself this question. Why does a governor-general arrive with twenty thousand soldiers?"

Armes placed the telescope back on the table and sat down beside Henry.

"Marie Louise?" Henry looked up expectantly.

"Safe at Sans Souci and happy to be there, I think. Everything goes well there. Your Dahomeys are a fine bunch of boys."

"I wish all my soldiers were like them. I handpicked those boys myself. Every one's over six feet tall—husky *brutes*

266

all of them. I've had time to train them and they can fight, those boys. But the others will fight, too. Just shake a chain and leg irons in front of them and they'll all fight like demons of hell, even though they've only a rusty machete to fight with."

Gradually the members of Henry's council drifted back into the room. Armes settled down to the prospects of a long night of endless verbiage, but Henry's assortment of generals and admirals was strangely quiet. They were all aware that Henry had stationed men throughout the whole city. Some were hidden in servants' rooms, some behind bales in warehouses, some in their masters' bedrooms, but each man had flint and steel and a wad of tinder in his pocket and a canteen filled with *clairin* which burned as quickly as naphtha. Each man's ear was tuned to the bugle call which Henry had told them to expect.

The hours passed slowly until daylight came. When the full light of day streamed through the windows, Henry dismissed the others, but asked Armes and Pompee to come with him. They climbed the wide stairs, slowly, step by step, to the floor above, and entered Henry's vast bedroom. A mulatto girl, sprawled naked on the bed, sat up and looked at them with frightened eyes, reached for her filmy *robe de chambre,* and scuttled from the room at Henry's command.

"Didn't need her after all. Thought I might with Marie Louise away," Henry half apologized. "If either of you wants her, you can have her while I'm dressing." His eyes opened wide in a question, but both Armes and Pompee shook their heads.

A fresh uniform was carefully laid out on a chair, the white breeches folded across the seat, the blue coat of a general of the Armies of France draped across the back. Henry motioned for Pompee to help him remove the high black boots that he was wearing, and when Pompee pulled them off, Henry wriggled his toes in the long white silk stockings.

"Silk stockings for a black stable boy, TiArmes." Henry smiled the ingenuous little-boy smile that always seemed so strange on his big face. "Goddamn it. I may be going barefoot again before long." He stripped off the soiled uniform and walked into the bathroom.

It was the first time Armes had ever seen Henry naked, and he marvelled at the massive strength of the man—the

267

broad sweep of the shoulders and the mighty arms—but the also noticed that good living had started a paunch, and that Henry was no longer the flat-bellied youth he had been at the Couronne.

When Henry had finished splashing, he returned and Pompee helped him into the clean clothing. He dressed himself slowly, and when he had finished, he buckled on the sword belt and the ornate gilt-scabbarded sword.

"General Henry Christophe is playing host to the French today. He must be dressed to receive them. The black stable boy may be willing to kiss the hand of the first consul's sister, but he'll be damned if he'll kiss the ass of the first consul's general."

They walked down the empty halls and out into the bright morning sunshine. An open carriage was awaiting them at the door.

"Drive to the quay," Henry told the coachman.

At the end of the long stone quay, Henry left the carriage and stood looking out to sea. His hand encircled Armes' shoulder and he pointed. A small boat was heading inshore, agleam with white paint and polished brass and the gay tri-color of France whipping in the breeze.

Henry's lips make a grim line. "You see, TiArmes, we are just in time. St. Domingue awaits France, not as a white mistress awaits her soldier lover, but rather as a black slave girl, cowering in the dark, awaits the brutal rape by her white master."

"I don't see you cowering, Henry." Armes noted Henry's varnished boots firmly planted on the stones of the quay.

"Ah, but I am inside, *mon frère*. I know it and now you know it, but Napoleon's boy general will never know it."

32

THE grandeur of Henry's full-dress uniform; the imposing appearance of his official staff lined up behind him; and his early-morning appearance on the quay were all wasted. General Leclerc was not in the boat. He had not deemed the meeting with Napoleon's "damned nigger upstart" of sufficient importance to come himself, but had sent a young ensign named Lebrun who, although one of the lowest-rank-ing officers on Leclerc's staff, was, nevertheless, a most personable young man. Pauline had seen to that! She had personally picked all of the younger officers on her husband's staff, and Pauline, like old Queen Maria Louisa of Spain, cared more for broad shoulders and a bulging pants' fly than she did for military experience. Let the older officers attend to military tactics while the younger ones entertained her, for, if she had to come to this out-of-the-way hole, being entertained was a necessity. She hoped to supplement her young men with some of the St. Domingue mulattoes about whose prowess she had heard such glowing accounts from her sister-in-law Josephine. Josephine should know! She was from Martinique, and surely the half-breeds of Martinique could be no better endowed than those of St. Domingue.

So, Lebrun was young and personable and charming, and so he continued to be after he had stepped out on the quay and greeted Henry with the correct salute. He was, however, most uncommunicative as he sat stiffly beside Henry during the short ride from the quay to the palace. No, he had no message from General Leclerc to General Christophe. Yes, he did have a letter addressed to former Governor-General Toussaint, which he could not of course hand over to General Christophe. Yes, he would wait while a messenger was sent into the interior with the letter and defer his return to the ship until he had received an answer.

Once alone in the palace with Henry, however, his ramrod backbone bent a little, and he confided most delicately and diplomatically that perhaps he did have a message for General Christophe from General Leclerc, to wit that, "if General Christophe were to hand the city of Cap François over to General Leclerc before Governor-General Toussaint were to arrive on the scene, General Leclerc would find means of heaping honors on General Christophe." Henry bellowed with rage and informed the fellow that he was not acting under Toussaint, the duly constituted governor of St. Domingue, and that he could and would take no orders from anyone else. Above all, he informed the pale Lebrun, he was not a traitor. Then he calmed down, somewhat ashamed of his display of temper, and informed Lebrun that he would dispatch messengers at once into the interior to deliver the letter to Toussaint. In the meantime, he suggested that Lebrun remain in the palace as his guest until the messengers returned with Toussaint's reply, which would probably be the next morning. Lebrun accepted; he had no other alternative. He knew full well he was being held as a hostage.

Henry quartered him in the finest suite in the palace. Even the quadroon girl who had been asleep in Henry's room that morning was provided for the ensign's pleasure, but he was watched like a single mouse under the surreptitious gaze of a hundred hungry cats. Not for a moment was he allowed to quit the palace, nor communicate with any of the *blancs* in the city. Even his dalliance with the quadroon girl was observed by a dark eye through a convenient keyhole, and it was afterward reported that he had a body as white as a fish's belly and could well take lessons in lovemaking from any black peasant.

As soon as Henry had disposed of Lebrun, he called Armes and Pompee back into the council chamber. Valentin Vastey opened the door for them and, as they entered, put his fingers to his lips to caution silence. Without uttering a word, he led them over to Henry, who handed Armes a small sheet of paper, covered with Vastey's copper-plate writing.

> *Even the walls have ears here. We cannot talk. You and Pompee leave now. Two miles out on the road to Milot, there is a ford. Await us there. Nobody must overhear what I have to say to you.*

Armes read it and handed it back to Vastey, who flicked it through a lighted candle until it burst into flames. Only then did Henry speak, and his words took the form of a commonplace greeting. Armes asked Henry's permission to return to Sans Souci, which Henry granted rather gruffly, angrily in fact, if no one had not seen him wink. Then, with a curt, *au revoir,* he turned to his desk to sign papers. After long practice he had learned to trace the crude letters that comprised his name.

Armes and Pompee found their horses waiting, already saddled at the palace steps. It was only a short way to the ford in the river, and when they arrived, there, they dismounted, tied their horses, and lounged on the grass of the riverbank. The place seemed strangely deserted. Usually there was a group of *lavandiéres* there, beating clothes

270

clean in the shallow waters, but today there was a Sunday hush about the place. Armes rightfully guessed that the excitement had drawn all the peasants into the Cap to gaze in awe out into the harbor where the great French fleet rode at anchor under the guns of little Fort Picolet.

Their rest was brief, for in less than a half-hour a cloud of dust down the Cap road betokened someone on horse back. As Armes surmised, it was Henry, and Vastey was with him.

Henry leaped to the ground and threw the reins to Vastey. He still had on his dress uniform, but it was soiled and sweat-stained now. Armes noticed his face. He saw a deeper sincerity there than he had ever noticed before, and mingled with sincerity was a deep urgency. Henry's warm brown eyes were pleading with him and, when he spoke, his words were even more urgent than his eyes.

"TiArmes." He seemed at a loss to know how to begin despite his anxiety. "I want to ask a favor from you—so great I do not know how to begin."

"That's easy, Henry. Just say the words one by one, until they're all out."

"If you refuse, *mon frère,* I shall understand, and I shall never hold it against you. You are the only white man I ever had as a friend, and you are the only real friend I ever had. You were my friend when Henry Christophe was a slave and had nothing but the pants and shirt he wore. It made no difference to you how little I had. Even if Henry Christophe were the king of St. Domingue, you would still be my friend. Not that there's any chance I might ever be king," he grinned.

Armes' thoughts raced back over the long friendship they had shared. He remembered the first time he had offered his hand to Henry. How that friendship had grown with the years! How deep the bond that existed between them!

"It must be important, Henry, or you would not have ridden all the way out here to discuss it."

"There are spies in the palace, TiArmes. That goddamned Telemaque has decided to cast his lot with the French. White money has bought his loyalty to me, although it was not worth a hell of a lot anyway. His spies are everywhere. I do not know whom to trust. Only you and Pompee and Valentin. That is why I am going to ask you to do a very difficult thing for me—a very secret thing."

"If I can do it, you know I will."

"It will mean that you will be separated from Athenée."

Armes bit his lips, regretting his ready promise.

"How long?"

"I do not know, but perhaps not too long."

"I guess it is no more difficult for me to be separated from Athenée than for you to be away from Marie Louise."

"You may be in great danger."

As I have been from almost the first day I landed in St. Domingue."

"And you might get badly hurt." Henry looked down at his hands. "By these, TiArmes, my own hands."

"Now I do not understand you, Henry. So far I have agreed to everything, to leave Athenée for a time; to expose myself to danger; yes, even to letting your hands hurt me. But why, man? Tell me everything."

Henry sat down heavily on the bank and motioned to the others to sit beside him.

"I need to know what's going on out there." He pointed in the direction of the sea. "On those ships. How can I find out? There's not a man I know who would not sell me out for French gold, except you two and Vastey. You could go to them, TiArmes. You're white. You know their ways and they would accept you. You could be in the enemy's camp, and they would not suspect you."

Armes interrupted him. "Not suspect me? How wrong can you be? All St. Domingue knows of our friendship and how close we are."

"But all St. Domingue will change its mind after tonight."

Armes' eyes questioned the statement.

"Yes, after tonight. If you agree to my plan."

"Proceed! Tell me about it."

"In a few hours you will return to the palace. I am having a state dinner tonight for the little ensign Lebrun. It is well that he sees how the Negroes live in St. Domingue. It is well that he understands we are not African savages with a bone through our nose, living in grass huts. Even now I have sent messengers to bring back Marie Louise's gold plate."

"Yes, Henry, and after you dine him on gold plate, then what?" Armes was becoming impatient.

"At the dinner tonight, Ensign Lebrun will sit at my right hand and you at my left. During the conversation, you will try to convince me, for Lebrun's benefit, that I should surrender to the French, give up the city, capture

Toussaint and Dessalines, and hand over everything, lock, stock, and barrel, to Leclerc. You understand?"

"Perhaps I am beginning to."

"Then, TiArmes, I'm going to get mad at you. Most awfully goddamned mad. Did you ever see me get mad?"

Armes laughed. "I've seen you approaching it, but I've never seen you really lose your temper, Henry."

"Then, by God, you will tonight. In front of all those dinner guests—in front of Lebrun and Telemaque and all those other weasel-hearted goddamned black niggers, I'm going to pound hell out of you, even though it breaks my heart. And you've got to hit it back, TiArmes. We've got to make it *très réaliste*. You and I are going to have one big fight there. I expect I'll muss you up pretty much and I hope you do me. But just before I kill you, my guards are going to separate us, and they are going to drag you away to your room. I'm going to give orders that you be hanged in the morning for having struck the governor of the Province of the North and a general in the Army of France. Or would you rather be shot, or drawn and quartered? You can have your choice of deaths as long as you are condemned to die in the morning. Are you ready to die?"

"Not by a damn sight! Not even for you, Henry Christophe, and when it comes to that mauling business, I hope you realize that you are strong as a bull. Try not to pack too much of a wallop into those fists."

Henry grinned. His teeth always seemed so startlingly white against the moist purple of his lips.

"Then, *mon frère*, when we have subdued you and I have sentenced you to death, we'll leave you locked up a little while. Now, Pompee"—Henry turned to face him—"it's your turn to play your part. Lebrun has seen you with TiArmes this morning. That son of a bitch, Telemaque, knows the relationship between you two. Whatever you say will be believed. I want you to make your way secretly to Lebrun's room after dinner. It will not be difficult, as Vastey will be in command of the guards. Tell Lebrun that Armes has been against me for a long time; that I have taken Sans Souci away from him; that he disapproves of all my actions; that he has been more or less my prisoner; that he wants to get away from me, and that he has valuable information about me." He looked at Armes. "Most of which will all be wrong, *n'est-ce pas?*"

"Don't worry, Henry. I can make up plenty of things

273

about you which the French will believe." Armes flipped a pebble at Henry's medals.

"Then, Pompee, tell the little French *fat* that you can bribe the guards." Henry flipped the pebble back to Armes. "Tell him you can arrange for TiArmes' escape if Lebrun will give him safe conduct on board Leclerc's flagship. Tell him you must go with TiArmes because I'll murder you anyway since you're his friend. If the little *pis-en-lit's* got only half a brain, he'll realize he's struck a gold mine."

Pompee nodded in agreement.

"Then, when you and TiArmes are with Leclerc, I'll have a firsthand source of information. TiArmes will tell you what he can find out and you can send the message to me through the drums. You'll be onshore in a short time. Leclerc will be landing soon because Fort Picolet can't hold out long against the French fleet." Henry stood up, slapping the dried grass from his breeches. "And now . . . what do you say, TiArmes?"

Armes remained on the ground. He picked up a blade of grass and drew it slowly through his fingers. Why was he bound to this man—this Henry Christophe? There was no use in asking himself—he was bound to him and he'd do what Henry asked. He'd leave Athenée and the comfortable security of Sans Souci. He'd accept the dangers that being a spy involved. Yes, he'd do all that for Henry Christophe, because he believed in him.

He stood up, took Henry's big hand in his own, and shook it solemnly. "I'll do it, Henry, for you, not for St. Domingue or to abolish slavery, or to beat the French, but for you." He glanced down at Henry's hand in his own. "But remember one thing! Easy on your punches! I'll not be much good to you if I'm carried out to the ship on a stretcher."

Henry's hand closed tightly on that of Armes. Always quick with his emotions, he blinked his eyes to keep back the tears. The words he wanted to say could not find utterance. Finally he spoke.

"I'll go back now, TiArmes. You and Pompee arrive an an hour or so before dinner, which will be at nine. Let Lebrun see us together before the dinner starts, but remember to disagree with me. Now go to Sans Souci, bid Athenée *au revoir,* get fresh clothes, and be back at the Cap in time." He walked over to his horse and slipped his foot in the stirrup. "Kiss Marie Louise for me, TiArmes. You know we are expecting a son."

"A son? A son for you, Henry. Are you sure it will be a son?"

Henry pointed to Pompee. "So say the *papaloi*."

"Then congratulations on my new nephew."

"Thank you for that, TiArmes." Henry turned his horse and rode down the dusty road to the Cap with Vastey. Before he turned at the bend, he stopped, rose in his saddle, and waved back at Armes. The resounding bellow of his laugh rolled down the road and enveloped Armes and Pompee. Henry raised his arm and shook his clenched fist at them. "Don't be afraid, TiArmes. This goddamned big hand of mine is gentle enough to handle a baby. It won't hurt much." They disappeared around the bend.

Pompee came up leading the horses. Armes leaned up against Tom and patted his sleek flank. "What do you think of Henry's wild scheme?"

Pompee helped Armes mount. "Do not let it frighten you, milord. When we get back to Sans Souci, I'll prepare an *ouanga* for you. It will keep you safe." He jumped on his horse. "One moment, milord." He reached in his pocket and drew out a clasp knife, then leaned over in the saddle, removed Armes' hat, and cut away a damp tendril of hair. "This"—he pointed to the lock of hair—"plus some other ingredients . . .—"

"Such as?"

"Dried leaves of the sacred *maupou* tree; the skin of a green snake which has been shed; a few drops of your urine; blood from a black cock; the ashes of a voodoo fire. All these, imbued with the *loa* of Ogoun Feraille, our god of war. With this *ouanga,* neither steel or bullet can harm you."

Armes spurred his horse. "You know, Pompee, in spite of my upbringing, my education, and my judgment, I believe you."

"And why not, milord? Have I ever failed you?"

"No."

"Then as Damballah, Ayda, Erzuli, Papa Legba, Agwe, Guede, Papa Zaca, Ogoun Feraille, and all the other gods of Dahomey bear witness, I never shall, milord."

Armes stood on the balcony at Sans Souci. He had kissed Marie Louise for Henry and was ready to leave with

Pompee, who was holding the horses at the bottom of the steps. When he saw Armes and Athenée coming out onto the balcony, he invented an errand in the back of the house. They were alone.

Armes was dressed for the dinner at the governor's mansion. The new style from France was becoming to him —the long tight trousers of white tricot, the velvet-collared plum-colored coat, abbreviated in front, long tailed in back. They combined to make him seem taller, broader, bigger.

Athenée turned him around like a tailor's dummy, devouring him with her eyes.

"Oh, *mon bien-aimé!* These last few seconds, I must fill my eyes with you, so that when you are gone I shall see you standing here in this place, so much a man. So much my man!" She leaned her head on his chest, holding him close and tight so that the clean man-smell of him filled her nostrils. His hand reached up and touched the softness of her hair and his eyes looked down on the one flawless cheek. He felt the beating of her heart so close to his.

"It's an old, old story, *ma petite.* Man goes to war and woman is left behind to weep; to stretch out her hand at night and feel the awful emptiness of the other side of the bed. Just so shall I reach out at night and find only a rough blanket instead of warm flesh. But it will not last forever, and when I come back I promise to do something special for you."

"Will it be what I hope it will be?"

Armes closed her mouth with his lips. "Yes, of course, but more than that. Pompee is sending TiTonTon, the dumb boy, up the mountain to build our *caille.* When I return, regardless of Henry or anything else, we'll go up there, just you and I, for a week or a month."

"We'll be just two peasants of St. Domingue."

"Just two peasants with a bed of yams in front of the *caille* and a bed of straw inside. During the day we'll work in the bed of yams and at night we'll work equally hard in the bed of straw."

She kissed him. "I'd rather be a peasant with you, Armes, in a bed of straw, than sit on the throne of France."

Pompee returned. Armes ran down the steps and leaped up on Tom. When he looked back Athenée had disappeared from the balcony. He was glad, for he did not want to see her as he left.

"Well, Pompee," he said as they passed the sentries at

the gates and came out onto the road to the Cap. "Did you make the *ouanga?*

Pompee handed him a little round bag, covered with crimson silk, suspended from a braided cord of multi-colored silk threads.

Armes hung it around his neck. "Thank you, Pompee. I'm going to need it. Did you make one for yourself?"

"It was not necessary, milord. If you are safe you will protect me. If anything should happen to you, I would have nothing to live for."

Armes turned in the saddle and looked back at the house. The late afternoon sun had gilded the white plaster and emblazoned the windows until they shone like beaten metal. He knew that Athenée was weeping inside, and that Marie Louise who carried Henry's heir was weeping with her. Suddenly he thought of that long-ago day in Cambridgeport when he had parted from Kitty. He wondered if he too had a son, and he resolved that as soon as he returned from being a spy in the French camp, he would send her more money. Perhaps it was not *when* he returned but *if* he returned.

He flicked Tom lightly with his riding crop.

"Let's get it over with, Pompee."

33

POMPEE'S strong arms rowed the little skiff swiftly through the smooth, oily blackness of the water. There was no moon, but the lights of the French fleet, twinkling in the distance, flecked the water with myriad paths of dancing brilliance. Armes slumped in the stern of the boat. His searching fingers found his split lower lip, which was swollen to twice its normal size, then wandered to his left eye, which was nearly closed by a puffy, greenish-bronze swelling. A gash on one cheek was already encrusted with dried blood, and purple fingerprints discolored his neck. While his fingers explored his outer wounds, his head throbbed with a dull ache, and his whole body was sore from the pummeling it had taken.

Pompee halted the steady rhythm of the oars, reached

in his pocket for a linen kerchief, soaked it in the water, and handed it dripping to Armes.

"Sea water's good for bruises," he said consolingly. "Hold it on your cheek. No doubt but what you've been in a fight."

"Henry needn't have been so damned realistic," Armes said a bit resentfully. "Man, when I saw that doubled-up fist coming toward me, I thought the end of the world was on its way. Looked like an oversized ham."

Pompee giggled as he resumed his rowing. "But you sure messed Henry up a bit. When he fell over backwards on the table, the crash of glass sounded like a thousand windows breaking. Marie Louise'll have to get herself some new wine-glasses. Hee, hee! Never thought I'd see Henry sailing through the air like a sack of sugar."

Armes attempted a smile, but his swollen lip prevented its forming. "I'll bet that was the first time anyone ever knocked Henry down."

"But what made poor Henry the maddest—or made him look the maddest was when you ripped those medals off his chest and flung them in his face. Oh my, oh my! And when you called him a stinking black nigger. That riled him."

"Did our fight look convincing? Do you think it fooled Lebrun?"

"If I hadn't known, I'd have sworn he was going to kill you. Even knowing, I was afraid. You're a big man, milord, but when Henry grabbed you by the coat and lifted you off your feet, I wouldn't have given a sou for your life."

"And do you know, Pompee, all the time our good Henry was whispering under his breath, 'Sorry, TiArmes, got to make it look real good. Smash me now.'"

"You sure smashed him, milord."

They rowed on a way in silence. The lights of the boats did not seem to come any nearer.

"Young Lebrun certainly fell for Henry's scheme," Pompee giggled again, "just like Henry said he would. I sneaked up to Lebrun's room, told him how you had been hating Henry for his treatment of the *blancs,* how you wanted to get away from St. Domingue, and how Henry was keeping you because he needed a white man to advise him. Lebrun fell right in with it. Asked me if Mr. Holbrook knew anything about Henry's plans and I told him you knew more about them than Henry himself."

"Then what happened?" Armes asked.

"Well, Lebrun hemmed and hawed a little and asked if there was a way of getting you out of the palace, so I told him there was a way but it would cost money, because I'd have to bribe the guards at the door of your room and find us a boat. So, he went over and opened his *portemonnaie* and took out a handful of gold pieces and gave them to me. "See!" Pompee reached into his pocket and drew out several *louis d'or's,* which he placed in Armes' hand. "You know the rest, milord."

"Yes, and here we are on our way to meet General Leclerc. Pray to your god, Damballah, that he won't throw us in chains."

"You need not fret yourself, milord. You have the letter from Lebrun and you're still wearing the *ouanga* I made for you."

Armes felt his inside pocket to see if the letter were safe. While his fingers toyed with the little talisman, Pompee rowed on through the darkness, until gradually the lights came nearer. Armes advised Pompee to head for the biggest ship—the one ablaze with lights—and soon Pompee pulled up alongside. As their boat bumped against the towering black precipice of the ship, a face and shoulders appeared over the high railing and a voice called out.

"*Attention!* Who are you and what do you want? State your business!"

Armes noticed the glint of light along the barrel of a musket as the soldier aimed it at them. He stood up in the boat, balanced himself precariously and called out, "Armes Holbrook, an American citizen, with an important message for General Leclerc from Ensign Lebrun."

Now there were several heads peering over the rail. The first soldier shouted down to them again. "Stand your distance until I communicate with the officer of the day."

Pompee dropped his oars and the boat drifted idly. Soon an officer's shako appeared and another voice called out.

"Who are you? State your business!"

Armes repeated his previous statement. There was a further wait of several minutes while the officer went to confer with a superior. There followed the sound of ropes slipping through davits and a boat was lowered. A rope ladder snaked down the side of the ship and soldiers swarmed down the ladder into the boat, followed by the officer with the shako. They rowed the few feet which separated them from Armes' boat and, when they were alongside, reached

279

over, caught hold of the boat, and held it. The officer was directly opposite Armes now and raised a lantern to scrutinize him carefully.

"You are a white man!" He seemed surprised.

"Yes."

"You have been injured."

"Thanks to General Christophe."

"And this man?" The officer indicated Pompee.

"My servant, sir. He and Ensign Lebrun together saved me from being hanged tomorrow morning. I have a letter from Ensign Lebrun to General Leclerc."

The officer reached an open hand across the few inches of water between the boats.

Armes shook his head. "My letter is to General Leclerc and Ensign Lebrun instructed me to give it to him and nobody else."

The officer placed the lantern on the seat beside him.

"This is a most difficult situation, Monsieur Holbrook. We have been warned to expect some unusual sort of ambush. However, as far as I can see, you are alone with this man here, and certainly two lone men cannot be dangerous. Have your man row you to the ship and come aboard, both of you. I shall hold you under arrest until I confer with General Leclerc." The two boats proceeded to the side of the ship, and Armes and Pompee followed the officer up the swaying rope ladder.

Armes was quite unprepared for what he saw. The entire deck was brilliantly illuminated, but it was hardly the deck of a man-of-war. Amidships the deck was covered with rich carpets, and varnished bulkheads reflected the lights of a hundred lanterns. Chairs and sofas more suitable for a salon than a ship were sheltered by brilliantly striped awnings, and the entire deck was a litter of satin cushions, velvet poufs, delicate tables and tabourets. He felt he had stepped aboard some floating palace rather than a ship of war. He stared in amazement while the officer called two grizzled veterans and said something which sent them flying below deck. They appeared in moments with leg irons and chains. The officer bowed to Armes.

"I regret, Monsieur Holbrook, but I must take all precautions." He spoke half apologetically as he searched Armes and Pompee for weapons and then snapped on the manacles. "It will only be for a moment. General Leclerc is dressing, and will see you shortly." He turned and left them

280

standing there, securely chained to a gun carriage, their every move watched by two soldiers.

"Well, here we are, Pompee," Armes whispered.

Pompee shook his head grimly as Armes continued. "It isn't every night I have a fight with the governor of the Département du Nord; am sentenced to be hanged in the morning; go for a boat ride at midnight; and end up chained to a French cannon."

"Sh-h-h!" Pompee warned, "someone is coming." He inclined his head to indicate a door that was opening slowly.

Armes followed the direction of Pompee's eyes. Indeed somebody was coming, and it certainly was not General Leclerc. It was undoubtedly the most beautiful woman Armes had ever seen. From engravings sent from France, he recognized her as Pauline Bonaparte, sister of Napoleon and wife of General Leclerc. She was taller than Armes had imagined a sister of Napoleon might be, for he had often heard him referred to as "the Little Corporal." And . . . she was far more beautiful than he had ever imagined from the poor prints he had seen. She was far more beautiful than any woman had a right to be. A thin white muslin dress of the exaggerated Directoire style revealed rather than concealed the white globes of her breasts. It was bound with a sapphire velvet ribbon high above her waist and fell in straight, narrow lines from the firm, forward-thrust breasts. As she stepped in front of one of the ship's lanterns, the dress disappeared almost entirely and Armes saw only Pauline—the smooth contours of her body, lightly veiled by the flimsy muslin. She walked slowly toward them, a faintly quizzical smile on her lips. Although it was obvious that she had seen them, she pretended not to notice until she was only a few feet away. Then she stopped, drew back in mock surprise, gasped in pretended fright, and surveyed them carefully from her vantage point.

Pauline's look was eloquent. Armes remembered having been undressed in public once before by a woman's gaze. That was when Topaze had appraised him. Now, for the second time, a woman's eyes slowly stripped off his clothes, garment by garment, until he stood before her in unashamed nakedness. Unconsciously his body responded to her eyes, which were too warm; her lips, which were too full; her breasts, which were too provocative; and her flesh, which was too tempting.

281

"Oh, la la, monsieur, but you did give me a start." Her words lilted trippingly. "I had not thought to find a stranger on my ship, chained to one of my cannons."

Armes bowed as cavalierly as his manacles would permit.

"C'est la guerre, madame! Is it war or politics that is credited with making strange bedfellows?"

She looked at him quizzically from under her long, darkened lashes. "We are not engaging in politics, monsieur, and as far as I know we are not at war and . . . *hélas,* we are certainly not bedfellows."

"At least we are not at war tonight, madame, as I am your prisoner, but there is a possibility that tomorrow night . . ."

"We might be at war, you and I? *Alors,* monsieur, why not? It appears that you might be a most worthy adversary in war." Her hand stroked the muzzle of the cannon. "Would I succumb under fire from your heavy artillery?"

"A question which I would be most happy to answer with proof whenever Madame finds it convenient."

She stepped around to the side of the gun carriage where he was chained, so close to him that the heady odor of heliotrope perfumed the air he breathed; so close he could see the outline of the hard rosy nipples of her breasts under the thin fabric.

"Who are you?" Her voice sank to a husky whisper. *"Mon Dieu,* tell me who you are!"

"My name is Armes Holbrook. And you, madame?"

"I am the wife of General Leclerc."

"My pleasure, madame. I regret I cannot kiss your . . . hand." He held up one arm as far as the manacles allowed. "Your husband's hospitality . . ."

". . . seems to be wanting. I have an idea you will not remain in chains very long. You will find I am not without influence with my husband."

"Merci, madame."

A detail of four soldiers, headed by a captain, came marching down the deck. It was the same officer who had questioned Armes in the boat. He drew a key from his pocket and unlocked the manacles and chains, tossed them to a soldier, and ordered him to release Pompee. Pauline had scurried off, but before she turned the corner of the deck, she halted and looked back at Armes. Both he and the captain noticed her smile. Armes returned it, and saw the captain blanch and stiffen.

282

"General Leclerc will see you in his cabin, monsieur. This way, please. Bid your slave come with you."

"Pompee is not my slave . . ." Armes began, momentarily forgetting his new role. Then he caught himself. "Thanks to Christophe we are not allowed to have slaves anymore."

The captain dismissed Pompee with a glance. They followed him along the deck in the opposite direction to which Pauline had fled, and down a curving flight of stairs to the deck below. The companionway was but dimly lighted, but an open door cast a brilliant block of light in the narrow hall. The captain waved Armes in. He entered alone, and the door was closed behind him. Pompee remained outside with the soldiers.

General Leclerc was seated at a desk. Beside him was his wife, but this was quite a different Pauline from the one Armes had met on deck. This was the sister of the first consul of France and the wife of the new governor-general of St. Domingue. She sat stiffly in an armchair of equal height to that of her husband, with a concealing lace shawl around her shoulders. Leclerc, beside her, was a handsome man, tall, slender, and more blond than brunette. He looked even younger than his thirty years, for his face was smooth, unlined, and almost adolescent. One felt he had carefully cultivated the wisps of side whiskers to make himself appear older. Now he tugged at them nervously.

"Monsieur Holbrook, I believe?" Armes was surprised at the youthfulness of his voice. It was difficult to believe that this callow-looking youth was one of Napoleon's most brilliant generals.

"At your service, General."

"I understand you have a letter to me from Ensign Lebrun, whom I sent ashore this morning."

Arms produced the letter and handed it to Leclerc. The general broke the seals, smoothed the paper out on his desk, and read it, with Pauline looking over his shoulder. He glanced at her for confirmation, and when she nodded her head in approval, he addressed Armes.

"You seem to come well recommended. But there is much I do not understand as to how you happen to be here. Explain, Monsieur Holbrook."

Armes recounted his Boston background, his reasons for coming to St. Domingue, his early acquaintanceship with Henry.

"In the Bouckmann uprising," he continued "Henry Christophe saved my life. Why, I do not know, except that when I was a guest at the Hotel Couronne while he was a slave there, I had been kind to him on occasion. The fact that he saved my life placed me under a certain obligation to him. As Henry Christophe rose to power, he came to demand more and more of my services. I tell you in confidence, General Leclerc, that Henry does not read or write. He needed someone whom he could trust to attend to these most important details, and he felt that he could trust me because at one time we were friendly."

Leclerc looked at Armes in surprise. "You were friendly with a *nègre*—an ex-slave?"

"Some of the blacks have admirable qualities, General. I have found them to be . . ."

It was evident that Leclerc wished to hear nothing in praise of the Negroes.

"Quite right, quite right! Please continue with your story."

"However, of late, I have frequently disagreed with Henry. In my opinion, which is shared by all the other whites, St. Domingue would be a thousand times better off as a French colony under a French governor than it is at present under the black rule of Toussaint, Christophe, and Dessalines, who are all ignorant, uneducated men. We require a stable government here in St. Domingue, and to attain it we need white men in power. The rights of the plantation owners must be restored. I know! I am one, or rather I was one until Henry preempted my plantation. Why should we sacrifice that which is legally ours? We should have it all back, and the only way we can get it is under French rule."

". . . and through a restoration of slavery, Monsieur Holbrook?" Leclerc leaned forward in his chair.

It was a difficult question for Armes to answer, because he was not entirely sure of Leclerc's sentiments. He studied Leclerc for a moment. Leclerc was a white. Logically he must be on the side of the whites. Therefore Armes must speak as a white plantation owner.

"Most certainly, General Leclerc! Slavery must be restored."

"In that I agree with you, Monsieur Holbrook, and so does the first consul. But we must proceed slowly. In the end, slavery will be re-established. Am I right, my dear?" He turned toward Pauline.

Pauline spoke for the first time. "The Revolution introduced some very admirable sentiments in France, monsieur, particularly those about equality. However my brother has abandoned that particular sentiment. He has proved that all men are not equal; otherwise my brother would not be first consul; my husband would not be a general with soldiers under him; and you, Monsieur Holbrook, a former plantation owner with slaves under you. No, there is no equality among men of the same color, therefore there can be no equality between whites and blacks—between superior and inferior races." She threw off the shawl from her shoulders and leaned slightly forward to display her breasts, conscious of Armes' eyes upon them.

"Exactly my sentiments, madame! And these sentiments of mine are shared by all the whites in St. Domingue." Armes was beginning to feel more secure in his position, and the breasts were certainly enticing. He advanced to the desk and placed both hands on it, leaning forward that he might see further down into the violet cleft under the muslin. *"Absolument!* There must be a return to slavery. A free nigger is a dangerous nigger."

Leclerc offered Armes his snuff box with an elegant gesture.

"Do be seated, Monsieur Holbrook. Please continue with your interesting history. I believe now that we see eye to eye."

Armes thought for a second. "Where was I? Oh yes! As time went on, Henry and I came to disagree violently about almost everything. He is a stubborn, arrogant, dogmatic egotist who can see only his own side of every question. He is a primitive tyrant who will trample anyone and everyone underfoot in his mad thirst for power. Conditions have been unbearable between us of late, and I was willing to abandon everything here if I could find some way to escape, but Henry never let me out of his sight. Although I have never been under arrest, I have been so closely watched that I am virtually a prisoner. And I have reason to believe that my life has been in danger. Whenever I disagreed with Henry, he would fly into a rage, as he did last night. That was, however, the first time he ever laid hands on me." Armes patted his scarred cheek lightly. "But I am glad to say Henry carries as many marks as I do."

"You say you were not a prisoner. Could you not have escaped?"

"A white man in St. Domingue who has been a friend of Henry Christophe's is a marked man, hated by whites and

285

Negroes alike. Where could I go? To the whites? Despite my efforts to help them, they all considered me a renegade. To the blacks? Not one, except my man Pompee, would have helped me. Had I managed to board a ship, my absence would have been discovered and the ship searched. However, when I learned that the French were coming, I was most hopeful, and this morning when your emissary arrived, I was sure I could bring matters to a head. I attended Henry's council of state this afternoon. I have always had the entrée and I immediately advised complete surrender to you. I pointed out that it was useless to resist. Henry became angry. We had a few unpleasant words, and he commanded me to leave Cap François and retire to my plantation, which is now his, but no sooner had I arrived there than a messenger from Henry also arrived and insisted that I return to the Cap with him and that I attend the state dinner Henry was giving that evening. When I entered the banquet hall, I discovered that I shared the place of honor with Ensign Lebrun —he on Henry's right hand, I on his left."

"How do you explain his sudden change of heart?"

"There is no way of understanding these niggers, *mon général*. Perhaps Henry wanted to show off. The presence of another white man besides your envoy would enhance his prestige. Perhaps he even went so far as to think that your man would feel more comfortable with another white man there. I do not know. It is next to impossible to explain how these niggers think. They act on impulse only. Remember, they are really savages, scarcely a generation away from Africa, with only a thin veneer of civilization."

Leclerc agreed. "Exactly! That is what General Rochambeau, my second-in-command, says. He has lived here in St. Domingue—he knows them."

"Then," Armes continued, "while we were eating, the question of capitulation to the French came up again. Some of Henry's staff were baiting Lebrun. It placed him in a difficult position, so I sided with him—there is a strange affinity between two white men when they are alone among a hundred blacks. The argument became heated. Lebrun was very diplomatic—he kept silent, but I talked. Gradually tempers rose, mine along with the rest. Then . . . well, everything happened very suddenly. I regret to say I have a very explosive temper. It is impossible for me to control it. The whole affair culminated in Henry rising from the table to dash a glass of wine in my face—see." Armes pointed to the purple stain on his cravat. "Well, that did it. I reached over and pulled off some of the fake medals on Henry's chest and flung them in his face while I called him a no-good black bastard that should be shoveling horse manure from the stables at the Couronne rather than sitting at a table, trumped up like a general. That started it. Henry and I had a free-for-all."

Pauline leaned toward Armes and smiled.

"From your looks, Monsieur Holbrook, I would say that this Henry Christophe must be a very powerful man to handle an adversary as strong as you."

"When you see Henry, you'll understand. He's as strong as an ox. He picked me up and threw me on the floor, but I rolled over and avoided the kicks from his heavy boots which he aimed at my face. I managed to get up on my feet and we grappled. I heard a crash and saw Henry's feet in the air over the banquet table. He recovered himself, leaped upon me, pinned me down on the floor, clutched his black hands around my throat, and nearly strangled me before he released me and placed me under arrest. Then and there he sentenced me to be hanged in the morning."

A wry smile changed the curve of Leclerc's lips.

"As a general myself, I can quite appreciate his actions."

Armes laughed. "Poor Henry! It was a sad blow to his dignity before your envoy. There is nothing Henry hates as much as to be laughed at, and today all Cap François is giggling about Henry sprawling in the lobster mayonnaise. However, my story ends, because my man, Pompee, knows more about subsequent events than I do."

"But this man is a Negro. How can you trust him?"

"A rather needless question, sir. If it were not for Pompee, this coming dawn would certainly be my last. There is one thing I will say about these niggers, General Leclerc. Some of them can be faithful—exactly as a dog is faithful to his master. Pompee is that type, absolutely devoted to me. I can trust him."

Leclerc rose from the desk, opened the door, and spoke a few words to the captain outside. Pompee entered. Under Leclerc's questioning, Pompee presented his version of the story as he had explained it earlier to Armes.

When he had finished, Leclerc held a whispered consultation with Pauline, which Armes could not overhear but only judge by the emphatic noddings of Pauline's pretty head. Leclerc also nodded gravely before addressing Armes.

"I think we shall take advantage of your knowledge of St. Domingue, as Ensign Lebrun suggests. Outside of General Rochambeau, we are quite unacquainted with the colony, and he has not been here for some years. Things have changed since then." Lebrun's finger pointed directly at Armes. "Monsieur Holbrook, would you be interested in serving France?"

"France and the whites and you, General, and you, madame." Armes caught a sidelong glance from Pauline.

"Then I shall commission you in the French army. Perhaps such a procedure is a bit unusual, but as both General Lafayette and General Rochambeau served under General Washington, I feel we can commission you to serve under the first consul. Shall we say the rank of captain, Monsieur Holbrook?"

Armes started to express his gratitude, but he was interrupted by Pauline. "Congratulations, Monsieur Holbrook, or should I say *mon capitaine*. We must see about a uniform for you, so that you may attend my *levée* tomorrow morning. *Hélas!* Your size! It is indeed a problem, for there are few men in France as tall as you. *Mais oui,* Charles"— she touched Leclerc's arm—"Captain Hoffman, the Alsatian! He is quite as *grand* as Captain Holbrook. Send an orderly to his cabin at once. Request the loan of one of his dress uniforms until such a time as our tailors can make one." She turned her radiant smile on Armes. "We'll have you a regular French captain by morning."

Leclerc stood up, signifying that the interview was over.

"We shall prepare a cabin for you, also such necessary things as you may need—razors, fresh linen, and the uniform Madame suggests. As for your servant . . ."

"Perhaps the cabin would be large enough for us both," Armes suggested.

"You mean you would sleep in the same room with a nigger?" Leclerc was astonished.

"If I may, sir. Here in St. Domingue we have become accustomed to two things—to black slaves and their services. It becomes difficult for us to do things for ourselves after a time. Pompee has always occupied a cot in my room and attends to all my needs. He is most invaluable when it comes to taking off my boots."

"Good God, man, I take off my own boots."

"But you will not, General, when you have established yourself in St. Domingue."

288

"I think we are going to like it here, Charles." Pauline's words were followed by a little laugh. "And I think we are indeed fortunate to have the services of Captain Holbrook. Most fortunate indeed. *Bonne nuit, mon capitaine.*"

Armes bowed to them both and, motioning to Pompee to follow him, left the room.

34

WHEN Armes awoke the next morning in the cabin that had been hastily prepared for him, it took him some time to orient himself and realize where he was. At first, it almost seemed he must be back on board the ship that had brought him to St. Domingue, but when his hand wandered to his face and he felt the swollen eye and the dried blood on his cheek, he recalled the events of the night before and understood exactly where he was. He was on board the French frigate and he was now a captain in the Army of France.

His vision was blocked by a narrow wooden shelf which extended above his bunk and, although it hardly seemed wide enough for a man to lie on, it was evidently where Pompee slept, for a pink-palmed black hand dangled over the edge. Armes banged with his fist on the board over his head, and Pompee swung his legs over and bounced down onto the floor. Before Armes could speak, Pompee cautioned silence by placing his finger to his lips and pointed to the ornamental fretwork which ventilated the cabin at the top. He leaned over, placed his mouth close to Armes' ear and whispered, slurring the Creole words so that it would be difficult for a Frenchman not familiar with the patois to understand what he was saying.

"We must take care. It is possible that we are being watched."

Armes noted the open fretwork and nodded his head in assent then, in French and loud enough so that he could be overheard, he spoke.

"Thank God, Pompee, we are out of the clutches of that black maniac, Christophe. Had it not been for you, *mon vieux,* my neck would have been considerably stretched by a rope by this time."

Pompee's French was not too good. He had always spoken

Creole, but if his French was not grammatical, at least it was understandable, and his reply assured Armes of their safety. He spoke at length of his admiration for Leclerc, the startling beauty of his wife, and his high regard for the French army. While they were talking a heavy rap on the door caused Pompee to turn and open it—only a few inches at first—to ascertain the identity of the knocker. It was a French soldier, evidently an orderly, for he wore a white coat with his uniform trousers. His arms were piled high with clothing—small clothes, uniform, towels, and a case of razors resting on top.

"Captain Hoffman's compliments to Captain Holbrook," he said as he walked into the cabin and laid a freshly pressed uniform on the bunk. "And Captain Beauchamp's"—he laid the case of razors alongside it. "And Captain Annency's"—he added the spotless linen to the uniform. "And Madame Leclerc's"—he put down the snowy towels and the bars of perfumed soap. His arm raised in a stiff salute to which Armes replied, he withdrew.

The razors were of fine Toledo steel; the towels with Pauline's monogram were soft and fluffy; the linen drawers new and of the finest cloth, and the uniform almost a perfect fit, even though Armes was fearful that the seams of the trousers would split with any undue exertion. However, when Pompee had finished with him, he felt quite presentable and not a little proud of his gilt-fringed epaulets. The swelling around his eye had gone down somewhat during the night, his lower lip had regained a more normal size, and the black crescent of court plaster on his cheek gave him a rakish air—not unlike a buccaneer. Pompee had clubbed his hair with a velvet ribbon and tied a stock high around his neck. Indeed, from what Armes could see in the miniature mirror, he looked quite presentable. The uniform was most flattering; he hoped Pauline would be impressed.

Not knowing where to go or what to do, he sat down again on the bunk, but his problem was soon solved by another knock. This time the door opened to disclose a young officer, tall, blond, ringleted, and perfumed.

"Captain Hoffman at your service, Captain Holbrook." He smiled and pointed to the uniform which Armes was wearing.

"Yours?" Armes nodded.

Hoffman's smile widened into a grin. "Madame requests that you attend her *levée*. Shall we proceed?"

Pauline's cabin could have made twenty of the tiny cubby-

290

hole Armes occupied. Were it not for the cant of the walls and the diminutive windows, Armes could have imagined himself in the Tuileries. The room was sumptuously furnished in the heavy Napoleonic style of polished mahogany with ormolu mountings. The ceiling simulated a field tent with broad stripes of red and white satin rising to a center pinnacle. Far and away the most imposing piece of furniture in the room was Pauline's bed, shaped like a swan and piled high with frothy pillows of lace. Pauline was sitting up in bed, dressed in a peignoir sufficiently flimy to show her rose-nippled breasts, holding court *à la reine*. The cabin was crowded with officers, all of them young, bowing over her hand, reaching for her fan, pouring her chocolate, retrieving the yapping spaniels which occasionally fell off the bed, or just staring at her, wide-eyed with admiration.

Hoffman pushed his way through the press to the side of the bed, clicked the heels of his polished boots together, and bowed low.

"Hans, *mon cher*. How delightful! It's always such a pleasure to see my big blond Siegfried." She glanced past him and caught Armes' eye. "And Captain . . . Captain . . . ?"

"Holbrook. At your service, madame."

"La! Such a difficult name to pronounce. I prefer your first name. Wasn't it *Canon*?" She winked at him intimately.

"Quite near, madame. It is Armes."

She extended her hand slowly.

"Now I remember. It is a most appropriate name for a soldier. I seem to remember that you are well-armed, *mon capitaine*."

He leaned to kiss her hand and whispered, "I believe I am, madame, but the final judgment must rest with you." His words were scarcely audible, but she heard them and allowed her hand to linger at his lips for an extra moment.

"I'd willingly detain you longer, Monsieur *Bien-Armé*, but my husband awaits a word with you, so I shall dismiss you this morning. However, in the future I shall not be so indulgent. We must find time to speak of your arms, which I fear would soon penetrate my weak armor."

"I shall anticipate that most interesting conversation, madame." Armes relinquished her hand.

"*Vraiment?*"

"*Certainement*, madame."

"Possibly when we are on land again?"

"*Mais oui*, madame."

Armes followed Hoffman from the cabin, successfully parrying the envious glances of the other young officers. Leclerc's cabin was next door. Here indeed was quite a different assemblage. Where youth, good looks, and virility had been conspicuously present in Pauline's, military experience and grizzled hair were more in evidence in Leclerc's cabin. Hoffman left Armes at the door and, as he entered, more than a dozen pairs of eyes scrutinized him. Leclerc was seated at the same desk, occupying one of the high-backed chairs. The other, where Pauline had sat the night before, was empty. Standing at one side was young Lebrun, looking tired and drawn after an apparently sleepless night.

Leclerc introduced his generals and his colonels quickly, explaining to them that Armes was the American they had just been talking about, then turned to Lebrun.

"Repeat your story to these gentlemen, sir."

The young ensign had apparently been dumbfounded with his reception at Henry's palace. Although he confessed he had not exactly anticipated a grass-thatched hut with a dirt floor, he had been entirely unprepared for the splendors of Henry's entertainment. He told of the magnificent dinner, the gold plate, the liveried servants, and the beauty of the palace. During his recital of the quarrel between Armes and Henry, he nodded and smiled occasionally at Armes to confirm their conspiratorial ties. Then he went on to tell of his bedroom, the furniture, the page boys who waited on him, even the beautiful octoroon who shared his bed.

"It will make an ideal residence for you, General, and for Madame. It is really a little Versailles, and I found it difficult to believe that I was entirely surrounded by Africans. It all reminded me a little of the days of Louis XV and the Parc aux Cerfs."

"Especially the mulatto wench." One of the colonels licked his lips in anticipation. "How did you like her?"

"She was beautiful sir, and shall I say—er—most talented?" Lebrun stammered and blushed.

"But what of Cap François?" a grizzled colonel demanded.

"One of the fairest cities I have ever seen," Lebrun replied. "Paved streets and imposing mansions, a magnificent cathedral and a splendid opera house. It is indeed a *petit Paris* but even more beautiful than Paris, for the sunny streets are lined with palms and tropical trees. One sees flowers everywhere—huge scarlet flowers, vines ablaze with cerise and crimson flowers—and orange trees in bloom. *En effet, messieurs, c'est un véritable Eden!*"

"How fortunate we are! And what defenses did you see?" another veteran asked.

"I regret I saw very little of the city—only what I saw from General Christophe's carriage during my rides back and forth from the quay. I saw no defenses on the waterfront with the exception of the little fort."

"Did you see any evidences of a large army?" This time Leclerc asked the question. "No, wait, Lebrun, perhaps Captain Holbrook can better answer that question. What is the size of Christophe's army?"

Armes knew that Henry wanted him to belittle his power and create a false confidence among the French. This was not too difficult. The truth was quite sufficient.

"Henry has only a small army," Armes replied. "He has one crack company which he calls his Dahomeys. They are the pick of all St. Domingue—tall strapping bucks who Henry has drilled to perfection. Naturally they are devoted to him, for he has indulged them until they have become the aristocracy of St. Domingue—haughty, supercilious, and insolent. They are detested by the other soldiers and all the civilian population." He hesitated for a moment.

"Go on, Captain," Leclerc urged. He turned to the others. "You see, messieurs, information like this could be obtained in no other way." There was a chorus of agreement.

"But except for the Dahomeys," Armes continued, "Henry has almost no army at all—at least nothing which France would consider an army. There are about four thousand so-called foot soldiers who drill when they feel like it, which is seldom. They are entirely unacquainted with the word 'discipline.' A soldier may disappear, spend weeks or months in the mountains, then reappear when he takes the notion, and nothing is said. These men have no uniforms; they wear what they have or what they can find. As for arms—almost nothing. But"—Armes emphasized the word—"do not underrate them; they are terrific fighters. And they are also most unreliable. At present they owe lip service to Henry because he is the strong man of St. Domingue today. But remember this! In the days of slavery here, the thing a slave most dreaded was to have a Negro master, for some free Negroes held slaves. They have the same feeling toward any Negro over them. They ony respect whites, and if France offered

293

them more than Henry Christophe, they would willing desert him."

Leclerc toyed with a miniature bronze cannon on his desk and Armes, remembering Pauline's conversation of the night before, wondered if the little cannon might not be symbolic of Pauline's desires. He smiled to himself as he awaited Leclerc's reply.

"What do you know about the governor of the West—Dessalines?"

Armes shook his head grimly. "I have met Jean Jacques and I sincerely hope I never see him again. He is a *brute* with a deep and bitter hatred for both whites and mulattoes. If Dessalines had his way, there would not be a person with a drop of white blood alive in St. Domingue today. Although Dessalines is a more ignorant man than Henry Christophe, he is a better soldier. He has a larger army than Henry, but I daresay it is no better disciplined."

"And Pétion, in Port-au-Prince?" Leclerc pushed the little cannon across the desk.

"I do not know him, sir. He is a mulatto, and more French than Negro—an artist, a dreamer, a visionary. Offer him a couple of pretty enameled crosses and you can buy him. As to his army,—" Armes snapped his fingers—"he has an oversupply of mulatto officers, but no privates."

He advanced a step towards Leclerc. *"Mon général!* You have here, so I was told in Cap François, over twenty thousand soldiers of France. Henry cannot and will not resist you. But Henry is a sensitive man, like all men whose beginnings have been humble." He looked under his lashes to see if Leclerc would wince, but the man's face was like marble. "Yesterday when Monsieur Lebrun landed in Cap François, Henry was hurt and disappointed. He had expected to see you, and not seeing you injured his vanity. That is why he has refused to act. His subterfuge is that he cannot act without the authority of Toussaint. Pah! That is a lie, conceived to hide his wounded pride. Above all Henry desires legitimate authority. He had rather be a general of France than a general of St. Domingue. Pin the Legion of Honor on his chest, give him a parchment heavy with seals and ribbons that names him to some exalted rank, and you will have Henry Christophe in the palm of your hand. My suggestion is that you write him a personal letter."

Leclerc stood up to signify that the conference was over. As the officers filed out the door, he detained Armes. When the door had closed behind them, he indicated a chair opposite him and bade Armes sit down.

"You think the letter might gain our peaceful entry into Cap François?"

"I do, General, but it must be most carefully composed. Henry is no fool. The letter must be friendly, but not too friendly. It must bear the weight of the authority of France without seeming to threaten. It must be definite, but most important of all, it must be written from one general to another."

Leclerc tugged at his side whiskers and seemed lost in thought. He spoke softly, quite oblivious of Armes' presence.

"Bonaparte has ordered me to conquer St. Domingue as a stepping stone to still greater conquests. He has given me wide latitude; told me to treat diplomatically with the Negroes; humor them at first and, once having gained their confidence, crush them. Perhaps"—he now seemed to be aware of Armes sitting opposite him—"perhaps you are right, Captain Holbrook. We shall win this Christophe over peaceably before we crush him completely. Let us write him —a letter from General Leclerc to General Christophe. Here" —he pushed a sheet of paper and a quill across the desk— "you write the letter, Captain, and if it seems adequate to me, I shall have it copied and sign it. Write, Captain Holbrook, and perhaps your words will save St. Domingue for France and bring a whole new world under our first consul."

Armes reached for the pen. How he wished he could write the message he really wanted to send to Henry—to tell him to burn the city, retreat to the hills, and leave nothing for the French but smoking earth. He glanced up and saw Leclerc's narrow blue eyes staring at him. As he pushed the bronze inkwell across the polished surface of the desk, Armes dipped the pen in ink and sent the quill scratching across the paper. Slowly the words took form—fateful words that marched across the white sheet.

To General Henry Christophe of the French
   Army of St. Domingue.

Mon General:

I learn with sorrow, Citizen General, that you have refused to receive the squadron of the French army which I command, saying that you have no order from the former Governor-General Toussaint to admit the rightful governor-general of the Colony, myself.

I have the highest respect for you, Citizen General. We have heard of your bravery in France. It will greatly distress me to count you among the rebels instead of a valued member of my own staff. However, I must warn you. If you have not delivered all the batteries on the coast tomorrow at daybreak and all the surrounding country from 1 Bonnet à l'Evêque to Milot, I shall disembark 15,000 soldiers of France and take the city of Cap François. I hold you responsible for the safety of the city and that the flames of rebellion do not break out before I arrive.

Leclerc
Governor-General of the Colony of
St. Domingue and General of the Army of France

Leclerc studied the letter carefully. Armes had inserted the two geographical names so that Henry would understand he had written the letter himself, and he was sure that Henry would not miss the implication of the last sentence.

Leclerc looked up at him. "The Bonnet à l'Evêque?"

"A high mountain that marks the boundary of Henry's jurisdiction."

Leclerc studied the letter a moment longer. "It seems quite in order, Captain, and most diplomatic. I shall have it transcribed and send it ashore by Ensign Lebrun. Possibly he will wish to renew his acquaintance with the beautiful octoroon who seems to be a part of the furniture of Christophe's palace." He smiled weakly and rose. "Thank you, Captain Holbrook."

"Armes picked up the little cannon on the desk and examined it. "A beautiful little toy, General Leclerc."

Leclerc smiled cordially and suddenly became a man instead of a general.

"Yes, isn't it? I value it highly, as it was a present from my wife."

"You are most fortunate to have such a charming wife."

Leclerc did not answer, but Armes noticed the distressed look in his eyes.

He bowed his way out and sought Pompee in his cabin. Pompee's fingers on his lips again cautioned silence. He beckoned to Armes to follow him and led Armes aft, down a narrow ladder and along a dark corridor which terminated in a narrow door, which Pompee opened. It was the officers' privy, perched precariously over the water, but closed with

296

a solid door. They sat down on the narrow bench and saw the sea sparkling below them through the double holes sawed in the planking.

"This is the only safe place on board to talk," Pompee whispered.

Armes gave a full account of what had taken place and repeated almost word for word the letter he had written for Leclerc. Pompee's head moved slowly up and down in approval. Once again they made their way up on deck, in time to see the gig with the tricolor carrying Lebrun toward the Cap.

Knots of officers crowded the deck, talking and pointing to various outstanding landmarks in the city. Dominating everything was the glistening white palace of Henry Christophe, set against the soft green verdure of the mountain. The spires of the cathedral soared above the city; the streets were thronged with people; the city seemed to be in a holiday mood.

Armes was hopeful that Pauline would appear, but throughout the morning he caught no sight of her. Evidently she remained below during the heat of the day. The morning dragged on slowly. Hoffman appeared and spoke to Armes, then introduced him to several new officers, who accepted him rather reluctanly. Fired by Lebrun's report of his experience with the mulatto girl, they questioned Armes about the women of St. Domingue and his detailed information quickly established a camaraderie between them. He gave them explicit directions as to how to reach the house with the red door off the Place des Armes, and all of them were eagerly awaiting the opportunity to land.

Toward noon, they saw the gig returning with Lebrun standing in the bow. As soon as the little boat hove to, he clambered up the ladder and dashed for Leclerc's cabin. Immediately the deck started to buzz with excitement, and conversations became more spirited as wild rumors made the rounds. Several of the officers left to go below to pack their gear in preparation for a landing, for it had been quite universally agreed that Henry would offer no resistance. Armes leaned on the rail beside Hoffman, idly watching the light on the water.

A cry from the lookout in the crow's nest shattered the gay exuberance of the deck. "Fire! Fire in the city off the starboard bow!"

Armes looked first at Henry's palace. Great flowers of

297

orange flame sprouted from the windows, followed by a somber pall of black smoke. Armes knew that Henry had kindled those fires himself—he was burning all that he had accumulated during his period of power under Toussaint. Now, all over the city, spirals of smoke could be seen—one, two, three, until it became impossible to count the various separate and distinct conflagration. Soon the separate blazes mingled as house after house, then street after street sent towering clouds of sparks into the air. Cap François was blazing! Cap François was dying!

All through the afternoon the flames rose above the Cap, leveling the fairest city of the West Indies, the *petit Paris* of the New World. When darkness came the fiery glow rose high into the purple sky. Fire! It was Henry's answer to Leclerc's letter. Fire! It was the Negroes' answer to Napoleon for, as the flames mounted higher, it would seem that even the little Corsican, sitting in the Tuileries, might see that ominous glow in the sky. It was the fire of Napoleon's defeat in the New World, and it had been kindled by a black slave.

Cap François burned all night. The rich warehouses of sugar caramelized the streets; coffee was roasted by the ton; rum blued the flames; and still the fire burned, marking the end of planters' mansions and peasants' *cailles,* marking the end of Cap François and presaging the end of French dominion.

Armes watched the holocaust with mingled joy and sorrow, knowing that Henry watched it, grim and determined from the hills behind the Cap. Pompee in the general excitement had found his way to Armes' side and, while he watched, he whispered to Armes in Creole.

"Ogoun Feraille, our god of war, will be happy tonight. Never before has such a fire been lighted to honor Ogoun. He will enjoy it, because he knows that Henry lighted it. The red in the sky tonight is the color of Ogoun Feraille; the red blood that will flow in the streets is the color of Ogoun Feraille; the red stripe in the flag of France is the color of Ogoun Feraille. Ogoun Feraille will conquer."

"When you say Ogoun Feraille, it sounds as though you mean Henry," Armes whispered.

"Henry *is* Ogoun! He is the horse that Ogoun rides. The gods of Africa have come to earth in St. Domingue and the *loa* of Ogoun Feraille rides Henry Christophe to victory. Yes, milord, Henry Christophe will conquer, but it will be a long hard road, for he has a hard rider on his back."

Armes heard his name spoken very softly behind him and turned to see a French girl, dressed in the black of domestic service. She came close to him and whispered.

"Madame requests your presence in her cabin."

He followed her down the deserted companionway and along the corridor. She knocked discreetly at the door and, when it was opened, motioned for Armes to enter.

There was no light in the vast cabin but the red reflection of the sky. Armes felt the warmth of lips on his own and reacted to the questing hand.

"We have only a moment, Monsieur Grand Canon," Pauline whispered, "but I could exist no longer without proving to myself whether or not you are a braggart."

"And what is your opinion now, madame?"

"That you have good reason to be a braggart, Monsieur Très Grand Canon, and that I shall anticipate seeing you again. Now go, *mon capitaine*, before we both lose our reason."

35

IT was rumored, and probably not without foundation, that when Pauline's gig touched the ruined quay in Cap François and she went ashore, she wept in disappointment at the desolation she saw. Armes was not in the same boatload, so he did not witness her tears, but he was near weeping himself when he saw what remained of the once beautiful and flourishing city. There was nothing, or almost nothing, left except a few gutted buildings; some tottering masonry walls; piles of smoldering ashes, and blackened trunks of trees. Not a single inhabitant, white, black, or mulatto, was in sight. The blacks had departed as conquerors with Henry Christophe; two thousand whites had accompanied him as prisoners of war; and the mulattoes had gone along because they could not remain and there was no other place to go except where Henry led.

Henry had established headquarters near Marmelade, back in the mountains, where he had joined forces with Toussaint and Dessalines. It was war now! Toussaint's hopes for a *rapprochement* with French authority were dashed to earth.

It was a triumvirate between Henry, Dessalines, and Toussaint now. But Toussaint had lost heart. He was old, he was tired, and he was heartsick. Not so Henry or Jean Jacques, whose youth fired them. The French in power meant a return to slavery. Kill them, starve them, burn everything that might succor them. And so it was done.

The desolation of the countryside made Armes fear for those at Sans Souci, but he discovered that Pompee had unlimited means of communication, and was able to report that all there were safe. Moreover, Pompee's sources of information told him that although Henry was nominally encamped with Toussaint and Jean Jacques in the mountains, he was actually using Sans Souci as a general headquarters for his own army and defending it with his gallant Dahomeys.

Cap François did not rise as a phoenix from the flames. There was nobody to rebuild it and nothing to rebuild it with. Those who drifted back patched and repaired what little was left standing, but there was very little to patch or repair with. Gradually the hostages which Henry had taken with him found their way back to the desolate city. They were released not for humane reasons, but for economic ones. Henry had nothing with which to feed them and no place to keep them, and he could not very well slaughter them in cold blood, as Dessalines advised. In the future he would feel differently, but for the present he was content to let them depart, although Dessalines insisted on a mass execution for the whole lot. Dessalines ruthlessly killed as many as he could, but those that escaped him straggled back to Cap François in the same clothes in which they had fled and which were, by and large, their only possessions.

It was their soft white hands, uncalloused from any labor, that salvaged the old bricks from rubble piles, erected jerry-built walls to provide tottering supports for palm-leaf thatches, and managed to scrape together an existence far worse than that they had formerly allowed their slaves. In fact, in not a few cases their former slaves built the walls and laid the thatches for them, out of some lingering sense of devotion, while others sat back and doled out precious foodstuffs that they had scavenged in payment for their former masters' labor.

Regardless of the needs and wants of the city, however, construction was immediately commenced on a viceregal palace for Pauline, to be situated on the spot she had chosen on a promontory overlooking the bay. It turned out to be a crude affair, built of felled plam trees overlaid with lath and plaster, but its ornate white stucco was temporarily imposing. When it was finished she transferred her young ladies and her officers from the ships and instituted a series of *fêtes champêtres* which were, she hoped, as royally bucolic as those the late Marie Antoinette had given at the Trianon. Pauline's ladies flirted behind their fans with the simpering young officers, played blindman's buff on the terraces and, within a few weeks, Pauline discovered she was bored to death with the new palace, her young officers, and most of all her ladies-in-waiting.

It did not take her long, however, to discover that what her sister-in-law Josephine had claimed about the mulattoes of Martinique held equally true about the mulattoes of St. Domingue. Pauline found them to be far more handsome and infinitely more interesting than even the most dashing French officers, with the result that Pauline lost her boredom and the palace was treated to a constantly changing retinue of imposing young mulatto footmen in tight-fitting livery which had been especially designed by Pauline herself to make the most of their obviously male charms.

Armes had seen almost nothing of her since landing at Cap François, mainly because Leclerc, who himself had seen little of Pauline, had demanded most of Armes' time and attention at Army Headquarters, which were now established at Fort Picolet. Armes had attended almost daily conferences with the governor, and had advised him with a fair amount of truth and a far greater amount of subterfuge, with the result that Leclerc was as ignorant as before, although he considered himself well posted.

In a swift reconnoiter, made on the same day they landed, Pompee had discovered a half-ruined house not far from the fort which he had skillfully repaired and furnished with odds and ends salvaged from half-burned buildings, with the result that Armes lived with a certain amount of creature comfort. But he was lonely for Henry and Marie Louise, for Sans Souci and Milot, and most of all for Athenée. The weeks since he had seen her had been magnified into years. Life without her was only half a life—she was his completion.

But even the memory of her could not entirely satisfy Armes. He could love that memory, but he needed something more substantial to fulfill his daily needs. These were satisfied, if only temporarily, by a Negress whom Pompee had installed in the house. Not that she satisfied them directly! Maman, for that was the only name she had, was a woman of enormous girth, who heaved her quivering corpulence around the house with a rapidity which amazed Armes. Her heart, which occupied practically all of her enormous pile of flesh, probably accounted for her name. She mothered Armes, petted him, spoiled him, and, in her desire to see him happy, presented him with a seemingly endless procession of coffee-hued wenches, all of whom she introduced as her nieces. To her way of thinking a man needed a bed partner as much as he needed his supper. She was an excellent cook, and her ability to choose nieces was quite in proportion to her ability to cook a tasty supper from one scrawny chicken and a single yam.

Although Armes welcomed each of the nieces warmly, slept with all of them, and then gently propelled them to the front door and out the next morning, Maman saw that all her efforts to bring about a lasting alliance were in vain. She continued to provide them, however, and Armes continued to enjoy them without realizing that the supply had run out and the same ones were reappearing in his bed. In them he found a temporary forgetfulness, but neither singly nor collectively did they dispel the image of Athenée.

Armes' loneliness was not without compensations. He knew that he had been of real help to Henry. When Leclerc, angry and impatient at having made no progress in St. Domingue other than the seizure of the ruined Cap, had heard that Henry had left the safety of Marmelade and Sans Souci and established a camp at Limbe, only about twenty-five miles away, he made plans to ambush and capture Henry there. These plans, owing to Armes' knowledge of topography, were mostly made by Armes, and consequently he was well-informed of every move which the French army was to make. All of which he relayed to Pompee.

The night before the proposed ambush Pompee called a voodoo ceremony in the big *houmfort* which had been hastily thrown up on the edge of the town. The French had thought it some sort of a native dance hall, which in truth it was most of the time. The drums sounded all through that night, and the heavy reverberations of the *maman* drum were relayed on to Henry's camp at Limbe. In the morning when the French soldiers arrived on schedule to carry out their carefully laid ambush, Henry and all his soldiers were gone and Limbe was smoking as furiously as Cap François had smoked.

Then, the denouement! Impatient at his ability to accomplish anything, exasperated at the unwillingness of the blacks to come out in the open and be conquered, Leclerc abandoned his pretense of upholding freedom and equality for the blacks. None of the blacks seemed to believe them anyway, so Leclerc jettisoned all his protestations of good will and showed his true colors in a public proclamation that the plantation lands were to be restored to their former owners and that slavery would be reestablished in the colony. Let the black bastards swallow that! What Leclerc could not win by strategy he would win in open warfare with thousands of good French soldiers to win it for him.

Even before the proclamation was out, Armes had Pompee relay this information to Henry, who published it in every city, hamlet, and *carrefour*. The drums carried it from mountain to mountain; it went over jungle trails by peasants on foot and on bourriques. Toothless old crones tottered from house to house telling everyone they could reach, and even children ran loose in the village shouting that one hated word —"slavery."

Leclerc had played into Henry's hands, and Henry had the situation he wanted. Thousands of black peasants who had been lukewarm in their attitude toward the war lost no time in making their way to Henry's camp. Although they were half-naked, undernourished, and armed only with machetes or farm implements, they formed a redoubtable army which swept Henry, by guerilla tactics, over the intervening miles and carried him almost to the gates of Cap François.

From Pauline's sagging palace, the young citizen-lords and citizen-ladies could plainly see the campfires of the Negro army, and it sent a delicious shiver down their delicate spines. Just think! Over there were thousands of black savages waiting to devour them, but of course they were safe with the French army to protect them. Oh, it was most titillating to be in such imminent danger!

Leclerc was in Port-au-Prince when he heard the news, and the majority of the French fleet was with him. At his orders, the fleet immediately headed out into the Gulf of Gonaïves, circled the great northwest point, and sailed between the island of Tortue and Port-de-Paix just in time to arrive at Camp François and save the city. Henry scampered back up into the hills, thumbing his nose at the French army, but the French at length had an immense victory to celebrate. But Leclerc realized his mistake and, on the heels of his touted victory, he issued another proclamation. Proclamations were a simple matter and he could publish one an hour if he wished. This time he completely reversed himself. He had been misunderstood! It was an error, or so he assured the blacks. A return to slavery had never been considered for a moment. It went without saying that the French loved their black brethren. *Naturellement,* they desired nothing but complete freedom for them. Mother France stood with open arms to receive her black children as full citizens of France. *Liberté! Fraternité! Egalité!*

Henry heard the second manifesto with grave suspicions. Having the whites as avowed enemies was far better from his point of view than having them as false friends. But the peasants believed Leclerc and his dusted-off words. To them the crisis was over, and they need fear slavery no longer. They drifted back to their women and their *cailles,* where a man could fill his empty belly with beans instead of mangoes and sleep in a bed with a woman instead of on the hard ground. Henry dispatched word to Armes through Pompee that his men were deserting him. Outside of his Dahomeys at Sans Souci, he had only a few ragged battalions left. What should he do? Armes sent him a one-word message—"Wait."

That night Armes sought counsel of Pompee. They considered Henry's predicament from all angles. Pompee paced up and down the room while he pondered the matter. Gradually his pacing slowed and he stopped in the center of the room, his face contorted, his body frozen in immobility. At first Armes thought that the fellow was ill, but then realized that he was in communication with one of his gods. After a few seconds, Pompee shook himself, opened his eyes, and resumed his natural expression. His words carried surety and conviction.

"Ogoun Feraille says it is better for Henry to surrender," he stated. "Henry can do nothing by fighting against the French, as he is outnumbered and overpowered. Henry has nothing left to fight with but courage, and the French have everything. We shall tell Henry to surrender, and he will gain in the end. There are other ways of killing the French besides shooting them with bullets."

"Such as, Pompee?"

"Just this, milord. I have banded all of the *papalois* and *mamalois* of St. Domingue together. Never before has such a strong invocation risen to our gods from the hearts of their faithful priests and priestesses. We have invoked their aid against the French army, and they will not fail us. Wait and see, milord. The French will die like flies. How? Ask me how, milord."

"Yes, Pompee, how?"

"*La fièvre jaune!* Yellow fever! It will soon be the time of the year when it comes, and it kills the *blancs,* but never harms the blacks. Nothing can stop it. Neither the medicines of the whites nor their doctors. It kills more surely than a bullet and almost as fast. It will come, milord, and soon."

Armes shrugged his soldiers. He had expected some well-laid scheme of rebellion, but this seemed too fantastic to be credible. Although he had witnessed the power of voodoo in the past, it hardly seemed likely that it could send a plague so perspicacious that it would be able to choose between black and white.

"Does your voodoo wish to kill me along with the rest of the whites? You say it spares none."

"Oh, no, milord! Although you are so unfortunate as to have a white skin, you are not white. The voodoo gods see you as one of us."

"Thank them for me, Pompee," Armes laughed. "You know, you may be right. There are times when I forget that I am white. I'm beginning to act like a Negro, think like a Negro, and even feel like one."

Pompee grinned and wagged his head. "Then go to the pale young general with the curly whiskers tomorrow. Tell him Henry Christophe, that poor *gros nègre,* desires to surrender. Tell him, however, that Henry will surrender only on his own terms and in his own manner."

"But what are those terms and what is that manner and how shall I tell Leclerc that I have heard from Henry?"

Pompee stood before him, his arms spread apart with the pink palms of his hands showing. "Oh, milord, you know what to tell Leclerc. You do not have to ask Pompee. The words will form themselves in your mouth as you stand before him. You can formulate Henry's terms of surrender as well as he can. You and Henry are brothers. Just think what you would want yourself and ask for it. That's all, milord, that's all."

The next day, Armes requested a private audience with Leclerc, and was told through an aide-de-camp that the general would receive him at the palace instead of the fort. It seemed that Leclerc was taking advantage of the lull in hostilities to spend a few uninterrupted days with his wife. Armes had Pompee brush his uniform, shine his boots, and take special care in shaving him before he set off for the palace. It was the first time he had been there, and what had seemed from a distance to be an imposing structure proved, on closer inspection, to be most disappointing. The tropic rains had penetrated the plaster walls and distempered them with great damp blotches. Termites had gnawed at the green lumber foundations, canting the walls out of plumb. Everything about the place looked like a temporary stage setting, ready to be struck at any moment.

A handsome mulatto footman led Armes to a small salon, opened the door, and announced him. Pauline was inside with her husband, and Armes' thoughts reverted to the night he had come aboard the man-of-war. Leclerc's greeting was friendly and military. Pauline, however, rose from her chair and glided across the floor to meet Armes.

"Oh, the American captain! How delightful!" Her sidelong glance was like soft fingertips caressing his cheek. "But you have been so rude, *Monsieur Américain. Très impoli!* You have not been to see me, no, not once, since we have been in Cap François. *Hélas!* It is such a deadly place." She tripped back to stand beside Leclerc's chair, composing a pretty little picture of uxorial affection as her fingers toyed with the fringe of his epaulets. Her petulant words caressed him. "Charles, I insist that you discipline Captain Holbrook immediately. Condemn him to a month of hard labor on bread and water unless he promises to attend my next *soirée.*"

Leclerc nodded at Armes and smiled wanly. "You have heard the lady, Captain Holbrook. Which shall it be, bread and water or cakes and champagne?"

Leclerc appeared tired and disillusioned. He had achieved success in his marriage to a Bonaparte, but the sad part was that he was in love with her. In that Armes did not blame him, for Pauline was indeed a women to be loved. But Leclerc was no fool, and he was well aware that he was sharing her favors with young French studs and mulatto stallions. Now, from Pauline's affectionate greeting to Armes, Leclerc could see that he had another possible rival. It was becoming tiresome. He sighed.

Armes looked past the general to Pauline.

"I can think of nothing more charming, Madame Leclerc, now that I have the general's permission."

"Why, Charles." Her fingers ceased twining the epaulets

and twined his whiskers instead. "Did you forbid Captain Holbrook to come here?"

Leclerc sighed again. "No, my dear, but you must remember we have been fighting a little war—only a little one, to be sure—but a war nevertheless, and Captain Holbrook has been my good right hand."

Pauline flounced down into her chair. "Then, Charles, loan me your right hand for a while. The war is over, or practically so. At least that is what you told me. You routed the niggers; you have driven them away from Cap François. They are returning to their homes. Now you have convinced Toussaint that he should return to law and order. That means the war *is* over, darling, doesn't it?"

Armes' attention jumped to the information about Toussaint. It was something he was not aware of. Evidently Leclerc had been in communication with the old man. Here was something of importance to relay to Henry. If it were true, it would be a very good reason for Henry's surrender.

Leclerc answered her patiently. "Yes, my dear, Captain Holbrook may attend you. And now, will you excuse us. We have things to talk about which would not interest you in the least—dull military matters which soldiers must discuss."

"Of course, Charles, and I have so many things to do to get ready for the ball tonight. You'll attend, Captain Holbrook. Remember, it is an order. It will be such fun. It's going to be *bal masqué* and nobody, absolutely nobody, must know who is who. I'm going as a shepherdess. Oh la la! Now I've let the cat out of the bag, but you will not tell a soul, will you, Captain?"

He assured her that he would not and that he would immediately forget what she had said. As she closed the door to leave, she made a little moue at him which the door hid from Leclerc.

Leclerc straightened the papers on his desk. "And now, Captain Holbrook, perhaps we can talk business. You wanted to see me about an important matter?"

Armes came over to the desk and sat down at Leclerc's nod.

"I have some rather strange information for you. I had a visitor last night."

Leclerc raised his eyebrows.

"Who?"

"A mulatto by the name of Valentin Vastey—friend, confidant, and secretary of a sort to Henry Christophe."

Leclerc raised his eyebrows even higher. "Ah, your erstwhile friend who condemned you to be hanged."

Armes nodded. "But, General Leclerc, you will remember my telling you the first night I met you that Henry is a very changeable man. He is ruled by the whim of the moment. I have no doubt but what, if he had executed me that morning, he would have wept before nightfall. You will remember we had quarreled that morning and he had dismissed me, only to recall me later and invite me to sit at his left hand during dinner."

"Yes, I remember."

"Apparently he has had another change of heart. He has approached me, in the person of Vastey, for help. He wants me to intercede for him with you. In other words, Henry desires to surrender, but on his own terms."

Leclerc tugged at his curling whiskers.

"With Toussaint casting his lot with the French . . ."

"Pardon, General, I did not know."

"Yes, it is settled. He will retire from public life to his estate at Ennery. He wishes to have nothing more to do with politics. He is turning over the governorship of St. Domingue to me but he, like Henry, has certain conditions."

"May I ask what they are?"

"A guarantee of complete freedom for all blacks; amnesty for all the rebels; and an equitable code of laws for blacks and whites. We are inclined to grant them, at least for the time being."

"And those are Henry Christophe's terms of surrender, plus one more. Henry wishes you to confirm his rank of general of brigade in the French army with a command to include his own company of Dahomeys."

Leclerc pushed his chair back from the desk and walked to the window, drew back the heavy brocade draperies, and stared out at the mountains. He knew that somewhere in their purple fastnesses, Henry Christophe was hiding. But Leclerc was uncertain. He wanted to be exactly sure of everything he did, and most of all he wanted to report to Napoleon that St. Domingue had surrendered to him—that St. Domingue in the persons of Toussaint l'Ouverture, Henry Christophe, Jean Jacques Dessalines, and Alexandre Pétion was once again safely under the tricolor of France.

The brocade fell back into heavy folds and he turned to face Armes.

"What is your opinion, Captain?"

"I cannot advise you, *mon général.* I can only say what I would do in your place."

"And what would that be?"

"I would meet Henry's terms. You have persuaded Toussaint to retire. Now, with Henry Christophe a general on your staff, it follows as night the day that Dessalines and Pétion will come over to your side, and you will rule St. Domingue. You can accomplish all this without firing another shot. What you do afterward about restoring plantation property and reinstituting slavery is your own concern. I am merely telling you what I would do now. I would get all my enemies together where I could keep my eyes on them."

"I think your advice is good, Captain. Tell me, can you get in touch with this Vastey?"

"I know where he can be reached."

"Then tell him that General Leclerc accepts General Christophe's terms and will be delighted to have Citizen-General Christophe as a general on his staff and his Dahomeys as a part of his command."

"I shall tell him, sir."

Armes rose to leave. As he stood up, Leclerc walked around the corner of his desk and faced him. The general fumbled with the medals on his right breast and detached one. He came closer to Armes, holding a bit of gold and enamel in his palm.

"The Cross of the Legion of Honor. It is my brother-in-law's most cherished decoration. I take pleasure in awarding it to you, Captain." He pinned the medal somewhat crookedly on Armes' coat.

For the first time since he had been with the French, Armes felt a pang of remorse. He had tricked this man, misled him, lied to him, and certainly intended to cuckold him, yet all the time Leclerc had trusted him. Treachery was an art, but not a virtue. He stuttered his thanks to Leclerc and, while he did so, he allowed a wave of pity to cloud his thinking. He felt sorry for the young man before him, beset with weighty problems of politics, government, and his own marriage. But the feeling was only transitory. The white face above the blue coat changed and he saw Henry's face. No, he had not dealt treacherously with Leclerc—he had dealt loyally with Henry. The tinseled bauble on his breast meant nothing— Napoleon had distributed them wholesale throughout Europe.

He bowed respectfully, however, and mouthed the necessary words. "I thank you, Citizen-General. I do not deserve this honor." He fingered the rounded points of the enameled star as he turned and left the room.

36

ARMES was reluctant to admit to himself that he was strangely excited over the prospects of the ball that Pauline was giving. Not only had she given him a special invitation, but she had apparently made a rendezvous with him by taking pains to inform him in advance of the costume she would be wearing. Try as he could to dispel the fascinating image of her as a shepherdess, he could think of nothing else. Even though half the ladies of Pauline's little court might choose the same exciting *masque*, Armes knew he would recognize Pauline even if she were wrapped in sackcloth. Nothing could disguise those special curves which Pauline alone possessed.

While his fantasies regarding Pauline did not erase his longing for Athenée—as a matter of fact they intensified it to the point that the more he thought about Pauline the more he wanted Athenée—he was aware of the fact that Pauline was near at hand, Pauline was lovely, and, perhaps most important of all, Pauline was willing. For what? Of that there was little doubt, for if Pauline could distribute her favors indiscriminately among her coterie of young officers and her pale bronze mulatto footmen, surely she would not be averse to making love to him.

Yes, he was excited over the prospect, and why not? Since he had left Athenée he had scarcely spoken to a white woman, and now the sister of Napoleon had deliberately placed herself in his path. Even if he wished, he could not refuse her, because she was not only Napoleon's sister but the wife of his commanding general. And Armes did not wish. He was not good at disciplining himself nor at practicing self-denial. He had been faithful to Athenée in his own fashion. The nightly advent of Maman's nieces had not counted, as they provided merely a physical relief and in no way affected his love for Athenée. His love for her, deep and abiding as it was, was not affected by his bed companions, and neither would it be by any momentary feeling for Pauline. That would merely be a delightful little adventure, the prospect of which was already making his blood tingle. All Pauline might be able to do would be to rob Athenée of a few moments of his thoughts, nothing else. As Maman's nieces had failed to do, so too would Pauline fail to disturb the deep tranquillity of his love for Athenée.

Thus he argued with himself and thus he almost convinced himself. Although Pauline occupied his thoughts, she did not penetrate far enough into his consciousness to unlock the door which guarded that other image—Athenée. But the prospects of the coming rendezvous added a new swagger to his walk, a new zest to his actions, and a new incentive to his thoughts. Just now he was a hunter, excited over the chase. He had located his quarry, and there remained only that one supreme moment of suspense. Would his aim be true? Would he be successful in the kill? He had never failed before— certainly he would not this time.

His spirits high, he galloped home from the palace, dismounted in front of his house, and started up the steps two at a time, whistling. Maman, on her knees scrubbing the threshold, blocked the doorway, presenting a huge expanse of white cotton cloth, curving over her monumental buttocks without a single wrinkle. Her head and shoulders were inside the doorway, and the song she was singing so vociferously had completely drowned out both his steps and his whistling. It was too inviting an opportunity to miss. His hand itched for contact with that huge target, and he lifted his arm exuberantly and brought his palm down sharply on the smoothly rounded protuberance that extended in such a tempting arc from his doorway. The contact was satisfying, the noise gratifying, and the result terrifying. Maman rose like an escaped balloon and her ascent was punctuated with yelps of surprise and pain. Without identifying the assailant, she accomplished a mid-air pirouette and caught Armes full in the face with her soapy rag.

Her unintelligible sputter of Creole gave way to deep guffaws of laughter when she saw Armes, and it took her several minutes before she could control the spasms that convulsed her. When, with heavings and gasping, she finally regained her breath, she lifted the hem of her skirt and gently wiped the suds from Armes' face, only to collapse again into convulsions of hilarity.

"Him's a-feelin' better, him is." She brought the words out in giggling gasps. "Him's coming to himself, slapping poor old

311

Maman's derriére. Him's my *gros blanc,* him is, and what's making him so happy today?"

"You wouldn't understand, Maman."

She closed one eye slowly until her cheek pouched up to her eyebrow.

"Oui, Maman know. Maman know what her *gros blanc* thinkin' 'bout. Him's finally got himself a white woman to sleep with and him's happy, so that makes Maman happy, too." She gathered up the pot of water and the rags from the floor and waggled down the narrow hall. Armes could hear the thunder of her laughter as she entered the kitchen, gradually diminishing in volume until it finally became a deep-throated chuckle. Pompee had evidently been in the kitchen, for he hurried into the salon where Armes was standing.

"I heard you laugh too, milord. Oh, it's good to hear you laugh again, and Maman's fairly purple in the face. Was it a good joke?"

"Just a little slap on Maman's fat ass which brought me a mouthful of dirty water and a compliment from her. She says I'm now a *gros blanc.* That's a compliment, isn't it?

Pompee grinned and shook his finger at Armes. "If you're a *gros blanc* to Maman, it certainly does mean something. Maman should know, she's had enough experience."

Armes sank into a chair and extended one foot for Pompee to pull off his boot. He placed the other foot again Pompee's rear and pushed while Pompee pulled.

"Tell me something, Pompee," he addressed the bent-over figure in front of him, "if you were to attend a big voodoo ceremony as chief *papaloi,* how would you dress?"

Pompee placed the boots in the corner and pondered the question.

"I suppose I'd wear the green silk trousers that TiTonTon embroidered for me, and I'd wind a bright red sash around my waist."

"Is that all?"

"No! I'd wind some cloth around my head and I'd stick the tail feathers of a rooster in it—white if I was seeking the *loa* of Damballah or Ayda, black if I was honoring Guede Nimbo, or red if it was for Ogoun Feraille."

"How about a shirt."

"No shirt, milord, but I have many strings of beads—very precious ones—made of the bones of a snake, which I would wear, and I would carry my *asson,* the gourd rattle decorated with snake bones."

Armes pictured himself in the barbaric costume and tried to imagine the effect it would make among the silken dominos and fanciful costumes that would appear at Pauline's ball. This, at least, would be different. He would represent the real St. Domingue, not a fake France.

"But why do you ask?" Pompee questioned.

"Just an idea, *mon ami*. I had thought of wearing a costume similar to yours tonight."

Pompee suddenly became apprehensive. "No, milord, no! You could not appear at a voodoo meeting without me, and if you did, it would not be fitting for you, a *blanc*, to appear in the robes of a *papaloi*."

Armes stood up and walked over to where Pompee was standing. He put his hand reassuringly on Pompee's shoulder and his words came slowly. "Believe me, I have no idea of ridiculing your religion. I only wish to honor it. Tonight the wife of General Leclerc gives a ball at her palace—a *bamboche*, you would call it. Ordinary clothes like these"—he slapped his thigh in the white breeches—"are not to be worn. Everyone who goes must dress like someone else and wear a mask. I had thought to show them what a *papaloi* might look like, for I know they have little or no idea what a *papaloi* is. I would like to wear your cloth if you would permit it. It would be no disrespect to your belief."

Pompee appeared relieved. "My clothes have no special significance. It matters not what I wear when I attend my *mystères*. I wear what I choose. But I could not let you wear the necklaces nor carry the *asson*. Those are sacred because they come from the snake, the symbol of Damballah. But I can get you beads of glass and wood, and I can make you an *asson* which will make just as much noise as mine. I'll be glad to help you, but . . ."

"But what . . .?"

"How can you represent a *papaloi?* Do you forget, milord, that your skin is not the right color. A white *papaloi?* Never!"

Armes laughed. "You were right, Pompee, when you told me that only my skin is white. Truly I am beginning to think like a Negro, for I had entirely forgotten my paleness. But wait! That night at Bouckmann's meeting . . ." He stopped suddenly. Again he saw the crucified figure of Ali on the ground, saw its agonized contortions, the bandaged head rolling from side to side, the cords bound around the delicate wrists and ankles. His gay mood evaporated. He could not go on.

Pompee opened the door of the half-charred armoire and placed the boots carefully inside. He turned and looked at Armes sadly. It had been so good to hear him laugh again. He must help him recapture that mood. Armes could not lose his joy.

"I know, milord. Henry blacked you with soot and you were blacker than I am. But that would not work tonight. You would soil the gowns of the French ladies when you danced with them. But Pompee knows a better way. There is a tree which grows here—I've seen one on the road to Petit Anse only about ten minutes away. The bark of the tree when boiled in water makes a deep brown dye. It is harmless to the skin and will not wear off. There have been times when some of our mulattoes have wished to appear darker and they have used it. It will wear off slowly and it will take you a week to be really white again."

Pompee's words had served to break the spell. Armes felt his euphoria returning.

"Quick then! My horse is saddled at the steps. With ten minutes to go and ten minutes to return, you'll be back soon. Strip the bark from the tree, Pompee, bring it back, and boil it up. The dainty demoiselles of France are going to dance with a *gros blanc* that will be a *gros nègre*. Let's see how they like that."

"I'm sure Madame Leclerc will," Pompee laughed as he grabbed his machete from the leather scabbard on the wall and dashed out the door. The hoofbeats of his horse receded into the distance, and Armes threw himself across the bed. Maman's deep voice came in patches of song from the kitchen; the white light of the afternoon sun was strained through the sackcloth at the window; and somewhere out in the street a wandering *marchande* sought purchasers for her *figs*. A little green lizard scuttled up the wall, his beady eyes concentrated on an unsuspecting fly. The quick tongue uncoiled and the fly disappeared.

Was that what was happening to him? Armes pondered the question. Was he losing his identity as a white man by long association with the blacks of St. Domingue? Should he give it all up, even Athenèe if necessary, and return to a more normal way of life among his own people in Boston? It might be better. He was slowly being assimilated. True, he had found great loyalty, devotion, and friendship among the Negroes. There was Pompee and there was Henry. Could he find any better friends in the world? The answer was no. And

314

there was no danger of his losing his identity as a white man. He never could as long as he had Athenée. She was the answer to everything. If she stayed in St. Domingue, he must remain. There would be, there could be no thought of his leaving. For too long now they had been separated. Suppose it were permanent?

He rolled over on his side, unloosened his belt, and kicked off his breeches. He would dismiss all serious thoughts from his mind and concentrate on the ball tonight. Let him think about Pauline's pink and white flesh after a surfeit of sepia-colored flesh; about the firmness of her breasts after the pendulous African breasts he had already seen too much of. Let him transport himself to the sweet little ladies of her court, the music of violins, the splash of champagne in glasses. He, a *papaloi*, a bronzed barbaric *brute,* in their effete midst— that was something to conjecture! A black savage in the perfumed decadence of Pauline's rotting palace; a primitive African flaunting his virility among the pomaded dandies. His black hands cupping her white breasts! Suddenly he saw it all so clearly—the strength and magnificence of Henry's purposeful hands compared to Leclerc's nervous fingers. He realized the firmness and the strength of the Negro in contrast to the indecision and the subservience of the white man. It made it clear to him exactly where he stood. On the side of the blacks—at least they were men.

His half-conscious thoughts wandered through the labyrinths of approaching slumber until they once again encountered Pauline. He drifted off into a satisfying dream which served to release his pent-up energies. How long he slept he did not know, but when he awakened, the light in the room was gray, and he saw Pompee standing in the door with a multicolored rainbow of silk over one arm and a steaming, vile-smelling bowl of dark brown liquid in the other.

He set the bowl down on the table and came over and shook Armes gently. "It grows late, milord, and we have much to do."

Armes shook off his drowsiness and raised himself on one elbow.

"*Merde!* What is that stinking stuff you have?" His nostrils dilated in disgust.

"It will not stink once it is on you, after it has cooled. Wait until you see yourself. Look!" He threw the armful of silks onto a chair, where they slithered to the floor in a shimmering cascade of emerald, magenta, orange, vermilion, and pink.

"And look!" He held out a gaudy gourd with strings of colored beads wired on the outside. "And listen!" He shook it and it rattled.

"You're absolutely sure that stuff won't make me smell like a latrine?"

"My word on it, milord. See, as it cools the odor disappears."

"Then let's get started. I'll need a bath and a shave first."

Pompee leaned over the bed and unbuttoned Armes' shirt.

"A big shave this time, milord. From here to here." His hand described an arc from Armes' chin to his groin.

"What in hell do you mean?"

"Blacks don't have hair on their chests."

"But I'll be goddamned if I'm going to . . ."

"Tonight you are going to be a *papaloi*, milord, and if Pompee has anything to say about it, you're going to look like the greatest *papaloi* this side of Africa." He reached for the second button on the shirt, but Armes sat bolt upright in bed.

"Damn this whole thing for a foolish idea," he sputtered as he drew the shirt off over his head. "Shaved like a stuck pig, dyed to look like an old saddle, and trussed out in green silk pants with chicken feathers in my hair. What a crazy idea!"

"It was your idea, milord, and now I am going to make sure that you are a credit to me." Pompee forced Armes back down on the bed and held him there with one hand while he reached for a bowl of lather with the other. He plopped a huge glob of lather onto Armes' chest, then another and another, and rubbed the white froth over his whole torso. Releasing Armes, who now had become entirely submissive, he slappety-slapped the razor on the strop. He was still laughing when he leaned over Armes, razor in hand. Armes eyed the razor apprehensively.

"You be goddamned careful with that razor, man. Don't let it slip. We can't disappoint the pretty Pauline tonight. She'd have no use for a bloody eunuch."

Pompee grinned as he scraped a sodden mass of curly black hair from off Armes' chest. The skin glowed pearly white in the path of the razor. Pompee's grin turned into an audible chuckle as he flicked more blobs of soapy hair onto the floor.

"That Pauline won't be recruiting any more yellow boys after tonight," Pompee chuckled. "Not after she sees what

316

a black man's like. Maybe those yellow boys have just been preparing her for what she's going to get tonight."

His chuckle was infectious. Armes began to laugh too.

37

THROUGH some devious means, known only to himself, Pompee had managed to discover a coach of sorts—aged and decrepit though it was—to convey Armes to the ball. Carriages and coaches were almost nonexistent in the Cap these days, but in some way this ancient vehicle had survived the holocaust and its driver, as were most of the blacks in the city, was a friend of Pompee's. In it Armes arrived at the palace with some semblance of style; at least he was shielded from the public gaze during the trip.

The final glimpse he had had of himself in the cracked and clouded mirror of his room had more than satisfied him. Pompee's bronzing process and his barbaric clothes had caused a change not only in Armes' outward appearance, but in his entire consciousness. In shedding his paleness he had become an entirely different person physically and mentally. The curving white feathers of Ayda Weydo, goddess of love, seemed to increase his stature, enlarge his thoughts, and magnify his virility. He felt capable of incredible things through a new and vital power that burgeoned within him. It was as though some inner voice kept reminding him that he was unconquerable, and that no person or thing could withstand the force of this hidden potency. He understood the expression "walking on air" when, as he descended from the ancient fiacre in front of the palace, his bare feet in their thonged sandals scarcely seemed to touch the earth.

Pompee had accompanied him, but as the carriage halted to let Armes out, he retreated into the shadows of the corner. Armes turned, conscious of the startled gaze of the sentries by the palace steps, and whispered through the raddled curtains of the coach. "In about ten minutes," he said. Pompee's grunt of assent was his only reply.

Resplendent in his regalia as a high priest of voodoo, Armes strode up the crumbling white steps of the palace, but

317

when he arrived at the door, two armed sentries barred his way, their crossed muskets forcing him back a step.

"No blacks allowed here," one of them barked. "Get going, nigger, this is no place for you."

"Put down your guns, men." Armes spoke softly but with authority. "Take care how you address an officer of the French army."

"An officer of France! Ho, ho! Did you hear, Jacques?" One sentry winked at the other. "A goddamned nigger walks up here, half-naked, and says he's an officer of France. Ho, ho!"

"Captain Armes Holbrook of General Leclerc's staff" Armes spoke louder. "If you need proof, call the captain of the guard. This is a masked ball"—he slipped the black mask over his eyes—"and I come in the costume I have chosen."

"But you're a nigger," the sergeant protested. "I'm not blind."

"A white one, however. See!" Armes pulled the gaudy sash down a few inches and permitted the sergeant to stare in wonder.

"Mon Dieu," he gasped, "the man's really white. Your pardon, citizen, I thought . . ."

"You were only doing your duty." Armes nodded. "You are to be commended. But now, if you will let me pass." He strode into the palace.

The long hall and the salons were brilliantly lighted but strangely deserted. The scrape of violins which came through the tall windows of the terrace, however, informed Armes that the ball was being held out of doors to combat the oppressive heat of St. Domingue. He was grateful that nobody had seen him enter the palace, and pushed open the door of what appeared to be a small cloakroom, hoping to locate a mirror that he might reassure himself that the various parts of his costume were in their proper places and that no seams had split. One glance in the tall mirror which he found assured him that everything was in order, and he crossed over to the small window, looked out, and listened. Here in the front of the palace, it was quiet and almost dark, lighted only by the flambeaux at the entrance. All of the festivities were confined to the broad terrace in the back where they received the cool breezes from the sea. As Armes peered out the window, his ears became attuned to the night sounds—the hoofbeats of horses on the drive, the crunch of wheels in the gravel as carriages brought other guests; then, when these had died away, he heard only the muted voices of the tropic night and the faint echoes of the violins. Pauline would have no moon for her party, but diamond stars were scattered on the black velvet of the sky.

His head out the window, he continued to listen, and then it happened. A violent eruption of sound cascaded down the mountain like a burst of seven thunders. The booming explosion of the great *arada* drum—a huge affair hollowed out from a tree trunk and played by six drummers—descended upon Armes. He had never seen one of these drums. They were far too sacred to be profaned by the eyes of one not initiated into the *mystères*. Nor had he ever heard one so near at hand before. The racket was ear-splitting. It echoed from hill to hill and writhed around the palace like a living thing. After the initial shock of its thunder, he heard the *maman* drum, the largest of the three *voodoo* drums, with the *papa* or *second* coming next, followed by the staccato rattling of the *bébé* or *boula*, the smallest of the drums. Their individual notes became synchronized and they struck up a rhythm, strong, primitive, and orgiastic. Even the windowpanes of the jerry-built palace chattered in their frames from the impact of the noise.

Armes smiled to himself. Pompee was on time to the minute. With a last glance at the mirror, he straightened his mask, left the room, and walked rapidly down the deserted corridor to the wide doorway leading out onto the terrace. The orchestra had stopped, drowned out by the deafening reverberations of the drums, and the frightened dancers stood frozen in their places. Mortal terror spread over the faces of the guests under their silken masks as the drums possessed them. Nobody spoke. Nobody moved. They only listened, transfixed by fear. The drums! The awful drums! The drums of doom that prophesied some savage massacre.

Armes paused on the steps leading down to the terrace. He was aware of the theatrical effect he must be creating, illuminated by the light of hurricane-shaded candles and blazing flambeaux. All eyes shifted to him as he slowly raised his arms above his head. Then, pitching his voice high above the pulsating clamor, he cried out.

"Oh-o-O-OH—ah-wah-WAH-WAH! Legba, *ouvre l'porte!* Damballah, come down to us! Ayda, bless us! Oh-o-O-OH! Damballah, Damballah, DAMBALLAH, DAMBALLAH WEYDO!" The shrill tones of the African names and the Creole words brought added terror to the guests, and they stared at him, eyes blazing through the holes of their masks. Some pointed with limp fingers; others screamed; and not a few fled down the steps of the terrace to the darkness below. A woman fell to the floor in a faint, her partner unaware of her plight as he riveted his eyes on Armes.

Then, suddenly as they had begun, the drums stopped, and Armes slowly descended the stairs, pausing on each step until he reached the terrace. His bare feet made copper splotches on the whitened stone. Silk trousers, full and wide as skirts at the bottom but fitting him like skin from the knees up, molded his thighs in vitriolic green and, as he moved, the sequin-embroidered cloth reflected the dancing candle flames. Around his waist there were yards of orange, carmine, yellow, and blue silk, interwoven to make a kaleidoscope of flashing colors. His chest glowed smoothly, reflecting highlights like a polished bronze statue where the strings of multicolored beads parted to reveal the warm flesh. Pompee's crowning touch had been to paint his nipples vermilion.

His lips, under the black curve of the mask, appeared wide and almost Negroid, like split pomegranates, parted to show the whiteness of his teeth. Around his head, Pompee had wound a tall conical turban of gold-shot flame-colored tissue from the top of which sprouted a crest of curling white cock feathers. The brown lobes of his ears peeped out from under the tight folds of the turban, heavily weighed with crude earrings of beaten gold which nodded with each descending step. In one hand he carried a long, rounded gourd which chattered from the network of wooden beads around it. The startled audience shrank back as he came down the stairs to stand, feet wide apart, hand on hips, immobile as a statue. A collective sigh escaped from the crowd as they saw him smile and realized that he was unarmed. Their initial shock had caused them to forget that this was a *bal masqué;* now with the remembrance they recovered their composure. The murmur of excited talk resumed and the violins twanged as the musicians retuned them.

As primeval Africa in all its savage grandeur put to shame the gaudy pretensions of cankered France, a shepherdess, dainty as a Sèvres figurine, disengaged herself from the arms of a medieval jester in red and yellow motley. With impatience, she shook off her partner's arm as he attempted to escort her across the floor. The dancers cleared a path for her—a wide expanse of waxed boards that stretched between her and Armes. Little running steps brought her up to him, and she stood before him, hands hidden in the wide panniers of flower-sprigged taffeta. With a mock curtsy, she sank to her knees.

"Welcome to my palace, oh Prince of Africa." Still half-kneeling before him, she lifted her face to stare into the glittering holes of his mask. Her voice sank to a whisper so low that only he could hear. "It would take more than a mask to disguise you, M'sieu Canon."

"I come not as a prince, *Mademoiselle Bergère,* but as a *papaloi* of voodoo, that strange Dahomean cult which your subjects here in St. Domingue practice. Tonight I am the high priest of Ayda Weydo, the love goddess of Africa."

"Then perhaps you can teach me a lesson . . . tonight?" She rose, and her hand toyed with the mass of necklaces on his chest. He felt the heat of her hand as it crept under them and pressed hard, palm down, against him and then was quickly withdrawn.

With a low bow which nearly dislodged his towering head-dress, he saluted her, then offered her his arm and led her across the terrace, timing his steps to the beating of the drums which had started up again. Now the big *arada* drum was silent, and the rhythm of the *maman, papa,* and *bébé* became slow and sensuous, exciting Armes as always. Although the eyes of all were upon them, they were oblivious to the stares. They walked alone.

"You are magnificent, Monsieur Canon," she whispered, "but I am almost afraid of you. There is something savage about you. See, I am trembling."

She was, but his low words quieted her. "I am no wolf that devours pretty little shepherdesses." His eyes dropped to the lacing that fastened her bodice and to the filmy lace that failed to hide the white globes beneath its froth. The orchestra had recovered from its fright and the music of the violins began. "May a high priest of Ayda dance with the queen of shepherdesses?"

They joined a group of couples forming a quadrille, and she floated from his arms into those of a Cardinal Richelieu, whose great red robe encircled her as he twirled her and re-turned her to Armes. He caught her and her hand lingered on his bare arm. Her fingers stroked it and then dug deeply into his flesh.

"The drums," she exclaimed, "they do something to me. Where do they come from?"

"My valet has influence with the voodoo drummers."

"Oh, if I could only hear them nearby. Could I see them?"

"You mean you would have them here? Here at the palace? Have you forgotten that they are Negroes—rough peasants from the hills?"

"Does that matter if I wish to see them?"

"No, madame."

"Then let us relinquish the dance and discuss it."

They walked to a bench at the edge of the terrace. Armes knew that the path from the hill where Pompee had stationed the drums passed directly into the palace road. By this time Pompee and the drummers should be coming down that path. Almost rudely, because he wanted to please Pauline and there was not a moment to lose, he excused himself and ran up the steps into the palace and down the hall, out the door through the main gates to the road. He was just in time. Pompee and the three drummers were coming down the road with their drums on their shoulders, all except the big *arada* drum which others were secretly transporting through the forest. Pompee recognized Armes from a distance and ran up to him. Armes explained Pauline's unusual request and Pompee listened attentively. When the three drummers came up to them, he conferred with them for a moment in a mixture of Creole and African dialect.

"Yes, milord, the boys say that they would like to see the inside of the governor's palace. They would like to drink the bubbling *tafia* of the general and see the white ladies dance. They say they are hungry and would like to taste the governor's food. They will come inside and they will play the drums for Madame."

Armes led them into the palace between the astonished sentries and out onto the terrace. They stood, barefooted, clothed in their poor rags, blinking in the bright light, but Pauline spoke kindly to them and led them to the musician's platform, where they squatted in a row in front of it.

She clapped her hands, and when the murmur of conversation subsided, she addressed her guests.

"*Mesdames et messieurs,*" she began. "Tonight I offer you something new and different—something you have often heard from afar in St. Domingue but never near at hand. His Eminence"—she nodded her head in the direction of Armes who was standing beside her—"the high priest of Ayda, has brought his drummers with him. They will now . . ." She stopped in exasperation. A light-skinned mulatto boy, dressed in the palace livery and carrying a silver tray piled high with little cakes, blundered clumsily through the door behind her. "Back, boy, back," she hissed at him. "This is not the time to serve refreshments."

He stopped abruptly, stared at her with eyes glazed with fright, and then turned quickly to seek the shelter of the door, but as he did so, he caught one clumsy foot in the other, tripped, and fell sprawling to the floor. The silver tray slithered across the boards, scattering the dainty pastries right and left before the drummers. Eager black hands reached for them and crammed them into wide-open mouths. Each cake was gulped down in a single mouthful, and they scrambled on all fours to gather them up, cramming two or three into their mouths at a time. Utter confusion reigned for a moment, followed by gales of laughter from the French at the sight of the black monkeys scrabbling about on the floor. But the drummers failed to mind laughter and returned to their drums, wiping their lips and laughing too. Pauline smiled indulgently at them, now picking stray crumbs from their fingers with their red tongues.

"You like my *meringues?*" she asked.

"*Meringue?*" one of them questioned, pointing to his mouth. "*Meringue? Meringue c'est bon!*" He gestured to the others. "*Meringue c'est bon?*" They answered him, "*Meringue c'est bon.*" With repetition it evolved a rhythm of its own, a haunting, toe-tapping rhythm which the *bébé* drummer caught with his fingers on the drum. So expert was his sense of rhythm that the drum actually spoke the words, "*Meringue c'est bon.*" A self-congratulatory smile appeared on his face and he tapped out the rhythm again and sang the words, "*Meringue c'est bon.*" As he continued to sing and drum, *papa* drum took up the beat and then the big *maman* drum responded. "*Meringue c'est bon. Meringue c'est bon.*"

Pauline's extended hands caught the gay rhythm and she clapped them in time to the beat. Armes carried it along with the cha-cha-cha of his *asson* rattle. She advanced toward him, her feet keeping time with the cadenced percussion while he came toward her, enfolding her in his arms. Their feet joined in the rhythm and they danced. One by one the fiddles improvised on the melody. Two by two the dancers caught the beat and took their places on the floor. The stately measure of the quadrille and the minuet were forgotten in the rhythm of the exciting new dance—the dance of the little cakes—the Meringue.

"*Meringue c'est bon!*"

Stilted words and formal phrases were lost in the wild abandon of the dance.

"Meringue c'est bon!"

Officers and ladies whirled together, clasped in each other's arms.

"Meringue c'est bon!"

Their feet pounded the boards to the new tempo so temptingly primitive.

"Meringue c'est bon!"

Then men clasped the women tighter and the women responded. Now no other dance would do but the new Meringue. The drummers entered into the spirit and carried on, with sweat soaking their thin cotton shirts. But the dancers were not so hardy; they had to rest. Order finally came out of chaos and the dances became shorter. The French musicians regulated their length by tapping the over-enthusiastic drummers on the shoulder when it was time to finish. Armes and Pauline had stopped dancing. They were both panting. Armes' back and chest gleamed with beads of perspiration, and despite Pompee's assurances, there were dark brown smudges on Pauline's dress.

"Now," she spoke softly, "now, while everyone is intrigued with the new dance. The second terrace below. There is a little grotto there. Let us go."

They slipped from the dance floor and ran down the steps, unobserved, to the lower terrace. She took his hand and guided him through the semi-darkness to the end of the terrace, then down a few more steps. He could see a rough rock formation where drooping ferns framed a black opening. She led him inside into the enfolding darkness. Her lips immediately found his and his arms enfolded her.

"Oh, Monsieur Canon." He could hardly hear her words. "Ever since you came aboard our ship I have longed for this moment. *J'aime votre grand canon parce que c'est maintenant le mien.* I have dreamed of it. Deny me no longer, Armes."

He had no words with which to answer her, nor breath to form them, for he could not relinquish her lips. His hand, black in the darkness against the dim white of her throat, caressed in moving circles that found her shoulder and then encountered the froth of lace, but the stays of her bodice denied him entrance until his fingers, seeking and fumbling with the knot of the lacing, untied it. The bodice parted and the whole cumbersome costume dropped from her shoulders. He released her for a fleeting second from his arms, but only

324

long enough to allow the mass of taffeta, lace, and whalebone to slip to the floor. Her hands had been unsuccessful in unwinding the interwoven strands of the sash that bound his waist, but he knew the secret and yanked it off. The green silk trousers slithered down his thighs and mingled with the sprigged taffeta.

Now flesh touched flesh in the cool, moist darkness, and hands were free to make all the delightful explorations that had been denied them. The hard points of her breasts pressed against him, and he felt her fingers pinching his reddened paps as his mouth glided over her flesh.

"You came well armed," she gasped.

"For your pleasure," he replied.

"And yours?"

"Can you doubt it?"

"Then now, now, now!"

Black fronds cast a ragged silhouette over the entrance to the grotto while the muffled sounds of the amorous Meringue drifted down from the terraces above, timing their bodies to its irresistible, primitive rhythm. His arms clutched her tightly to him and a thousand rockets burst into flame in his head, to send their tingling sparks throughout his viens. He slumped forward, his knees buckling under him until only her arms held him erect. But she would not accept his defeat, nor allow him a moment to recapture his breath; her lips, her fingers, and her body continued their urgent solicitation. Despite her frantic efforts, her importuning was in vain. His desire for her was now as completely dead as though it had never existed. His only wish was to get away from her, if possible without offending her. But the excuses he would have made were never spoken, and he was spared the lies a man must invent to escape from an unsatisfied woman.

For suddenly the music stopped and in the quiet that followed they heard a man's voice . . . another man's answering. Now Armes could see them—black shapes of two men in uniform before the curtain of ferns. His hands pressed gently against Pauline's mouth. They stood, tense and rigid, momentarily expecting discovery. While she stealthily reached down, picked up her dress, and slid into it, he managed to get back into his trousers and rewind the sash. The voices outside continued.

"It is my husband and General Rochambeau." Her words were barely audible in his ear. "Do not fear—if we make no

325

noise they will not enter. Charles detests this place. He says it is the haunt of lizards. We are safe here."

They could now distinguish words. "Well, Charles"—it was Rochambeau speaking—"you have rewon St. Domingue for France. Congratulations! Word was received tonight that Henry Christophe has surrendered and will come to the Cap. We shall treat with him for a while, give him a pretty cross to hang on his chest, humor him a bit, and then . . ."

Armes could not see the gesture Rochambeau made, but he could imagine it. That gesture would neatly sever Henry's head from his body.

"Yes, *mon general*," Leclerc answered. "Our task here is nearly finished. But we must not forget—this is only the first step, and the next one is more important. St. Domingue is ours, but St. Domingue has only a minor place in the plans of the first consul . . ."

"But that minor place is important, *n'est-ce pas?*"

"Most important. My brother-in-law has conquered the Old World—all of Europe, except Prussia and Austria, and he does not need them."

"But don't forget England," Rochambeau cautioned.

"Bah! We are at peace with England." Leclerc dismissed Great Britian with a snap of his fingers.

"Exactly, and that leaves us a free path to the New World, to which this minor place of St. Domingue is the important stepping stone. Already our agents in Canada and Louisiana have convinced the French there that they should revolt. And as for these infant United States, we shall conquer them more easily than we have the blacks of St. Domingue. Soon the new empire of Napoleon will extend over two continents."

"Did you say 'empire,' *mon général?*"

"And why not—has there ever been a greater empire?"

Leclerc shook his head. "But Napoleon is not an emperor."

"Ah, but he will be soon, *mon cher* Charles. A late dispatch that arrived from Paris this evening confirms the fact, and probably by now he already is. And what will that make you Charles? A royal prince, at least, because you are married to the Princess Pauline."

"Mon Dieu! She *will* be a princess. I never thought of that." He started to walk away, but stopped and retraced his steps, to lay a hand on Rochambeau's shoulder.

"You know your orders, General. Prepare at once to transfer troops to conquer Louisiana. Tell Paris the time has come to send reinforcements. Ready the fleet to carry fifty thousand soldiers to Louisiana. Those Americans will capitulate without a struggle when they see the brave soldiers of Napoleon on their soil. The French in Canada will join them, and all of North America will bend the knee to His Imperial Majesty, the Emperor Napoleon the First of France and the world. And, General Rochambeau, my wife will be a princess of the blood royal."

Their footsteps crunched on the gravel path and up the stairs to the terraces above. Before they ascended the second flight of stairs to the brilliantly lighted terrace, Pauline's fingers clutched at Armes again, and he knew that as much as he desired to be quit of her, her persistence would force him to stay even against his will.

"Only once, *mon cher?*" Her lips sought his. "It was too quick, *Monsieur Grand Canon*. Surely you can accomplish a second *coup de canon*."

Diplomacy was necessary. The news of Henry's surrender had made him free—free to go to Athenée as quickly as he could. He cared no more for this imperial harlot. But he must be diplomatic. She must not read his thoughts. He gently disengaged himself from her arms.

"Your Imperial Highness," he said, and he would have bowed low had she not been so near. "A moment ago I was with the wife of General Leclerc and, as the old saying goes, 'All is fair in love in war.' But now I am with the sister of the Emperor of France. I cannot aim so high."

"I would imagine the canon is capable of aiming as high as it wishes." Her tantalizing fingers resumed their coaxing. "But perhaps it is that you do not love me."

"Let us say I love you, but I respect you even more. Remember, I am only a poor American, as much a masquerader in my French uniform as I am in this toggery. To such as I an Imperial Highness does not distribute her favors. Let me remember only this one thing—that tonight I held a charming woman by the name of Pauline in my arms and that together we explored the very depths of joy. But let me forget, from this moment on, that I ever dared look at the sister of the Emperor Napoleon."

She moved away from him. Her voice changed from the soft tone of an amorous woman to the firm one of a princess. "You are right. I must remember, at least for tonight, when it is all so new to me, that I am an Imperial Highness. Perhaps tomorrow I shall regret it, as I am sure I shall, so will you call on me tomorrow?"

She gathered up her skirts and walked to the entrance of the grotto. A look assured her that there was nobody about. She extended her hand to Armes.

"I almost regret now that I am an Imperial Highness, and so far beyond your reach. Yes, let us return, Armes."

He looked up and saw Leclerc leaning over the balustrade, looking down at them. Armes nudged Pauline, and she too saw him. When they arrived on the upper terrace, Leclerc stared at them grimly. He did not know where they had been in the lower darkness, but from the disheveled clothing, he had a pretty good idea of what they had been doing. His eyes noted the careless lacing of Pauline's bodice and the slackness of Armes' sash.

"*Tiens,* Charles, it is so much cooler on the lower terrace near the sea. Captain Holbrook offered to escort me there . . ."

He cut her short. "I desire to speak to Captain Holbrook. Your pardon, madame."

She blanched, bowed curtly to Armes, and walked away. He turned to face Leclerc.

"After tonight, Captain Holbrook, we shall no longer need your services in the French army. You are discharged from further duty."

They were the most welcome words Armes had ever heard.

"Merci, *mon général.*" His heart had never felt lighter as he walked across the terrace.

38

THE scented night air rushed past Armes' face as he and Pompee galloped over the miles between Cap François and Sans Souci. To Armes it was like a fine vintage wine; it exhilarated him, inflamed him, and animated him, but at the same time soothed and cooled him. For the first time since he had left Athenée standing on the balcony of Sans Souci, he felt like a free man, and it was wonderful to taste liberty again; to ride through the velvet night; to anticipate Athenée and know that in a few paltry moments that anticipation would be a reality. It seemed almost impossible to believe that the insubstantial dreams of the past weeks could ever again materialize into warm flesh, but they would, and soon. He spurred his horse on.

The back of his hand brushed roughly across his lips as he tried to erase that last lingering touch of Pauline's mouth. He cursed himself for a hot-blooded idiot and wondered now why he had ever desired her after the long procession of French officers and mulatto footmen who had preceded him. The very thought of her repelled him, and he wished, now that the fire of his passion had been quenched, that he could have seen her a few hours before in the same light as he regarded her now. What was she? Nothing but a common whore with an omnivorous appetite for men. Another Joanna of Naples, whose soft flesh was the battleground for countless minions. Better to forget her! Repudiate the whole sordid affair in his mind and pretend it never happened. Surely this one brief moment of infidelity to Athenée could not weigh heavily on his conscience against the many nights he had longed for her even while in the embraces of Maman's nieces.

He had quitted the palace as quickly as possible without being actually rude. When he left Leclerc, the Negro drummers were still thumping out the measures of the Meringue, and Pauline's ball had deteriorated into a peasant *bamboche* as orgiastic as those the Negroes held in the mountains. The loose-lipped lasciviousness of the officers and the half-closed eyes of the demoiselles had repulsed him in his moment of satiety. But although they disgusted him, he had achieved a new and vociferous popularity among them. His walk across the floor had been in the manner of a small triumph. Dancers stopped him, congratulated him on the originality of his costume and the importation of the drummers; joked with him through innuendos; and generally impeded his progress. He hastened through the press of bodies—*"Mais oui, mademoiselle"; "Merci, monsieur"; "Certainement!"; "Enchanté!"*— spouting a whole string of civilities as he was accosted.

Armes had sighted Pompee standing beside the drummers, and when their eyes met, he made an almost imperceptible inclination of his head that sent Pompee scurrying out into the hall. Not wishing to be faulted for boorishness, he approached Pauline and went through the formality of kissing her hand. As he bent over it, he heard her whisper.

"Tomorrow, Monsieur Grand Canon, here at the palace at four in the afternoon. We shall resume our gunnery practice. A single shot from a cannon does not entirely guarantee its efficiency, *n'est-ce pas?*"

Armes abandoned her hand and straightened.

"He knows." His eyes turned in the direction of Leclerc.

She shrugged her shoulders. *"Eh bien!* And why shouldn't he? A man who is incapable of satisfying his wife most certainly should know when she has found a man who can. At four, Armes?"

"He has discharged me from his service."

"But I have not from mine. At four!"

Armes shook his head. "At that time, madame, I shall be many miles away from here. My regrets, madame."

Pauline realized that she had lost her little game, and she was incapable of accepting defeat gracefully. The purr in her voice disappeared.

"Then I dismiss you also, Monsieur One-Shot. After your inability to repeat your performance tonight, I doubt if you would ever be able to satisfy me."

Armes bowed low. "I shall have my servant Pompee search among the peasants of St. Domingue, madame. Without a doubt he can locate a black stud who will meet all your requirements." Before Pauline could think of words to answer him, he turned on his heel and left.

Pompee had been waiting for him in the hall.

"Let's get out of this goddamned place, quick." Armes lost no time in gaining the door.

The road in front of the palace and the streets were practically deserted at that late hour, which was fortunate for Armes, as his fantastic costume went unnoticed during the walk back to his house. Once inside the poor shack he had called home, he routed Maman out of bed, had Pompee explain to her that they would not be coming back, presented her with the contents of the house, and prepared to leave. A certain amount of brisk scrubbing removed a small amount of Pompee's dye, and he became more *café au lait* than *café noir*—a mulatto rather than a Negro. While he was attempting to achieve some degree of whiteness, Pompee had saddled the horses. They were ready to go. There remained nothing to do but quiet Maman's copious tears with a playful slap on her fat ass, jump into the saddle, and eat up the miles between the Cap and Sans Souci. Between Armes and Athenée!

It was long past midnight when they arrived at the gates of Sans Souci. Despite his surrender to Leclerc, Henry had not relaxed his vigilance, and one of his Dahomeys was posted as sentry. Armes' failure to know the password temporarily

330

barred him from entering, but the sentry routed out a sleepy officer who was acquainted with him. He regarded Armes' color and his French uniform with open-mouthed astonishment, but he allowed him to pass. They encountered another sentry, sleeping blissfully on the lower step that led to the balcony, but Armes was able to step over him without waking him. The house was entirely dark. He groped his way through the hall, located a candlestick on the console, and lighted it. As the familiar surroundings emerged from out of the darkness, he realized that the long time of waiting was over. Pompee glided down the hall to see if Henry was there and to wake him, while Armes hesitated before the door of his own room.

The candle seemed superfluous. Better to surprise Athenée in the dark. He blew it out and placed it on the floor. Then gently, without the slightest creak of the hinges, he swung the big door open. The shuttered windows gave little light, but he did not need even their meager illumination. Taking care not to wake her, he tiptoed to the bed and stood over it a moment, listening to her measured breathing. As his eyes became accustomed to the darkness, he could make out the shadowy outline of her face on the pillow—the chiseled profile that he knew and loved so well. He knelt beside the bed and lightly, like the wing of a bird brushing the meadow grass, his lips touched her cheek. She stirred in her sleep and murmured a word—a soft word that he could hardly catch, but he knew that it was his name. This time his lips slowly moved toward her mouth. She stirred again and sleepily responded to his kiss.

"Athenée, Athenée." The syllables of her name contained all the suppressed longing in his heart. "Athenée."

She awoke. She was not startled; there was no surprise in her immediate recognition of him. "My very dear," she whispered, "you have come back to me."

"And did you ever doubt that I would?" His lips pressed more closely.

"No, beloved, at least not until this very night. All the time that you have been away, I have felt secure in your love. I knew that wherever you were, some invisible cord bound us together, but tonight, for some strange reason, when I went to bed I was frightened. The cord seemed broken, and I felt that I had lost you. I could not sleep, so I lighted a candle and lay here looking at the ceiling until the candle burned down. That must have been an hour or so ago, and suddenly

I felt the cord between you and me tighten again. I knew then that I had found you and that I had never lost you. I slept, and as I slept I dreamed of you, but my dreams were all mixed up. I seemed to confuse you and Pompee . . ."

"Hush! It was only a dream, beloved, but more true than you can imagine. You'll laugh when I tell you, but let's not talk about dreams now. We've both dreamed long enough. Now at last we are here together and nothing else matters, because this time it is not a dream."

Her encircling arms brought his head closer. The buttons of his uniform made cold circles on her flesh, and yet they proved to her that he was real; that he was there; that he was Armes; and that he was hers. Nothing else mattered to her; nothing to him.

How long he remained there on his knees beside her bed he did not know. The minutes were unnumbered. Time stood still, and together they tasted eternity.

"Your heavy coat," she whispered, "must you keep it on?"

"But if I take it off, I shall have to relinquish you, even if but for a moment."

"Can't you do that?"

"No." His voice caressed her. "Because if I do take my arms away, you might vanish into thin air. I know all too well. Too many times of late I have held you in my arms, only to awaken and find that you had vanished. Coat or no coat, I cannot lose you this time."

Her fingers sought the buttons on his coat. One by one she undid them until she could loosen one arm and slip the sleeve over it. Once loose, she replaced it around her shoulders and removed the other arm, slipping the coat sleeve from it. The coat fell in a shapeless mass on the floor.

"But you have no shirt on under your coat and . . ." Her avid fingers explored his chest. Immediately she sat up in bed and pushed him from her. *"Mon Dieu!* Get away from me. You are not Armes! Who are you?" Even in the dim light she could see the darkness of his skin in contrast to the whiteness of her own. She recoiled from him in terror. "You are not Armes, but who, in the name of God, are you? You speak with his voice, you kiss with his lips, but you are not he."

He laughed and sought her again.

"May not a man shave without being repudiated by his wife?"

"Shave? Since when have you shaved more than your face?"

"Only tonight, darling, and that too I shall explain to you later. Oh, *ma chérie,* there is so much to explain. It will take hours and days to relate it all."

"For a moment I was frightened. I thought perhaps you might be one of Henry's Dahomeys." She pressed her cheek against his chest. "It prickles."

"And it will probably prickle more as it grows out." He was laughing now. "There was a masquerade at Pauline's palace tonight. You were right in your dream about me and Pompee changing places. Tonight I borrowed his *papaloi* finery for a costume. And I invented a new dance also. I gave them the Meringue, and I imagine they are still dancing it if they have any strength left. But that is not all. I kissed Pauline's hand and addressed her as 'Your Imperial Highness.'"

"You kissed her hand. I hope it was only her hand you kissed."

He so wanted to confess to her. The words were on his lips that would shrive his soul, but he withheld them. Some other time. Some other place. Under some other conditions. This moment of reunion was far too precious to spoil.

"Yes, I kissed her hand." At least it was no lie. "But not like I am kissing your mouth, your cheek, your shoulders, your . . ."

There was a knock at the door. Armes relinquished Athenée and walked over to open it.

"Henry," he exclaimed, "Henry Christophe!"

"TiArmes!" The booming welcome of Henry's voice set the crystal pendants on the girandoles to tinkling. "TiArmes, you have come back." He halted on the threshold, the folds of his long white nightshirt trailing on the floor behind him. Marie Louise looked in through the crook of his elbow.

"Welcome back, Armes, welcome back to Sans Souci," she said.

"Yes, welcome back, TiArmes," Henry bellowed again. "It's good to see you. It's damn hard to lose a friend." He lifted the candle he was carrying and looked more closely at Armes. "Come out of the shadows, man. *Mon Dieu!* What have we here—some goddamned high-yellow, bright-skinned *affranchi?*" He brought the candle closer to Armes' face. "Look, Marie Louise, my brother is becoming more like me every day. Pretty soon he'll be as black as I am. Man, how come you turned mulatto?"

"At first I was afraid of him, Henry." Athenée threw a

robe about her and climbed down from the high bed. "But black or white, it's Armes, and see"—she rubbed her fingers over his glabrous chest—"he's no longer a bear."

"The man's really turning black," Henry guffawed. "He's got no more hair on his chest than I have. Welcome to our ranks, TiArmes."

It was Armes' turn to laugh. "Yes, Henry, I *am* turning black, and in more ways than you think. But this"—he indicated his skin—"is not the way I mean. Pompee tonight turned me into a better Negro than you did with your soot, because this will not wash off. But the Negro part of my mind will not wear off, *mon vieux*. The more I saw of the whites, the more I was convinced that your cause, Henry, is the right one. Yes, the hair on my chest will grow again, the dye that Pompee put on me will wear off, but my thoughts will not change. That I can promise you, Henry Christophe." He strode to the door and called down the hall. "Pompee, Pompee, come here at once. We're having a family reunion and we need you, man."

Pompee's "coming" drifted up the long corridor.

Armes placed one arm around Henry's nightshirted shoulder and gathered Athenée and Marie Louise under the other. "I do not know what relationship we bear, one to the other, but this I do know, I love you all. You, Athenée, I love more than life itself. You, Henry, I love as I would have loved the brother I never had. And you, Marie Louise, I love for your goodness and your sweet gentleness and for the son you are going to bear Henry. And you, Pompee"—he stopped as Pompee entered the room—"I love as a man loves his own shadow, for he knows that it is a part of him."

Henry—tall, pompous Henry Christophe, general of the Army of St. Domingue—grabbed the flowing tails of his nightshirt high above his knees with one hand and his wife with the other and spun her around in the parody of a dance. Armes clapped his hands, repeating the rhythm that had been pounding through his head since he left the palace. *"Meringue c'est bon!"* he shouted. *"Meringue c'est bon!"*

Marie Louise pushed Henry away with a frown: "Stop it, you big ox! Have you forgotten that I am *enceinte*? You never will remember." She snatched Henry's nightgown, which was now up to his thighs, and pulled it from his hands so that it fell to the floor. "Armes, what are you shouting about? *Le meringue c'est bon?*"

"Just foolish words, Marie Louise, but I think, Henry, that

tonight in the palace of Napoleon's sister, your people have made an important stride toward nationalism. Just as the music of the 'Marseillaise' united France under the Revolution, so will the music of the Meringue of St. Domingue unite her sons. St. Domingue? No, not St. Domingue. That is a French name, and we want nothing from the damned French. We are not French, Henry. We are a new race in a new country. What did this island used to be called before the Spaniards found it? The name the Indians called it?"

"Haiti, milord," Pompee prompted him. "It meant 'high place' in the Carib tongue."

"Then, Henry, let us name this 'Haiti.' Let us strive, you and I and our brother blacks, to make this a veritable high place—a nation—a nation so high that all the world will look up to us. Haiti, Henry! Haiti!"

Henry's eyes searched Armes' face. "Haiti, TiArmes! It is a good name. We shall remember it. We shall cast aside St. Domingue, with all its accumulated sorrows, its cruelty and oppression and bloodshed. Yes, TiArmes, it shall be Haiti for you and me and the other men of color. I like the name. Someday this will be Haiti, and may the white god of the Christians and the black gods of Dahomey look down on Haiti and bless it." His big arm reached out and drew Marie Louise to him. For a long moment his eyes rested on Armes and Athenée, and there was a quiet benediction in them. He and Marie Louise turned and left the room. Pompee followed them, closing the door softly behind him. Before the door closed, shutting out the narrow slit of light that came from the hall, Pompee spoke.

"C'est une bonne nuit," he said softly. "Bonne nuit, mes enfants." The door closed, and Armes and Athenée were alone together.

39

AFTER his long absence from San Souci, Armes for the first time realized how wonderful it was to be home; to wake up in his own bed; to open his eyes to familiar surroundings; and to see the impression Athenée's head had left on the pillow beside him. Now, once again, he was Armes Holbrook of Sans Souci, and that was far more satisfying than being Captain Armes Holbrook of the Army of France. Free of military discipline once more, he could stretch out his long legs, punch the pillow into a more comfortable shape, and doze off again. But this morning, the first after his return from the Cap, he was anxious to greet his own world again, so he jumped out of bed, donned a cool silk robe, and presented himself at the breakfast table. Henry was yawning and rubbing the sleep from his eyes; Marie Louise sat quietly, her face star-lit with pregnancy; Pompee grinned from his accustomed chair; and Athenée sat cool and immaculate behind the tall silver coffee urn.

Between mouthfuls of crusty *pain-rôti*, dripping with butter, Armes spoke across the table to Henry.

"We have some serious business to discuss this morning, *mon frère*."

"And I have serious business to attend to this morning, TiArmes." Henry sipped the strong black coffee, his eyes lowered and a grave frown on his forehead. "It's a job I don't like—getting ready to go to the Cap and turn myself over to little-boy General Leclerc. Tell me, TiArmes, shall I go to the Cap as a free man and remain as a prisoner. Is it a trap? Can I trust France?"

"That's exactly what I want to talk to you about, Henry." Armes took another huge bite of toast, which he washed down with hot coffee. "But let it wait until we finish breakfast. We are here in Sans Souci. The French are in Cap François. So let's forget about them until we finish breakfast, and then we can get together and damn their souls to hell."

Athenée extended her hand across the smooth mahogany and placed it on Armes'. "Sometimes I envy you for having been in the Cap. So little happens here at Sans Souci. Tell us, for Marie Louise and I are both dying to know, is Pauline so very beautiful?"

Armes gulped his coffee, playing for time until he could control his voice.

"Everyone says that she is a very beautiful woman," he said noncommittally.

"But we are not interested in what everyone says," Marie Louise interrupted. "We want to know what you say. You have seen her."

"And kissed her hand," Athenée added. She looked straight at Armes.

"I'd call her good-looking." Armes nodded his head

thoughtfully. "But of course, being Napoleon's sister, her good looks have been exaggerated, and now that she is to be an Imperial Highness she will be considered even more beautiful. Napoleon has been made Emperor of France and that makes her a princess. Now everyone will be loud in her praises and every woman will be aping her. Tell me, do you still copy her dresses?" He felt that he had turned the conversation very neatly.

"Heavens, no! We are making dresses for Henry's new son. It *will* be a son, won't it, Henry?" Athenée asked.

He grinned back at her and nodded his head.

In one way Athenée had been right, that little had happened in Sans Souci, for the even tenor of life had gone on there. But, in truth, much had happened during Armes' and Pompee's absence. The little village of Milot had grown, sprawling out haphazardly below the big house. Henry's Dahomeys had built houses for themselves and taken wives and now were busy begetting sons to increase the population of the village. Work had progressed on the church and already the circular walls had risen. A weekly market had been instituted to which peasant women brought produce from over the hills—carrying it miles over mountain trails. One house, larger than all the rest, had been built by one of Henry's Dahomey captains, who had installed in it a group of dusky charmers. Their services found a ready market with the soldiers, and there was always a line of them in front of the door. In fact, with a church, a voodoo *péristyle,* a marketplace, and a thriving whorehouse, Milot had become a real town.

Outside of that, little had taken place at Sans Souci except the everyday problems, and on that particular morning, Pompee had one of those to report. When he had gone out before breakfast to check on plantation matters, he had been informed that TiTonTon, the mute boy, had disappeared. Not only had TiTonTon vanished without leaving a trace, but two fine mules, two *bourriques,* two cows, two goats, and a collection of farm implements were all missing.

"I'll send a squad of Dahomeys after him," Henry quickly volunteered. "They'll track the thieving bastard down."

Pompee motioned for the boy who was serving at table to leave the room and then leaned forward to speak quietly. "No, Henry, let everyone think he skipped away, decided to become a *cultivateur,* and stole the things to start his farm. Actually he went on my orders. Just between ourselves, he

337

has gone to the Bonnet à l'Evêque to start work on Mon Repos. We must keep it a secret."

"Ah, the Bonnet à l'Evêque," Henry said. "You remember, TiArmes, I spoke to you about building a fortress up there."

Armes acknowledged the remark by nodding his head.

"And if I had one there today," Henry sighed, "I'd send a little note to the French. It would have just three words on it—*Merde! Merde! Merde!* Then I'd take my Dahomey boys and we'd go up to the Bishop's Hat and spit down on the French bastards."

Marie Louise turned on him. "Stop it, Henry! I'll wash your mouth out with soap and water. The very idea of your saying such nasty words right here at the breakfast table in front of the Vicomtesse and your own wife. Shame on you, Henry Christophe! Now apologize to Athénée."

Henry grinned shamefacedly. "My apologies, madame, but as far as I am concerned the only word I want to say to the French is . . ."

"Henry!" Marie Louise shut him off.

When there was no more coffee left in the big silver urn, they pushed their chairs back from the table and wandered out onto the balcony. Marie Louise informed them that she had something more important to do than sit and listen to Henry's dirty words, and left for the kitchens to supervise the day's menus. Athénée decided that the floors needed waxing, and she departed to round up the servants for the task. Pompee excused himself after a few moments.

"I'm riding up to le Bonnet," he said in parting. "I want to help TiTonTon with the work up there. I suppose you two are too busy to come." He added the last merely out of politeness, for he knew that Armes would not leave on his first day back, and Pompee was glad of it, for he wished to go alone. It had been a long time since he had seen TiTonTon and he was anxious to be with him again.

"Much too busy, Pompee," Armes declined. "Henry and I have too much to discuss this morning."

". . . and too much to do," Henry added.

Pompee left and they were alone.

"I hope I didn't hit you too hard that night," Henry chuckled. "You sure did a lot of damage, TiArmes. You know, for a moment, when you sent me crashing onto that table, I almost thought it was real. I got mad and had to keep telling myself, 'Henry, Armes is doing this because you asked him to,' but I couldn't seem to pull my punches."

"You damned well didn't. I can tell you that." Armes thrust out his lower lip. "Here's how I looked when I landed on Leclerc's ship—one eye closed and my lower lip bigger than yours."

"Must have been pretty big." Henry tugged at his own lower lip.

"It was, but I think Pauline found my battle scars most interesting."

"Only your battle scars?" Henry closed one eye knowingly and leaned forward in his chair. He lowered his voice. "I've heard about the pretty Pauline. Seems she's drained all the white fellows and has started in on the mulatto boys. Why, we had one bright-skin come out here from the Cap. Said he'd been working at her palace there, but from what I could judge, he'd been doing most of his work in bed with Pauline and her girls. Said Pauline's got one mulatto boy who gives her a bath every day. Tell me, did you get any of that high-class stuff?"

"More about her later," Armes promised. "Now let's talk about Henry Christophe."

"Yes, about me, TiArmes." Henry became serious. "The French have received my note of surrender and agreed to my terms. It was the only thing I could do. Outside of my Dahomeys, I haven't a soldier left. My army fought well enough when I needed them. They were brave and we battled the French to the very gates of the Cap. My boys like to fight, but they do not like sitting around on their ass doing nothing. So they drifted off, each man to his own *caille* and his own woman. If I needed them, they'd come back, but they have no arms to fight with and I have no money to buy them. So, *mon frère,* I have surrendered as you suggested. Now I want to know how Leclerc's going to receive me. You've been with him: you ought to know."

"With honors, Henry," Armes assured him. "Of that I am certain. Yes, with honors. They'll even pin one of these on you." Armes fished in the pocket of his robe and drew out the Legion of Honor, which he tossed to Henry. "Or take this one if you want it. Leclerc gave it to me."

Henry caught it and examined the enameled star on its gaudy ribbon as it lay in his hand.

"But can I trust them, TiArmes?"

"No! Not for ten minutes at a time! Watch them every

single moment, for you never know when the blow will fall. But have no fear for the present. They need you now. They've got Toussaint and they've got you and they will continue to need you until Dessalines and Pétion have also surrendered. If they harmed you, they know they could not get the others. But as soon as the other two surrender, then watch out! For the time being you are the cheese in the mousetrap, set to catch Dessalines and Pétion, so you'll be well treated. But"—he pointed his finger at Henry to emphasize his words,—"when they get you all together, then watch out. So play along with them for the present and they will play along with you. Eternal vigilance is the price you must pay for association with them. I know; I've been with them. Sure, they'll make you a general; they'll pin a couple of stars on you; they'll give you a command; they'll even let you keep your Dahomeys for the time being, but be careful."

Henry placed both hands on his knees and spread them apart. His eyes followed a small black ant that was crawling across the floor. It neared the sole of his shoes. Henry lifted his foot and the ant crawled underneath. The foot came down quickly.

"Like that, TiArmes?" he asked. "I walk into their trap and they close it on me. Is that the way?"

"No, Henry! Look." Armes pointed to the ant which had miraculously escaped and was crawling away. "They won't close the trap on you. Just as a tiny pebble saved the ant, so will you be saved. You've got a pebble on your side."

Henry's eyes questioned him. "You mean . . .?"

"Your African gods, Henry. I've come to believe in them. I've seen what they can do. Pompee has shown me. Pompee prophesies the end of the French army in the Cap."

Henry nodded knowingly. "I know. The fever, TiArmes."

"So Pompee tells me."

Henry slapped his knee with a resounding whack. "I hope he's right. I'm not a *papaloi* and I don't put much faith in voodoo, but the fever does come, and when it strikes it hits only the whites. Every year there is a little bit of it, but once in a while it hits hard. Some fifteen years ago it came and they carted the bodies of the whites away in tumbrils at night. They couldn't make coffins fast enough to bury them. Thank God it never touches the blacks."

"Pompee assures me that I shall be safe. He says the only thing white about me is my skin." Armes looked down at his

340

brown hands. "And that isn't very white now. I'm more black than white, despite my color. I feel at home with you, and I felt like an alien with the French."

"It's true, TiArmes! You know, if a white man told another white he' had a black soul it would be an insult. If a Negro told a white man he had a black soul, it would be the end of the black man. But I, a Negro, am going to tell you, a white man, that you have a black soul, and I know you will not take it as an insult."

"No, Henry. I feel flattered and I thank you. But now, there is something else I must tell you, which is important to me."

Henry signaled for him to proceed.

"I love this island, this Haiti as we call it now."

"Yes, now it is Haiti," Henry repeated the name.

"As I said, I love this island," Armes continued, "but although I forget the fact at times, I have a country, too. And, Henry, I love the United States. One cannot forget the land of one's birth or ever stop loving it. A man loves his wife as I love Haiti, but he loves his mother as I love the States. Henry, the States are in danger."

"The States, TiArmes?" Henry nearly fell off his chair. "Surely Napoleon doesn't have his greedy eyes in that direction."

"Surely he does. St. Domingue is but a stepping stone, a base of operations, a headquarters for the French. They will assemble an even bigger army here, then sail for Louisiana. Their agents have been working on the French there and on the French in Canada. Once landed in Louisiana, Napoleon plans to conquer all the United States and Canada. I know! I heard Leclerc himself taking it over with Rochambeau."

Henry pondered Armes' words carefully. With head bowed on chest, he looked up quickly at Armes.

"But this is good for us in Haiti, TiArmes."

"Good for you that France conquers the world, that Napoleon becomes Emperor of all North America as well as Europe?"

"*Mais non*, but France shall not conquer the world."

"How do you know?"

"Because you, TiArmes, are going to prevent it. Tomorrow you will go to Durham, Brown and Company in the Cap, if there is anything left of them."

"Yes, they are still here."

"And you will tell them, *mon frère*, all that you have just

341

told me. They are English and they do not love Napoleon. Tell them that as America is now in danger they had better spend a little money and break the egg before the eagle is hatched."

"You mean . . .?"

"I mean this. England and the United States can supply me with arms, and I can lick the French before they ever get a chance to land in Louisiana."

Armes shook his head. "The United States is not at war with France, and for that matter neither are you. Tomorrow you go to Cap François as a bona fide general in the French army."

"And tomorrow you go to Durham, Brown, TiArmes." Henry stood up, and it seemed to Armes that he grew inches taller as he raised himself to his full height. "We fight fire with fire. The French think they are tricking us. *Mais non,* it is we who trick them. With help from the United States and England, and Damballah's yellow fever if he ever gets around to sending it, we'll wipe out the French and change St. Domingue to Haiti. You'll do it, TiArmes?"

"I had in mind doing something like you suggest, but I thought of going to the American consul."

"Bah," Henry spat over the railing. "He couldn't do anything. This isn't government business that requires hemming and hawing and a lot of papers all bound with red tape. Listen, *mon frère!* The English and the Americans are men of business. To them their dollars and their pounds are their most precious possessions. They'll do anything to protect their business. And . . . they're smart enough to know that if France holds Europe and North America, they're out of business. To hell with the governments, it's the businessmen we want. Men like your uncle in Boston. Have Durham, Brown get in touch with him. He'll believe them if he knows the word comes from you. Tell him the story and he'll carry on from there." Henry walked over to the steps that led down from the balcony. "Things are working out for us, TiArmes. I don't know if it's because Pompee and his dancing *hunsis* kill a few black cocks and drink their blood or whether your white God has seen the blacks suffer enough or whether it's all up here"—he rubbed the thick wool that covered his head like a close cap of shiny black astrakhan. "But this one thing I do know, TiArmes. Someday I'm going to stand right here and look out over these green valleys and say, 'Henry Christophe, this is all yours, and no goddamned white man is ever going to take it away from you.' "

"And when that day comes St. Domingue will be in good hands."

"Not St. Domingue. Haiti!"

"Haiti then—God bless her."

Henry walked down the steps. He spoke briefly to the soldier who was on guard duty.

"Call a meeting of my officers at once. Then inform all sergeant-majors in the company that I want every man to spend the rest of the day getting his uniform ready. Tomorrow before dawn we march to Cap François. I want every uniform clean; very button shining; every boot polished. Now, go!"

He turned and looked up at Armes on the balcony.

"We'll show them what our nigger army looks like, eh, TiArmes? Wait until they see my Dahomeys tomorrow, all shined up with spit and polish. I only hope the poor bastards can get their boots on over their big feet. They've been going barefoot too goddam long." Henry stepped over to stand directly beneath Armes.

"Do you think there's any chance I might make out with that Pauline while I'm in the Cap? I'd like to tell my children that I laid Napoleon's sister."

Armes leaned over and winked at Henry.

"A very big chance, if you wear your tightest pants, Henry. You see, Her Imperial Highness the Princess Pauline is a very military-minded young woman. Her particularly specialty is ordnance. She wants to know all there is to know about big cannons."

"I think I could teach her along that line."

"Ah, but there is one catch to it, *mon brave*. Pauline likes cannons that fire salvo after salvo, one right after another."

"Then I'm her man, TiArmes."

"More power to you, Henry. I wasn't."

40

HENRY Christophe had surrendered to the French, but on his own terms. He intended to enter Cap François not as a defeated general at the head of a tatterdemalion band of

343

stragglers, but as a conquerer. He had planned it that way and, although he was not aware of it, the French were planning to receive him as such. Leclerc was desirous that Henry's reception should be regulated by the strictest protocol and lack nothing in the way of military honor. He desired the news of Henry's capitulation and his reception at the hands of the French to spread quickly through St. Domingue, because he hoped it would influence Dessalines and Pétion to lay down their arms also. That would come later, Leclerc hoped; now as much as it galled him—brother-in-law of the Emperor Napoleon—he would concentrate on Henry Christophe, general of the Army of St. Domingue, ci-devant governor of the Province of the North, and onetime stableboy at the Hotel Couronne. While Leclerc went about his stiff-necked plans for the reception. Henry was busy at Sans Souci.

Shortly after midnight, when the cool breezes from the ocean swayed the palm fronds, Henry, at the head of his company of Dahomeys, left Sans Souci for the Cap. It was a ragged-looking crowd of soldiers—an army of black peasants, barefooted, dressed in odds and ends of nondescript clothing and led by a general wearing a worn and crumpled uniform astride a piebald mule. But, despite their appearance, the army marched with military precision, and every man carried a carefully wrapped bundle on his back, even the general. And although he rode a mule, he led a white horse.

Armes accompanied them, and Pompee, tired from his long day's journey to the little valley atop the Bishop's Hat, paced his horse beside that of Armes. At first Armes thought it better that Henry go without him, but as Henry pointed out, they were now able to be friends again in the eyes of the French. Hadn't Armes arranged the terms of Henry's surrender with Leclerc? Didn't he now wear the *Légion d'Honneur?* And why? Because he had won a victory for the French by bringing Henry to the city. Therefore, it was only natural that they should be friends again, *n'est-ce pas?*

"The enemies of today are the friends of tomorrow in St. Domingue," Henry explained. "Today Jean Jacques and I are friends: Toussaint and I; Alexander Pétion and I! Tomorrow, who knows? Today we are united under one cause—hatred of the French and a desire for freedom. But wait, TiArmes, until we have gained those ends. Then things will be different. One of the four of us will be stronger than the other three. Then the three will hate the one. Therefore,

344

have no fear that the French will call you a turncoat or point you out as a renegade, either for your desertion of them or of me."

He convinced Armes.

Henry rode along at the head of his column. Vastey and his officers followed him, with Armes and Pompee riding among them. The moon rose late that night, painting the dusty roads ahead of them with silver. By two o'clock in the morning it was as bright as day. Moonlight highlighted damp ebon skins, picked out the silver trappings on the saddle of Henry's horse, and turned the black, plodding shapes into men. But the splendor of the night made the shabby retinue appear even more unkempt and ragged. White dust rose around them as they trudged on. The powdery clouds, kicked up by the shuffle of bare feet, settled on the men's close-fitting caps of black hair and on their faces until they took on the appearance of gray wraiths, marching silently in ghostly formation through the tropical night.

Tonight there was no singing. They marched in silence, accompanied only by the sluff, sluff, sluff of bare feet. It was an unreal army, moving toward an unknown fate, but it was not a defeated army. As they passed peasant *cailles* along the road, they could see fires burning in front of them, with a knot of people standing out in clear silhouette against the orange blaze. When Henry passed they cheered him in hushed voices as if loath to break the eerie spell of the night and the plodding men. They greeted him as *"mon général,"* *"sauveur,"* and *"libérateur."* They walked slowly alongside his mule and placed their hands lovingly on the stirrups. Henry reached down and took their work-calloused hands in his and clasped them tightly, and they went back to their *cailles* glorified at having touched him. No longer were they slaves but free men, and as long as the tall, young Negro, their own Henry Christophe, rode for them, they were safe. He had their trust and their confidence and, to prove it, they draped his saddle with woven garlands of heavy-scented tuberose, hibiscus, and wild orchid. As a child comes to its father for reassurance, they came to him, and he comforted them and sent them back to their homes.

Armes and Pompee rode along slowly with the procession. Pompee had been brimming over with news on his return to Sans Souci, but the preparations for leaving had made it necessary for him to postpone telling it. Now, he leaned over and placed his hand on the pommel of Armes' saddle, reining Lalla until her nervous steps more nearly coincided with the slower ones of Tom. Armes was dozing—the slow cadence of the march was soporific. Pompee had to speak twice to gain his attention.

"TiTonTon has done a wonderful job at Mon Repos."

"Mon Repos." Armes repeated the unfamiliar name; then its significance dawned on him. "Of course, Pompee! How stupid of me. I was half asleep."

"No wonder! From Madame's ball to Sans Souci and now back again."

"From captain in the French Army to voodoo *papaloi* to Armes Holbrook of Sans Souci! From white to Negro to mulatto! Now I'm playing wet nurse to Henry's Dahomeys. Did any man ever have so many roles in so short a time? But tell me about your TiTonTon."

"He is a good boy, milord, and has served you well. You would not recognize the little valley of Mon Repos today, although it is just as lovely as it was before. The little brook still wanders through it, but most of what was grass is now grain—maize and millet." He went on to describe the transformation of the mountain valley. The little knoll was now crowned by a substantial *caille*. Its doorway faced the blue Atlantic far, far below, its rear the granite ramparts of the Bishop's Hat. TiTonTon had labored well. The heavy corner posts supported a low thatched roof and the walls were woven of sturdy branches daubed over inside and out with mud which had dried to a hard, masonry-like surface. TiTonTon had even limed it so it glowed white in the sunshine. Inside there was a hard-packed earthen floor and crude, primitive furniture which Pompee and TiTonTon had made. Beside it, but sufficiently far enough away so that both *cailles* afforded privacy to their occupants, stood a smaller house, equally well constructed. This one, Pompee informed Armes, was for TiTonTon and himself, for Pompee wished TiTonTon to remain with him should they ever go there to stay.

"But when is all this going to happen, and why?" Armes was curious.

"We do not know now, milord, but the time will come. You will see. You and Madame and TiTonTon and I will be safe at Mon Repos."

"Are you sure nobody knows about it? You know how news travels in St. Domingue. Let a person go into a closet and sneeze and within five minutes the drums have carried the news from Cap François to Jérémie."

"Nobody knows," Pompee assured him, "but you and I and Madame, Henry, Marie Louise, and TiTonTon. The Bonnet has always had a bad name among the peasants. They believe it to be the haunt of *loups-garous*, and nothing could persuade them to go there. Fortunately TiTonTon is not afraid. As one of my *hunsis* he has faith in my protection."

Armes' head nodded slowly in time to Tom's steps. He was thinking.

"I cannot seem to remember the boy much. I do recall a dumb boy coming to us after the Bouckmann rebellion. Athenée recognized him and asked me if he might remain at Sans Souci. Seems she had nursed him at St. Gabriel. But I do not think I ever spoke more than a couple of words to him."

Pompee smiled in the darkness. "Yes, milord, you did speak two words to him, and those two words gained you his devotion for life. You do not remember what they were?"

"No."

" '*Pauvre enfant!*' That is what you said to him after you called him over to you. You were sitting on the lower step at Sans Souci and when he sidled up to you, trembling like a frightened rabbit, you motioned to him to come closer. He came and stood between your knees, not knowing whether you were going to whip him or kill him. You opened his mouth gently with your fingers. I shall never forget the look of horror on your face. Then you patted him affectionately on the head and said '*pauvre enfant.*' Not only that, but you reached in your pocket and took out a handful of sweets and gave them to him and sent him on to the fields. That was the first time in his life a white man had ever spoken kindly to him, and the first present he had ever received. He has never forgotten it."

"But if the boy cannot talk and cannot write how can you understand him?"

"It is not difficult when you know him. The contortions of his face, the expression of his eyes, and the few grunts he can make, coupled with the play of his hands, speak almost as well as words. At times I forget he does not talk."

Armes had never been particularly interested in the development of the mountain sanctuary. The whole scheme had seemed fantastic to him, and had it not been that Athenée had fallen in love with the spot and Pompee's insistence that

347

the work be carried through, he would probably have dismissed the matter in the press of more urgent things. Now he was beginning to become interested. He asked other questions—about the mules and donkeys that TiTonTon had taken with him, about the garden, the *caille,* and the development of the little valley.

Pompee had a ready answer for all his questions, and while they rode along in the night, Armes began to visualize the farm from Pompee's words. He saw it as primitive and earthy, secluded from the world, and he could see its possibilities as a refuge from the constant seesaw of St. Domingue politics.

"You've done well, Pompee, you and TiTonTon. As soon as I can I'll go up and visit it. Tell me, is there anything I can do for your TiTonTon? I'd like to repay him for what he has done for me."

Pompee had an answer to that question, too. "The boy is crazy about music. To one who cannot sing nor make a noise, something that speaks is most important. He drums on a board, keeping rhythm by nodding his head up and down. He so wants to make a noise, but he wants that noise to be beautiful. I gave him a *vaccine,* the little bamboo flute that the peasants play, but it does not express him sufficiently. If you could give the boy a guitar, milord, you would make him happy."

Armes agreed and they rode along. They were nearly to Cap François and the moon was paling in the sky. The first streaks of the false dawn were coloring the east. When they arrived at the ford in the river where Armes and Henry had planned their quarrel, he saw Henry raise his arm and heard the command to halt repeated along the column. They stopped, then another command brought them to the edge of the stream. Half of them crossed over and the company lined up on both sides of the little river.

Henry rose in his stirrups and addressed them.

"You have your orders, *mes enfants.*" He was laughing in a most unmilitary manner. "You have your orders which I gave you, and I have mine which my wife gave me. Into the river, all of you. Leave your cast-off rags on the bank and forget them. Scrub yourselves clean with sand and leaves so that no dainty Frenchman will find it necessary to place his handkerchief to his nose and say that all black soldiers stink. When you have finished scrubbing yourself, put on your uniforms and line up for inspection. If any man lacks a button or if any button does not shine so that I can see my face in

348

it, that man will wish he had never been born. Now, *mes enfants!*" Henry slid down from his mule and started to strip off his own worn uniform.

Standing there naked in the cool, pale light of the eastern sky, he reminded Armes of some heathen god of ancient Egypt whose sculptured bronze had come to life. Henry walked over the close-cropped grass to the river. He stepped in, ankle deep, and jumped back.

"It's goddamned cold, this water," he called to the naked men who stood poised on the bank. But he stepped in again and strode out, flinching as the cold water slapped against his belly, then plunged head first. One by one his men followed him, and from both banks they dived in until the water was churned white. Armes still sat on his horse. Henry swam over within shouting distance. "TiArmes, TiArmes," he called. "Are you afraid of a little water?"

Armes felt curiously conscious of his white skin. It separated him from all the rest. He wished to be identified with them—to be one of them—rather than feel a barrier of color between them.

Henry called again. "From the waist up, TiArmes, you're nothing but a goddamned *affranchi* like little Valentin here." He reached out and grabbed the little mulatto who was near him. "And see what we do to mulattoes, TiArmes." He ducked Vastey, then lifted him clear of the water in his huge arms. "Come on, TiArmes! You're a mulatto from the waist up and a white man from your waist down." Then, in anticipation of his joke, he roared with laughter. "But it's from the waist down that counts in a man's life, and if the fair Pauline prefers you to her mulatto studs, you have nothing to be ashamed of. "Come on, TiArmes! Let us scrub that *affranchi* dye off. Be all white again. God knows our army needs one white man."

Armes had shed his clothes almost before he touched the ground. He ran along the riverbank until he was abreast of Henry, plunged in, and swam out. Before he reached the spot where Henry was, he dove and swam underwater. His hands encountered the hard calves of Henry's legs, grabbed them, and twisted them until Henry's big feet, not too securely planted on the sandy bottom, were dislodged. There was an immense splash and Armes rose to the surface to see Henry floundering in the water.

Then Henry was after him. He was more powerful than Armes and his quick strokes brought him to Armes in a second. Henry grabbed him by the back of the neck with one hand and pushed him down under the water while the other hand reached down for a handful of white sand. He lifted Armes, sputtering and struggling, and scrubbed one of his shoulders vigorously. "I'll make a white man of you yet," he bellowed.

"If you leave any skin on me." Armes wriggled out from under Hanry's clutch and leaped on Henry. They wrestled in the water until Armes managed to push Henry under. When the big fellow came up for air, he held up both hands in surrender. "You win," he cried. "You goddamn *blancs* always win in the end."

Henry and his army scrubbed themselves clean in the little river. Their black skins shone like hard polished ebony; their white teeth gleamed like the pebbles in the river; and their skullcaps of wiry wool were pearled with water. Then they dried themselves with handfuls of grass and aromatic leaves, romping in wild horseplay in the light of the new sun. When they were dry, they carefully unrolled the parcels they had been carrying on their backs all night. They dressed themselves carefully in the gaudy uniforms that Henry had supplied them when they were the guard of honor of the governor of the North. They donned the sleek white *tricot* breeches, the gold-laced coats of scarlet, the high polished boots, and the plumed shakos. After they had finished dressing, they lined up, four abreast, in the road—a long column of white and scarlet and gold and . . . black. Henry's white horse had been combed and curried, and he mounted and rode slowly down the line. They all met his inspection proudly. Not a button failed to shine; not a boot that didn't reflect like a mirror.

Henry was satisfied. He wheeled his horse to the center of the road. The drummers with their big, red-tasseled drums fell in behind him. Then came his mounted officers, together with Armes and Pompee, who felt somewhat shabby in their travel-stained white linen, and then the Dahomeys—Henry's pride. The drums ruffled and they started toward Cap François. The sweaty rags of common peasants were abandoned and forgotten on the banks of the river. Now they were soldiers of Henry Christophe, following their general into the city—not as a surrendered battalion but as proud conquerors.

For a mile outside the city gates, the road was lined with blacks, all in their holiday clothes. They were out to welcome back their governor, their general, their Man. Many had known Henry before in his slave days at the Couronne. Some had envied him, some had disliked him, some had ridiculed him, but today they all loved their *gros nègre*—their Henry. The French heard the cheering long before he came in sight, and Leclerc looked down the street from his position before the steps of Pauline's palace.

Both sides of the street were lined with French soldiers, stiff and proper in their parade uniforms, all standing rigidly at attention. Wobbly arches of palm fronds spanned the street —quickly improvised in the early morning hours. Some boasted letters picked out in blossoms, "Bienvenue, Henry." Although poor Henry could not read them, he could wave back to the women who threw bouquets of scarlet poinsettias between the serried ranks of soldiers.

Leclerc's face paled as he saw Henry advancing on his white horse. He bit his lips with nervousness, and so much forgot himself as to pluck at his whiskers with his long, pale fingers. But he sat his horse straight, like the general he was, and, as Henry neared him, he dismounted.

When Henry was about fifty paces from Leclerc and his staff, Armes heard him give the command to halt. The drums continued, and the black boots of the soldiers marked time on the cobbles, magnifying the beat. Henry's horse reared up, but the long years Henry had spent in the Couronne stables stood him in good stead. He calmed the horse and dismounted, handing the reins to Vastey. With a pompous stride he walked toward Leclerc, and the equally stiff and pompous Leclerc advanced to meet him.

"This," Armes thought, "is a vital moment in the history of St. Domingue. How will Leclerc receive him? What will he do? Will he do the right thing in the right way? Will he forget that Henry is a Negro and receive him as a brother general? Will he, if only for one moment, let Henry feel that they are equals?" He knew Henry was thinking the same thoughts. But he also knew that the first gesture would have to come from Leclerc.

The two men were facing each other now. Only a couple of steps separated them. "Oh God," Armes prayed, "let Leclerc put out his hand. Let him embrace Henry. Let there be just the slightest, momentary contact of white skin and black—just enough to save Henry's pride."

Leclerc stopped, clicked his heels together, and drew himself up as straight as a ramrod. Henry's actions followed Leclerc's. Leclerc's right hand rose in a stiff salute. Henry's followed just as stiffly. Leclerc bowed stiffly from the waist. Henry's bow was even stiffer.

Leclerc spoke. "General Henry Christophe?" They were proper words, but their inflection should not have formed them into a question. By so doing they denied Henry's identity.

"General Leclerc?" Henry's question boomed out over the tricolor cockades of the French.

Leclerc was nonplussed. He could not very well answer "yes" to the question, but habit caused him to incline his head.

"May I present you with the First Dahomean regiment of St. Domingue, *mon général?*" Henry was being generous.

"The Army of France is happy to welcome you and your regiment, General Christophe. Please conduct your men to barracks and report to me at Headquarters in an hour. We shall discuss your command more in detail." He saluted smartly but mechanically, waited to receive Henry's answering salute, then turned abruptly on his heel and walked back to his horse. Henry duplicated the motions, mounted his horse, and turned to his Dahomeys.

"You are now soldiers of France, *mes enfants.* Follow me! Forward, march!"

The drums rolled and the column fell in behind Henry. Armes fought to keep back the tears of anger that stung his eyes. He knew with an overwhelming sense of certainty that the hatred Henry had previously had for Leclerc was now increased a thousandfold. He knew that Henry's injured pride would never let him rest until he had humbled Napoleon's pale young general. He knew . . . and he was glad, for he realized that of the two men who had faced each other only a moment before—the white general and the black general—Henry Christophe was the stronger and the better man.

41

A CHAGRINED Armes and a rebellious Pompee watched Henry's broad back as his white horse led the smartly stepping column of Dahomeys in a slow march down the street from the palace. Their black boots and white breeches moved in perfect unison with the drums, and their shakos made a brave show in the sunlight. Leclerc and his staff immediately dismounted and disappeared into the doorway of the palace. Apparently he had never noticed Armes' presence. The rattle of Henry's drums grew fainter, and the red coats of the Dahomeys faded into the distance. Here, where a few moments before two opposing factions had faced each other in a guarded truce, there was nothing left but the brilliance of the morning sun, glinting on the empty cobbles.

Armes and Pompee turned their horses and walked them along the street. Each had business to attend to, and they agreed to meet again two hours later in the *Place*. Pompee went to pick up some odds and ends that Armes had left in the Cap; offer Maman an opportunity to go to Sans Souci if she so desired; and then meet with one of the other voodoo *papalois* of Cap François. Armes had important business to transact with Durham, Brown and Company.

Their stone building near the waterfront had been one of the few left standing after the fire. Although it had been gutted on the inside, it had been repaired, and now presented nearly the same appearance as before. It still appeared more English than French—more London than St. Domingue.

The black boy that met Armes at the door was as decorously attired in gray cloth as though he had been in Mr. Frothingham's office in Boston. He seemed to be familiar with Armes' name. He requested him to wait a moment, disappeared behind a green baize door, and returned quickly to usher Armes into an office paneled in rich dark wood. An elderly man, thin of face with a high domed forehead over which a few wisps of white hair were carefully arranged, glanced up from the papers on his desk as Armes entered. He motioned Armes to a high-backed chair and transfixed him, like a butterfly on a pin, with his icy stare, while he carefully folded his hands around his little waistcoated melon of a stomach and waited.

"I am Armes Holbrook, sir." Armes felt he had to say something to break the strained silence.

"John Avery, Mr. Holbrook." The name was bitten off precisely.

"Thank you." Armes inwardly damned the man for a pompous idiot, but he proceeded. "I would like to ask you a question."

The thin lips became even thinner. "Pray do."

"Are you an Englishman or an American? I know that both are interested in this company."

The pale blue eyes did not blink—they stared intently at Armes. "Before I reply to your rather impertinent question, Mr. Holbrook, I might ask if you are an American or a damned nigger rebel of St. Domingue?"

The coolness of his reception was raising the fire of Armes' temper.

"In that case, sir, I would tell you it was none of your business, but I would still ask you my question."

"Although I can hardly understand what difference it might make to you, I shall tell you that I am a citizen of the United States, although I have spent most of my life in London, Jamaica, and St. Domingue, where our company has offices. I might add also that I have the pleasure of knowing your guardian, Mr. Frothingham, in Boston."

Armes felt that the man wanted to add, "And small credit you are to him," but nevertheless he felt relieved. His muscles lost their tenseness and he relaxed in the chair.

Avery's voice continued in its chilling monotone. "I have followed your career of late, Mr. Holbrook, and I must admit I do not care for you, your actions, or your associates."

"I presume you refer to my friendship with Henry Christophe."

"I most certainly do! A blacker rascal I have never heard of."

"General Christophe is hardly to blame for the color of his skin."

"I do not refer to the color of his skin, Mr. Holbrook, but to his character."

Armes could feel the blood flushing his cheeks, and he presumed that his ears were scarlet. A glance at his hands made him conscious of their brown dye, and he knew Avery must be wondering about his mulatto coloring. With his voice carefully controlled, he looked straight at Avery.

"Pardon me, sir. Let us divorce myself and my actions and your opinion of both from the matter which I wish to discuss with you. I have not come here to talk about my good friend General Christophe nor myself. I am here to discuss something far more important than either of us—a grave danger that threatens the United States and England."

Avery smiled, for the first time, as if it hurt him to do so.

"Is this another scheme of yours, young man? The French may have been hoodwinked by your sudden about-face in regard to Christophe. I was not. However, it was none of my affair, so I did not interfere. At the moment England

354

and France are at peace. Therefore I am duty bound to recognize General Leclerc as the rightful governor-general of St. Domingue. As to Henry Christophe and you, Mr. Holbrook, I consider you both rogues, rascals, rebels, and troublemakers despite the fact that Chistophe was received in Cap François this morning."

Armes jumped up and walked over to Avery's desk. He planted both hands firmly on it and leaned over until his face was only a foot or so away from Avery's. The old man did not retreat an inch. He glared back at Armes in defiance and started to speak, but Armes' words, shouted in anger, drowned him out.

"Mr. Avery, I don't give a hoot in hell whether you like me or whether you approve of me. Please understand that. But you are going to listen to me if I have to throttle you and beat my words into your stupid head."

Avery's eyes flashed fire from under his scraggy brows. "I am compelled by force and threats to listen, so I shall, but regardless of what you say I shall not believe you."

"But listen to me nevertheless. In your eyes I may be a renegade, a deserter of my race . . ."

"A wastrel, a libertine, a seducer of women, a rake, a liar, and a disgrace to the white race, to mention but a few of your more admirable qualities, Mr. Holbrook."

Armes clenched his hands so tightly on the rim of the desk that the knuckles turned white under the brown dye. He was firmly resolved to control his temper—not to let his fingers tighten around the scrawny neck of the old man until he had said what he wanted to say.

"You are not complimentary, Mr. Avery, but I shall have to admit the truth of what you say. There are one or two other things you did not mention. I have also become a heathen in that I believe in the voodoo gods and am a wearer of fetishes. But let me remind you of one thing, old man. I can be all of these things and maybe more, too, but I can still love my country. Now, goddamn your narrow-minded, puritanical soul, you listen to me and believe me. North America is in grave danger, and when I say North America I mean my own country of the United States and England's Canada."

Avery sank back in his chair, his mouth open in astonishment.

"You do speak like a man who is not afraid to state his convictions."

"I am. Now listen, Napoleon has his eye on North America. Orders have already gone to Paris, directly to the Tuileries, to send fifty thousand soldiers to St. Domingue in the biggest fleet France has ever assembled. Why? Just to conquer Henry Christophe? Hell, no! St. Domingue is merely a stepping stone on the route to Louisiana, and with those fifty thousand Frenchmen, Napoleon is going to sweep over the United States, conquer it, set up one of his brothers as king in Washington, and then proceed to Canada, where the French will welcome him with open arms. That, Mr. Avery, is what I would like to pound into that wooden skull of yours."

It was Avery's turn to stand up. You've some scheme afoot, Holbrook. I don't believe you."

"If you don't believe me, God help you, old man! The blood of tens of thousands of peaceful citizens of the United States will be on your hands, for they will soon be dead from French bullets. Just because you don't believe me."

Avery came out from behind his desk, tiptoed over to the door, and opened it carefully. He peered up and down the hall to satisfy himself that nobody was listening. Then he returned to his desk.

"Are you sure of what you are saying, Mr. Holbrook? You must have some foundation upon which to base your statements."

"I have. I overheard a conversation between Leclerc and Rochambeau. I can vouch for the truth of every word I say, and although I may well be the scoundrel you accuse me of being and perhaps even worse, the fact remains that I still love my own country enough to tell the truth. It is the truth, so help me God."

"Are you referring to Jehovah or Damballah?"

"Sometimes I wonder if there is any difference."

Avery sat down, and Armes could see that the old man was deep in thought. When he spoke it was almost in a whisper.

"Bring your chair over here next to mine, Mr. Holbrook. Although these walls are thick and that door is strong, we cannot take any chances on being overheard. Your information possesses all the qualities of gunpowder . . ."

"And might save a lot of gunpowder in the end."

"Exactly!" Avery was becoming more friendly. "When did you hear this information?"

"Last night at the masked ball at the palace."

The thin lips curved into a smile. "Oh yes, I heard you

were there. You must have been quite a sensation. Rumor has it that you were singled out for marked attention by Madame Leclerc."

Armes grinned self-consciously. "News does travel fast here in St. Domingue. But it was entirely through Madame's attentions that I happened to hear what I did. She and I were in a very compromising position in a rather dark and hidden spot."

Avery actually laughed. "Ah, that is something I had not heard. Dear, dear. Must I add 'adulterer' to your already long list?" The cold blue eyes warmed with a little twinkle.

"I'm afraid so. But being an adulterer with Pauline is not very difficult, provided one has the necessary qualifications, which she seemed to feel that I had. At any rate, Pauline and I were engaged in a rather intimate *rendezvous* in the grotto on the lower terrace of the palace. By a coincidence Leclerc and Rochambeau, who were also seeking privacy but for a different purpose, stood directly before the entrance to the grotto, naturally entirely unaware that it was occupied. Therefore, Mr. Avery, I can assure you that I am telling the truth. General Leclerc had no idea that his conversation was being overheard by his wife and her lover. His words were intended for Rochambeau's ears alone."

Avery gave a thin, dry laugh which turned into a cough. "Heh, heh! So you and the fair Pauline were fitting the horns on Leclerc's head while he and Rochambeau were discussing the future of America. Heh, heh! You know, Holbrook, I'm beginning to like you, although you're a bloody rascal. Stealing a man's wife right out from under his nose."

"It might be more correct to say that Pauline stole me, Mr. Avery. But that is not important. Do you believe that I am telling you the truth?"

"Under those circumstances, I must confess that I do."

"Then listen, sir." Armes outlined the ideas that he and Henry had discussed the day before. Wouldn't it, he urged, be better to help Henry Christophe clandestinely rid St. Domingue of the French than to allow them to use St. Domingue as a way station for the American continent? It was merely a matter of supplying Henry with money, arms, and ammunition against the time when he could use them. It was a matter of sailing boats coming in the dead of night to a deserted beach and landing those precious arms to be stored in some hidden cache in the mountains. It was a matter of Negro dominion in Haiti as compared to French dominion in North America. It was a matter of life or death to the United States.

Avery listened attentively, considered the matter carefully, and then spoke deliberately. "I have a ship leaving for New York tomorrow. One of my men is returning. He is a most trustworthy man. Through him I shall have our New York office get in touch with Mr. Frothingham in Boston. Moreover, I shall personally vouch for the truth of the matter. However, young man, these are dangerous words you have just spoken to me. They could cause both of us to face Leclerc's firing squad tomorrow. There is only one loophole. You say Madame Leclerc heard this disclosure also? Might she not suspect you if the information leaked out?"

Armes brushed the question aside. "Considering what was happening to Pauline at the time, I doubt if she even heard what her husband was saying, and if she did, she is hardly in a position to tell her husband of my presence. I cannot picture her confessing that she overheard him while she was cuckolding him with another man."

"Quite so. We are safe on that account. Who else knows about this?"

"Only General Christophe."

Avery shook his head. "That's bad. I don't trust him."

"But I do, Mr. Avery. Henry Christophe is the most honorable man I have ever met. If Henry asked for my right hand he could have it."

"There must be something in the man to inspire such devotion. You know, Holbrook, I am beginning to wonder if I might not have misjudged you."

Armes smiled. "Not too much, Mr. Avery. You see I really am a wastrel, a libertine, a seducer of women, a renegade . . ."

"Granted! But I think you are perhaps more than all these things. You seem to have a cool head to offset your hot blood. Between the two of us perhaps we can save the United States from Napoleon. There is a certain subtle diplomacy in business, Armes, that does not exist in governments. We move faster and we accomplish more. If Napoleon takes over North America, it will not only mean the end of the United States but the end of Durham, Brown and Company. So you see, we have a selfish interest in the matter."

Armes relaxed in his chair. "Then I shall hear from you later, Mr. Avery. I shall be interested to know Mr. Frothingham's reactions." He stood up, prepared to leave.

The old man also stood up and came closer to Armes. He

put his thin hand through Armes' elbow and walked with him to the door. "The fair Pauline," he tittered. "You aim high, my boy."

"The credit all goes to Pauline, sir. Believe me, if ever man was raped by woman, I was by Pauline. But willingly, sir, willingly." Armes turned and grasped Avery's thin white hand in his large brown one. He shook it solemnly. There was much about the man that reminded him of Mr. Frothingham. He turned the doorknob and partially opened the door. For the benefit of a clerk who was passing in the hall, he made his voice casual, and said, "Then, Mr. Avery, my credit is still good here?"

"With recent receipts from your guardian in Boston, Mr. Holbrook, your balance now stands at £ 75,853, plus a few odd shillings and pence. I would consider it passing good."

Armes waited until the clerk had passed, then lowered his voice.

"Transfer another £ 50,000 to the account of Henry Christophe. That's how much I believe in him."

Avery bowed and slowly lowered one eyelid. "I always say that when a man backs up his words with his money, he believes in what he is doing. I can see that you are thoroughly convinced that the dark gentleman you mentioned is worthy of your trust."

"Of that I can assure you," Armes answered.

"Then I shall try very hard to consider him worthy of mine."

"You're not making any mistake, Mr. Avery." Armes held out his hand and Avery shook it hard. Armes felt that he had made a new friend. As time went on, he was to discover that he had.

42

PEACE—a troubled and uncertain peace, but peace nevertheless—settled over St. Domingue. Only a few days after Henry's triumphant entry into the Cap, a weary old man who had carried the heavy burdens of the blacks on his shoulders, Toussaint L'Ouverture, came quietly and without fanfare to the city. No battalion of Dahomeys in brilliant uniforms escorted him. He came alone with a few stragglers, tired, dirty, and hungry behind him. Toussaint came to the French empty-handed, with only one request—that the Negroes be guaranteed freedom forever. The request was all too readily granted. Leclerc was ready to concede anything in order to make a favorable report to Napoleon, knowing that anything he said could be unsaid as quickly as it was glibly promised now. Having delivered himself, Toussaint asked for permission to retire to civil life with his wife and family at his little plantation at Ennery. Leclerc granted this also. He was glad to be rid at last of the First of the Blacks.

Followed then Jean Jacques Dessalines, and another French general was added to the roster of Napoleon's army. Where Henry Christophe had been all spit and polish in his immaculate uniform, Dessalines appeared purposely as disgraceful as possible. His torn and ragged uniform was encrusted with the dirt of the road, his boots were unpolished, and his once white breeches were greasy and grimy. Where Henry's wide brown eyes had looked straight at Leclerc, Jean Jacques' eyes avoided the gaze of the white general. He had never broken his vow. He never would. The hatred that Dessalines had for all whites extended to every man, woman, and child whose skin was pale. The sight of white skin inflamed his basest passions. Like the *bandera* waved before a fighting bull, it engendered an uncontrollable desire to kill without mercy. So, Dessalines hung his huge, misshapen head in front of Leclerc, and only half listened to the Frenchman's words. Jean Jacques knew that if he raised his head and looked the man in the eye he would kill him. Patience was a difficult lesson for Dessaline, but he was forcing himself to learn it. The stakes were too high to let his temper rule him.

A few days later Alexandre Pétion, the slim, pale mulatto who had been reared in luxury and educated in France, arrived from Port-au-Prince to receive a third generalship in the French army. Leclerc sighed with relief. *"Une famille jolie,"* he wrote to Napoleon, blissfully confident of his own ability to outwit the four black leaders. He liked Pétion—so did Pauline—and Pétion, homesick for the boulevards of Paris, cooperated with Leclerc. Even the surly Dessalines dissembled his intense hatred with a thin veneer of cooperativeness, and Henry joined him, both in dissembling his hatred and in paying lip service to Leclerc.

And it was Henry who hatched the idea of obtaining the guns for the blacks. Henry was clever, and he never forgot anything that might stand him in good stead. Now he remembered. Some years before, Sonthonax, the commissioner whom the brave new French Republic, at that time brimming over with its idealistic doctrine of liberty for all, had distributed over twenty thousand muskets to the slaves which the Republic had so enthusiastically "liberated." These guns were now scattered all over St. Domingue from the Cap to Les Cayes—useless ornaments on the wattled walls of peasants' *cailles* because no ammunition had ever been issued to go with them. But the guns were still there, and even though many of them had never been used, they were in good condition, for the peasants revered them and carried them in the voodoo processions around the *houmfort.*

Without mentioning the fact that the guns were worthless without ammunition, Henry mentioned their existence to Leclerc, and convinced him that they were a threat to the French and should be safely in Leclerc's own hands. Leclerc was convinced, but as he wanted to rid himself of Dessalines' rank musk at his staff meetings, he dispatched Jean Jacques to round them up. Henry lost no time in convincing Leclerc that Dessalines and his men were not enough to do the job properly, and maneuvered Leclerc into appointing him also. Henry conferred secretly with Dessalines, and for once they agreed on something. Henry accomplished his *coup de maître,* and Leclerc congratulated himself that he had done the same, for he had not only gotten rid of Dessalines and his stink but of Henry and his Dahomeys.

The two generals departed, dividing their command to comb the island from *caille* to *caille* to search out the French muskets. They ferreted them out in every obscure hut in the colony. Henry dictated a letter telling of their success to Leclerc. The muskets were in his hands, please send instructions as to how he was to deliver them to the Cap. But if he could make a suggestion? As roads were practically nonexistent and transportation was mainly on the heads of peasants and on the backs of *bourriques,* wouldn't it be much better, Henry inquired, to cache the guns in various forts throughout the island? Then, if they were needed in any particular spot, they would not have to be transported all the way back again. Of course, General Leclerc must not think that he was offering advice to his superior officer, but it seemed to him . . . And it seemed a feasible plan to Leclerc also, so he agreed. He had formed the habit of saying *oui,* and Henry's advice did seem logical. So, having recovered the greater part of the twenty thousand muskets, Henry and Jean Jacques made sure that they were safely locked up in strongholds in the mountains.

When they returned to Cap François, Henry made quite an impressive ceremony of presenting the keys to those strongholds, tied with a wide tricolor ribbon, to Leclerc, who commended them both and awarded them the Legion of Honor, although he neglected to kiss either of them on the cheeks. Neither Henry nor Jean Jacques was hurt by the withholding of Leclerc's kiss, and they much admired the pretty white-enameled stars with their gay ribbons. They served to remind them that while Leclerc had the keys, they had the guns. *Voila!*

During the weeks that Henry was running about, collecting guns from peasants' *cailles,* Armes delighted in a long breathing spell at Sans Souci, uninterrupted by politics, crises, or diplomatic cat's-pawings. For the time being, neither Henry nor Leclerc required his services and, although Pauline may have desired them, she could not ask for them. Consequently Armes settled easily into the old routine, and his life progressed as peacefully as it could on the brink of a volcano which, while it only occasionally spouted brimstone and sulphur, was often heard to utter deep rumblings in its interior.

Henry was now in command of the garrison at Dondon, high up in the mountains. He was so far away that it had been impossible for him to arrive in time the night Marie Louise was taken with labor pains, but he managed to get there, in a wild dash down midnight mountain peaks, in time to hear the first weak squalls of his newborn son. For it was a son, as Henry had been so certain. Marie Louise wanted to name him Henry, but Henry desired a more prophetic name, and decided on Victor. The same priest in the same rusty cassock who had married Henry and Marie Louise christened the baby, who was strong, fat, and good-natured—three characteristics which remained with him as he grew to young manhood.

During the few days that Henry remained at Sans Souci, he beamed in pride of his new fatherhood. Marie Louise's eyes became even more soft and beautiful. Athenée clucked over the infant like a mother hen with one lone chick, and even Armes looked down into the cradle and poked his big finger at the baby, which only caused it to wrinkle up its monkey face and scream. Pompee, strangely enough, did not seem to rejoice in the new arrival, although he was more

362

devoted and paid more attention to little Victor than all the others did. When he cried, Pompee picked him up and cradled him tenderly in his arms, patting him and crooning as he walked. But when he looked at the little Victor, there was sadness in his eyes. Pompee seemed to sense some dark cloud in the little fellow's future, but he mentioned it to nobody, not even Armes.

After his short period of exuberant fatherhood, Henry departed for Dondon, and Armes was left to contemplate his wide fields. It came as rather a surprise to him when one day, after luncheon, Pompee suggested that they leave that evening for Mon Repos. It would be better to go by night, he suggested, as they would be unlikely to meet anyone.

"Except the *loups-garous*," Armes grinned.

"Any man who got safely out of the clutches of Pauline need not fear a *loup-garou*," Pompee grinned back at him.

They agreed to start at sundown, and although the mountain trail was difficult in the moonlight, they arrived in the little valley before the moon set. Armes halted his horse by the brink of the waterfall and looked out over the silver mist that covered the valley. Ghostly rows of shoulder-high maize marched across it, and on the other side of the stream a waving field of millet rippled like a millpond in the spectral light. The dark shape of the two *cailles* on the knoll loomed up over the silver mist—a big one and a smaller one beside it.

From inside the small *caille*, they heard a dog bark, softly at first and then louder. The door was pushed open and the animal dashed out, coming at them across the field with deep-throated growls. Pompee spoke sharply to him, and he subsided into tail-wagging, but not before he had awakened a flock of chickens, roosting in an avocado tree, whose lord and master, with a mistaken idea that it was morning, sent forth a clarion call that echoed against the granite cliffs of the Bishop's Hat. A donkey brayed, an ox lowed from the rough corral, and then a light appeared in the doorway of the *caille*. The slender silhouette of a nude man patterned itself blackly against the orange glow. Pompee called out and the figure ducked back from the door only to reappear clad in a pair of pantaloons. As they rode across the field, the light moved from the small *caille* to the larger one. Pompee cautioned Armes, "He's shy, this boy. His affliction has made him avoid people. Do not be surprised if TiTonTon seems ill at ease with you at first."

Armes' finger pointed over his left shoulder to the bulky package tied to his saddle. Pompee's white teeth flashed in the lambent moonlight. Happiness to Pompee meant making somebody else happy, particularly TiTonTon.

The thin orange light of the candle, streaming through the door, disclosed a young man in his late teens or early twenties whose thin, flat belly seemed hardly strong enough to support the wide sweep of his muscular chest and shoulders. He hung his head as they appeared, so that Armes could not see his face, but as he dismounted from his horse and approached the door of the *caille*, he could see the nervous twitching of the muscles in the boy's arms. TiTonTon raised his head for one sweeping glance at the two men, then lowered it again, but in that one instant, Armes glimpsed the fine sculptured forehead, the large intelligent eyes, the flattened nose with its wide nostrils, and the Negroid lips of the true African. The boy was from one of the superior tribes—Mandingo, Hausa, or Dahomey.

TiTonTon bowed low as he ushered them into the hut. It was larger than Armes had expected, with a clean-swept, hard-packed dirt floor. A thick woven mat of banana leaves occupied one corner in place of a bed. Two crude chairs and a table completed the furnishings, except for a scrubbed iron pot, a machete, and a cumbersome iron spoon. The walls were the chief decoration of the hut. They had originally been white, but now they were covered with murals, and although the art was primitive and highly colored, it was delicately limned. Looking around at them, Armes saw the daily life of Sans Souci—workers in the cane fields, the big house, the village of Milot, the *houmfort*, the voodoo processions, the drummers, and the weekly *bamboche*. The pictures covered the rough walls with the richness of a medieval tapestry, and gave warmth and color to the whole interior.

Armes was astonished. He looked at Pompee, who indicated TiTonTon standing against the wall, his big hands nervously interlacing their fingers in front of him.

"You did all these?" Armes asked.

The black head nodded.

"But it's wonderful."

The shoulders shook a little.

"And I thank you for all the work you did."

Pompee drew out one of the chairs from the table for

Armes to use and then seated himself on the other. Armes continued to stare at TiTonTon.

"You are TiTonTon. I remember you at Sans Souci."

The boy lifted his head to steal a quick glance at Armes, then ducked it down again.

"You have been a good boy," Armes continued. "You have worked hard outside and you have done all this in here." His arm sweep indicated the walls. "I appreciate it."

This time the boy's glance lingered a little longer on Armes' face. Then suddenly he ran across the room to fling himself on the floor and clasp Armes' knees with both hands. His wide lips stretched to a thin line over his teeth, and he struggled to express himself until his forehead was beaded with sweat, but only a few guttural sounds came out of his mouth.

"He's trying to thank you for thanking him," Pompee said quietly.

Armes reached down and put his hands on the boy's shoulders. "Stand up, *mon homme!* You do not have to kneel before me. Look, we are going to sleep here tonight, and when daylight comes, we are going to take a look at all you have done. Then we shall leave so that we may arrive at Sans Souci before breakfast. Pompee!" He turned in his chair. "How about getting the blankets from the saddles. And," he added with a quick wink at Pompee, "the bundle I carried up the mountain."

Pompee left and TiTonTon got to his feet to stand awkwardly in front of Armes. He kept his eyes on his big bare toes, then gathered courage to look up from under his lashes at Armes. A smile convulsed his face. Armes felt that the boy had smiled rarely in his lifetime, but now his whole face was illumined. Again he struggled to speak but, as gestures were his only language, he stepped nearer to Armes, reached for his hand, picked it up, and kissed it. Armes felt embarrassed; there was nothing he could do nor say except pat the boy on the shoulder. It was like patting a big, overgrown puppy who was trying in his own inaudible way to express his love for his master. Pompee's arrival with the unwieldy bundle was welcome. Armes pointed to the bundle and then to TiTonTon.

"It's for you, boy. Unwrap it."

TiTonTon advanced slowly to the table where Pompee had placed the bundle, staring at the object with awe. The fingers of his right hand pointed to his chest. "For me?" they queried.

"Yes, for you," Armes assured him.

TiTonTon carefully untied the hempen twine and unrolled the fabric covering. The neck of the guitar appeared from the wrapping, and the boy stopped suddenly to gaze at it with unbelieving eyes. It seemed incredible to him that it could actually be his, but a wave of Armes' hand directed him to proceed. When his trembling fingers had finished unwinding the cloth, he lifted the guitar reverently in his arms. Then he replaced it on the table, knelt before it on the floor, and stroked it lightly and lovingly with his hands. One finger plucked tentatively at the strings; a low note of music vibrated through the room, and with its sound, TiTonTon burst into hysterical sobs. Tears coursed down his cheeks, but he brushed them away and stood up. New life seemed to enter into him. He lifted his head proudly, cradled the instrument in his arm, and swept his hand over the strings. As though a miracle had happened, he stood transfixed. Evidently he had seen a guitar before, for his fingers tested the tune of the strings and he cocked his head first to one side and then to the other listening. His ear attuned to the sounds, he tightened some keys, loosened others until he seemed satisfied, then sat down, cross-legged on the floor, with the precious instrument in his arms.

A strange melody poured forth from the instrument. The guitar spoke—music such as Armes had never heard before, an unearthly primitive song that was full of suppressed longings. The tones seemed to become words. They told of bitter anguish and sorrow, of loneliness, isolation, and ridicule. They pleaded for understanding; they begged for friendship; they prayed for love. Then the chords changed and there was an interval of peace and quiet, of hushed tremolos in which Armes saw sunrise and moonrise and heard the rushing water of the little stream in the mountain meadow. The black fingers muted the strings and the last vibrations died away in the *caille*. TiTonTon looked up directly at Armes, and the smile reappeared on his lips. The fingers of his left hand sought the frets, and one finger of his right hand plucked a string. The guitar spoke. It became a human voice which talked in words of music. "*Je vous remercie, milord,*" it said with twanging strings, and Armes understood.

"*Mon Dieu!* He's speaking with the guitar. Did you hear it, Pompee?"

366

"I did, milord. I knew what would happen. That is why I asked you to buy it for him."

TiTonTon laid the instrument carefully back on the table. He gathered up a blanket and spread it carefully on the woven mat for Armes, smoothing it carefully with his overgrown hands. His finger, pointing to the other blanket and then to the second *caille,* indicated that he would take Pompee's blanket over there. Then he came and stood in front of Armes, knelt before him, and drew off his boots. Each boot he fondled lovingly and placed them side by side on the floor. For the second time that night he reached for Armes' hand. This time he placed it on his close-cropped kinky hair. Again Armes patted him as he would a dog and started to speak to him, but Pompee advanced to the door of the *caille* and held up his hand for silence.

Far below them the drums were sounding as they did every night in St. Domingue. They had become so much a part of his life that Armes was unaware of them, but as he listened, he detected a new rhythm—one that spoke of impending danger. He listened attentively, but since the night of Bouckmann's massacre, he had never been able to read the meaning of the drums. But as he listened, he saw a look of terror spread over Pompee's face. TiTonTon must have understood the drums too, for he jumped up and ran to the door.

"Peace has lasted too long in St. Domingue," Pompee said with a quaver in his voice. "Now war starts again."

"What has happened?" Armes rose from the chair and went to the door. The full yellow moon was sinking and the shadows of the trees were creeping over the valley.

"The French have arrested Toussaint. They have captured him through lies and deceit. He is now a prisoner aboard a warship heading for France with his wife and children. Oh, what a terrible thing to do to a . . ."

"Poor old man whose life has been dedicated to freeing his fellow men," Armes finished the sentence.

"But that isn't all, milord. The drums have another message. The fever has struck Cap François. Today there were ten deaths, tomorrow there will be twenty, and a week from tomorrow there will be hundreds. Leclerc and his wife have left Cap François and fled to the island of Tortue, where they think they will be safe. Stupid fools! Do they think the arm of Damballah cannot reach from Cap François to Tortue? Even if the general fled from here to Paris, he could

367

not escape the vengeance of Damballah. Why does the poor fool try?"

"We all want to live, Pompee, and life is just as precious to Charles Leclerc as it is to us." He placed his hand on the black satin smoothness of TiTonTon's back as the three of them stood in the doorway of the *caille*.

"Listen, boy." Armes gave him a little push. "In my saddlebag, you'll find a bottle of rum. I brought it up here, thinking we might need it to warm us and take the chill of the mountain air out of our bones. Go fetch it! And then go to your *caille* and bring back yours and Pompee's mats. We're all going to get drunk tonight—so goddamned drunk we'll forget all about the French and the fever and everything else. I don't want to get drunk alone. Go, and let's see if for one night we can't forget the whole damned, stinking mess."

TiTonTon looked to Pompee for affirmation.

"Do as milord says. TiTonTon. We'll all get drunk together, and between the rum and our company perhaps we can make milord forget. Run, TiTonTon."

43

"IT'S WAR!" Henry banged his big fist down so hard on the breakfast table at Sans Souci that the Sèvres cups chattered in their fragile saucers. "War, I tell you! Now the French *cochons* have shown their filthy hands. With Toussaint arrested and carted off to Paris, what assurance do we have? Who's next—Christophe of Cap François, Dessalines of St. Marc, or Pétion of Port-au-Prince? One of us, you can be damned sure, is slated to go. Which one?"

"What are you going to do?" Armes leaned across the table. "What's your next move, Henry?"

Henry considered for a moment. He became somewhat calmer. "In an hour I'm leaving for Dondon. I've made my plans. I'll not declare war openly and show my hand at once. For the time being I'm safe. The French have buried me in the fortress of Dondon as commanding general of that latrine. *Merde!* Do you know what the fortress of Dondon is?" He glared the question at them. "Do you?"

Armes shook his head in denial.

"Well, the whole goddamned thing isn't bigger than this house—just whacked together out of logs and mud. That's my command now. But"—his voice dropped—"I'm glad. They intended to bury Henry Christophe in the mountains, and that's just what Henry wanted. Do you know, TiArmes, what I have in that goddamned, puny, little fort?" His eyes blazed as he awaited Armes' answer.

"I have a pretty good idea."

"I have over eight thousand French muskets, everyone of them cleaned and oiled. And, thanks to you, TiArmes, and that good Mr. Frothingham in Boston and Durham, Brown, I have plenty of lead and powder for those guns. And that isn't all. . . ."

"No?"

"No! Not by a damned sight! There is a parade ground in front of my fort, and every day I drill the ass off my army. Every one of my Dahomeys has a squad of ten men under him. Five hundred Dahomeys—ten men each—that's five thousand men, TiArmes. And these men are soldiers! They're no higgledy-piggledy army of stupid peasants and *cultivateurs*. They haven't much in the way of uniforms, but they can slice a man straight through with one swipe of a machete. They can shoot, too, and they can march and obey orders."

"And Dessalines?" Athenée asked the question this time.

"The same."

"And Pétion in the South?"

Henry nodded his confirmation.

"Then tell us, what are you going to do?"

"It won't be an out-and-out war," Henry informed them. "More or less a series of armed raids—guerrillas, as our friends in Santo Domingo say—little wars. A group of my men will strike at a French plantation near the Cap. They'll take the owners prisoners, drive off the cattle, lay waste the fields. Of course *I* shall know nothing about it. Then, before the French have time to do anything, there'll be another raid in the vicinity of St. Marc, then another down around Port-au-Prince. A lot of little fires, TiArmes, that the French won't be able to put out, for as soon as they stamp one out, another will start."

So it started. Plantation after plantation which had been rebuilt and put into operation after the Bouckmann uprising went up in flames. Field after field became torches in the night. The savage drums sounded through the hills; the Negroes swept down from their hidden bivouacs in the mountains, and in the morning, death and desolation marked the countryside. Once again the *blancs* fled to the cities. Leclerc braved the fever and returned from Tortue and called his generals together. This time Christophe, Dessalines, and Pétion were not invited to the conference. This time, although Leclerc presided at the head of the conference table, Rochambeau took the floor. He had been a plantation owner in St. Domingue himself. He knew how to deal with niggers, he said.

"What are we waiting for?" he cried. "Must we keep up this stupid pretense of fraternity with the niggers any longer? No, I say! Either St. Domingue belongs to France or it belongs to the stinking blacks. Which shall it be—ours or theirs?" He stood up and faced Leclerc. "*Mon general,* it's up to you. Give the word. Let us exterminate the blacks. Let's rip them apart and spill their guts over the whole country. They're no damn good anyway except to fertilize the fields. Let's wipe the island clean of them. Then, when St. Domingue belongs to us again, we can replace them quickly. Africa's reservoir is full and England cannot stop us from getting them. What do you say?"

Leclerc, pale and wan, his long fingers trembling in his curly beard, hated Rochambeau, because he knew that where he himself was weak the other was strong. He knew that while his own tired mind occupied itself with his wife's blatant infidelities, the other was planning battles and strategies. But as much as he hated his second-in-command, he knew that Rochambeau was speaking the truth. Cooperation had failed. Extermination was now in order. He lifted his hand for silence.

"You have heard General Rochambeau," he said. "Do you agree with him?"

There was a chorus of *oui's*. It was settled as easily and as quickly as that. Death to all the blacks.

Leclerc pulled the bellcord beside his chair.

"Let us drink to a white St. Domingue," he said.

When the Negro footman entered, Leclerc ordered wine for his staff. It was brought quickly and the silver salver and the glasses placed on the wide table. As the servant circulated among the officers, pouring the wine, Leclerc stood up.

"Issue orders for the immediate arrest of Generals Dessalines, Christophe, Pétion, Rigaud, and all the rest. And now, *mes amis*, a toast. To Dessalines, Christophe, and Pétion.

370

May they follow Toussaint to France and rot in the same dungeon with him."

While the officers drank, the footman bowed and left the room. Five minutes later, an aged Negress—a superannuated old crone who pared vegetables in the palace kitchens—hobbled out the back door and made her way down the street. Old and lame as she was, she knew where she was going and exactly why. She hurried as fast as her old legs would carry her to a palm-thatched *caille* on the edge of town. In a few seconds a man came out of the *caille;* a second followed him, and then a third. They departed in opposite directions. That night the drums carried the message the old woman had delivered—that orders had been issued for the arrest of all the Negro generals. Henry received the messenger before he heard the drums. Dessalines got the message from the drums before the messenger came. It was further to Port-au-Prince, but the drums carried the message over the mountains to Pétion. There was no need for Henry to escape. He was safe at Dondon, but both Jean-Jacques and Pétion marched from their posts, their armies behind them.

The three of them met in the mountains. Now, for the first time, the blacks had a real army. They had guns, they had ammunition, and, most important of all, they had a united purpose. From now on it was black against white, without any reservations, and this time fortune favored the blacks. They had a powerful ally—the yellow fever.

It was, as Pompee had said, striking fast, multiplying its destruction day by day. Cap François, besieged by the blacks from without, was besieged by an even fiercer enemy from within. French soldiers in their heavy woolen uniforms dropped like flies in the streets. There was nobody to bury them, and their corpses bloated in the tropic sun until nightfall, when squads of Negroes, once more demoted to the status of slavery, came out with ox-drawn tumbrils and gathered up the bodies, carting them to the edge of town where they were thrown into pits of quicklime.

Each day the fever increased. It spared none of the whites, but never touched the blacks, who seemed to be immune to it. Beset by fever, Cap François turned to feverish indulgences. Drunkenness, rape, and thievery ran hand in hand with the plague. The wine shops did a thriving business until their owners, in the midst of serving a glass of rum, grabbed the edge of the bar and fell to the floor. The whorehouses made plenty of money until the soldiers who patronized them stretched out, clutching at their throats, their bodies rigid, their breath coming in gasps, their black vomit staining the filthy sheets where they had anticipated ecstasy instead of death.

The fever was no respecter of persons. It crawled among the petty bourgeoisie who kept the stores and shops; it led a death march through the barracks and into the officers' quarters. Finally it extended to Tortue, to which Leclerc had returned, and laid its hot hand on his brow. He died, twisting on the white linen sheets, while Pauline wrung her faithless hands in the corridor. She managed to squeeze out a few tears—not very many—and had what was left of him sealed in a lead coffin and loaded on board a frigate. Then she collected her brocades together, took her two favorite mulatto studs along to make the voyage less boring, and accompanied Leclerc's putrid flesh to Paris.

Rochambeau was in full command. For the first time he had a free hand, and he used it to levy bitter punishment on every black in Cap François and on every Negro prisoner his men captured. He marched them through the streets of the Cap, handcuffed man to man, loaded them in boats, and then took them a little way out from shore, not too far for those on land to enjoy the spectacle. Then, at a word of command, the first black in the string would be pushed overboard, and the entire screaming line would follow him into the water. A most pleasant diversion while it lasted, but it did create a problem. The next incoming tide washed the bodies ashore, and the stench of rotting flesh was disagreeable. Another method had to be devised. Several were. Negroes were sent to dig their own graves, then ordered to stand in front of them while they were shot. Others were spread-eagled against walls and flayed alive. This became Rochambeau's favorite pastime, and several of his soldiers were most adept at it. First an incision with a sharp knife from shoulder to shoulder. Then the trick was to loosen just enough skin to get a firm grip on it with both hands. A quick pull!—and the skin was torn off with a ripping sound which did not drown out the screams of the victim. The man was left to hang there until the flies finished him off. Unfortunately the skin was too black to make good parchment.

Between the whites' massacre of the blacks and the fever's massacre of the whites, the population of Cap François was diminishing fast.

372

Everything, no matter how unimportant, that went on in the city was promptly reported to the Negro generals. Pétion and Christophe had agreed that Dessalines should be in supreme command, and they were wise in their agreement, for Dessalines was more of a military man than either of them. He was cruel and ruthless, but he was shrewd when it came to military strategy. The brain under his thick black skull never rested. He commanded his army with a sure hand and won victory after victory over the French. Dessalines seemed to be everywhere at once, striking at the French from every direction. The one place in all St. Domingue which he had always avoided was Sans Souci. This, and the people on it, were under the protection of Henry Christophe, and Dessalines grudgingly respected Henry's wishes.

One afternoon, however, when Henry was at Dondon, Armes heard a flutter of drums down the road. Through the dust, he saw a ragged column of soldiers with an even more ragged general riding ahead of them. It was not Henry, of that Armes was sure, so he waited on the balcony until the troops halted at the gates and the commander rode up the graveled drive. Armes recognized Dessalines, travel-stained and dirty. He did not lift his face to Armes when he spoke, and there was neither friendliness nor respect in his tone.

"Où est le général Christophe?" he demanded sullenly in his guttural Creole.

"He left this morning for Dondon. He said he was to meet you there."

"Merde! So he was. But I had other business to attend to. I'll camp here for the night."

Armes descended the steps. "We at Sans Souci are happy to welcome the illustrious General Dessalines. May we prepare a room for you?"

Dessaline's fingers tightened their grip on the saber at his side. He nervously pulled it a few inches from its scabbard.

"I'll not accept favors from any goddamned *blanc.*" Saliva bubbled in the corners of his lips and ran down his chin. "Take your room and ram it up your goddamned white ass. I don't want it. If I did, I'd take your whole house, and if I wanted to sleep in it, I'd sleep in it, and if I wanted to burn it, I'd burn it. Don't come crawling to me with your hospitality, *blanc.* The only reason your head is still on your shoulders is because Henry Christophe is so stupid he thinks you are his friend."

He wheeled his horse and started down the drive. Armes

stood still and watched him depart. A short distance down the drive, Dessalines turned his horse and trotted back.

"Get your horse, *blanc*, and follow me!"

"Is that an order from you, General Dessalines?"

"It goddamned well is, but have no fear, *blanc*, you'll return to eat dinner with your Vicomtesse. I have something I want to show you. I want you to see how Jean Jacques Dessalines deals with the whites."

The general sat his horse impatiently while Armes summoned Pompee, gave orders to have his horse saddled, and inquired if Pompee might accompany him.

"The great *papaloi?*" For the first time Dessalines raised his head and looked at Pompee, but lowered it again under Pompee's direct stare. Armes knew that Dessalines might be the bravest man in St. Domingue, but that he feared one thing——the voodoo gods which Pompee represented. "Why not, bring him along," Dessalines answered with an offhand gesture.

The soldiers were making camp in the little square of Milot when Armes and Pompee arrived, riding behind Dessalines. Fires were burning and a supper of sorts was being cooked. The women of the village had come out with fruit and vegetables as an excuse to search for relatives or friends among the ranks. Others, their husbands being long absent, were searching for lovers for the night. Over in one corner of the little *place*, Armes noticed a group of whites. He did not know how many there were, but he judged them to be about fifty. He saw several young women, an elderly couple, and a group of adolescents and children.

Dessalines dismounted and motioned for Armes and Pompee to do the same, and the three of them walked over to the group of whites. As Armes approached nearer, he saw that their hands were tied behind them with strong cords of white hemp. Evidently they had marched a long distance, for their faces showed great strain. They were not permitted to sit down but were kept standing. Dessalines' soldiers, who were guarding them, saw to that.

"Your countrymen, Monsieur Holbrook." Dessalines waved in the direction of the miserable group.

"What do you mean *my* countrymen? I am not French, I am an American."

"And so are these, all Americans. They thought they were safe, hidden away in a little village up in the mountains where they had fled to escape the fever in Cap François.

Safe? They should know no *blanc* is safe when Dessalines commands."

Armes walked over to the group and spoke to one of the men. "Is it true what he says? Are you Americans?"

The elderly man answered, "It is true. We are, all of us."

"Please, sir, may we have water? We are dying of thirst. a woman pleaded in desperate tones.

Armes strode back to Dessalines.

"You cannot harm these people. They are not French. They are no enemies of yours. The United States is not at war with Haiti."

Dessalines spat on the dusty ground and scuffed his boot viciously over the spittle. "Bah! They are *blancs*. I shall kill them."

"No, General Dessalines." Armes spoke very softly and deliberately. "You shall not kill them. I forbid it."

The Negro threw back his ugly head and laughed maniacally.

"You forbid it! You? Ha-ha-ha! Why, you're nothing but a goddamned *blanc* yourself. You forbid it? Ha! No *blanc* ever forbids Jean Jacques anything. Oh no, *blanc*, I didn't have you come down here to forbid that these people die, but to tell me how they shall die. Do I shoot them one by one? Or would you prefer that I have my men stand at fifty paces and fire point blank at them? Perhaps you'd rather I had them skinned alive. That would be a pretty sight, and one which Rochambeau would enjoy. Or we can march them over to the sea and drown them like kittens. I could suggest burning them or, although it's a dirty job, my men could beat them to death with the butts of their muskets. Come, *blanc!* How shall we do it? Which of the many different ways that Rochambeau has found to kill our people do you prefer for yours?"

Armes kept silent, but he was thinking fast. He turned toward Pompee, hoping to catch some sign of encouragement, but Pompee was staring at the cowering mass of whites. Armes faced Dessalines.

"Look at me, General Dessalines!"

Involuntarily the man looked up, but he lowered his head immediately.

"I shall not look at you, *blanc,* because if I did I would kill you."

"You do not look at me because you are a coward and do not dare face me. You asked me how these people shall die and I'll tell you. Shoot them, one at a time, by the best marksman in your corps. Understand?"

Dessalines grunted.

"But remember this." Armes leveled a steady finger at him. "Every time one of your soldiers puts a charge of powder in his musket, every time he rams down a ball of lead to shoot these people, you, General, you consider one very important thing. It's American powder and lead that you are using to kill Americans. It was paid for by Americans, shipped to Haiti by Americans to help you, General Dessalines, win your independence from the French. Now, go ahead! Shoot them with their own bullets, and by Damballah, the great serpent god of Dahomey, it will be the last powder and lead you will ever receive from the United States. Shoot them, General Dessalines, and then let your powder trickle away until you and your men are left with empty muskets to fight the French. Shoot them! Yes, shoot them, and I promise you that I shall cut off your supplies from the United States. And dead or alive I can do it, General Dessalines."

The big Negro backed away a step, then suddenly looked up until Armes could see the yellowish whites of his eyes. Armes could see fear there. He waited for Dessalines to speak, and when he did, his words were almost a whisper.

"You swore by Damballah, *blanc.* What does Damballah mean to you, you puny, white-livered Christian?"

"I swore by Damballah because I believe in Damballah, you ignorant, black-bellied bastard who would bite the hand that's feeding you. If you dare to kill these people, I'll call on Damballah to destroy you."

The quick tropical night had fallen as they were speaking. Dark clouds scurried across the sky, blotting out the thin crescent of the new moon. Suddenly a brilliant flash of blue-white lightning zigzagged down the side of the Bishop's Hat. The crash of thunder that followed was deafening, and its reverberations echoed among the distant peaks. A torrent of rain descended, and in the next blinding flash, Armes saw Dessalines' face for the second time. Now there was terror in his eyes; his lips were slavering; the black cheeks looked like wet ashes.

Pompee knelt on the ground, tore his shirt off, and let the driving rain pelt his chest. A small green snake curled in his hand. "The gods have spoken. The gods have spoken," he chanted.

376

Dessalines' voice roared above the thunder. "Take the prisoners away," he shouted. "Release them. Send them back to the Cap. Get them away from here, but do not harm them."

The soldiers fumbled with the prisoners' thongs, surprised at their general's commands but obeying them.

Dessalines reached out his hand and grabbed the shoulder of Armes' coat. His powerful fingers dug deep into the flesh under the light fabric. Armes could feel their power, and he knew they were trembling with suppressed rage. Dessalines spun him sharply and flung him away. Armes stumbled and would have fallen, but Pompee sprang up from the ground and steadied him.

"You gave orders to General Dessalines," the enraged general was screaming. "You a *blanc!* I've never taken orders from a white before. Even when I was a slave I had a black master. I shall not forget, never. Someday I am going to have the pleasure of killing you. Someday the voice of Jean Jacques Dessalines will be supreme in St. Domingue. When that day comes, regardless of Henry Christophe or anyone else, I shall kill you, and *mon Dieu,* how I shall enjoy it."

He turned and walked into the blackness of the rain and the night.

"You have made a dangerous enemy tonight, milord." There was a tremor of fear in Pompee's voice.

"He has always been my enemy."

"But you have made a powerful friend."

"Who?" Armes asked.

"Surely you cannot doubt that Damballah answered you with the thunder? Never in my life have I felt the *loa* come so close and so suddenly."

"You think . . . ?"

"I think you are favored of the gods, milord."

The lights of Sans Souci beckoned to them through the downpour.

44

THE laurels of victory, nurtured by his quick and daring moves, multiplied on Dessalines' brow. His armies harassed the French everywhere and at all times, and in addition to his own victories, his generals, Christophe and Pétion, won others. Wherever Dessalines appeared the French were vanquished, and slowly, village by village, mountain by mountain, they retreated in straggling remnants to the north, until finally the city walls of Cap François marked the limit of French-controlled territory.

As much as Armes disliked and disapproved of Jean Jacques personally, he was compelled to admit the Negro leader's military genius, and to pay silent tribute to the uncouth ex-slave who confounded the armies of France and their war-baptized generals. Dessalines was cruel with a feral cruelty, but he was not a whit more so than the French. Every Negro prisoner they took was tortured without mercy so, in retaliation, every white that fell into Dessalines' hands was even more fiendishly tortured.

Henry and Pétion were more lenient, although as reports filtered in from the Cap of the inhuman torture which Rochambeau meted out to the luckless blacks, Henry's face hardened as he viewed his white prisoners. But he did not kill them. Henry was looking ahead into the future when St. Domingue would not longer be St. Domingue but Haiti. He realized that in order to exist, the infant country must depend upon trade, and trade would, of necessity, be with white nations, because there was no other Negro nation in the world with which to trade. So Henry sat in stern judgment upon his white prisoners, imprisoned them, robbed them, starved them, and then magnanimously freed them, and did the latter so graciously that when they departed they blessed him and called him their savior. In this way he gained friends among the whites, and although his hatred for them was possibly as deep as that of Dessalines, they were not aware of it and were grateful to him.

Armes had never accompanied Henry into the field. He was quite content to remain at Sans Souci and direct the activities of the plantation. Occasionally he and Pompee rode up the Bishop's Hat to Mon Repos with loaded pack mules behind them, and more and more Armes was absent from Sans Souci at night on the business he had inaugurated with Mr. Avery. Messengers came often to the big house—men whose rolling gait showed them to be more accustomed to the deck of a ship than dry land. Armes would talk with them behind closed doors, and they would depart together to some lonely cove on the shore, where the dark silhouette of a sailing ship stood out against the evening sky, and where could be heard the sound of muffled oars bringing small boats in through the surf with precious cargoes of ammunition for the black army. Although the ships flew no flags, their men spoke with the accents of Maine, Massachusetts, and Virginia; of Liverpool, Bristol, and Southampton; of Montreal, Quebec, and the Maritimes.

One afternoon, as Armes was stretching and yawning on the balcony after his noontime *somme,* Henry came riding up, accompanied only by a small detachment of his Dahomeys. He had, he said, been delayed by a skirmish in the neighboring valley, where his men had come upon a number of French soldiers rooting in the ground. Food was scarce in the Cap, and the unfortunate inhabitants who had survived the plague were now starving, as Dessalines had cut off all sources of supply to the city. Henry's men had encountered the French soldiers—merely walking skeletons with a covering of leathery skin over their bones—gnawing on some raw yams which they had discovered. The Dahomeys had killed them on the spot, relieved them of their guns and ammunition, and then ridden to Sans Souci. Henry's Dahomeys were not as spruce as they had been on the day they marched into Cap François, but what they lacked in gaudy uniforms they made up in increased military bearing. The boys were glad to be back home at Milot; Armes heard them shouting as they rode up the road.

It was a happy reunion. Marie Louise, with the infant Victor in her arms, ran down the steps to greet Henry. Athenée hurried to the kitchen to see that some of Henry's favorite dishes were prepared, and Pompee led the general's horse around to the stables.

Henry climbed the steps wearily, one at a time, flung himself into a chair, pulled Marie Louise and the baby down on his broad arm, stretched his long legs in the soiled white breeches and dusty boots out in front of him, and sighed.

"It's good to be home again, TiArmes, but I must leave at midnight. I go to join Dessalines, who is coming up from the south." His voice sank to a whisper. "Tomorrow we join forces to attack the forts that guard the Cap. Tomorrow, with Ogoun Feraille's help, we will take the Cap and write the last chapter of French dominion. They cannot escape. We have news that the English fleet has them bottled up by sea, and we have them surrounded by land—Jean Jacques, Pétion, and I."

"Tomorrow?"

"Yes, tomorrow! St. Domingue will end and Haiti begin."

"Then rest here now, Henry, until it is time for you to leave," Armes counseled. "Go to your room, bathe, eat, and then sleep until midnight. As for me, I shall take leave of you now, for I shall have to leave soon."

Henry shook his eyes wide open with an effort and lifted his head long enough to look at Armes. "Why? Where?"

"A messenger arrived this afternoon. The American sloop *Polly Ann* from Charleston is anchored two miles off Bas Limbé in the Bate de l'Aeul. She has a shipment of small cannon which she is going to bring in tonight at moonrise I have promised to be there. We have to arrange for oxen to haul the cannon and balls."

Henry's long legs jackknifed, and he sat erect in his chair.

"Did you say cannon, TiArmes?"

"Yes, cannon!"

"Then Ogun Feraille is surely with us. Only yesterday Jean Jacques was saying that if he could have more cannon, he could bring the French to their knees in hours. More cannon! That is the one thing they have which we need. That is why we have hesitated to attack the forts of Cap François. TiArmes, I cannot rest now. I cannot even have those few hours with my wife behind the closed doors of my bedroom, the thought of which has been tantalizing me for a week. I go with you, TiArmes. When do we start?"

Armes pulled the gold repeater from his pocket. "It's only three o'clock, Henry. Would an hour with your wife be enough?" He glanced at Marie Louise and watched the red blush creep into the dark smoothness of her cheeks.

"No, not enough, TiArmes, but better than nothing." He stood up, lifted both his wife and his son in his huge arms, and carried them off down the hall. Within an hour, he reappeared, clean and fresh in a sharply pressed uniform. His face had lost the haggard look it had when he arrived. Now he was rested, refreshed, and anxious to leave.

They departed, with the guard of Dahomeys, late in the afternoon, skirting the Cap by narrow trails through the foothills. When the road widened so they could ride abreast, Henry questioned Armes.

"That place up on the Bishop's Hat—is it ready?"

"More than ready. We have carried many supplies up there. Even a bed."

"A most necessary piece of furniture, as I found out this afternoon," Henry guffawed. "Time was, TiArmes, when a dirt floor or a mat of woven leaves suited me fine, provided the wench was fleshy enough. But I must be getting soft. Now a dirt floor is too hard, no matter how well padded the wench may be, and a leaf mat scratches my knees. Henry Christophe has become accustomed to a soft mattress and linen sheets. He laughed again. He had forgotten his original question.

"But you asked about Mon Repos," Armes reminded him.

"And so I did. Are you sure nobody knows about it?"

"Quite sure, Henry, TiTonTon has never seen anyone up there and I am certain nobody has ever noticed Pompee and myself going there. Pompee says the peasants fear *loups-garous* on the Bishop's Hat."

"For once we can be thankful for the poor bastards' superstitions."

The narrowing trail forced Armes to fall behind. When it widened again, he came abreast of Henry.

"Now, *mon frère,* tell me why you ask about Mon Repos."

"Because someday soon I am going to send you there. Jean Jacques makes no secret of his boast to kill you. He told me about your intercession for the Americans. You were too smart for him, and Jean Jacques does not enjoy being outwitted, especially in front of his men."

"He should be grateful to me, Henry, not only for the *affaire Américaine* but for another big favor I once did him."

Henry raised his brows and pursed his lips.

"Yes, a favor," Armes continued. "I gave him Topaze."

"That slut!" Henry spat on the ground. "Do you know what she did?"

Armes did not reply for a moment. The mention of her name brought back the magic of her musky perfume, the silken feel of her tawny flesh, and the moist pleasure of her lips. He cursed himself for the fantasy her memory painted in his thoughts. "No, Henry," he answered at length, "I do not know."

"She and a mulatto buck, one of Jean Jacques' lieutenants, fastened the horns on his head. He caught them together. With one stroke of his sword he castrated the fellow and left him to bleed to death."

"And Topaze?"

"Jean Jacques stripped her naked. Then he had all the soldiers in his camp line up, facing each other in two rows, and he made her march down between them. He told them they could use her as they wanted to, and it was hours before she stumbled off into the woods, naked and alone. She managed to survive; how I cannot imagine, but she did. Now she roams the woods and roads between St. Marc and Port-au-Prince, asking everyone for Jean Jacques. Poor demented thing, the peasants call her '*Souillée*,' the defiled one, but"— Henry paused for a moment—"that is hardly the right name for her. She was more *souillon* than *souillée*."

They rode on in silence. Now that Armes could no longer curse Topaze, he found he could pity her, and lament that such superb beauty of face and body had come to such an inglorious end. Whether or not he had ever loved her, he had enjoyed her. There was something she did to a man which set every nerve in his body a-tingling, separately and collectively, until it seemed his skin could no longer contain him. God, how he had enjoyed her! He hoped he would never see her again. It would be too pitiful to see the wreck of her beauty.

Their way passed through the little town of Cagnette—a mere cluster of peasant *cailles*, then out onto the road to Limbé, a more pretentious village, and turned right toward the little fishing village of Bas Limbé. It was dark when they arrived on the beach, and Armes lighted a lantern, covered it with a dark cloth, then signaled to the ship out in the bay. A blinking light from the ship answered and, having established his contact, he rode back through the little town. At a hut on the outskirts, he spoke a few words to the man sitting on the doorsteps, and soon eight teams of oxen were pulling as many wooden-wheeled carts toward the beach. When they arrived, the first small boat with two small cannon had already beached, and men from the ship, aided by men from the village, were unloading. A man in a short coat and leather sailor hat came up to Armes and spoke to him in English. Armes pointed to a high mound of well-filled bags, piled above the high-water mark.

"Coffee?" the man asked.

Armes nodded.

"That's what they want in Charleston. As each boat comes in, we'll reload and take the coffee back to the ship."

For a couple of hours the boats came in with cannon and departed with coffee. When the last cannon rested on the sand and the last bag of coffee was in the boat, Armes spoke to the man.

"Good night, sir, and thank you."

With a few feet of water between him and the shore, the

man called back to Armes. "You're a white man and I can tell by your talk that you're an American. What in hell are you doing here with these niggers?"

Armes started to answer him, but Henry restrained him. "That was English," Henry said, "but I understood some of the words. He wanted to know what you are doing here. Am I right?"

"You are."

"Sometimes, TiArmes, I wonder the same thing myself. Is it because of Athenée?"

"Yes, Henry, it's Athenée, but she is only a part of it. There's another part called Henry Christophe."

Henry turned his back quickly and mounted his horse. He rode down to the oxcarts, directed them to take the road to the Cap, then wheeled his horse and returned to Armes.

"We ride to join Dessalines."

"And the cannon?"

"The drivers know the road, they will follow."

"But, Henry, I certainly do not want to see Dessalines."

"You won't. There's a company of my men stationed to the west of Dessalines' camp. When we arrive there, I'll send an escort to Sans Souci with you. I'll not have you riding alone tonight, TiArmes. Not after what you just said to me. You know, TiArmes, I am really not a general, no matter how much I try to make myself think I am. Underneath all this"—he pointed to the gold epaulets—"There is nothing but the stableboy at the Couronne. And I can never forget, TiArmes, how you held out your hand to him and how you asked him to have a glass of wine, and if you think Henry Christophe is a part of your life, what in hell do you think TiArmes means to me, *mon frère?*"

"Just that, *mon frère.*" There was nothing more that Armes could say, but he felt a little extra circle of warmth around his heart. They rode in silence, watching the moon rise through the tangle of trees, watching the stars fleck the black night, listening to the throbbing of drums in the distant hills. The drums! Could Armes have understood their message that night, he would have known that they were sounding the death knell of France. This was the last night that France would hold her colony of St. Domingue. Tomorrow it would pass out of existence, and even its name would be forgotten.

They rode on through the night. The still-glowing embers of a campfire caused Henry to dismount, examine it, and then remount. He decided that his detachment of troops had been camped here earlier in the night but had now moved on. Unbeknownst to Henry, Dessalines had planned an earlier attack on the French forts. His messengers had been unable to locate Henry, and Dessalines had moved Henry's troops up to concentrate with his own.

Henry seemed a little worried over the fact that his men were not where he expected them to be. They rode on, galloping now, until they reached a sentry outpost. The picket recognized Henry, informed him of Dessalines' immediate need for him, and passed both of them through the lines. They kept on until Henry passed one of his own Dahomeys and discovered that the main body of his troops were in Dessalines' camp. The Dahomey waved them on, and soon they arrived at a *caille* which some *cultivateur* had abandoned. A light shone through the rough doorway. Henry motioned to Armes to stop.

"Dessalines is in there. Do not follow me in. Keep out of sight, TiArmes, but don't leave here. A white man is not safe out alone tonight of all nights. I'll go in and talk to him, and when I finish I'll come out and send you home. Wait for me, but keep out of sight."

Armes agreed to Henry's plan. He sat his horse for about an hour, then slid off for a more comfortable seat on the grass. The moon started its descent, and the fresh breeze of dawn rustled the leaves in the trees. Armes realized that when daylight came he would be in full view. He had decided to move back into the trees when he saw forms in the doorway and recognized Henry and Dessalines as they came out, followed by a number of Negro officers.

It was fast growing light. Dessalines spoke to a man beside him, who left immediately. He reappeared in a few moments and brought a drummer along with him. The fellow carried a French drum, draped with the tricolor flag. At Dessalines' command, he raised his sticks and the drum rolled, bringing the soldiers running to circle around Dessalines and his officers. Armes got caught up in the mob, which pushed him along with them, and as the drum continued its rolling, more soldiers jammed up behind him. Henry's army had joined with the soldiers of Dessalines, and they were all there in a stamping, milling mass—dirty and bedraggled, their eyes heavy from sleep, their mouths slack, scratching themselves in their half-nakedness. Closer and closer they pushed up to the *caille* and the group of officers. Armes could see Henry searching frantically in the crowd until his eyes finally met those of Armes. He gave a quick shake of his head, and Armes knew that Henry regretted his being there, but also realized that it was impossible for him to get out of the crowd without causing noticeable confusion. Henry's frown cautioned him to stay, and Armes sought shelter behind the broad shoulders of a tall Dahomey.

Dessalines yelled for a chair to be brought from the *caille*, and an officer ran in and dragged one out. First Dessalines tested his weight on it, then mounted it and surveyed his men.

His small eyes, hidden by the heavy brows, looked out over the sea of black faces, resting on a single face momentarily and then shifting quickly to another. Armes was thankful for the huge back of Henry's Dahomey in front of him for, by crouching down a little, he was able to hide himself from Jean Jacques' fiery eyes.

Then Dessalines started to speak. Words rolled out of his mouth, and as he spoke he worked himself up into a hysterical frenzy.

"Sons of Haiti," he cried, "sons of slaves! That is what you are—black slaves and sons of black slaves. And that is what you will be as long as the French remain on this island. Today we are going to push every white son-of-a-bitch into the sea. Today will mark the end of white man's rule here. As long as there remains one white bastard on this island, you will never be safe, and so I say *Death to all the whites,* every goddamned one of them."

The crowd, pressing closer together, wedged Armes against the man in front of him. He turned and stared hard at Armes, then nudged his neighbor. They talked, raising their voices until they made a disturbance that interrupted Dessalines. His rapid glance settled on the gesticulating men.

"Quiet down there," he yelled at them. "Listen to what your general has to say."

The man in front of Armes called out, "A *blanc,* mon général, there's a *blanc* here beside me."

"What?" Dessalines screamed like a man possessed.

"A *blanc!* A *blanc!*" Those surrounding Armes, emboldened by the first man, hollered in unison.

"Then bring him here!" Dessalines barked the order.

They pushed Armes through the ranks until he stood in front of them all, directly under Dessalines on the chair. The general looked down at him. His patriotic hysteria was now tinged with the dementia of his hatred.

"Oh, you, *blanc!* You're Henry Christophe's *patron*—the

385

self-styled friend of the blacks. What are you doing here, you goddamned, pale-faced, white-livered fool?"

"He is here because he came to bring you cannon, Jean Jacques—cannon, which arrived last night from Charleston; cannon, that will help us take the city of Cap François; cannon, that will drive the French into the sea."

"Cannon, did you say?" Dessalines stuck out his chin as though he were disputing Henry.

"Yes, cannon, General Dessalines," Armes said.

Dessalines bit his thick lower lip with his stained yellow teeth. He looked straight down at Armes, right into his eyes.

"I told you, *blanc*, that the next time I saw you I was going to kill you. I had just decided that I was going to do it now, but I have changed my mind. I shall wait until the next time you cross my path. General Christophe tells me that you have brought cannon to us tonight. Those cannon have saved your miserable life."

"Here they come now." Henry pointed down the road to a rising cloud of dust raised by the plodding oxen.

"So, *blanc*, your life is spared for the present. With these cannon I shall take the forts of Cap François. No, I shall not kill you this time, but I am going to use you to teach my men a lesson." He pointed to the soldiers around Armes. "Tie the *blanc's* hands and force him down on his knees in front of me."

Armes caught a quick look from Henry. "Don't resist," it said, so he stood still as one of the soldiers whipped his belt from his pants and secured Armes' hands behind his back with it. Black hands pushed him to his knees in front of the chair on which Dessalines was standing.

"Now, white man, kiss the toe of a black man's boot." Dessalines' boot came forward to within an inch of Armes' mouth. "Kiss it, you bastard, kiss it, or, cannon or no cannon, I'll slice off your head."

Armes leaned over and brushed his lips against the toe of the dirty boot. He continued to kneel there, not daring to lift his head and look up at Dessalines.

"Jean Jacques!" Armes could hear Henry's horrified words. "No! Stop! He's my friend! He's a friend to us all."

"Cover General Christophe, my soldiers," Dessalines said, "and if he makes a move, shoot him."

It was a moment before Armes heard the drizzle and felt the warm stream of liquid spattering on his head, soaking his hair and running down his cheeks. "Oh God, not that," he

386

prayed, "not that," but it was happening. The hot animal stench and the knowledge of what it was caused him to retch, and his own sour vomit spilled from his mouth. He cringed from his own debasement and the extent to which Dessalines was humiliating him. By this one unspeakable action, Dessalines was expressing his contempt for the entire white race, and his own ascendancy over them. Armes' impulse was to jump to his feet and use his head as a battering ram in Dessalines' belly, but the thought of Athenée restrained him. His death would profit nothing except a sop to his own honor. Let Dessalines degrade him! It would wash off, and he would live to protect Athenée. The stream diminished to a trickle and then stopped. Armes looked up to see Dessalines buttoning his breeches.

"I piss on you, *blanc,* and all like you! Look, my soldiers, see how the white man cringes below the Negro's boot." He leaped down from the chair and kicked Armes on the side of the head, then with his foot pushed him down in the dirt. "It is an omen! Today all whites will be under the soles of our feet."

Armes saw Henry's fingers clutching at the hilt of his sword, and knew that Henry too was fighting to control himself. But their passivity saved their lives.

Dessalines, supreme in his victory, turned and faced his generals, but as he did so, his eye caught the French tricolor, fastened on the drum. With a quick step for so big a man, he wrenched the drum free from the leather strap that fastened it to the drummer's shoulder. His hands clawed at the flag until he ripped it from the drum. With both hands, he raised it aloft, and the sun, breaking through the high palms, illumined the red, white, and blue stripes. Bearing it aloft, he walked toward Armes, who was still sprawled in the dirt. Vaulting up onto the chair again, Dessalines waved the flag.

"The flag of France, *mes enfants!* And now"—His hands tore at the thin fabric, ripping down the seam between the red and white. "And now—" He ripped the cloth again and the white parted from the blue. He flung the torn white strip down, and it slowly settled on Armes' body. With the blue stripe in one hand and the red in the other, he joined them together. "Voila! The flag of Haiti! Today marks the end of the whites. Today marks the end of the flag of France here. There shall never again be anything white in Haiti!" He signaled to the drummer, who brought his drumsticks down on the drum. "Form your battalions, *mes enfants,* under the red and blue flag of Haiti. March, march to victory and the end of the whites!"

Dessalines jumped down from his chair and ran ahead of the drummer, the two ragged strips high over his head. Armes struggled and managed to get to his knees and then to his feet. Henry ran over to him, unbuckled the belt from his wrists, and chafed them until the circulation started.

"Mon pauvre TiArmes! How much you have had to suffer through your friendship for me. But I tell you this, TiArmes, if Jean Jacques had killed you today, he would have had to kill me too. As it is we are both alive, and that is all that matters. He humiliated you and in so doing he humiliated me, for everyone knows our relationship. But I could not kill Dessalines today. Forgive me, TiArmes, for not killing him, but if I had killed him or he had killed me it would have split our ranks, and all our long struggles against the French would have been of no use. At the very end, they would have won. Can you forgive me, TiArmes?"

"I do, Henry. Your hands were tied as well as mine. Now we are both safe, for he seems to have forgotten me."

"No, he has not forgotten you nor his promise to kill you." Henry drew a soiled kerchief from the sleeve of his coat and handed it to Armes. "Wipe his filth from your face, *mon frère,* and leave now for Sans Souci. Four of my boys will accompany you to guard you."

"I feel as though I can never hold up my head again."

"You will, when you see Athenée, and know that you are alive to protect her. Listen, TiArmes. Leave for Sans Souci now. If the battle goes in our favor today, Jean Jacques will be the strongest man in Haiti. He will rule, TiArmes, and he has a long arm. As you see, even I cannot protect you, and who knows the fortunes of war—tonight I may be dead. So go now, and when night comes, take Athenée and Pompee and go to Mon Repos. Marie Louise and little Victor will be safe at Sans Souci, but you will not be any longer, for as far as I know you and Athenée are the only white people left around here. Go, TiArmes, and the greatest love any man, black or white, ever had for another goes with you."

A bugle sounded, and Henry ran to leap on his horse and take his place at the head of his Dahomeys. Armes slowly wiped his face with the piece of linen and threw the sodden mass on the ground. One of the four Dahomeys who had been left behind to accompany him leaned over to brush the dirt from his clothes, another found his horse and led it over, a third helped him into the saddle, and the fourth spoke to him.

"M'sieur Armes, don't mind that Dessalines. He's sort of crazy, that one. We're General Christophe's boys, m'sieur, and all of us like you."

Armes managed to smile at them. Their concern made him feel better, and he felt that as soon as he reached the nearest brook and could wash his face, he might manage to get to Sans Souci. But of one thing he was certain. He could never tell Athenée about what had happened. He could never tell anyone.

45

THE rattle of muskets and the boom of cannon were already heralding the approach of battle when Armes rode away from the encampment of Dessalines that morning—his soul as besmirched with hatred as his body was with filth. The four giant Dahomeys that Henry had insisted accompany him were kindly and solicitous in their manner toward him, and their pity was evident in the extra pains they took to be friendly while they led him over the little back trails that wound up into the foothills and skirted Cap François. When they had climbed the highest eminence of all that looked out over the waving green sea of forests, Armes could see the beleaguered city below, with the black tide of Dessalines' army frothing at the gates, battering down the resistance of the French.

Despite their friendliness, the four soldiers with Armes were restless. He knew that they were bored with the dull task of escorting him, and were missing the excitement of the battle, so when he had reached the top of the last hill, and saw Sans Souci spread out peacefully before him, he dismissed them.

"Thank you, M'sieur TiArmes."

"Don't think anything of what General Dessalines did. He's a crazy man!"

"If you need us, we'll go all the way with you, m'sieur."

"You're a good friend to General Christophe, m'sieur. We're good friends to you, too."

He waved them on, and they bid him a laughing farewell while they galloped off, slapping the flanks of their horses with their pink palms and flashing white-toothed smiles at him in gratitude for their dismissal. Armes rode on alone, glad to be rid of their joviality, that he might concentrate his thoughts on his hatred for Dessalines. That Jean Jacques would seek his death was a certainty. Even Henry could not help him now—only the hidden valley on the Bishop's Hat.

Sans Souci was strangely quiet when he arrived, and for the first time in many months, he rode unchallenged by sentries through his own gates. The guards had heard the noise of battle and had ridden off to join their comrades. When Armes reached the house, Pompee came out to meet him on the balcony.

"You should not have gone away without me, TiArmes. Even Henry cannot protect you as I can."

"But your gods protected me, Pompee. Sometime I'll tell you what happened to me this morning, but you will not believe it, for you will not believe that one man could do such things to another."

"Are you hurt, milord?"

"Only my pride, Pompee."

"Then that will heal. My thanks to my gods."

"And while you're at it, Pompee, thank them for bringing Ali to us that night." Armes jumped down from his horse. "The little fellow knew what he was talking about. I understand now, and I'm glad Mon Repos is waiting for us. It may save our lives. We go there tonight."

"And now, milord, you do believe?" Pompee's question was more of a statement of fact.

"And now I do believe." Armes ran up the steps and into the house. Hours of anxious anticipation had attuned Athenée's ears to the long-awaited sound of his steps. She ran through the dim coolness of the hall to meet him and sought the welcome solace of his arms. His lips brushed her hair, and he found momentary forgetfulness of the grim humiliation of the morning. She turned him slowly toward the door of their room, walked sideways in his embrace, and steered him through the doorway. Gently and without speaking she undid his garments, and as he walked across the room, the filthy, sweaty clothing fell to the floor, and one by one he stepped out of them.

"Hush, don't speak, my love. Don't try to tell me about anything," she murmured. "Something terrible has happened to you. I can tell by the look on your face, but I do not want to know what it is now. I can only rejoice that you have come back to me unharmed. I couldn't sleep this morning— I got up at dawn, fearful that something was happening to you. I haven't rested since. But now I thank God you're all right. Now I want you to get into your bath and think about nothing at all until . . ."

"Not even of my deep, unchanging love for you?"

"Well, that, of course, always."

"I think about it always," he said grimly. "I thought about it today, while I was undergoing the most profound humiliation a man can suffer. I kissed Dessalines' filthy boot this morning, Athenée, and while I was kissing it, I thought of you, and it was the thought of you that kept me from shoving my fist into his ugly face."

Athenée kept her eyes lowered, so that Armes could not see the tears that overflowed them.

"Don't think about it anymore, my darling. It's all over now." She moved off toward the door. "Let me tell the cooks to prepare a huge breakfast for you. I'm sure you are famished."

"Yes, you'd better go and get my breakfast ready. Otherwise my filthy body will overpower my mind, and . . ." He made a lunge for her, but she skillfully eluded his grasp.

"You take your bath," she laughed back at him. "You smell as musky as a cane-field buck at noonday. While you're in the tub I'll sit on the edge and feed you an omelet and *croissants* dripping with butter the way you like them, and pour you cup after cup of coffee and then, after that . . ."

"After that, my good woman, there'll be no midday dallying." He shook his finger at her. "We shall have work to do and plenty of it. We leave Sans Souci tonight."

"Leave Sans Souci?" her fright was apparent. "Where are we going?"

"To Mon Repos."

She relaxed. "Oh, up there? I'm so glad." She hurried out to the kitchens as he slid into the water.

When he had finished and dressed, they called Pompee and Marie Louise, and the four of them sat in conference around the dining-room table. There were many plans to be made. Marie Louise, it was decided, would remain at the plantation as Henry had wished. In her capable hands, the place would function as efficiently as though they were all there. Pompee would summon Maman, who had moved out to Milot, to look after Marie Louise, and Maman was better protection than a whole company of soldiers. As Sans Souci since the Bouckman rebellion had ostensibly belonged to Henry Christophe, things would be safer now than ever before. That much was settled.

Pompee was going to Mon Repos with Armes and Athenée, where he would be their *liaison* with civilization. He might not be able to be with them all the time, but he would come whenever he could, stay with them as long as possible, leave for his ever increasing priestly duties, and then return again. They would have TiTonTon with them on the mountain.

"But Athenée, *ma cherie*." Marie wrinkled her pretty little nose. "You will be so lonely up there all alone with nobody but Armes and that stupid lout, TiTonTon, who cannot even talk. You'll have nobody to discuss the latest Paris dresses with, nobody to decide on the length of a hemline or the set of a piece of lace."

"Up there, Marie Louise, the hemline will not make much difference, and I'm afraid there will not be a single piece of lace."

Marie Louise pouted. "And all your pretty dresses?"

Pompee interrupted her. "Madame must wear the dress of a peasant woman, and milord must dress himself like the poorest *cultivateur*. A dress of blue cotton for her; white pantaloons and sandals for him. Ah! That reminds me. The tree which grows the bark I need grows quite a distance from here."

Armes threw up his hands in despair. "Not more of that stinking stuff you prepared for me the night of the palace ball. *Nom d'un chien*, no, Pompee!"

"*Mais oui*, milord! It makes a very fine mulatto out of you, and Madame will be a beautiful octoroon."

Armes pursed his lips in disgust. "Not Athenée, too!"

Pompee nodded his head portentously. "*Mais oui, Madame certainement!* Who knows? Some day some peasant might be seeking a lost goat on the mountain. He would stumble on Mon Repos. He'd see two white people there. Immediately he'd hot-foot it to his *caille*, important with news. He'd blab it to his wife, and with such a morsel of gossip, she'd tell her neighbors at market and before long they'd know it in St. Marc. No, you must darken your skins. I will show you the tree. We'll locate one on the mountains, and you must keep the preparation always at hand."

Armes spread his hands out on the table in a gesture of helplessness.

"*In-sha-Allah,* as Ali would say. Poor little fellow! If it were not for him, we wouldn't have Mon Repos today. You know, Athenée, we've been proctected by love—Ali's, Henry's, Marie Louise's, and Pompee's."

"We are fortunate," Athenée said.

"And how fortunate I am." Marie blew a kiss to Armes across the table. "More fortunate than even you know, for the next time I see Henry I can tell him that he is going to have another son."

Athenée moved her chair close to her, petted and cooed with her as women do under such circumstances. She glanced up at Armes, and he saw a fleeting look of loneliness in her eyes, but it passed in a moment and she smiled again. He realized that there was a part of life which even his love could not fill; that even while her arms held him, they ached for a tinier head than his to nestle at her breast. Pompee broke the mood as he slid his chair away from the table.

"The bark from the tree." He waved and was gone.

But while he was away they were busy with preparations. Armes tested a fine pair of French dueling pistols he had purchased in the Cap months ago, and laid in a plentiful supply of lead and powder. Marie Louise walked over to the village of Milot and returned with Maman, who carried an armful of freshly laundered clothing. There were three dresses of rough blue denim, shapeless and ill-sewn, for Athenée. There were several baggy pairs of pantaloons for Armes, made of heavy white cotton, devoid of buttons and with a drawstring to fasten them. There was a shirt of striped red and white, also devoid of buttons, with long tails in front to be tied around his waist. There were crude leather sandles with rawhide thongs for both of them.

Armes and Athenée each went through their personal belongings—all the necessary impedimenta of civilization. Almost everything that had seemed so important to their existence they discarded one by one as worthless trifles. Armes saved a set of English razors, and Athenée added a pile of fine French soap. She wanted to bring a heavy gold-backed hairbrush, but Armes shook his head and substituted a plain wooden one and a comb of tortoise. What else did they need?

"Warm blankets," Armes suggested. "It gets cold on the Bishop's Hat at night."

"Not with you there, *mon cher*," she answered, "and the warm little shelter I shall find with my head on your arm and my cheek against your chest."

"But blankets, nevertheless," he insisted.

"And sufficient pots and pans," Marie Louise, always practical, said. "Copper ones that you can shine with sand from the stream, and heavy iron ones that will make a savory stew."

"Needles and thread." Athenée sought them in her work basket.

"Hammer and nails." Armes made a note of them.

"Flour, sugar, salt, and coffee," Marie Louise added, starting an inventory of her own.

Armes walked to the massive armoire which stood against their bedroom wall. He rummaged in it for a moment and then stood back, choosing carefully. At length he reached in and drew out one of Athenée's gowns—a pale satin that shimmered with the greenish blue of the sea. This he placed carefully on the bed, then added a crisp white linen suit of his own. Little white satin slippers took their place on the floor beside the shiny black boots which so completely dwarfed them.

"On our mountain, we shall live like peasants," he said, "and God alone knows how long we shall have to stay there. But we must not get to thinking like peasants even though we live like them. We shall pack these clothes carefully and hide them in our *caille*. Once a month, Athenée, we shall put them on so that we won't forget who we are." He looked at her for confirmation.

"Then add this, *mon cher*." She took a heavy cut-glass bottle from her dressing table. "A whiff of attar of roses will surely remind us what we are. And these." She opened her jewel case and took out a parure of emeralds—necklace, tiara, bracelets, and earrings—which she placed on the bed. Her glance caught the satin slippers. "Fie on you for a stupid man! What good are slippers without these?" She held up a pair of gossamer silk stockings.

They packed them away. Out in the kitchen Marie Louise was banging pots and pans together. Soon they heard Pompee's steps in the hall, and once again Armes smelled the foul stench of steeping bark.

Not long after, Pompee and Marie Louise appeared with

394

steaming bowls of the dark brown liquid, left them in the room, and departed. Athenée undid the buttons on Armes' shirt and slipped it off. She dipped her sponge in the liquid and made a wide circle on his broad back, then added eyes, a dot of a nose, and a gash of a mouth. He retaliated by adding a brown spot to each of her cheeks.

"Shall we try one coat and be an octoroon or a second coat and be a quadroon?" he laughed as he daubed at her shoulders.

Her finger tested the grinning face on his back and finding it dry, she kissed the crudely drawn mouth. "How about ten coats, and you'll be as black as Henry himself?"

The whiteness of their skins disappeared as the deep rich sepia replaced it. They finished and walked hand in hand to the big pier mirror in the corner. For a second they could not believe it was themselves that they saw reflected, but it was Athenée's lips that smiled back and Armes' mouth that laughed at her.

She turned and laid her hand on his chest. The hair had grown out again and made a thick mat of close tendrils in which she could lose her fingers.

"We have forgotten something," she said.

He slapped her hand playfully. "Not by a damn sight! I'm not going to shave my body again. There's going to be one *gros nègre* in Haiti with a hairy chest and if any stupid peasant should wander up the mountain and see it, I'll hang by my arms from a tree and pretend I'm a baboon."

"Then he'll run down to his wife and tell her that the biggest ape in the world is loose on the Bishop's Hat . . ."

". . . wearing white cotton pantaloons and a red striped shirt."

They dressed in the rough peasant garments, touching up their arms and legs where the clothing did not cover them.

Armes shuffled toward her, speaking in broad Creole.

"This *moun* wants you for the *bamboche* tonight, little yellow girl."

"This little yellow girl wants this *gros nègre* for more than the *bamboche* tonight. Why don't you visit my *caille* later on this evening, and we'll . . ."

"Hussy!" Armes slapped her derrière. "Come, woman, cast these shameful thoughts from your mind. Let's finish our packing."

That evening, a little procession could be seen forming at the back of the house. At the head of it was a young, well-built Negro, sitting proud and upright in his saddle. Behind him was a beautiful octoroon woman, dressed in a rough blue dress, who quieted her nervous mare, calling her Lalla. A giant mulatto in a red-and-white striped shirt and white pantaloons mounted his horse in back of her, as he spoke to a young Negress standing at the door.

"Good-bye, Marie Louise, for now. We'll return to Sans Souci, and very soon, I trust."

"Oh, I hope so, Armes—Athenèe. Please be very careful. May God be with you."

Armes, Athenée, and Pompee waved at her and started off. She stood at the door, waving at their backs, until no trace of them could be seen.

46

THAT night as Armes, Athenée and Pompee climbed the dark trails of the Bishop's Hat, the all powerful Haitian army, under General Jean Jacques Dessalines, captured the city of Cap François, and with it all St. Domingue. The French tricolor which had flashed its red, white, and blue of defiance over all Europe and through Africa as far as Egypt was lowered from the flagstaff atop Fort Picolet, and the white flag of surrender was raised. The unconquerable army of Napoleon stopped short and admitted its defeat at the hands of an illiterate bush Negro, born in the Guinea swamps of Africa, sold in slavery to a Negro master in St. Domingue, and raised to a life of degrading toil.

Jean Jacques Dessalines was a great general and a great man—one of the greatest the world has ever produced. He was ugly of countenance, uncouth of manner, illiterate and uneducated, and yet these defects never impeded his greatness. He hated the whites—all whites—with a fanatical bitterness which exceeded that of a Mohammedan *hashshashin*, but he must not be judged by his extreme cruelty to them, for he had witnessed their cruelty to those of his own race and, to his primitive mind, there was only one course of action—the pursuit of savage vengeance. But Dessalines as a conqueror was strangely compassionate toward the vanquished French. He allowed them to depart in peace, and even sent provisions to the starving regiments. But even with his permission, they could not leave. The English fleet blockaded the harbor entrance of the Cap, so Rochambeau and his soldiers surrendered a second time, and left St. Domingue by English escort to his Majesty's colony of Jamaica.

French rule in St. Domingue was ended, and so was St. Domingue. Henceforth it was to be known as Haiti, the High Place, as the Indians had called it. It was an infant state, weak, depleted, war-torn, and poverty-stricken, but gloriously free.

Later, after that fateful night of victory, the generals were to meet at Gonaïves. Pétion, the proud *affranchi* from the mulatto South; Christophe, the mighty black from the North; Dessalines, the conqueror; and all the other generals, colonels, majors, captains, and lieutenants in their fanciful uniforms were to come together to decide the fate of the mewling nation. First of all, Haiti was going to need a head, and it was only natural and right that they would turn first to Jean Jacques, the conqueror. His genius had won their liberty for them. He should be rewarded, and he would be. They would be unanimous in electing him captain general for life, ruling under a constitution drawn up, so they were to boast, with the blood of a white man for ink, his white skin for parchment, and his skull for an inkwell. It would be a wordy document, which would set forth few principles except the exclusion of the white man from any participation in the government of Haiti for all time to come. Haiti would be for the blacks, and that term would include not only the Negroes but the multi-hued mulattoes of the South. There would be no more distinctions; octoroons and quadroons, griffes and maramous—in Haiti they would all be *black,* and if they were Haitians they would remain black.

St. Marc and Gonaïves had always been home to Jean Jacques, and he was to remain there, content to be in familiar surroundings. Henry would return to the Cap as governor of the Province of the North once again, and Pétion would depart to govern the *affranchi* Port-au-Prince. But Dessalines, always unpredictable in his moods, would never care for the responsibilities of government. He was a soldier, and as such he would never be able to develop any interest in the intricacies of foreign commerce, and the baffling economics of balanced trade, the workings of justice. As he could neither read nor write, he would willingly delegate these distasteful chores to the only ones who could—the educated

mulattoes. It would be exactly as they had planned and
desired. But Jean Jacques was a soldier, and having conquered the French, there remained nothing for him to fight.
For a while, the utter annihilation of all the whites on the
island would amuse him, and he would derive some satisfaction from hunting them out. Just as the kings of France
had hunted stags in the forest of Fontainebleau, so Jean
Jacques would set his hounds on the trail of those luckless
whites who were hiding in the mountains, run them down,
and slaughter them one by one. When there were no more
whites left to kill he would be reduced to his palace pleas-
ures—his many mistresses, his orchestras of violins, his imported wines, and his exotic foods.

Henry, however, was no Jean Jacques. Secondary to Dessalines in military ability, Henry would prove himself the
world's most able administrator, Under his capable hands,
the crumbling city of Cap François would be transformed,
with new buildings, new roads, new administrative systems,
and a great new prosperity. The fields around the deserted
city would be hacked free of weeds, and soon undulate with
the green waves of sugar cane. Commerce would start with
the United States and England, and white factors from these
countries would find a welcome in the Cap. While Jean
Jacques debauched in his plaster palace with all his pretty
little girls—black, brown, sepia, tan, and yellow—Henry
would be working. But he would not be working alone.
Armes Holbrook, from the top of the Bishop's Hat, would be
there to guide him, counsel him, scold him, reprove him,
become angry with him, forgive him, and, through all, love
him.

47

A HEAVY mist enshrouded the Bonnet à l'Evêque that
night while the little caravan of three ascended the mountain over a ghostly trail, penetrating the veils of pale vapor
which swirled around them as though to keep their journey
secret, and closed again behind them to obliterate the signs
of their passing. Near the summit the fog increased in density, and they proceeded blindly until they heard the rushing
sound of the falls. They climbed to the lip of the cataract

to see the little valley of Mon Repos spread before them, wraithlike and shrouded. When they stopped to rest their tired horses, the plaintive notes of a guitar floated through the darkness, and they could see a haloed beacon of yellow light which beckoned from the smaller *caille*.

The guitar stopped suddenly on a high note of fear, and the light was immediately extinguished. Pompee called softly across the meadows, and the bass string of the guitar answered. "Who comes?" it asked, and Pompee identified them. The first they saw of TiTonTon was the disembodied gleam of his teeth in the darkness, then his body emerged. He stood by the trail and allowed Pompee to pass, with only an affectionate pat on the knee to welcome him, but when Athenée came up to him, he took her reins and led the horse through the field up to the big *caille*. His eyes worshiped her, and when Armes helped her down from Lalla, the boy stood there shyly, his head ducked low, waiting for her to speak to him.

"This is TiTonTon," Armes said as he brought the boy closer. "TiTonTon, this is Madame."

"TiTonTon and I already know each other. He is a good boy."

He stole a look at her and grinned, then he and Pompee disappeared with the horses. Armes and Athenée walked together to the house, but before they neared the entrance, TiTonTon ran ahead and produced a light, then ran back to Pompee. Only that lone candle was burning when they stepped inside. Armes closed the door to keep out the damp chill, opened his hands wide in a welcoming gesture, and waited expectantly for Athenée to speak.

She inspected the room carefully. It had changed since Armes' first visit. Now there was a real bed in the corner in place of the mat of plaited plantain leaves. It was a huge mahogany four-poster, draped with netting, such as some looting peasant might have found in an abandoned plantation house and appropriated for his own. The crude tables and chairs had been replaced by more comfortable ones—handcrafted, but not as primitive as those Pompee and TiTonTon had fashioned. Finely plaited mats of grass covered most of the earthen floor; a wooden bowl of yellow *figs* and green limes made a note of color on the table; and a long-necked gourd on the wall trailed a spray of orange flowers which TiTonTon had gathered. The flowers, the fruit, and the shadows which the dancing candlelight threw on the gaily

399

painted walls gave a carnival air to the room, which seemed to signify that they had been expected.

Athenée continued her inspection, then pulled one of the chairs back from the table and sat down.

"What shall I say, my beloved?" She looked gratefully at Armes. "I'm speechless. You never mentioned the painted walls."

"TiTonTon did them as a surprise for you."

"The lad's a genius. I shall never feel lonely when I can see all this life around me. You know, Armes, I feel at home. How little matters the glory that was St. Gabriel; the beauty and ease of living of Sans Souci. Here we have no polished floors, no gilded furniture, no crystal chandeliers, and yet the place breathes a welcome."

"Then you think you can be happy here?" There was a note of anxiety in Armes' words.

"I named it Mon Repos," she said, "and that is what it shall be. Our place of rest and refuge. But who am I to question it?" She looked down at the coarse blue cotton and the brown hands folded in her lap. "And who are you either, *mon gros nègre*?" She smiled up at Armes' dusky features. "Yesterday I was the Vicomtesse de St. Gabriel, worthless as the title is. Tonight? Tonight, what am I?"

Armes made a courtly bow. "You could be the wife of TiArmes, the Haitian peasant who has carved out a little field for himself on the side of a mountain."

"Yes, I could well be the wife of a Haitian peasant, for most of them marry without benefit of bell, book, and candle." She sighed and gave him a penetrating look. "Shall I be that, Armes—just that—your wife while we are here alone on the mountain?"

"I've always wanted you for my wife at Sans Souci. I could want you no more at Mon Repos."

Her hands plucked fitfully at the coarse cotton of her dress. She seemed to be making a momentous decision. Her face brightened and she went to the door, calling out into the night. "Pompee!"

TiTonTon appeared from out of the blackness into the light, devouring her with the eyes of an adoring spaniel. He pointed to the door of the other *caille*, imitated a man riding horseback, then brought the imaginary horse to a stop, dismounted, and tied the horse. He looked up at Athenée to see if she understood.

"He's trying to tell you, my dear," said Armes, "that

400

Pompee went outside to unsaddle the horses and tie them for the night. We can't let Tom and Lalla eat our millet, because it's all we have. I think Pompee's coming now." He peered out into the night, took a few steps into the darkness, and came back carrying one of the panniers. Pompee carried the other.

"What do you want Pompee for?" he asked Athenée.

"Hush!" She placed her fingers to her lips, and waited while Pompee unfastened the covers of the baskets. "Pompee, when slaves married, and even today when a man takes a woman to his *caille,* they do not always marry in the Christian church, do they?"

"The slaves never did, madame, but today if a man has enough money to pay the priest, he goes to the church with his woman and they are married."

"But if he has no money, what then?"

"Then they just 'jump the stick,' or if they are followers of voodoo, they go to the *papaloi* of their village and are wed by the ancient Dahomean ceremony."

"But only if the man has no money?"

"*Certainement!*"

"Armes," she called, "come over here."

He walked across the room and stood over her as she knelt by the panniers. She reached up and slid her hands slowly up and down the curve of his thighs. He regarded her, puzzled. Then she got to her feet and carefully examined the shirt he was wearing. She seemed satisfied and nodded her head in approval.

"What's the matter?" He did not try to cover his amusement. "What are you smiling about? Are you planning to sell me in Jamaica or Cuba? If so, the usual procedure is to have a slave strip so you can finger him thoroughly."

She shook her head. "I do not need to see you naked to know that you would bring a good price on the block. No, that was not it. Those trousers, Armes! They have no pockets, and neither has your shirt. Do I make myself clear?"

"No pockets? *Nom de Dieu,* I do not understand you, woman. Did the *loup-garou* that roams this mountain steal your wits on the ride up?"

"Oh, Armes! Like all men, you can be so dense when I am trying to be subtle. Remember what Pompee said? When a peasant has money he goes to the church to be married but when . . ."

". . . he has no money, he goes to the village *papaloi*. If I have no pockets, I have no money. Is that it?"

"It most certainly is."

"Despite the fact that there is a leather pouch in that basket with several hundred English guineas in it . . ."

"I don't care what's in the basket. I'm talking about the man who stands before me. As far as I can determine he is a poor Haitian peasant—just a mulatto *cultivateur*. He has brought a woman to his *caille*. Perhaps because he loves her."

He waggled a brown finger at her. "Ah, now you are certainly wrong. There is no 'perhaps' about it. He damned well does love her."

Armes looked at Pompee, trying hard not to laugh.

"Ah, Pompee, these women! How unpredictable they are! Beg them to marry you and they will refuse you. Grovel in the dirt before them and they will answer 'no.' Then suddenly on some dark night, high on a mountaintop, for no reason at all, they decide they want to get married. It's beyond me—I can't explain it."

"Perhaps I can, milord." Pompee looked from Armes to Athenée. "Madame does not wish to marry you in a church before a priest, because then she would be bound to you forever. I understand there is no separation in the Christian church."

"We call it divorce, Pompee."

"No divorce, then. But there is with us. The Goddess Ayda who stands guard over marriage never wants a man and woman to live together without love. When love dies the marriage should end. Either one is free to leave. That is our belief."

"And that is the only way I will be your wife." Athenée was serious now. "If at any time I think it is better for you that I leave you, I must feel free to do so. Be that as it may, even now, I cannot marry you, my dear, unless you ask me."

"And so, for the thousandth time, Athenée, I ask you to marry me by whatever rite you ask."

"Then will you marry us, Pompee?"

"Yes, I shall marry you. I will say the words that will make you Milord's woman. But let me ask you this, madame. You do not do this in sport? You do not do it to ridicule my gods?"

She placed her hand reassuringly on his. "Oh, Pompee, dear Pompee, you know me better than that. I respect you as I would a priest of my own church, and I shall respect

402

any ceremony you perform that will bind us together. I shall feel as wholly married with your words as I would standing before the high altar in the cathedral with a mitered bishop before me."

Armes interrupted her. "We already have the bishop's miter, my dear. As a matter of fact, we are standing on it."

She came closer to him and hooked her arm in his.

"Pompee, here we are! Will you proceed?"

"Do you but sit here a few moments"—he indicated the two chairs—"and you, TiTonTon, you are a *hunsi kanzo*. You have passed through the voodoo fire, and you can act as *houngenicon*—my assistant. I, the *papaloi*, will now raise you to that rank."

Pompee and TiTonTon busied themselves unpacking the baskets. They sought the bag of meal that Marie Louise had packed and, when they had located it, Pompee opened it and handed it to TiTonTon.

"Draw the checkered heart—the *vévé* of Ayda—on the floor. We shall use the table for an altar." He found another candlestick and put a candle in it and lighted it. Then he placed the candles at each end of the table. While TiTonTon was drawing the complicated *vévé* on the floor with cornmeal, Pompee left. He returned with something in his hand— a smooth round stone, black in color and polished as though it had often been handled. "A *pierre loa*," he explained as he placed it on the table between the candles. "I carry it in my saddlebag. The *loa* of Ayda resides in this stone."

His whispered words sent TiTonTon outside again, and shortly the boy returned with a white rooster and a white hen, their legs tied together, under one arm, and a *papa* drum under the other. He put the fowls down in one corner, where they crouched, and went over to add a few finishing touches to the *vévé* on the floor. Pompee smiled at the boy in approbation and called Athenée and Armes before him. Both he and TiTonTon removed their shirts, and he asked Armes to do the same. Pompee knelt, touched his head to the floor, and then motioned to Armes and Athenée to kneel before him. TiTonTon crouched on his heels at Pompee's side. His hands struck the drum, and the white cock struggled to free itself from its tethers, while the small white pullet clucked frantically.

Pompee started to chant—a strange, meaningless jumble of words that were full of rich charm and throaty fullness. As he chanted, he started to sway in time with the increasing tempo of the drums. TiTonTon soundlessly joined in the chant and the motions. As usual, the drums exerted their strange fascination over Armes, and their rhythmical beat, like a giant pulse, caused a swelling desire within him. The chanting continued for a long time, until at length it ended and Pompee, seemingly in a daze, stood up, reached for a crude iron brazier that was under the table, and ignited the half-burned charcoal in it with one of the candles. It did not catch readily, but when he leaned over and blew on it, a glow appeared and the charcoal burst into flames.

When the fire was burning brightly, he moved the brazier and placed it directly in front of Armes and Athenée in the center of the *vévé*. Again he started his chant, and once again TiTonTon pounded the drums in a frenzy. The rooster had ceased his struggles and the little hen had become quiet. In the chanting which Pompee kept up to the cacophony of the drums, Armes could catch the names of voodoo gods— Damballah and Ayda. Gradually, as the sweat-covered torso of the young priest swayed before him and the chant continued, Armes could feel himself become entranced. It seemed to him that he had stepped outside his own body. He glanced at Athenée; she too seemed somewhere in another world, for her eyes were glazed and unseeing.

Armes was never exactly sure of what happened after that, nor could Athenée later recall any of the events clearly. He knew he must have been under some form of hypnosis, because certainly the things he saw happen never could have happened. He saw Pompee reach for the white fowls, take one in each hand, and swing them around his head. He saw the wings flapping, heard the death rattles, saw the wings become quiet. Athenée must have seen the same, for he heard her gasp. Pompee laid the lifeless bodies of the birds on the floor, with the hen in front of Athenée and the cock before Armes. At a motion from Pompee, TiTonTon got up, separated the netting that surrounded the bed, gathered up the dead fowls from the floor, and laid them side by side on the bed, covering them with the sheet. He returned, his bare feet making no sound, and reached for a *vaccine*—a bamboo flute —that hung near the gourd of flowers, then squatted again near Pompee. A strange haunting music came from the flute, rising and falling in cadence with Pompee's chanted words. The music stopped, and TiTonTon moved over on his knees beside Pompee, who reached up, still on his knees, and pinched the candle flames out. The only light in the room was the glowing flames of the brazier. Taking a mouthful of rum from a bottle by his side. Pompee squirted it into the fire so that the flames rose up, blue and bright.

Armes could see Pompee's face through the fire, but it was the face of a stranger, far different from the familiar features of the wide-browed, handsome Negro youth. Now the eyes narrowed to slits; the flat nostrils twitched; the wide lips parted to bare the white even teeth. TiTonTon had also changed. No longer was he a youth but a young girl, softly feminine, with the eyes of a coquette under his long lashes. Pompee's hand reached toward Armes through the flames, and TiTonTon's came seeking Athenée's. Armes unconsciously reached out his hand toward Pompee's; Athenée, forced by the same compulsion, touched TiTonTon's, and all their fingers met in the moist warmth of Pompee's palm. Slowly Pompee drew their hands toward him until they were directly over the blazing brazier. Armes saw the blue flames creeping around his own wrist and licking his fingers, but he felt no sting of fire, no sharpness of pain, and he knew that Athenée did not either. Still clutching their hands, Pompee and TiTonTon stood up, lifting them with them. They straddled the brazier, letting the flames play against their cotton-clad legs, then took a step forward out of the blaze, scuffled out the *vévé* with their feet, and pressed their bodies close to those of Armes and Athenée. Armes felt the smoothness of Athenée's cheek against his own, the sweaty hardness of Pompee's chest, and he could smell the musk from TiTonTon's armpits. For a long moment the four of them stood closely pressed together in a quadruple embrace, their breaths mingling. Then Pompee released them, rekindled the candles from the flames in the brazier, and clapped his hands smartly together.

Like a person suddenly awakened from a dream, Armes looked around. Once more the room assumed reality for him. He felt that he had traveled many miles to some far planet and had returned again to familiar surroundings. He saw Athenée blink and shake her head, and he looked at Pompee's face, but now it was once again Pompee, and TiTonTon had ceased to be a girl and was once more a grinning boy.

"That, milord and madame," Pompee said in his natural tones, "makes you something different from what you were before. Once you were a man and a woman. For a few moments you have been Damballah Weydo and his wife Ayda Weydo. Now you are no longer man and woman, you are both. You, milord, are not wholly male, for you have taken on a part of Madame, and you, madame, have received a part of Milord, and we, TiTonTon and myself, are a part of both of you. The *loa* of Damballah came to you, milord, through me, and the *loa* of Ayda was imparted to madame by TiTonTon."

Armes laughed to cover his nervousness. He had been through a strange experience which he could not understand. Now he wanted to hear his own voice. The familiar ring of his own laughter would reassure him that he was not just dreaming. But he felt he must justify such laughter. He looked toward the bed.

"We're married now, Athenée. Pompee just killed two of our best chickens to do it. Did you have to kill them, Pompee?"

"Kill them, milord?" Pompee laughed in response. "I killed no fowl tonight."

Armes dashed across the room to the bed. He raised the sheet and stared. There on the bed, nestled closely together, were the white cock and the little white pullet. Their beady eyes reflected the light of the candles and, as Armes looked at them in astonishment, the rooster stood up, threw back his head, and crowed in triumph.

TiTonTon ran over and swept them off the bed into his arms, stroking their feathers. He started toward the door, and as he passed Pompee, the man put his arm around the boy's shoulders and drew him close in an affectionate embrace.

"You saw this boy tonight as a woman, milord, for TiTonTon is always ridden by the *loa* of Ayda. That's what makes our union so perfect." He paused for a moment on the threshold to place his shirt over TiTonTon's bare shoulders.

"That was a good omen, milord and madame, when the rooster crowed. Damballah blesses your marriage tonight." He paused a moment. "And ours." They walked out into the darkness, their bodies touching, and Armes closed the door.

With Athenée's hand in his, he crossed the room, snuffing the candles out as he went. The fire was dying in the brazier and sent up weird shadows on the painted walls. It flared up, suddenly lighting the room for a moment to disclose the blue denim dress on the floor covered by the sprawling legs of the white pantaloons, and died. The only light in the room was the pale glimmer from the lighted window of the other *caille*, then that was extinguished, and there was complete

darkness. Inside the *caille*, it was quiet except for the soft
little sounds of love from the bed. Outside, the drums
sounded from mountain to mountain, bearing the news of
Dessalines' victory over the French.

48

ONE sun-drenched day followed another at Mon Repos.
Cool nights, when the mists blew down from the granite peak
of the Bishop's Hat and enshrouded the little *caille*, alternated
with other cool nights, when the moon cast a brilliant light
on the little valley, painting the landscape in a vivid black
and white like an engraving by Piranesi. The sun-filled days
brought work to both Armes and Athenée; the cool nights
brought rest and the assurance of a closer union. A new pattern of life was developing for Armes, in which he was
relegated to second place—an apprentice to the superior
knowledge of Pompee and TiTonTon. His booklearning had
never taught him their primitive methods of wresting food
and sustenance from the soil. They had become the teachers;
he was only the willing pupil.

Pompee remained with them on the mountain most of the
time, but on occasions he would leave them, disappear down
the mountain trail, and be gone for a day or two, sometimes
as long as a week. His religious duties throughout Haiti demanded his presence at many ceremonies. Gradually he was
welding together a hierachy of *papalois* and *mamalois* in
every city, town, and village. Although each of them was
supreme in his own *houmfort,* all looked to Pompee as the
grand master of their tightly woven organization. His aim
was to stamp out the vicious Petro rites and substitute the
old Rada belief—the pure Dahomean religion—with its bene-
ficial influence. In this he was becoming successful, and
magie noire, the black magic of Petro superstition, was fast
losing ground. Petro *bocors* were leaving Haiti to seek refuge
in Martinique, Cuba, and Grenada, translating their evil rites
into *obea* and *nañigo* imitations of the real voodoo. Pompee
had become the Hermes of the Rada believers—the messenger
of the gods who conducted them to the mystical "Back There"
of Dahomey. *Papalois* in remote parts of the island expectantly awaited his arrival, as well as the latest news which he

brought. And there was always something new to tell these days.

Dessalines' hold on the people was fast weakening. He had allowed himself to be surrounded by ambitious mulattoes— men who were determined to grab the reins of government from the hands that had been so strong with the saber but were now so weak with the pen. They were succeeding because Jean Jacques had no faculty for government. His contribution to stable government, or so he believed, had been to exterminate the whites; he had hunted them down in his own province—in the mountains, in the cities, and on the plains. He had slaughtered them unmercifully, ripping them apart with the ferocious boar hounds which he had imported from Cuba, crucifying them and torturing them, until there wasn't a white person to be seen in the entire vicinity of St. Marc.

Despite Jean Jacques, Armes and Athenée still lived happily at Mon Repos. Their secret had been well kept. They were unmolested on the Bonnet.

Only once had intruders entered their small Eden. It was on a day that Pompee was away, and Armes and TiTonTon were working on the edge of the valley. They had planted yam vines there and were cultivating them one afternoon when they heard voices below. Cautiously and noiselessly they crept to the rim of the valley where they were screened by vines and underbrush and peered down the mountain. Two Negroes, dressed in peasant's clothing, were climbing up the rise. Armes was relieved to see that they were not soldiers, and when he noticed that one of them carried a rope halter, he was certain that they were searching for a mule or a *bourrique* which had strayed away.

Even the most simple-minded peasant, however, was a threat to their security. Let a stranger look at the cultivated fields in the little valley and he would know that the place was inhabited. From their sheltered spot, Armes and TiTon-Ton watched the men climbing ever nearer. There seemed to be no way to halt them. Armes considered running back to the *caille* for a gun, but taking the lives of two innocent men was repugnant to him. TiTonTon, his eyes on the approaching men, crept close to Armes and laid his hand reassuringly on Armes' shoulder, pushing him down even lower, and then pointed to himself. He was trying to tell Armes that he would take care of the situation, and although Armes could not imagine what means the boy would employ, he had learned to respect TiTonTon's intelligence. He obeyed the command and flattened himself on the ground to wait.

TiTonTon slipped off the ragged shirt that he was wearing and wriggled out of the loose pants. He gathered up handfuls of the dry dust and rubbed them over his body until the rich brown of his skin became gray and streaked. Then he stood up. His face quickly lost all expression, his eyes became lack-lustre and vacant, his cheeks sagged, and his mouth hung open with the slackness of stupidity. All the life and vigor of youth fled from his body, his shoulders slumped, and his feet stumbled over the ground with uncertain steps. In an instant he had transformed himself into a walking specter—a weird unearthly being that advanced slowly over the rim of the field, dragging its clumsy feet through the patches of yams.

Looking neither to the right nor the left, his wide-open eyes glazed, he started down the hill directly in the path of the two men who were coming up. Their banter ceased and they stopped in fright, as TiTonTon, accompanied by a shower of small stones, advanced toward them. He gazed straight ahead, staring through them instead of at them. Terror made them speechless, but one of them had sufficient presence of mind to cross himself, while the other reached inside his shirt and clutched at a *ouanga* that hung around his neck. As TiTonTon neared them, he let forth the series of bestial grunts that were his only words.

They stared at him, rooted to the spot in horror, until he was only a few paces from them, then one of them screamed a single word—"zombé"—and as the shriek echoed among the hills, they gained courage from their ability just to make a noise and fled down the mountain, falling, rolling, regaining their feet, and falling again, TiTonTon waited until they were out of sight and climbed back to where Armes was lying in the grass. He grinned broadly and went through an elaborate pantomime, during which he threw himself on the ground, dribbled handfuls of earth over himself, closed his eyes, then stood up again, and walked slowly with the same foolish expression on his face that had terrified the men. It was too complicated for Armes to understand, but when Pompee returned that night and Armes related the experience, Pompee doubled over with laughter. He called TiTonTon to him, patted him on the shoulder, rumpled his woolly hair, and kissed him on the cheek.

"We'll have no more visitors from that direction," Pompee

assured them. "They will never dare step foot on the mountain again."

"But why?" Athenée asked.

"Because they thought TiTonTon was a zombé."

Neither Armes nor Athenée understood the word, and Pompee went on to explain.

"There are certain secrets that the Petro worshipers alone know. One of these is the power to revive people already dead and bring them back to a certain state of life whereby they breathe and move as a living person. They even understand in a limited way, but they are people without a soul. When the Petro men hear of a death, they go at night and see if they can dig up the body. If they are successful, they perform certain incantations over it, and bring it back to this form of half-life. We call the creature that they have made a *zombé*.

"This creature has no will of its own. It will follow commands given to it, work, perform simple tasks, and do them in a mechanical fashion. It makes a cheap servant, for it can be fed on nothing but a little millet. There is only one restriction—the *zombé* must never taste salt, for if he does, he crawls back to his grave and back to death. Some peasants believe that to look a *zombé* in the face causes death. That is why these men will never come here again."

"But all that is too fantastic to believe." Athenée shook her head.

"Fantastic, madame? No! Unfortunately it is true. Have you not noticed how we bury our dead with extreme care, usually within sight of our *cailles* or at a *carrefour* where there are many passersby? We always put heavy slabs of stone over the graves and cement them well, *n'est-ce pas*?"

"*Mais oui*," she agreed.

"In this recent war, there have been many dead left unburied, so today there are many *zombés* in Haiti. They do their daily work on distant plantations mechanically, without knowing what they do. These strangers mistook TiTonTon for a *zombé*, so they fled in fright because they knew they must be near the dwelling of a *bocor* who might fall upon them as a *loup-garou* and drink their blood."

Athenée called TiTonTon over to her. He threw himself at her feet and rested his head in her lap, nuzzling against her like an overgrown puppy. She stroked his head.

"What a good boy he is, but, *hélas*, he can never talk," she said sadly. "And although his guitar speaks for him with

410

the beauty of his own music, it is hardly intelligible. What a horrible thing—never to be able to communicate one's thoughts. And I feel responsible for it because he was a St. Gabriel slave whom my husband tortured."

TiTonTon stroked her hand and shook his head sideways to indicate he absolved her of all wrongdoing.

"But he shall," she insisted. "There is no reason why he cannot communicate with other people. He can hear and he can understand; therefore he can learn to read and write. Paper and pencil can be his tongue."

Pompee nodded in grateful approval. "You have no idea, madame, what a wonderful thing it would be for him. He does so want to talk. There are millions of things he is dying to say. It would open up a whole new world for him. But, he still would not be able to talk with me, because I cannot read or write."

"Then you both shall learn. How better could I spend my time here than in teaching you?" She walked over to the table and brought back her Bible and her prayer book. Both TiTonTon and Pompee stared at the printed words that she showed them.

From that day on, she set aside some time each day for their schooling, and when TiTonTon and Pompee returned from work in the fields, their black wool damp with moisture from their baths in the river, Athenée patiently taught them. It was difficult at first—for them as well as her—for they had a hard time connecting the strange symbols with the words they spoke, but she persevered and so did they. Gradually the letters became familiar to them, and then the letters joined together to form words.

They started first with simple words, written on a dried plantain leaf with a charred stick. Then, returning from a visit to Cap François, Pompee brought paper, pencils, ink, and quills, and it became easier for them all. They copied their writing from the fine copperplate hand of Athenée until both could write with facility. Both were intelligent and quick to learn, and once having grasped the idea, they progressed rapidly.

One of TiTonTon's happiest days came when he ran down to the field where Armes was working, took a sharp stick, and printed in the earth, "Supper is ready."

Armes read the words and sensed the pride of achievement that lay behind them.

"Supper is ready, TiTonTon?"

The sharp stick traced the words, "Yes, milord."

"And are you hungry, TiTonTon?"

"Je meurs de faim," the stick wrote, and he bulged out his belly and patted it.

"Then we'd better hurry." Armes laid down his hoe. "Can't have any starving boys around here. Did you tell Pompee?"

"Pompee's already at the house," the stick wrote.

"Then come, we'll race to the house to see who gets there first."

TiTonTon's big feet raised up miniature tornadoes of dust as he ran to the *caille*, but Armes' long legs overtook him. They reached the door breathless.

"We've got a hungry boy here," Armes panted. "Needs his supper quick."

Pompee pointed to the floor, and Athenée turned them both around and pushed them out the door.

"Shame on you both, coming here to eat all covered with dust from the fields. Look at my clean floor with those big footprints on it." She pointed to TiTonTon's dusty footprints. "Now go, both of you, down to the stream, and wash yourselves clean as you always do before eating. And here"—she reached for an armful of clean white clothes and handed them to Armes—"we dress for dinner tonight."

Armes saw the white linen suit he had brought from Sans Souci. After he and TiTonTon had scrubbed themselves clean with leaves and white sand, and after he had dressed in his white suit and TiTonTon in his clean blue denim, they walked back to the *caille*. Athenée was seated at the table, strangely unfamiliar in her dress of sea-green satin, with emeralds sparkling in her hair and ears. There was a white cotton cloth on the table, the candles were lighted, and a delicious aroma assailed their nostrils.

"What is it that smells so good?" Armes asked.

"It is a special *ragoût* of chicken, maize, and mushrooms. And here"—she lifted another cover and waited for Armes to sniff again—"are some of your own yams, made doubly delicious by the fact that you raised them yourself. And this" —she pointed to a sodden white mass on a wooden plate— "I'm not too sure about this. It is my first attempt to make cheese from goat's milk."

He walked around to the side of the table and kissed her. Pompee came to stand behind her chair, his black hands resting gently on her white shoulders. TiTonTon knelt and laid his head on her knees. Suddenly he jumped up, ran to

412

the little box where she kept paper and pencil for him, and scribbled fast.

"We are the happiest family in the world. Let's never leave Mon Repos."

Athenée shook her head sadly.

"I wish we never had to leave, TiTonTon," she said.

"Maybe we never shall," Armes said. "Jean Jacques Dessalines is about my age, and he may outlive us all."

49

ALTHOUGH Armes filled his days on the mountain with hard, tiring work, he did it more by choice than actual necessity. He was not wholly dependent on the produce of their acres, but he enjoyed the primitive satisfaction of being self-supporting, in spite of the gifts which Henry and Marie Louise were continually sending. Such gifts were always welcome, because they were a surprise and provided them with things they did not raise themselves. Marie Louise's gifts were practical ones—candles, food delicacies, pots, pans, sheets, and blankets. Henry, on the other hand, was more unpredictable—the bundle might be a bulky one with several yards of purple-and-gold embossed velvet, or a tiny one in Pompee's pocket with a pearl brooch for Athenée; it might be a dozen bottles of watercress-flavored rum, a sack of chickpeas, or a side of bacon. But whether it was an enameled snuffbox or a bag of apples with the frosty savor of New England, the pleasure of opening the gifts was always the same.

Presents were not, however, the only means of communication between Mon Repos and Sans Souci. Pompee always returned with a saddlebag overflowing with letters or documents, to each of which Vastey had attached Henry's query or request for advice. Armes spent most of his evenings studying these papers, making a notation here or a question there, and at length writing out his advice and recommendations. It was mainly through Armes' instigation that Henry embarked on a broad venture of foreign trade, with the results that ships were now arriving at all the main ports of Haiti, and particularly Cap François. They came mainly from the United States and England, though there were some from

Holland, Denmark, and Spain. Also lively inter-island trading had developed between Haiti, Cuba, and Jamaica, as well as many of the smaller islands.

Henry had two crops which he was developing—sugar and coffee—which were supplemented with valuable hardwoods, some indigo, a little rice, beans, and other agricultural products.

Internal progress was discouraging and slow. The big sugar mills were nothing but rusted scraps of broken machinery; the once lush fields were overgrown with rank weeds; the coffee bushes in the hills had become choked with creepers and tropical growth. But the greatest problem of all was labor! The slaves had gained their freedom from the *blancs*, and they understood that to mean that they had gained their freedom from work forever. The whip of the overseer and the threat of the big house had vanished. Now they were free men. To hell with work! Nobody could tell them what to do.

Dessalines in his tawdry palace at St. Marc was not able to tell them, and he was the only man who had the authority. Dessalines thought himself supreme. *"L'état, c'est moi,"* was his attitude. Haiti was being governed by his whim of the moment, provided it met with the approval of his mulatto aides. Although Jean Jacques did not realize it, they actually governed him, and they governed Henry as well. Whatever progress he made in the North was immediately thwarted by Dessalines' mulatto lieutenants, who were not anxious to see any power or influence slip through their delicately manicured yellow fingers into the strong black hands of the governor of the North.

Few of the blacks shared Henry's energy for work. Those few who were ambitious cooperated, but the majority could see no reasons for breaking their backs in the hot sun when there were plantains hanging from convenient trees and wenches to sleep with in their *cailles*. Henry raged in frustration, but continued to build in every way possible. At times it seemed pointless, especially when he had to turn over all his hard-won receipts to Dessalines to squander on his twenty mistresses in their twenty separate palaces.

Henry himself was living frugally at Cap François and Sans Souci. He had burned his great palace by his own hand, and he was not anxious to build another. Henry feared Dessalines' jealousy, and he knew that any expression on his part to live in a manner that equaled that of Jean Jacques would soon mean that Henry's head would be missing from his body.

It was a time of careful planning, watchful waiting, and desperately slow progress for Henry. He fretted continuously. "There is so little time and so much to do," he kept saying.

"So little time and so much to do" was indeed Henry's greatest problem. He harbored dreams of a perfect state, and he knew that perfection could be obtained only by everybody else working just as hard as he did. But . . . nobody did, and nobody wanted to, except perhaps Valentin Vastey and Armes. But Henry kept on working—all day and far into the night. Even when his second child, a daughter this time, died, Henry kept on working, and although his kiss for Marie Louise was as tender as ever, his mind was far away, devising new rates for duties and customs, or wondering if he could scrape together enough coffee to fill the holds of the two ships which Mr. Frothingham had sent from Boston.

A four-day absence at the sacred waterfall of Saut d'Eau, where he had presided at an important conclave under the maupou trees, had necessitated Pompee's absence from Mon Repos. On his return he had stopped in the Cap, and as always he came back with a bulging saddlebag. When he had emptied it on the table in the *caille,* he lifted his hand to signify to Armes that that was not all, and sat down on a chair to remove one of his boots. From inside the lining he produced a small folded piece of paper. The writing was Vastey's, but the signature was a sprawling *Henry,* the only word he knew how to write. Armes read it over and then handed it to Athénée, who read it aloud.

Mon frère:

Don't be surprised when you see two Haitian peasants arriving at your *caille* this afternoon, and for God's sake, do not shoot them, because shooting the governor of the Province du Nord and his wife would certainly be considered high treason.

Henry

Preparations started at once. Athénée passed out brushes and brooms to TiTonTon, Pompee, and Armes, who promptly abandoned them and wandered out to the fields to see how things looked out there. She managed, however, to corral TiTonTon and separate him from the other two, but every time he passed the door in the course of polishing and scrubbing, he wistfully looked out to see if he could glimpse the two men. Pompee had been away for several days, and Ti-

TonTon wanted to be with him. The glorious fact that he was now able to write and communicate his thoughts to Pompee was a never-ending wonder to him. However, his loitering in the door was discouraged by Athenée, who wanted the *caille* to be even more spotless than it always was.

She was proud of her little home at Mon Repos. It was her own. St. Gabriel had been the home of her parents, and on her return it had been René's. She had never dared allow herself to think of Sans Souci as home, but this mud-daubed *caille* with the thatched roof belonged to her. Here on the mountain she was Armes' wife, and that gave her a vested interest in Mon Repos. Everything in the little house had taken on a deep personal meaning for her. She loved the rough pottery which she washed herself, the few shining pieces of brass and copper which she scoured in the white sand of the brook, and the bright curtains at the windows which she had stitched. She was always smoothing an imaginary wrinkle from the big bed, picking up a scrap of lint from the floor, or scrubbing the tabletop to a new whiteness. This was her home and Armes was her man, and she lived every day as it came, trying to keep the fear of tomorrow out of her heart. Someday that tomorrow would come and she and Armes would have to leave the mountain and then . . . She didn't want to think about that.

Those troublesome thoughts were not for today! Today Henry and Marie Louise were coming. It would be good to see another woman again; to talk of inconsequentialities such as gowns and parties. Gowns and parties! She thought of the green satin dress and hesitated. She looked at the brown dye on her arms. No, today she was a Haitian peasant woman, and the blue denim dress would be better. It was not so shapeless now that her needles had altered it. She set out the crock of brown dye on the table for Armes.

"Clean clothes for you, my lady." She took the broom away from TiTonTon. "But first run and tell Armes and Pompee that they too must make themselves presentable. Tell Armes he's almost a white man again and he needs a touching up, and he's got to shave and I have water heating, and I have ironed a white shirt for Pompee and it's waiting for him and . . . what on earth are you doing?" TiTonTon was searching the *caille*. "Oh, your paper and pencil! Now where did I put it?"

TiTonTon grinned, rummaged on the shelf near the door, and produced his materials. While he dashed out of the

416

house he waved them at Athenée, as much as to say, "How do you expect me to tell them all these things without my paper-and-pencil tongue?"

Soon the three of them were back, their heads dripping wet. Pompee picked up the clean white shirt and with Ti-TonTon departed for their own *caille*. Armes shed his damp clothes and stood still while Athenée painted him with a dye-soaked rag, sputtering as he always did at the odor of the dye. Each time it happened he swore that he wished he could change his color and be as black as Henry.

"If I've got to be a Negro, I'd rather be a real one," he said.

"There's a place on your shoulder that needs another coat." Athenée turned him around. "But actually, Armes, the sun has turned you so dark that you could almost be a mulatto without the dye."

He shaved, while she dressed, and when she had finished, he looked at her in astonishment, startled to see the old familiar veil across her face. It saddened him, for she had never before worn it at Mon Repos, and he knew that she was accustomed to appearing before Henry and Marie Louise without it. He looked at her, a question in his eyes. His look spoke more than words, and she answered him.

"It has been so long since I have seen them, my dear, and I feel more comfortable this way."

"But, darling, it's only Henry and Marie Louise."

"I know, and I am really ashamed of myself, but suffer me to have my whims. I feel better with it—more confident, happier. Do you really mind?"

His "no" was not positive, but he humored her. He himself had entirely forgotten the stain on her face, for he saw only the perfection of her other side, but he knew that she could not forget it. She had lived with it so long and cringed from it so often that it had left its mark on her mind as well as on her face. So, let her wear the veil today if it made her happier. Why should he force her to do otherwise?

It was shady outside the *caille*, and they went outside to wait. TiTonTon, whose hearing was more acute than the others, after two false alarms announced Henry's arrival. He heard the hoofbeats ascending the trail. They waited, accusing him of jumping the gun again, but this time he proved to be right, for, in a few moments, the top of a wide-brimmed straw hat appeared by the waterfall, followed by Henry's grinning face, with Marie Louise behind him. It had been a

417

long time since Armes had seen Henry in anything but a general's uniform, and he was hardly prepared for the giant black peasant with sweaty shirt and rolled-up trousers that sat his mule so casually, or the little round-faced woman in blue denim with her head bound up in a cerise cloth that followed him. But it *was* Henry and Marie Louise, and they all ran across the field to greet them.

Henry jumped down from his mule, and bruised his bare foot on a stone. He greeted them with a string of foul oaths while he danced one-footed in a circle, holding onto his bruised toe.

"I told you that would happen! I told you!" Marie Louise sputtered as ineffectually as ever. "But you *would* do it. You said you wanted to come barefoot and you did. I knew what would happen."

"Who in hell ever heard of a goddamned Haitian peasant wearing high boots?" Henry stopped swearing long enough to answer.

"You just wanted to come barefoot, Henry Christophe. That's the only reason. You said it had been years since you felt the earth under your toes and it would feel good, and no matter what I said, you insisted . . ."

"Oh, for the love of St. Ursula and her eleven thousand stupid virgins, will you close your mouth? I am enjoying going barefooted and I damned well intend to continue enjoying it, so shut up! Armes!" He held out his huge hands toward them all and gathered Armes and Athenée into them. Then Armes helped Marie Louise down from her donkey. Henry nearly shook Pompee's hand off, and then was introduced to TiTonTon, who was so awed at being presented to the great General Christophe that he could only hang his head and dig a hole in the dirt with his toe. His fright passed quickly, and in a few minutes he was scribbling on a piece of paper, which he handed to Henry. Henry examined the words as though he could actually read them, then handed the paper to Marie Louise, who could.

"Bienvenue à Général Christophe," she read aloud. Henry went over and clapped the boy on the back, nearly throwing him off balance. In a matter of minutes they were back on their old familiar footing. It was wonderful to be together again, and there was so much for them to see. Henry must look over the farm and Marie Louise must examine the *caille*. What did it matter if the farm looked small and insignificant to Henry or the *caille* poor and primitive to Marie

418

Louise? Neither of them mentioned it, exclaiming over it and complimenting Armes and Athenèe. Perhaps they envied them a little, too.

After a midday meal, which Henry admitted was one of the best he had ever eaten, he and Armes sought the shade of a tree outside, while the wife of the governor of the Province of the North helped the former Vicomtesse de St. Gabriel wash the pottery plates and mugs. TiTonTon accompanied Pompee to their *caille*. Pompee explained that he had not slept for two nights, and TiTonTon was always able to sleep any time and any place. Actually, after four days without Pompee, he had been anxiously awaiting a chance to be alone with him on the braided mats of their *caille*.

It was pleasantly cool out under the tree, and Henry wriggled his bare toes in the grass, leaned back, and looked up through the leaves. Armes stretched out on the ground beside him. The drowsy hum of insects, the muted sounds of the women talking in the *caille,* the warmth of the sun filtering through the trees, and the distant music of the waterfall all lulled Henry.

"TiArmes?" He lifted himself slowly up on his elbow and regarded Armes.

"Yes, Henry."

"It's good to see you again, *mon frère.* I've missed you."

"And I've missed you, Henry."

Henry took a deep breath, closed his eyes for a moment, and seemed content. "It's not very far from here to Cap François as the buzzard flies, but it might be a million miles away. Everything in the city was in a turmoil this morning. The anteroom was full of people waiting to see me. Valentin had a long list of appointments I was supposed to keep. A pile of papers awaited my signature. The mayor of Cap François was giving a dinner for me. Do you know what I did, TiArmes?"

Armes shook his head.

"When I saw Pompee come in this morning I got so lonesome to see you, I left everything and sneaked out the back door and rode to Sans Souci alone, made Marie Louise dress up like a peasant, and brought her up here. Armes, I want to talk."

"Well, then, let's talk, Henry."

"First about Dessalines. I have a lot to tell you about him, but perhaps most important of all is the fact that he has given up looking for you. Mon Repos has hidden you well."

"Are you sure?"

"Almost. I know he has been searching for you without avail. A week or so ago, he sent one of his damned bright-skinned spies up to the Cap. The fellow came to me and inquired about you. Said Jean Jacques wanted to send you to England as the first Haitian ambassador to the Court of St. James. Of course I knew the bastard was lying, so I told him that you and Athenée had fled to Jamaica. I had just received a letter from there and I picked it up and waved it in front of Jean Jacques' man so he could see where it came from. Told him it was from you. Must have convinced the yellow bastard, but that's only a part of the news. Wait till you hear this!"

"More about Dessalines?" Armes asked.

Henry nodded assent. "Big news! You are now living in an empire, TiArmes," he sneered. "Yes, an empire, with that Dessalines, whose mother was certainly screwed by an ape, as Emperor. Jean Jacques the First of Haiti!"

"So what does that make you, Henry? Grand Duke, Prince Regent, Heir Apparent, Crown Prince, or what?

"Not a goddamned thing! The selfish bastard says there'll be only one title in Haiti—his own. Since Napoleon crowned himself Emperor of France, our Jean Jacques decided he could crown himself Emperor of Haiti. The son-of-a-bitch doesn't even know what the word 'empire' means." Henry sighed. "Oh, TiArmes, sometimes the whole thing is more than I can stand. I work and work and work and get every-thing ready and then I get an order from His Imperial Majesty, *Merde* the First, countermanding everything I have done. Money, money, money! That's all he wants! He'd rather have a centime in his hand today than put it to work to bring in ten centimes tomorrow. He doesn't give a damn about Haiti. Give him something to eat, pour some rum down his throat, slip a wench or two into bed with him, and he's satis-fied."

"Yes, I imagined he'd be like that," Armes agreed.

"But where are we going, TiArmes? Sometimes I think it would have been better if we had made a deal with the French. *Vraiment!* It couldn't be any worse than it is now. If we could have kept the French and abolished slavery we might have been better off."

"What seems to be your most pressing difficulty, Henry?" Armes hitched himself up to a sitting position and slipped

420

off his own rough shoes. Henry's liberated toes looked much too comfortable.

"Money, TiArmes! Money! Dessalines devours it, and the awful part of it is we haven't any to be devoured. Not a goddamned sou! All we have in Haiti today is the money that comes from other countries. All the French gold we had has disappeared. Nobody knows where it is. Probably the stupid peasants buried it in their back yards. Today we are using English pounds, American dollars, Spanish pesetas, and Dutch guilders, but we have very few of them, and no money of our own. Pétion, the poor fool, is coining money of tin, but even the peasants know that it is worthless and will not use it. Money is our most important problem, but there are others."

"Such as . . . ?"

"Laziness! Trying to get these black bastards off their fat asses to do an honest day's work. We can't go on like this. Life isn't a perpetual holiday, even for free men. We've all got to work and build and create a race of men that take pride in themselves. Oh, TiArmes, there's so much to do and so little time to do it in and you and I can't do it all alone."

"Henry." Armes was thoughtful and serious. "If you were in Dessalines' place and had absolute power, could you solve your problems then?"

Before answering, Henry considered the question carefully. "I think so, TiArmes. Yes, I know I could, because I know what's best for these people. If my word were law, I could make them go back to work. I'd stand over them with a whip if necessary."

"But Henry, wouldn't that be slavery? Isn't that what you have just freed them from?"

Henry shook his head. "No, TiArmes, it would not be slavery. When a man is a slave he works without having anything to look forward to. Each day he works and all he gets is a little something to put in his belly. He doesn't even know his own children, for they are taken away from him and sold. Sure, I'd make them work, and work hard . . . there's no disgrace in that. All the time they were working they would be building a better country for their children to live in. And then when those children grew up they'd have an even better country. You take a calf, TiArmes. Sometimes if you want it to drink milk, you hold its nostrils until it cannot breathe and it opens its mouth. Then you pour the milk down its throat. You do it because you know it's for the animal's good. TiArmes I hate to admit it, but these niggers are little more than animals, the way they've lived and bred. To the French they *were* animals. Now I've got to teach them, and they may not like it, but it will be for their own good."

"I guess you're right, but you'll have to wait. The way Jean Jacques is going he can't last much longer. I've seen by the papers you've sent me that unrest is brewing in the South. Pétion and his mulattoes are against Dessalines."

"Yes, they want to get the power into their dirty yellow hands."

"Then wait, Henry, wait! But while you are waiting lay your own plans well. Develop your ideal state in your mind. Aim for perfection. Have everything in readiness when the times comes. If anything happens to Dessalines, you must be ready to seize the government before Pétion and his Port-au-Prince-clique can get it."

Henry stood up. "I'm thirsty, TiArmes. Let's go to the *caille* for a drink of water."

"Sit down! This is more important. Now listen to me! If Pétion gets ahead of you, split Haiti. Let him and his mulattoes rule the South. You don't want them anyway: they're troublemakers."

Henry sat down again quickly. "And I'll take the north. By God, you're right, TiArmes. Jean Jacques won't last much longer, and Pétion can have the South and his thin-nosed yellow bastards along with it. I'll take Cap François and the North, and we'll make it the best goddamned state in the world. I'll be President." He gulped. "But just now I'm so thirsty I can't talk anymore. I'm drier than a Dominican whore at ten o'clock in the morning. Come!"

Armes spied TiTonTon, yawning in the door of his *caille*. He called to the boy. "Fetch a gourd of water for Henry."

"Fetch two gourds, boy! Fetch a dozen. I could drink the brook dry."

TiTonTon dashed into the *caille* and came back with two gourds dripping with water. Henry grabbed them, drained them dry, and put them down on the ground. While he was drinking TiTonTon ran back to the *caille* and quickly appeared with two more gourds of water for Armes.

Armes drank, placed the gourds on the ground alongside those of Henry, and stared at them. For no apparent reason,

422

he lined the four of them up at his feet and studied them carefully.

"Goddamn it, man," Henry laughed, "didn't you ever see a gourd before?"

"Perhaps I never really have."

"But man, they're all over Haiti in every peasant's hut. Everyone in Haiti uses them a hundred times a day. Why, if it wasn't for gourds, the peasants would die. They couldn't fetch water, they couldn't eat, they couldn't even piss in their *caille*."

"And that's it, Henry. We've solved one of our problems. When you become President of Haiti, there's your money." He pointed to the four gourds on the ground. "Right there, see it?"

Henry shook his head. *"Tu pauvre!* Are you crazy—*fou?* Some Petro *bocor* has put a curse on you. Better have Pompee kill a couple of roosters and burn a few *maupou* leaves to free you from the spell."

Armes was patient. "I'm not crazy. I mean every word of it. Listen! Let's say you are in power and you can enforce any decree you make. You have the army behind you, so . . ."

"I go out and pick all the goddamned gourds in Haiti and use them for money."

"Exactly. You said the peasants couldn't live without them."

"They can't."

"Then take their gourds. Take every gourd in Haiti. Send your soldiers out to gather them. Bring them back into the towns and the cities. Guard them as if they were gold. Then set a price on every gourd. So much coffee, so much sugar, so much indigo, so much mahogany for one gourd! If the peasant needs the gourds, he'll find something to buy them with if he has to go to work to get it."

Henry sat still, gazing up through the leaves at the sky. Suddenly he reached down, picked up one of the gourds, and jumped up. He fondled it in his big hands. "Mon Dieu, TiArmes, you've not only solved one problem but two. I'll collect every gourd from here to Jérémie. I'll strip every tree of the big ones and every vine of the little ones, and if any black son of a bitch dares to hold out one gourd on me, I'll throw him in prison. Then, when I have all the gourds in Haiti, the peasants will come crawling to me, their hands full of produce of some kind. I'll take their coffee, their beans, and their sugar, and I'll ship them away and in return I'll get

423

gold and silver. Then I can make coins and have money, TiArmes, Haitian money."

"But you'll have to wait, Henry," Armes cautioned.

He looked down at Armes and winked. "I'm damn good at waiting, TiArmes. I've waited a long time, and it won't hurt to wait a little longer. But now waiting will be easier, because I've got a plan that will keep the army busy, set the peasants to work, expand commerce, and finance the country, thanks to you and these four gourds."

"We'll have more plans," Armes assured him as they started to walk toward the house. Henry stopped, turned around, and went back to gather up the gourds.

"Better watch after these, you peasant," he laughed. "Pretty soon you'll come begging to Henry Christophe, with a bag of coffee on your old woman's head, and you'll say 'Henry, give me a gourd. Sometimes I have to piss in the night and my old woman won't let me piss on the floor. It's too far to the door and there may be a *loup-garou* outside waiting for me. Give me a gourd, Henry.'

"Then I'll say, 'TiArmes, you no good peasant bastard, here's your gourd, but give me that bag of coffee on your old woman's head, so I can ship it to Mr. Frothingham in Boston. He'll pay me good solid money for it.' He put his big arm around Armes' shoulders and walked along with him. "You see, TiArmes," he confided, "that's why I wish I was a *blanc*. You *blancs* got brains; all we blacks have is an itch in the pants."

"Then I must be black, because that's about all I seem to have these days, *mon frère*."

"Put on a little more of that dye, man. I've seen you white and I've seen you mulatto, and now I'd like to see you really black."

"And some days I wish I were," Armes confessed.

That evening, when Henry and Marie Louise departed for the trip down the mountain, Henry paused for a moment on the brink of the waterfall and shouted back.

"Here's a vine with six gourds on it, TiArmes. Guard it carefully. Maybe it's the only way I can pay you back for all I owe you." His laugh echoed back above the sound of rushing water.

424

50

"WAKE up, milord! Wake up." It was the first time Pompee had ever come unbidden to the big *caille,* and he was knocking frantically at the door. In his early-morning haste, he had not even bothered to tie his white pantaloons around him, and clutched them at his waist. Again and again he banged. "Wake up, milord, there's a squad of soldiers coming across the fields." Without waiting for an answer, he pushed the door and dashed into the hut, ran over to the bed, and shook Armes' shoulder.

"Soldiers, milord! They are coming across the field."

Armes sat up, trying to shake the sleep from his eyes. "Soldiers? What kind of soldiers?"

Pompee ran back to the door, tying his trousers together as he went. TiTonTon was outside, shielding his eyes from the morning sunshine, trying to identify the uniforms.

Pompee squinted and recognized the bright red coats and plumed shakos of the Dahomeans.

"They're Henry's men, milord." The tension in his voice eased. "Thank God they're not from Dessalines."

Armes made a grab for his clothes as he jumped out of bed, shook the hair from his eyes, and ran outside. The soldiers were only a few yards away, and one of them, an officer, dismounted and walked over to Armes.

"We seek a M'sieur Holbrook." All the officer could see was a stalwart mulatto in peasant's clothes.

"Yes," Armes nodded.

"M'sieur Holbrook, a white man, who is a friend of General Christophe's."

"I am he," Armes affirmed his identity. "Perhaps General Christophe neglected to tell you that I have become a mulatto, but only temporarily."

The officer looked down at Armes' brown hands and shrugged his shoulders ever so slightly, as though his disbelief was not his fault.

"And I have the honor to be a friend of General Christophe's," Armes went on. He motioned with his head to TiTonTon. "The saddlebags inside," he said, and when

TiTonTon brought them out, Armes showed the officers Henry's initials stamped in gold on the leather.

The officer seemed convinced. "I am Lieutenant León Bois, at your service." He clicked his heels together smartly and bowed. "I bear a message from General Christophe."

"Thank you for coming."

"General Christophe desires me to inform you that His Imperial Majesty, the Emperor Jean Jacques Premier of Haiti, was ambushed and killed on the road to Port-au-Prince yesterday. General Christophe is leaving at once to confer with General Pétion, and when he returns he requests your presence at Cap Haïtien."

"Cape Haïtien?" Armes repeated; the name was unfamiliar to him.

"Formerly Cap François. General Christophe feels that the name of a French king is not fitting for a Haitian city."

Armes hesitated for a moment before answering the lieutenant.

"You go now to rejoin General Christophe?"

"We do."

"Then advise General Christophe that I shall be at Sans Souci, awaiting his commands, when he returns. Do you have any idea of when that might be?"

The lieutenant started counting on his fingers—so many days to ride to Port-au-Prince, so many days for the conference, so many days to come back. "Not less than two week, I would say, monsieur."

"Then be so kind as to inform General Christophe that I shall await him in two weeks at Sans Souci."

The lieutenant clicked his heels again, remounted his horse, gave the command to his men, and led them down over the rim of the valley.

Armes watched their departure with mingled feelings. He looked around him—at the crude peasant hut with its thatched roof and mud-daubed walls, the grain and the vegetables which he had planted; then he lifted his head to the dark majesty of the stone summit above them. All this had been his, every leaf on every tree, every blade of grass, every stalk of grain. He loved it all, and never before had realized quite how much he loved it. He looked down at his hands, brown-stained and calloused from work, and he understood how their strength had grown from the hard work they had done in the fields. The strength in his hands and the burgeoning strength of his body reminded him of Athenée and he ran back into the *caille* to awaken her, but she met him in the doorway.

"I heard." Her eyes were forming tears.

"We are free now. We need never fear the vengeance of Dessalines again. Our death sentence has been lifted and we can leave all this and return to Sans Souci.

She turned her head from him and walked across the room. Before he followed her he called Pompee and suggested that he ride down to Cap François—no, Cap Haïtien —to get the latest news.

"Yes, milord," Pompee agreed, "and this time, may I take TiTonTon with me? He has never been to the Cap and it would be a wonderful experience for him."

Armes assented. He walked over to where Athenée was sitting at the table, her arms folded on the scrubbed white boards and her head bowed in utter dejection on them. Her shoulders shook with her sobbing, and when Armes came to her and tenderly lifted her face in his hands, he saw wet streaks on her brown cheeks.

"Are you then so sad that we must leave Mon Repos?" he asked gently.

"It's silly of me, of course," she said, making an effort to regain her composure, "but I was hoping that all this would not end quite so soon. For the first time in my life I have really lived. I have known what it is to be gloriously happy."

"But those days at Sans Souci?"

"I was happy there too, but it was never the supreme happiness I have had here. This has all been so wonderful, you and I together on top of the world, living in a little kingdom of our own. I've never had to think of your leaving me—even for one night. I've awakened so often, reached over and felt the warmth of you beside me, and then thanked God silently and gone back to sleep."

"And I too, darling. I've done the same."

"Oh, Armes!" She shook her head sadly. "Have you ever stopped to think what perfection we have achieved. There has never been a single cross word, a single disagreement, a single unhappy moment between us. But now I am afraid of facing the world again, and that it might mean our separation."

He ran his fingers lovingly through her hair. He too realized the bliss that Mon Repos had brought them. He had discovered the joy of living close to the earth. During all the time they had been at Mon Repos he had wanted no other woman but Athenée. The old insatiable desire for conquest had ceased, and he had been content to return to her after a long day in the fields. In her he found all the delights of all the other women in the world. They had passed their evenings together under the green-black sky, listening to the notes of TiTonTon's guitar falling like drops of silver in the soft night air. He remembered the crisp, cool evenings, when the air rushed down with a chill from the barren summit, and they closed the door of the *caille* to sit before the welcome warmth of the charcoal brazier and watch the shadows of the flames bring the painted walls to life. Then there was always the wide warm bed and the touch of their bodies, and the completeness of his satisfaction which left no room for any other desire.

He sighed. "But, darling, we have already had this perfection that nothing can ever take away from us. We cannot bury ourselves here on this mountain, forgetting the world. We may look like peasants, dress like peasants, and live like peasants, but we are not peasants. There is a whole world before us—a world of achievement. We cannot forsake it all for a mountain valley and a few acres of millet."

"No, of course not." She managed a wistful smile.

"Besides," he continued, "I feel my work here in Haiti is almost over. Henry Christophe has nearly reached the top. I want to help put him there and then . . ."

"What then?"

"I want to take you with me back to Boston. Or to London, or Paris, or wherever you might like to go."

"And leave Sans Souci?"

"Yes, and Haiti. I've grown to love this country and its people, but there are times when I long to hear my own language spoken."

She looked at him doubtfully. "You would take me with you? Even with this?" She pointed to the purple stain on her face. "No, darling, you would be ashamed of me."

"Listen." He shook her shoulders. "If we ever do quarrel it will be because of your sensitivity. Why can't you forget that? I have. You say you love me. Suppose today I went out to cut down a tree and the axe were to slip and I gashed my arm so badly it had to be amputated. Then, because of that physical defect, I suppose you would stop loving me. Would you?"

"No, I'd love you all the more."

"And so do I love you all the more."

"But that is not love. That is pity, Armes."

"So, your love for me would change to pity."

She shook her head in indecision. "I don't know, I don't know, Armes."

"And I suppose because I want you every night more than I ever wanted anything before, that is pity. Not by a damn sight, Athenée. A man may pity a woman, but that doesn't make him want to sleep with her. You should know by this time that my acts of love are not mere deceptions, made out of pity. Good God, Athenée, what do I have to do to prove that I love you?"

She rose wearily from her chair, but she did not look at him. Her fingers nervously plaited the thick cotton of her dress. Her voice choked.

"You wish me to go with you?"

"Certainly."

"And your plans for the future include me?"

"Naturally. How could I plan without you?"

"Then, Armes, beloved, go ahead and plan, and be happy in making those plans."

He opened his arms and she crept inside them. She clung to him tightly as though it were their last embrace and she was about to lose him forever. Their lips found each other's, and for a long time they stood close together, until he pushed her away gently, sat her down in a chair, and dropped on his knees before her.

"A little more of that and we would spend the rest of the day together here inside." He lifted one corner of her skirt and wiped her eyes gently. "Today will be a holiday from work. Let's pack a little lunch and climb higher up the mountain, until we can see all of Mon Repos stretched out before us. The hot sun of Haiti will shine in our faces, the cool winds of the mountains will fan us, and when we return tonight we shall have a picture of Mon Repos so firmly etched in our minds that nothing can ever erase it. Someday when you and I have grown old together, we'll take each other's hands and walk back in memory to this little valley, and know that no two people ever loved each other so much before or since as we do today. But hurry and get ready, for if we dally longer here we'll end up barring the door, closing the curtains, and . . ."

It was her turn to push him away, and she busied herself with packing the lunch. Later they climbed the mountain and found a grassy spot high above, which looked down on the *caille* and the little brook. Athenée's gaze rested there, but Armes looked out beyond to the sea, glittering blue in the sunshine. Athenée did not see the ocean; she saw only the few days they had left at Mon Repos. She reached for Armes' hand and held it gently in her lap. A tear dropped on it and he chided her, but she informed him that women sometimes cry from happiness as well as sorrow. He believed her, but she knew that she had lied to him for the first time.

When the sun had set and they descended the mountain to Mon Repos, they found candles lighted in the *caille* and Pompee and TiTonTon awaiting them. TiTonTon was jubilant, his pencil hopped from word to word as he told them of all the marvelous sights he had seen in the city. Pompee waited patiently for him to finish. When he had, more because his fingers had become cramped from writing than any other reasoin, Pompee related the news he had gathered about the death of Dessalines.

It seems that the mulattoes of the South had finally rebelled against him. The yellow men had gathered an army together and marched on Port-au-Prince. Pétion had not stopped them, and had surrendered the city, keeping his own command. When word of the coup reached Dessalines, he bellowed like a bull in his palace and ordered his soldiers to turn out. Once again the old war-horse felt the thrill of battle as they marched along the dusty roads to Port-au-Prince. Dessalines, the Emperor of Haiti, rode at the head of his column, and when they neared the sprawling city of Port-au-Prince, he saw a contingent of soldiers coming down the road to meet him.

"The yellow sons-of-bitches," he shouted to his officers. "They're afraid of Dessalines and they've come to surrender. They know their Emperor."

He spurred his horse and galloped on to meet them, quite unaware that none of his own soldiers followed him. Suddenly a shot rang out. Dessalines' horse fell under him, but he struggled to his feet in the dusty road. The troops of Pétion surrounded him, and he realized that they had not come to surrender but to kill him. He kept them at bay with maniacal fury, swinging his saber in wide circles, and the fearful curses that spilled from his lips almost saved him. The rebels were almost persuaded. This was the Lion of Haiti, the brave Dessalines who had led them into battle, who had driven the French from the island and won freedom for them. They were almost persuaded, but not quite. Surprised to find himself alone among enemies, he called on his own soldiers, but they sat their horses impassively, daring to disobey him for the first time.

Another shot split the shimmering air. Dessalines fell, sprawling across the dead horse. He was not dead, but it would have been better if he had been, for they fell upon him in a saturnalia of violence, hacking at him with their sabers, pounding his mutilated body with musket butts, and riding their horses over him. It was all over in a few minutes, and the first Emperor of Haiti had become a mass of bloody meat which stained the white dust of the road crimson. That mass of mutilated flesh was all that was left of Jean Jacques Dessalines, who had been born a slave and died an emperor.

With wild yells of jubilation, the soldiers of Dessalines galloped up to embrace the rebels from Port-au-Prince, and together the two armies rode in triumph to Port-au-Prince, stopping only long enough to spit on or further desecrate the bloody corpse in the road. The dust from their horses' hooves settled on him, and they left him in the sun. There he remained all day while curious peasants passed back and forth in a steady procession, stopping, staring, and passing on.

Late that evening, a bedraggled figure crept out of the brush that lined the road. Timidly she hobbled along, the filthy rags of coarse sacking which covered her dragging in the dust. The peasants in the road made way for her, and as she passed they whispered *"Souillée,"* the defiled one. When her halting footsteps brought her to the body of Dessalines, she unwrapped a cloth from around her waist and spread it on the ground. Inch by inch she rolled the shapeless mass onto it and then with all her strength she tugged at it. It was a heavy load, for Dessalines had been a huge man, but she dragged it slowly along the road, leaving a red trail behind her, then across the grass which bordered the side of the road and into the forest. All night long she sat laughing and weeping in lonely vigil beside the corpse. Peasants, staring through the bushes, saw her caress the mass with loving hands, then throw her body upon it in an attempt to make love to it. When morning came, she scooped a hollow in the black moist dirt and rolled the body into it, covering it with rotted leaves. When she had finished she laughed and limped off into the forest.

Pompee finished his tale and got up to leave the *caille*,

431

beckoning for TiTonTon to follow him. He halted in the doorway for a second and looked out into the night.

"He was a wicked man, that Jean Jacques Dessalines, but he was a great man—greater than the good Toussaint, greater even than our Henry. Now he is gone, and we must forget his faults and remember only his greatness. Whatever Haiti is to be in the future, it will be Jean Jacques Dessalines who laid the cornerstone, and every Haitian for generations to come will honor him, even as I who hated him for his cruelty do him honor this night." He stepped out and TiTon-Ton followed him.

Armes closed the door and blew out the candle. The darkness of the night outside was filled with the throbbing of the drums, beating out the message that Jean Jacques had passed through the open gate of Papa Legba. But their pulsing rhythm brought back to Armes a remembrance of the tawny limbs and hot kisses of Topaze, now *Souillée*, wandering alone in the midnight forests. It was only momentary, for he looked up to see Athenée awaiting him.

51

THERE was little to pack at Mon Repos. All of the trivia which had been so important to them on the mountain was practically worthless at Sans Souci. The hoe that had fitted so well in Armes' hands, that he had wielded so vigorously, and that had been such a constant companion now became just another hoe. It was no longer a friend. The two brass candlesticks which Athenée had polished so lovingly every day, delighting in their soft sheen, now turned into a pair of ordinary candlesticks, hardly good enough for the kitchen at Sans Souci. Everything on the mountain had lost its value except in memory. What did it matter now whether the avocado tree behind the *caille* bore fruit or not when there were hundreds of trees on the big plantation? Why bother if the bougainvillea which Athenée had planted beside the doorway ever bloomed? Once she had lovingly trained its thin green shoots to climb the wall of the *caille*, watching for each new leaf with tender solicitude. Now whether it lived or died made little difference.

Pompee did not want to abandon TiTonTon to pursue a

solitary existence up there, and yet neither Athenée nor Armes wanted to think of Mon Repos reverting back to weeds again. The *caille,* though crude and lacking in grace and comfort, was, nevertheless, far better than most of the houses of the *cultivateurs,* and it seemed a waste that it should not be used or that somebody should not reap the benefit of the crops which Armes had planted and tended. Pompee as usually finally solved the problem.

"You remember Maman?" he inquired of Armes.

"As if I could ever forget her." Armes recalled the smoothly rounded buttocks that he had slapped so gleefully.

"Maman is married again." Pompee spent a minute in mental arithmetic. "I believe this is the seventeenth time, or so she told me. But this time I think Maman has met her match, at least in size."

"Impossible! There is no *gros nègre* to match Maman."

"Yes—Simon! He was one of Henry's Dohomeys until he grew so fat they couldn't find a horse in Haiti that would carry him. He's probably twenty years younger than she, but they make an ideal pair."

"What's Simon doing now?" Athenée asked.

"Nothing." Pompee shook his head. "That's why I was thinking about Simon and Maman for Mon Repos."

"Perfect." Athenée was overjoyed. "Here it is all ready for them—*caille,* fields, livestock, and everything."

So Maman and Simon came up the mountain, which presented quite a problem in itself. They made it on foot, in easy stages, camping out overnight on the way, and when they arrived they were charmed with the prospects. Simon had been a farmer before he was a soldier and loved the land. Although a woman of the town, Maman, with a man of her own, was content to bask in Simon's smile wherever that might be. On the same day they arrived and installed themselves in the *caille,* Armes and Athenée departed with Pompee and TiTonTon.

None of them could bear to look back as they started down the first steep descent by the waterfall. None of them ventured a backward glance, for to each of them Mon Repos had given a special sort of quiet security. To Armes and Athenée it had meant the full blossoming of their love. To TiTonTon it had brought a means of communication, and with the ability to express himself, he was no longer an awkward, bashful boy. His knowledge of writing had changed his whole personality, as the days of hard work in the fields

433

had broadened his chest and increased his stature. No longer was he a lumpish lout of a boy but a man, carefully patterned after his idols, Armes and Pompee. Pompee too had found peace on the mountain, for he cherished the love that had developed between TiTonTon and himself. As Athenée had shown TiTonTon the mysteries of words and letters, so had Pompee taught him the *mystères* of loving and being loved.

Each of them felt, as they left the little *cailles* and the peaceful valley, that they were leaving much of themselves behind. In the years to come, they would look back on this interlude, passed in a primitive way, as a time when they had, as the psalmist sang, been led beside the still waters, lain down in green pastures, and felt their souls restored.

The last pictures of Mon Repos they saw were the ebony, full moons of Maman's and Simon's faces; their broad, white-toothed grins; and the branches of the trees around the waterfall etched against the blue sky. The cherubim with the flaming sword now guarded the gates of Paradise and they could never return, for they were not truly of the soil. The days they had spent as peasants had been only a masquerade from which they knew they would someday return. That day had come, and it was a day of deliverance to all but Athenée.

But painful as it had been to leave Mon Repos, it was wonderful to be back at Sans Souci. Henry and Marie Louise welcomed them, open-armed, at the head of the balcony steps, and in the joy of *bienvenue,* they forgot Mon Repos. Yes, it was really good to be back again. It was good to sit at the polished mahogany table and eat the delicious food. It was good to see the sparkle of wax candles and the gleam of silver. It was comforting to feel the heated water of their bath, the cool linen of their sheets, and the overall joy of a well-ordered household with a multitude of servants to anticipate all their wishes.

The question of what was to become of TiTonTon was still unsettled. He had become so close to them at Mon Repos—so much a member of the family group—they did not wish to part with him. Here again, Pompee, who seemed to be able to solve every problem, made an excellent suggestion. Why shouldn't Armes take advantage of TiTonTon's new ability to write and employ him as his secretary? Indeed, the boy had developed such facility in penmanship that he could write almost as fast as another could talk. Armes, who loathed letter-writing, accepted the idea, and TiTonTon was installed in a little office under the balcony with his inkwell, quills, and papers. Pompee changed to one of the big rooms on the main floor, with a wide testered bed, and took Ti-TonTon in with him.

When Henry was at Sans Souci, he used the boy almost constantly, relieving Vastey of much of the work of letter-writing. Armes also found himself sitting more and more in the little office, dictating long letters to Henry when the latter was in the Cap. There was little trace now of the shy youth who had been all hands and feet in the sleek, well-groomed young man dressed in crisp white linen, who not only handled much of the business of the plantation but whose fingers guided the rising star of Henry Christophe by even lines of fine copperplate writing in the most elegant Parisian French.

Yes, Henry's star was rising, and he regarded himself as the rightful ruler of Haiti. Certainly he had that right. He and Dessalines and Toussaint had been the three stalwarts who had broken the shackles of slavery to win victory over the French. Toussaint had had his day as governor-general of St. Domingue under the French. Then followed Dessalines with his tenure as governor-general for life and his transition to Emperor of Haiti. All this time Henry had waited patiently. Now it was his turn. He had been appointed provisional governor of Haiti by the assembly that met in Port-au-Prince after Dessalines' assassination with the understanding that he would be made governor for life. But Henry had not reckoned on the intrigues of the Southern mulattoes. They had suffered one black, Toussaint, to rise to power; they had allowed another, Dessalines, to don the ermined robes of empire, and their light skins had cringed when they made obeisance to these two blacks. Never would they suffer a third! Henry Christophe was in the North; Pétion and his assembly were in the South. Henry was miles away in Cap Haïtien, so the provisional assembly felt safe in ignoring his delegates. Dictated by the mulattoes, who now called themselves the *élite*, a new constitution was authored which granted Henry the empty title of President of Haiti, but stripped him of all power and invested it in the predominantly mulatto senate. Under these conditions, Henry would have been a complete nonentity——a ruler in name only, a meaningless figurehead.

When they offered this empty honor with their false smiles

and reassuring bonhomie to Henry Christophe, he would have none of it. He flung it back in Pétion's face, and defied the soft-spoken mulatto with the threat of an army which he marched to the very gates of Port-au-Prince. Henry and his army remained there while Pétion trembled, until Henry grew tired of frightening him and marched his men back to Cap Haïtien. Screw the yellow bastards! That's about all they were good for. Henry didn't want the South with its intrigues and its plots. Give him his own black North. Let the goddamned *affranchis* cut each other's throats! He was through with them. With an arbitrary line which was never too clearly defined, Henry split Haiti into two countries, North and South, and made his return to Cap Haïtien a triumphal procession. Let Pétion be President of the South— all Henry wanted was his own familiar North with Cap Haïtien, Haiti's most prosperous city, as its capital. He'd take the fertile valley of the Artibonite and the rich Plain du Nord. Let the mulattoes have the swampy jungles and the high mountains of the South and the West. Henry took the part of Haiti that mattered, and he lost no time in proclaiming himself President of the State of Haiti. He saw to it that his powers were equal to Dessalines'. Pétion with his tin money and his second-rate city of Port-au-Prince was ignored, and if he wished to call himself President of Haiti, it mattered little to Henry, for it was an empty title, and the world would accept only Henry as Chief of State. Henry could have conquered the South but he didn't have time, and he didn't want the goddamned place, anyway. The game wasn't worth the candle.

Together he and Armes drafted the new constitution of the North, and TiTonTon wrote it out. Many of Henry's grandiose ideas were tempered by Armes' sound common sense, so that in the end it was a fair document, even though a dictatorial one. It was received, voted upon, and naturally accepted by the assembly that Henry had handpicked. In his constitution, Henry had been ambitious. He, who could not read or write himself, decreed universal education, the founding of schools, freedom of religion. Henry honored Roman Catholicism as the state religion, for Catholicism had the respect of other governments whereas voodoo had none. But in his heart, Henry had never abandoned voodoo. He knew that it would flourish and hoped secretly that it would, for he had never lost faith in the ancient gods of Dahomey. Henry had other plans, too—military, civil and economic. Some of them, Armes felt, were too fantastic to consider, but Henry overruled him.

"I often think of the Bonnet à l'Evêque," Henry said one evening as he and Armes were poring over papers in the salon at Sans Souci.

"And so do I," Armes answered thoughtfully. "There are times when I wish we were all back there. I've never been able to forget it."

Henry laid down the big palm leaf fan he had been waving and leaned across the table. "You think of it as peace, TiArmes, but I think of it as war. I envisage a fortress there, rising from the top of the peak. Napoleon has not forgotten us, *mon frère*. Not by a damned sight! Some morning we shall awaken to find another French fleet off Cap Haïtien. Therefore I dream of a fortress on the mountain. It would be invincible . . ."

"And impossible!"

Henry banged the table. "Nothing is impossible.

"Henry, Henry." Armes yawned. "Let's go to bed. You're half asleep now and dreaming. We had all we could do to get a bedstead up the mountain. You would not even be able to get one cannon to the summit. Forget it, *mon frère!* Let's go to bed."

But Henry waggled his fingers in impatience. A deep new line appeared across his forehead. His face became stubborn and determined.

"No, TiArmes, *I* couldn't get one cannon to the summit, and why should I? I'm President of Haiti, and I do not drag cannon from one place to another. But . . . five hundred men could get one cannon to the summit of le Bonnet, and if I want five hundred men to do it all I have to do is tell them."

Armes stood up and walked around the table. He laid his hand on Henry's shoulder.

"Yes, Henry, you are the President of Haiti, but, President Christophe, such thoughts are dangerous for a man of your position. Remember Jean Jacques? He was Emperor of Haiti, and now he's nothing but a mass of rotting carrion flesh. And you're not Jean Jacques, Henry. You couldn't be, because you're a bigger man and a finer man in every way. Don't become a petty tyrant. Develop Haiti! Increase her trade and her riches. Show the rest of the world what a Negro can do. Show them and make them respect you,

437

and through you every other Negro in the world. But keep these other thoughts out of your mind."

"But it would be for their own good, TiArmes, for their protection from the French."

"We do not always like to do things that are for our own good. You order five hundred men to drag a cannon to the top of the Bishop's Hat and every one of them would hate you. Then another five hundred men to drag another cannon and five hundred more would hate you. Forget it! You're not the stuff that despots are made of. Lead your people, Henry my brother, but do not lead them back into slavery."

Henry lowered his head into his big hands and sighed.

"Dreams, dreams, dreams, TiArmes. I want to do so much. I want a school at every *carrefour,* and I want that school filled with happy children. I want to see the harbor of Cap Haïtien filled with ships from all over the world, bringing their riches to Haiti and taking ours away. I want to see the city of the Cap as the fairest city in the world. I want to see every peasant in Haiti secure in his own *caille* on his own land. I want to do all this, TiArmes, and what do I have to work with?" He looked up at Armes, and there were tears in his eyes.

"This." Armes lifted Henry's hand as he had lifted it once before. "This, Henry Christophe! But it will take time. Rome was not built in a day, you know."

"Time is something I do not have."

"We are both young, Henry boy! The years stretch ahead of us instead of behind us."

Henry shook his head. "There is so little time, TiArmes, and so goddamned much to do."

Armes reached down and placed his hands under Henry's armpits and dragged him up to a standing position.

"You're a *gros nègre,* Henry," he laughed, and punched the barrel chest.

Henry feinted and then started to laugh.

"Remember, TiArmes, the time you sent me sprawling amongst the crockery?"

"Can I ever forget it." Armes rubbed the side of his face. "Maybe I'd better beat you up again when you get these wild ideas into your head. But come, let's forget Haiti for a while and the fact that you're its President. Let's go out on the balcony and join the ladies. Listen! I can hear TiTon-

Ton's guitar. He's sitting on the steps and the moon is rising and there are people out there who love us."

They walked down the hall toward the big double doors that framed the malachite and marcasite night. TiTonTon's guitar broke into the rhythm of the Meringue, and somewhere up in the mountains behind Sans Souci a *maman* drum spoke. Another drum on another mountain answered, but tonight the rhythm was a joyous one that spelled peace and happiness—a man's own *caille* for himself and his woman, with the scented darkness around them for a coverlet.

The dresses of the ladies made white blurs in the night as the two men stepped out onto the balcony. Henry sank into a big chair next to Marie Louise and Armes let himself down onto the floor beside Athenée. Her fingers curled the damp tendrils of his hair, and his cheek felt the warmth of her skin through the thin muslin of her dress. Pompee's tall figure emerged out of the darkness and lay down on the steps beside TiTonTon. The last fluttering notes of the Meringue splintered into motes of moonlight.

For a long time nobody broke the silence. Henry's hand sought that of Marie Louise and enfolded it. Armes turned his head to press his lips against the thin tissue of Athenée's dress, and TiTonTon's hand stroked the close-cropped head of Pompee in his lap. Henry drew Marie Louise over onto his knees; Athenée bent over and Armes half raised himself to meet her kiss; TiTonTon's fingers traced the outlines of Pompee's lips and Pompee shifted his head in the other's lap.

How long they sat there, each in his own contentment, Armes did not know, but when the full moon rose and flooded the balcony with its pale silver, Pompee sat up and TiTonTon picked up his guitar. The music started again, and Pompee's rich full voice rose in a mystic African chant. The words were unknown to Armes, but he knew that Pompee was invoking his gods for all of them, and that somewhere in the night, the black gods of Dahomey were hearing Pompee's prayer and granting it. Here, in this strange land, Armes had found peace.

52

HENRY Christophe of Haiti was not only one of the world's greatest Negroes but one of the world's greatest men. Although his rule extended over an area which included less than one-half of Haiti, which in turn represented only half the island of Santo Domingo, his greatness was not bounded within those narrow geographical limitations. Henry's innate intelligence combined with his unbounded energy to give him stature both as a man and as a ruler. He entirely transformed the north of Haiti, and he did it in a very short time. From the ashes of Cap François, he built the city of Cap Haïtien, and he built his city well. From the tangled, weed-infested fields, he built a vast agricultural system. Without knowing how to read and with his ability to write limited to his signature, he set up an educational system and established a press. Without ever having practiced commerce, he built a vast commercial empire which extended to the United States, England, and Europe. From the obscure beginnings of slavery, son of a nameless father and mother, he was to found a legitimate monarchy and a nobility.

True, the peasants groaned under the load of work that Henry imposed upon them, but they worked and they produced and in turn they enjoyed the prosperity that their industry brought. Henry had recognized the practicality of the matter of the gourds that Armes has discussed with him and sent his soldiers throughout the North, commandeering every gourd, large or small, green or ripe, from the trees and vines. These were all brought to the Cap and stored there under heavy military guard. When a peasant in his lonely *caille* went in search of a gourd for his daily use, he discovered the only way he could obtain one was to load his woman or his donkey with sugar or coffee or cacao and exchange that produce for gourds. This he did, and he found that Henry had placed a fair value both on the gourds and the produce. In turn Henry exchanged that produce for gold and silver, and with it minted money which bore his own sculptured face. It was only natural that he should call his monetary unit a *gourde* and even today, all Haiti reckons its wealth in *gourdes*.

Under Pétion, conditions were different in the South. Henry's peasants were wont to look with envy on the easy-going life their brothers led in Port-au-Prince and the western peninsula. There they danced all night and slept all day, but, alas, their stomachs were always empty, and Pétion's worthless tin coins could purchase nothing. Then Henry's peasant's took a second look at their sturdy *cailles,* their flourishing farms, their hard-paved roads, and their shimmering city of the Cap, and although they grumbled they returned to their work.

Henry himself was a glutton for work, and he expected everyone else to do as much as he did. Vastey and the other secretaries were continually on the run while TiTonTin, now now graduated to a coat of gold-embroidered turquoise and white pantaloons which fitted him like the skin of a sausage, wrote reams and reams of dictation. Of necessity Armes was drawn into this avalanche of work, and when faced with the piles of documents on his desk, he swore he had never worked harder, but he enjoyed his role in building this infant nation.

As Henry divided his time between the Cap and Sans Souci and insisted on discussing every important move with Armes, it meant they were both always on the run. They even discussed state matters while on horseback and while eating, until Athenée put her foot down and banished arguments at the dinner table. For there were arguments! Often Henry and Armes engaged in violent altercations, during which Henry would bang the table and their voices would rise in the heat of anger. The chandeliers would quiver and secretaries would quake, and then suddenly either Henry or Armes would become calm and start laughing at their own stupidity. Then Henry would stretch his hand across the table to Armes and they would forget their differences and smile shamefacedly at each other. Sometimes Armes accepted Henry's point; at other times Henry would bow to Armes' judgment. With that particular item amicably settled they would proceed to the next.

Henry had decreed Roman Catholicism as the state religion and, as the head of state, he and Marie Louise attended Mass punctually every Sunday. It was one of the few times during the week that he and Armes were separated. One hot Sunday morning Henry arose early at Sans Souci, and with Marie Louise drove off in the cumbersome coach he now used to Cap Haïtien, to attend Mass in the cathedral.

The church at Milot which Armes was building was not finished as yet, so the Cap was the nearest place to go. With the new road between Milot and the city, it was an easy journey, and allowed Henry and Marie Louise to be back in time for Sunday dinner, which they had in the late afternoon. After dinner, Henry had the table cleared, rang for TiTonTon, and spread his papers out before him. As usual, Armes' chair was beside Henry's, and while daylight lasted, they pored over plans, reviewed new laws, and instituted new programs until it became so dark they could not work. Henry was about to ring the bell for candles, but Armes threw his quill down on the table and stood up, stretching his arms and taking a deep breath.

"Mon Dieu, Henry." Armes stretched again. "This is Sunday. I've had all I can take. Dismiss TiTonTon and let's join the ladies on the balcony." He shook his head to gain a degree of wakefulness, but Henry remained seated. He fumbled among the documents on the table, for, although he could not read, he had an uncanny faculty for identifying papers.

"Now this, TiArmes"—he held up a folded parchment—"is the authorization for the new school at Plaisance?"

"Yes, Henry," Armes yawned.

"And—" He reached over and picked up another paper. "This is a statement from London showing our balance in the Bank of England to be close to one million pounds?"

"Yes, Henry."

He shuffled the papers into an untidy pile. "Where is the paper from Mr. Frothingham in Boston that itemizes our latest shipment of coffee?"

"Under your right hand, Henry."

"And the grant to Monsieur Cuchatelier for the cacao plantation?"

"Under the other, Henry."

"Now, shall we allow M. Rocourt and Mr. Layden to form a partnership to export mahogany?"

"Oh, for heaven's sake, yes!" Armes turned in quick anger and walked toward the door. "We argued about it for half an hour and you decided in favor of it."

"TiArmes, come back here!" Henry barked, and slapped the table with the flat of his hand.

Armes had reached the door by the time Henry's command halted him. He turned quickly, piqued with Henry's tyrannical tone of voice.

"Yes, your Majesty! What in hell do you want now?"

Henry lifted his head quickly and darted a sharp glance at Armes. His voice was no longer imperious.

"What did you say just then, TiArmes?"

"I said, 'Yes, your Majesty.'" Armes was losing his temper. "Anyone would think you were some goddamned king and I was some sniveling secretary you were ordering about. Well, let me tell you this, Henry Christophe . . ."

"Don't say it, TiArmes." Henry was out of his chair and across the room. He reached for the bronze handle of the door just as Armes' hand touched it and held it so fast that Armes could not turn it. "Forgive me, *mon frère*. Forgive me, but repeat those words you said to me."

Armes' anger passed as quickly as it had come. He laughed. "Your Majesty?"

"That's it. Those two words." Henry pursed his lips together tightly and Armes, through long association, knew that some important pronouncement was to be made. Henry slowly raised his hand and looked at it. He clenched it into a tight fist and then opened it slowly until his fingers were cupped around an imaginary globe in the palm of his hand. "Your Majesty," he whispered to himself, and then repeated it aloud. "Your Majesty!" He spun Armes around and led him back to the table, pulled out a chair, and pushed him into it. Henry stood in front of Armes—his legs wide apart, his feet firmly planted on the floor, his big hands straining at his trouser pockets. "Say it again, TiArmes, say it again."

"His Majesty, Henry Christophe the First, King of Haiti." Armes was surprised at the intensity of his own words.

"That's it, TiArmes! That's what we need. That will make the world sit up and take notice. What do they care in Europe or America about a black Henry Christophe who is President of Haiti and only half of Haiti at that? Not a goddamned thing! They look across the ocean and say, 'See that silly nigger over there in Haiti, pretending to be a president. Ha! He won't last long.' But, TiArmes, if that silly nigger were a king . . ."

"Like Jean Jacques was an emperor?" Armes said with disgust.

"No, never! Jean Jacques was never a real emperor. It just suited him to take the title. It was his whim, and who paid any attention to it? He had no court to back him up. But I would be a real king, TiArmes, with my own nobility around me. Not only would I satisfy these greedy Haitians,

443

but I would command the respect of the world. And I promise you this, I'd *work* at being a king, so that the whole world would respect me."

All the love that Armes had for the man before him came to the surface. He saw the logic of Henry's reasoning, and he knew that it did not stem from purely selfish impulses. Yes, Henry wanted to be great, but he wanted to make Haiti great through himself.

"Yes, Henry, you *could* be a king. You would not be like Jean Jacques. No! Because you are a far greater statesman than poor Jean Jacques could ever be. He hated me and I never had any love for him, and yet I do not believe there was a greater military genius ever born than Dessalines. But he was a general, not an emperor. As for you, Henry, I do not belittle your military successes. You won them fairly and you were a good soldier, but you were not a brilliant one like Jean Jacques. As a statesman, as a president, yes even as a king, you are far greater than Jean Jacques, and you are without peer today. Italy had her Lorenzo, France her Napoleon, England her Pitt, and the United States her Washington. Haiti has you, Henry, and you are the equal of any of them."

Henry's hands were trembling with emotion. "You really think so, TiArmes? Look, you and I are alone together. You have no need to flatter me. You never have, because you are not like the others. Between you and me it has always been man to man, brother to brother. If you want to call me a son-of-a-bitch, you do, and if I want to tell you you are a goddamned bastard I do. If anyone else called you that I'd kill him, and if anyone called me that I think you would too. No matter what we have ever said to each other, it has never affected this." Henry put one hand on his heart. "Has it?"

Armes shook his head slowly. He remembered how often they had cursed each other, only to end up laughing and slapping each other on the back. "No, never, Henry."

"Then, TiArmes, tell me the truth, such as you have never told me before. Am I, Henry Christophe, worthy to take my place with the other crowned heads of the world? Remember who I am. They were born to kingship; I was born to slavery. While I was shoveling horse shit at the Couronne, they were being rocked in gilded cradles. While I was whoring after street girls, they were tucked in silken sheets. And,

444

TiArmes"—his voice sank to a whisper—"did you ever hear of a black king?"

"It isn't so much the color of a man's skin," Armes reassured him, "or where he was raised or who his parents were. None of these things fits him for kingship. It is the man himself that matters. I shall not flatter you, Henry. I have no reason to. Our friendship was never built on flattery. I'm no fawning toady who wants to get a plantation for his son or a rich husband for his daughter. I've never asked but one thing of you, Henry, and that's your friendship, and I already have that, so what need have I to flatter you? So, I say to you now, without guile or flattery, that you could be one of the greatest monarchs in the world today."

Henry—big, bluff Henry—was sobbing. Great tears rolled down his cheeks, and his shoulders heaved under the tight-fitting blue broadcloth. Armes was at a loss what to do. He had not realized the depth of Henry's ambitions. Now he saw them plainly, and he realized that Henry longed for more than the petty presidency of Haiti. Henry wanted a place in the world. He wanted to show the world that a Negro could be king. With kingship he hoped to draw the admiration and respect of the world not only to himself but to the race he represented. Henry's kingship would confer nobility on every Negro everywhere. The slaves of Louisiana in the cane fields could wipe the sweat from their brows and think of Henry Christophe, an ex-slave, now a king. The Negroes in Jamaica and the slaves of Cuba could see in Henry's regality a hope for themselves. Even in Africa, black men in loincloths would hear of Henry Christophe and feel a thrill of pride that one of their race had attained such eminence. Henry Christophe, king of Haiti! Henry Christophe, the Negro king! Henry Christophe, the first of the blacks. His Majesty, Henry Christophe!

Armes waited for Henry's sobs to subside. He fished in his pocket for a handkerchief and handed it over to him. Henry reached for it, looked up, and smiled. It was the smile of a little boy who has cried his heart out.

"If you ever tell anyone of this, TiArmes, about me blubbering like a schoolgirl, I'll . . ."

"I'll not include it in your biography, Henry."

"Well, TiArmes, we have more work to do."

"But not tonight, Henry."

"No, not tonight," Henry agreed. "And yet there is this one thing I must say to you, TiArmes. I *will* be King. There will be no difficulty about it, for my assembly will vote on it, especially if I dangle a list of titles in front of them. And then, when I am king, TiArmes, I want you to be my prime minister."

"Me, a prime minister?"

"And why not? Louis XIII had his Richelieu . . ."

"Whom he hated. No, Henry, when you become King of Haiti, I shall leave you."

"Then I'll be goddamned if I ever want to be King." Henry banged his fist on the table.

"Quiet, *mon frère!* Listen to reason! If you were King and I were your prime minister, do you know what the world would say?"

Henry considered the question carefully. "Yes, TiArmes, they would say that Henry Christophe was just a stupid nigger and that all the brains belonged to a white man. You are right."

"I know it, Henry. So when you become King of Haiti, I shall leave you. Not because I want to, but because it is best for you. A Negro king and a Negro kingdom do not want a white man as a prime minister. The world is so constituted today that the white man would get all the credit. As a king, you must stand on your own two feet." He looked down at Henry's brilliant boots. "And I think they are big enough for you to stand on."

"Once again you are right, TiArmes." He shook his head thoughtfully. "But I shall miss you. How can I get along without you?"

"I'll be in the States, Henry, and I'll be watching you and always in touch with you. And I must confess that as much as I love you and Haiti, it will seem good to be home again. I've had enough of the sun, and I want to feel the cool breeze of a New England October. I want to wake up and see the ground covered with snow again. I want . . . but never mind, we must tell the ladies our momentous news."

"I wonder how Marie Louise will like being queen of Haiti," Henry chuckled as they walked toward the door.

"And I wonder how Athenée will like being Mrs. Armes Holbrook of Boston," Armes added thoughtfully.

"Marie Louise will like it." Henry's red tongue made the circuit of his lips.

"I hope Athenée will. Once she told me she would never leave Haiti with me."

Henry's arm encircled Armes' shoulders. "Don't worry,

446

TiArmes, women are changeable creatures. Athenée will go with you wherever you go. She loves you."

"Perhaps she loves me too much, Henry."

They opened the big double doors and walked out into the hall and onto the balcony. They had important news that would change the quiet existence of the two women they sought. The news would make one of them a queen, but it would be a sentence of death to the other.

53

ATHENÉE did not sleep that night. Although Armes was in a jubilant mood when they separated from Henry and Marie Louise, she could not match his gaiety. Once inside their room, he was like a boy anticipating a school vacation, bubbling over with plans for their future. They would soon be going to Boston. They would have a home there—a red-brick, bow-windowed house on Beacon or Mount Vernon Street with a white paneled drawing room and Hepplewhite chairs. Of course they would not stay all the time in Boston. They could spend several months a year traveling; they could go abroad; they could do this and they could do that; and naturally they would always be revisiting Sans Souci and Henry.

His enthusiasm for the future continued after they went to bed and, from making plans, he drifted into making love, but for the first time, her ardor did not equal his, although in his great happiness he did not seem to notice. Afterward, he pulled her close to him, so that her head nestled under his arm and her cheek was against his chest. He sighed wearily and contentedly and promptly fell asleep. Fearful of disturbing him, she did not move but lay there calmly, her thoughts racing in mad circles as she felt the smoothness of his skin and the firmness of his muscles against her. She heard his even, untroubled breathing, so peaceful in contrast to her wild thoughts. She felt the slow, metronomic beating of his heart, and compared it to the fluttering of her own. Gently her fingers explored his sleeping body, touching all the beloved and familiar places that now seemed so distant, and so soon to be lost. She loved him more than ever, but loved him now with a sense of farewell, as though a slowly descending curtain was about to separate them and shut out their love. She longed for the night to extend into eternity, that she might lie forever sheltered in his arms, glorified in his complete possession of her, with no dawn to sever the feeling of oneness.

The night passed slowly for her while she reached her momentous decision, and the dawn came all too quickly. The heavy scent of jasmine faded with the coming of the light; the drums in the mountains grew quiet; the night noises ceased; and a cool breeze wafted fresh fingers of air through the slatted jalousies. In the half-light and the damp coolness, she reached down and pulled the linen sheet away from his body. Her eyes hungered for the glory of him stretched out beside her. It seemed that she could never surfeit herself with the sight of him or the feel of him. She felt she must, under this new and strange compulsion, imprint every detail of him indelibly on her mind through seeing him, touching him, breathing in the male scent of him, and tasting the faintly salty tang of him on her lips. Her welling desire made her wish that his sleep would change to an eager wakefulness, but her better judgment kept her from interrupting his sleep. Her desire must have transferred itself to his unconsciousness, however, because he stirred in his dream and pulled her to him. But she gently disengaged his searching lips and his questing hands and crept to the other side of the bed, lying there a moment in indecision before she sat up and parted the flimsy netting. With a gentle movement that would not awaken him, she stooped to pick up her gown from the floor where he had flung it in his ardor of the night before. With stealthy movements, she slipped it on, tiptoed across the room, and closed the door carefully behind her.

The early-morning light painted the floor of the hall with a square of pale sunshine. The candles guttered in the silver candelabra, and there were white pools of wax on the floor under the crystal chandelier. The entire house was wrapped in sepulchral stillness—a depressing quiet compared to the bustle of day. Her bare feet made no noise on the polished boards as she moved noiselessly down the hall to the door of Pompee's room. Her knock was gentle but imperative. In a second, the door opened a crack, and a slit of Pompee's face appeared. His eyes stared at her in disbelief and fright.

"Madame, are you ill, or milord?" His voice was husky, his words blurred.

"No, Pompee, neither. Forgive me for waking you so early

448

in the morning, but I must have a word with you. It is important," she added, "so important to me."

"*Certainement,* madame." He closed the door all but the merest crack. "I shall dress and meet Madame in the salon."

She shook her head. "Not there, Pompee, no!"

"Then in the garden, madame?"

"No." She held up one foot. "I have no shoes and I do not wish to disturb Armes to get them. When you have dressed I shall come in."

"But TiTonTon, he is here."

"Awake?"

"Yes."

"It doesn't matter. What I have to say can be said before him also." She hesitated. "Close the door and dress, Pompee. Open when you are ready but be quick, my feet are chilled."

He closed the door, only to reopen it and drop an over-sized pair of old felt slippers at her feet. She slipped into them, and waited until he admitted her. TiTonTon was sitting up in bed, a white sheet wrapped around his tobacco-brown nakedness. Pompee had hastily donned shirt and trousers. He motioned her to a chair and sat down on the bed beside TiTonTon.

"Madame is distressed over something." His voice was warm with sympathy. "And she did right to come to Pompee, for she knows that Pompee's life is hers to command." TiTonTon reached on the floor beside the bed for paper and pencil and hastily scribbled, "And TiTonTon's too. It is all for Madame."

"Thank you both, *mes amis,* but it is not your life I am thinking about. It is my own."

"Then Madame is ill. But have no fear. The English Dr. Duncan that Henry Christophe brought to the Cap is a learned man, and if he cannot cure her, Pompee will."

"Yes, Pompee, I am sick. But Dr. Duncan's nostrums cannot cure me, nor your prayers either, not even the love I know that you and TiTonTon have for me. My sickness is not one that a person dies of. How I wish it were. It would make things so much easier for everyone."

Pompee did not answer. He and TiTonTon looked at her with troubled eyes, not understanding.

"You are my friends." It was a statement, not a question. She pointed from one to the other.

They hastened to reassure her, but she waved their words aside. "I need no reassurances from you—that is why I have come to you for help. Last night my whole life changed. I have known this change was coming for a long time, but I have tried to dismiss it from my thoughts and live in a fool's paradise. I should have known that such great happiness could not last, but I hoped it would. Now I can hope no more. So I have come to you, begging your help. May I have it?"

"As I said before, with my life, and I will answer for TiTonTon, too." Pompee's voice trembled.

TiTonTon wound the sheet about him and slipped off the bed. He came over to Athenée and huddled on the floor beside her, his head against her knee. She put her hand on his head to comfort him and drew strength herself from the contact.

"I know you will try to persuade me not to do what I propose to ask of you. Do not try to dissuade me. My mind is made up, and if you do not help me I shall have to do this thing alone."

"Whatever it is . . ." Pompee began.

"Do not promise rashly, Pompee. You may not want to help me when you know that the one thing I desire above everything else is merely to die."

Pompee leaped from the bed and was at her side. "Oh, no, madame! I could not promise to help you in that, not even if you asked me."

"Oh yes you can, Pompee, if you know it means my happiness and Armes' happiness. Is not that what you wish for both of us?"

He nodded his head slowly in agreement.

"Then listen carefully. Henry Christophe is about to become king of Haiti."

"And how does that concern you, madame?"

"I am happy that Henry is to be king. He deserves it, but Henry's crown means that Armes will be leaving Haiti, and he insists that I go with him. That I cannot do. Believe me, I cannot."

"But why, madame? Milord loves you so very much and you love Milord. . . ."

"The very reason why I cannot go with him, Pompee. I love him too much. I cannot bear to see his love for me die."

Pompee started to pace the floor, walking up and down the narrow space between the bed and Athenée's chair.

"But why, madame, why do you think of such a thing? In all the time you and Milord have been at Sans Souci his love for you has never cooled. He loves you today more than ever. I know, because I know Milord."

"Yes, you are right. Armes does love me, and that makes my problem more difficult. You ask me why I think of such a thing, Pompee. You ask me?"

"Yes, Madame, I do ask you."

"Then look at me, Pompee. Look! Look at me as though you had never seen me before! What do you see first? This!" She pointed to the purple stain on her face. "Look well! If you had never seen me before and were now presented to me for the first time, your eyes would recoil from me. You would be embarrassed. You would try not to look at this ugliness and pretend you did not see it, while all the time your eyes would stray to it, and you would cover your confusion with a forced courtesy and inane words. Yet all the time you would be thinking, 'Poor woman, poor unhappy woman,' and next you would think, 'Oh, her poor husband, to have to look at that every day.' Oh, I know, Pompee, I know how unkind the world can be. I know how everyone would talk and ask each other if they had seen poor Armes Holbrook's wife. I cannot bear it, Pompee! I cannot go with him, loving him as I do, and make him an object of pity and ridicule among his friends in Boston. I cannot tie him to such an existence as he has here in Sans Souci, and yet I cannot go with him. I cannot sacrifice him to my love. He must be free."

TiTonTon clung to her frantically, sobbing on her knees. He had forgotten his paper and pencil, and was trying to comfort her with strange wordless noises. Pompee stopped his pacing to stand in front of her. "But, madame, have you thought of Milord? Consider him and the sorrow he would have in being parted from you."

"I have thought of it, Pompee, far more than my sorrow in being parted from him. Death is the only thing that can separate us. If I were to flee from him he would follow me and find me. And death is not an inconsolable sorrow. His grief would last a while, but once away from Haiti he would leave his memories of me behind. Someday he would meet another woman and he would forget me, but he would never forget me if I were to live. Therefore I want to die, and I have come to you for help because I am afraid to die."

"*Mais non, madame, c'est impossible!*" Pompee shook his head in unison with TiTonTon. "You ask me to kill some-

451

thing I love, and I love you, madame. How could you imagine such a thing?"

"Because you do love me, Pompee. You are wise. You are a great *papaloi* and you know the secrets of the herbs that grow in the field, the leaves of plants, the bark of trees and their roots. Among these are things that stupefy the senses; that kill without pain or suffering. You could prepare such a thing for me and put a few drops in my coffee or wine and serve it to me. I would merely fall asleep and die. It would free me and it would free Armes. Will you do it, Pompee?"

He came close to her and leaned over until his eyes were on a level with her own. "Never, madame." TiTonTon looked up at her, and his lips silently formed the same word. He placed a restraining hand on Pompee's arm as Pompee started to speak, ran over to the bed, trailing his sheet behind him, and snatched up paper and pencil. His fingers shook so he could hardly scribble the words on the paper, which he then handed to Pompee. Pompee read it carefully, then crumpled the paper and flung it on the floor. He started to pace the room again, and while he walked up and down, TiTonTon's eyes followed him hopefully. Suddenly Pompee stopped, dropped to his knees, flung his arms wide, and moved his lips in a silent prayer. The quietness of the room was broken only by TiTonTon's bare footsteps as he hurried across to Athenée and laid his clumsy hand reassuringly on her shoulder. Pompee got up from his knees and stood in front of her.

"Let me say that I know that you are sincere, madame, and that this is something you greatly desire. I believe you. I believe that your love for Milord is so great that you would sacrifice yourself to make him happy. I have never known greater love, and I respect you for it. But consider this! My love for Milord may be as great as yours, and I do not want to hurt him."

"But you will help me, Pompee?"

"Yes, I shall help you, but in a way of my choosing. There is such a terrible finality about death, madame. When Guede Nimbo opens the black gate there is no return. But, there is another gate which sometimes opens. Papa Legba stands guard at the gate of the gods, and through it they may come to earth. To the gods nothing is impossible. I would like to open Papa Legba's gate for you instead of Guede Nimbo's."

"I do not understand, dear Pompee."

"You cannot, and I cannot explain it to you. I can only say this. Perhaps—only perhaps—my gods can solve your

452

problem, and you may still live. However, you might die in the attempt to live. It is impossible for me to say, but if you are willing to die for Milord, then you should be willing to take an equal chance and live for him."

She shook her head in incomprehension.

"Oh, madame, let me try," he pleaded. "Let me try to save you. I do not know if I can. My gods are powerful, but I have never asked so much of them before. I cannot do it alone. It will take the combined powers of myself and all the *papalois* and *mamalois* that I can call to me. But if you are willing I will try."

"I do not understand, but I have faith in you, Pompee."

"Then let that faith sustain you. Milord does not intend to leave Haiti at once?"

"Not until after Henry's coronation."

"And that will not be for some weeks at least."

She agreed.

"Then, madame, I shall start to make preparations. Today I shall send out word to every voodoo priest and priestess to meet me at the Saut d'Eau near Mirebalais as soon as all the details can be arranged. The Saut d'Eau is the most sacred place in Haiti, because the *loas* of our gods live in the giant *maupou* trees there. You will have to go with me and you will be gone several days—perhaps a week or more. And, dear madame, it may be that you will never return. That is a chance we take."

"And Armes," she asked. "Must he go with us?"

Pompee shook his head. "No, Milord could never witness that which must take place at Saut d'Eau." A note of fear crept into his voice. "We must, however, take Henry into our confidence, and have him fabricate some errand that will take Milord away for a few days. It can be arranged, do not worry, and Milord will suspect nothing. You and Ti-TonTon and I will go together. Marie Louise could go too, but I fear that now that she is to become Queen of Haiti, she would attract too much attention. But you will need a woman with you—I know, we can take Maman."

"If we can find a horse big enough for her," TiTonTon scribbled.

"I leave everything in your hands, Pompee. I trust you and TiTonTon." Her two hands grasped theirs. "I shall be ready when you say the word."

"Then, madame, try to forget all this for the present. Live these coming days as if you expected a miracle to happen.

453

One will happen, I assure you. Either you will be the happiest woman in the world or you will pass through that dark gate that Guede Nimbo opens for you—the gate that opens only one way."

"As though a miracle would happen . . ." She repeated the words after him, and as she opened the door of Pompee's room she turned toward them, hands outstretched. "As though a miracle *will* happen, dear friends."

She closed the door behind her and shed the big slippers before slipping down the hall to their bedroom. Armes was lying in the same position as when she left him. She stripped off her dress and dropped it to the floor, parted the netting and lay down beside him. He half woke, stretched out his arms to enfold her, and drew her close to him. His lips nuzzled hers. She felt the strength of his arms around her and nestled her head against the warm security of his chest. Pompee's words came to her again. "As though a miracle would happen."

Armes' hands caressed her softly, and as her hands touched him she had no doubt of the strength and enormity of his love. That in itself was a miracle.

54

HENRY'S necessary preparations before assuming the crown of Haiti prolonged his own and Armes' absences from Sans Souci. There was so much to do and the time was so short in which to do it. Just as Henry had anticipated, he had encountered no difficulty with his assembly. It had complied with his wishes and conferred majesty upon him, but majesty was bringing with it a host of complicated plans and procedures and a multitude of matters of protocol and infinitesimal details of minute but important problems. Marie Louise also found it necessary to spend most of her time at the Cap, for if Henry was to be King, Henry must have a palace. There was nothing suitable in the Cap—Pauline's had tumbled into ruins soon after she left—so several adjoining houses had to be hurriedly pieced together and converted into a palace of sorts behind an imposing but false stucco facade. The country was scoured for furnishings which had survived revolution, fire, and pillage, and a sufficient number was unearthed in peasants' huts and the palaces of Jean Jacques' mistresses to be refurbished and decorate the palace quite regally. Hundreds of workmen thronged the place, plastering, painting, polishing, and decorating. With plenty of money—for the treasury was now full—anything could be accomplished, and the palace transformation was not only sudden but in quite good taste.

There were coronation robes to be made; gowns for Marie Louise; a crown to be fabricated almost overnight by European goldsmiths, as well as royal decorations of the order of Saint Henry which would confer nobility on Henry's subjects. In this anthill of feverish activity, Henry was tireless and Armes exhausted. Marie Louise, her mind a whirl of gold fringe, seed-pearl embroidery, white satin, Gobelins tapestries, and Savonnerie carpets, had finally succumbed to exhaustion and insisted that Henry return to Sans Souci for at least a day and a night for, as she put it, "It isn't going to be any use for you to be a king, Henry, if I perish of exhaustion before I am crowned, and you have to ascend the throne alone. If I don't get a breathing spell, I'll go to sleep during the ceremonies."

Armes had looked at her gratefully and added his plea for a respite to hers. Despite the fact that causing any cessation of Henry's activity was like trying to halt a tropical hurricane, he grudgingly acquiesced, primarily because he wanted to try out his new and immense gilt coach. It was truly a regal vehicle, and few would have suspected that it had been made over and enlarged from one which Pauline had abandoned. Although its gilt was new and fresh and the white velvet upholstery hot and uncomfortable, it was sufficiently regal to awe the Haitians, including Henry himself, even though the immense crown atop it which sprouted black ostrich plumes wobbled precariously during its progress.

The peasants turned out en masse to watch the coach's passing. For weeks the drums had carried the story; night after night they had throbbed from mountain to mountain that Haiti was now a kingdom and that Henry was its monarch. Black faces were lined up along the road, and as the coach passed they made deep obeisance. Their shouts of "Vive le roi" transformed the short journey from the Cap to Milot into something like a triumphal procession. Marie Louise napped in the satin-tufted corner, awakened sufficiently now and then by a particularly vociferous burst of cheering to wave her hand languidly. But Henry never dozed.

455

He sat stiffly erect beside her, facing Armes who rode backward. Henry's broad smile greeted each of his subjects, and although he bowed to them all, actually he saw nothing but a blur of black faces. For he was busy thinking, trying to solve the thousands of petty problems that perplexed him. It was one thing to found a kingdom; it was another to regulate court etiquette, inaugurate a complete peerage, and prescribe the length of ladies' dresses, the amount of bosom they could show, and the colors they might wear.

He stirred uneasily in his seat and his boot nudged that of Armes.

"Did TiTonTon bring the portfolio with my papers?"

Armes pointed to the rear of the coach. "He has it with him outside on the footman's box." Armes had seen to it that the papers were placed outside the coach, for Henry would have pored over them all the way, and Armes was tired of explaining and arguing.

"Then stop the coach!" Henry reached for the bullioned tassel beside him. "Here!" He stuck his head out the window and yelled at the coachman, "Pierre, stop! Tell TiTonTon to bring the portfolio down to me. TiTonTon, fetch me the portfolio! No, wait! Come inside here with it. We'll need you. Open the door, TiArmes. Let him in." While Henry confounded them all with contradictory orders, TiTonTon fumbled with the folding steps until Henry reached down a gigantic blue-sleeved arm, caught him by the coat collar, and hauled him in. "Drive on, Pierre, drive on!" Having created utter confusion, he sat back on the seat mopping his brow.

In the excitement Marie Louise had awakened, but when she saw they had not yet arrived at Sans Souci, she pillowed her head on her hand and closed her eyes again, then opened them and looked resentfully at her husband. "Henry, are you going to keep me awake with your chatter? Because if you are . . ."

"Quiet, woman!" he bellowed. "Oh, ah . . ." He lowered his voice both in volume and in pitch. "I mean, please be still, your Majesty."

"Don't you 'Majesty' me, Henry Christophe, and don't you think for one minute that after all these years, I'm going to jump when you speak and start calling you *sire,* either. I married you as plain Henry and I'll call you Henry and . . ."

"You'll call me *sire,* too, whenever anyone else is around."

"Pouf!" She stuck out the tip of her tongue at him. "I suppose because Armes is here and poor TiTonTon, I must wait

456

for you to address me first and then answer *sire*. Well, let me tell you that when we are *en famille* . . ."

Henry's temper passed quickly and he held up a restraining hand.

"Sh-h-h, *ma chérie!* That's just what I wanted to talk to you about. We have a kingdom in Haiti, but we lack a royal family. Outside of me and you and the children we have no family at all, unless there are some goddamned black cousins climbing trees back in Africa. And . . . in a kingdom as important as Haiti is going to be, we're damned well going to need a royal family."

She shook a menacing finger at him. "I'm not going to have any more children."

Henry winked at Armes and shook his head at her. "That's for me to say, but that is not exactly what I mean. What I am trying to say, if you would keep your goddamned royal mouth shut long enough to listen to me, is this—we do not have a family. We have Armes and Athenée, but they are not our family."

"Why, Henry?" She leaned over and touched Armes' sleeve. "Could anyone ask for a better brother than TiArmes? Athenée has been both a mother and a sister to me. I've gone to her with every problem I have ever had, and she has never failed me. Do you think it has been easy for me— a poor ignorant girl who was brought up to make beds and count linen at the Couronne—to adopt the airs and graces of a queen? Where would I have learned except from Athenée? How would I have known how to dress, to deport myself, to be what I am today if it had not been for her? You, Armes, you answer me."

"You did not have to learn, Marie Louise," he smiled. "Royalty is natural for you. It was already there inside you; Athenée just helped bring it to the surface."

Henry cleared his throat and assumed a grave expression. "If you think Athenée has done all that for you, what do you think Armes has done for me? If Athenée has been more than a sister to you, certainly Armes has been more than a brother to me. He is the only man in Haiti I can trust. He has never failed me. So I say, Marie Louise, whatever we two are today we owe in some part to these two people. How can we repay them?"

She considered the question thoughtfully, and when she spoke, she was speaking almost to herself, although her eyes were dancing as she regarded Armes. "Money? No, money could never repay what you and Athenée have given us from your hearts. Land grants? Heavens no, you wouldn't want any more than you already have at Sans Souci. Jeweled decorations? You had the Legion of Honor, Armes, and it did not make you any greater. Perhaps a tiara of diamonds for Athenée? Bah, she would never wear it." She turned to Henry and spread her hands wide in a gesture of helplessness. "In truth, *sire*"—the word was heavily accented—"we cannot ever repay them except to continue to love them like our own brother and sister."

Henry slapped his broadcloth thigh with a resounding smack. "Just like a fool woman. She squats on the pot six times before she starts to pee."

"Henry Christophe! If you're going to be a king you'd better learn to talk like a king."

"What's the matter? I said 'pee' didn't I, not 'piss'?"

"Well, Louis of France would never have said anything like that."

"Probably he was too goddamned elegant to even pee. Oh, will you keep still? We're wasting time and words. Go to sleep and let me talk to Armes. Listen, TiArmes, and don't make me repeat it, because the King is a busy man and he doesn't have time to say things twice. From now on you and Athenée are legally our brother and sister. See!" He grabbed the portfolio from TiTonTon and dumped the papers out on the floor. They fell in a jumble, but Henry fumbled through them and found one with ornate ribbons and a big blob of red wax affixed to it. "See," he cried, "the Great Seal of Henry Christophe, and though I can't read a damned word it says, I can *tell* you what it says. It says, Mister Armes Holbrook, that from today you cease to exist. There is no more Mister Armes Holbrook in Haiti. He's over —*tout fini!* As far as Boston is concerned, you can be Armes Holbrook if you want to, but never again here in Haiti. Not by a damned sight!"

"Then, for the love of God, who am I?"

Henry threw back his head and roared. "Look at this!" He shoved the crackling parchment into Armes' hand. "Look! You're the goddamned younger brother of his Majesty, King Henry Christophe. See!" His black finger pointed to the words.

Armes took the parchment and held it toward the window. He read the beautiful hand-lettered script slowly.

". . . and we, through our royal rights and prerogatives invested in us, do hereby announce to all the people of this, our Kingdom of Haiti, that the said Armes Holbrook is hereby adopted as blood brother to ourselves and that he is a member of our Royal Family of Haiti and is to be known henceforth as the Prince Royal of Haiti. He is the only man besides our son, the Crown Prince Victor, that may be addressed as His Royal Highness."

Henry chuckled, leaned over, and searched for another document. "Here, read this, too." He poked the second one at Armes, who read it, following Henry's finger.

". . . and that the said Athenée de St. Gabriel is hereby adopted as a blood sister to ourselves and that she is forthwith to be a member of our Royal Family of Haiti and to be known henceforth as the Princess Royal of Haiti."

Armes shook his head in disbelief. He looked first at Henry, who was grinning broadly, and then at Marie Louise, smiling gently. He could not find the words he wanted to say, and when he tried to speak his voice broke. "I don't . . . I mean . . . I can't . . . Henry, you wonderful idiot you! I'm the proudest man in the whole world. This is the greatest honor any man ever had, and I shall treasure it and hope that as long as you live, you will be proud to call me your brother; as proud as I am to be the Prince Royal of Haiti. Man, oh, man." He was laughing now. "Just wait till Mr. Frothingham hears of this. Can't you see the old boy addressing a letter to me—to 'His Royal Highness, the Prince Royal of Haiti.' How his pen will splutter! And he'll say, 'That Armes Holbrook, never thought he'd amount to much.'" He won't believe it, and I really can't believe it myself. Me, Henry, me! A prince, and not just any little two-penny prince either but a prince royal. And Athenée, a princess!"

Henry nodded with smug satisfaction.

"But it won't be so much of a change for her," Armes said. "She's already been a vicomtesse. But for me, whew!" He wiped his brow with a handkerchief.

"Ah, but that is not all, *mon prince*." Henry fumbled and picked up a third document from the floor. "I think this is the right one. Do not bother to read it, I shall tell you."

"What, another surprise?"

"Perhaps this one will not be so pleasant. However, it's up to you. This is a bill of sale for Sans Souci. I want to buy it, TiArmes. I think you will find the price fair."

Armes reached for the paper and glanced at it, astonished at the figures he saw. Immediately he tore it in two and handed it back to Henry.

"You cannot buy Sans Souci, Henry. You may be king and you can do almost anything you want, but you cannot buy Sans Souci because it is already yours. If it hadn't been for your standing guard on the night of Bouckmann's rebellion, Sans Souci would be nothing but a heap of ashes. And you protected it during Dessalines' government. I want you to take Sans Souci for yourself when I leave Haiti."

"Thank you, TiArmes."

"On one condition, Henry."

"And that is?"

"That you tear the house down and build your palace there. I do not wish you to remain in the Cap. You are too close to the people there. Follow the example of Louis XIV who moved his palace from the Louvre out to Versailles. Make Sans Souci another Versailles, Henry."

"But that is just what I wanted to do, TiArmes. Sans Souci has been the only home I have ever known. When I sit on the balcony there and look off, across the fields, I feel at home. That is where I want my palace."

"Then build it there, Henry, and may you and Marie Louise always know peace where the four of us have lived so happily together. 'Sans Souci,' Henry. We say the words so often, we forget their meaning. 'Without care.' And speaking of Sans Souci, here we are."

The wrought-iron gates swung wide for the gilded coach and they rolled up the graveled drive. Athenée had seen them coming and was waiting to receive them, Pompee by her side. As the coach stopped, Henry stepped out, followed by Marie Louise and Armes. Henry halted at the foot of the steps, looked up at Athenée, and bowed.

"The King and Queen of Haiti have come to honor their sister, the Princess Royal."

Athenée waved her hand in greeting, believing that Henry was jesting.

"Why, Henry . . ." She was laughing.

Armes dashed up the steps two at a time and took his place beside her. He knelt on one knee and extended a welcoming hand to Henry and Marie Louise below.

"The Prince and Princess Royal of Haiti are pleased to welcome your Majesties."

Henry offered Marie Louise his arm and they ascended the steps regally. When they reached the top, Henry glanced over his shoulder to TiTonTon who was collecting the papers from the floor of the coach. "Would the Baron de TiTonTon be so kind as to deliver our documents to the Comte de Milot"—he indicated Pompee—"and we command the Comte de Milot and the Baron de TiTonTon . . ." Henry stopped and began to laugh. "TiTonTon! Now that's a hell of a name for a baron. Sounds more like some nigger slave boy. TiTonTon! Got to change it. What are we going to call this fellow?"

Athenée entered into the persiflage and swept an exaggerated curtsy before Henry. "If I might suggest, *sire,* TiTonTon's destiny has brought him to associate with a king and a queen, so why not name him Baron de Destinée?"

"That's you, my boy." Henry pointed down to TiTonTon. "From now on you're the Baron de Destinée. But as I was saying, I want you and Pompee—no, damn it, the Comte de Milot—to dine with us tonight. You two are part of the family too."

Something about Henry's tone hinted to Athenée that he was not merely joking with them.

"Are we rehearsing something?" she asked, looking from one to another. "I do not quite understand. I thought we were jesting."

"No, my dear, Henry is not jesting." Armes was still holding the papers in his hand, and he passed them to Athenée. "Read this." He waited for her to read the two parchments, and when she glanced up at him, scarcely comprehending what she had read, he continued.

"Tonight, my dear Princess, you take your place among the dynasties of the world. You are a peer of Pauline, for as she is the sister of an emperor, you are now legally the sister of a king. Athenée de St. Gabriel has ceased to exist. From tonight on, you are only Athenée of the House of Christophe. Athenée, my darling, we are the peers of all the Hapsburgs of Austria, the Hohenzollerns of Prussia, and the Hanovers of England. Today, by a stroke of the pen, Henry has made you a royal princess." He leaned over and lifted her hand. "Princess Royal of Haiti, I kiss your hand."

She turned to Henry. "You mean I am really . . ."

"My sister, the Princess Royal of Haiti." Marie Louise embraced her.

"And Armes?"

"My brother, the Prince Royal," Henry grinned. "I should have said *our* brother, but I can never remember to think of myself as *we*."

"Then good Pompee is really the Comte de Milot?"

Henry nodded.

"And TiTonTon?"

"As you named him—the Baron de Destinée, and don't ever call him TiTonTon again."

With Marie Louise's arm still around her, she stepped close to Henry.

"I remember on the day that you and Marie Louise were married," she said, "I asked you to kiss me, Henry, and you did, albeit somewhat unwillingly, because you did not think it proper for a Negro to kiss a white woman. And now the tables have turned, Henry Christophe, and a white woman kneels to kiss your hand. Yes, Henry, I kiss your hand, as my sovereign, and in doing so I honor you." She stood up. "And now if you'll bend down, I'm going to kiss Henry Christophe because I love him."

He bent down and she kissed his cheek. "You are a fine king, Henry, and a great man, and I thank you and I love you. But now, *sire,* will you excuse me for a moment?"

He nodded and she ran into the house, only to reappear in a few moments.

"Shall we dine *en famille?*" She beckoned them to come inside. Henry and Marie Louise entered first, then Armes, who offered her his arm, and finally TiTonTon and Pompee.

The footman had been coached by Athenée only a few moments before, and he was still trying to remember his lines as he tapped three times on the floor with the long pole of the candle snuffer. Then he announced to the vacant room:

"His Majesty, the King of Haiti."

Henry marched in solitary grandeur to the head of the table.

"Her Majesty, the Queen of Haiti."

Marie Louise tripped into the dining room.

"His Royal Highness, the Prince Royal of Haiti."

Armes squeezed Athenée's hand with the crook of his elbow.

"And Her Royal Highness, the Princess Royal of Haiti."

They walked in slowly.

"His Excellency, the Comte de Milot."

Pompee walked with measured tread to his seat with all the dignity of an African potentate.

"The Baron de Destinée, *homme de cour*."

TiTonTon carried himself ramrod straight.

Athenée looked around the table. For a few moments she had forgotten her own great sorrow, but now it returned to her. She dismissed it immediately. How could she let it intrude when all the rest were so happy and—what was it that Pompee had said? 'Act as though a miracle would happen.' Well, one miracle had happened and, oh God, let the other one happen. Through long custom the footman started to serve her first, but she directed him with her eyes to Henry, then lowered her head.

"Our Heavenly Father, grant, we pray, wisdom and strength to our sovereign."

"And to all his family," Henry added.

55

DURING the fortnight that followed Athenée's elevation to royalty, her life changed little, except that the house servants addressed her, when they remembered it, as *altesse* instead of madame. Armes was away during most of the days, coming to Sans Souci late in the afternoon and departing early the next morning. Always, however, when he was forced to spend the night in the Cap, he managed to send a courier to tell her he would not be home, and although she dreaded the nights without him, Pompee stayed close to the house, watching over her. Neither of them had ever mentioned anything more about their previous conversation, but each appreciated that the other had not forgotten. There was a new look of tenderness in Pompee's eyes when he regarded her, and he was always presenting her with little gifts—a bunch of wild orchids, a curious bit of raw gold twisted into a brooch, or a fantastically carved little statuette of some African god. With both TiTonTon and Armes away, they ate their meals together in the dining room, facing each other across the expanse of polished mahogany, each conscious of the other's unspoken thoughts, and each talking of matters of everyday triviality.

Armes had been away for the night and, unable to sleep, Athenée arose early, but Pompee was already in the dining room when she entered. As she turned the ivory spigot of the coffee urn, his words caused her hand to shake so that she spilled the coffee on the table.

"Ce soir! Tonight!" He looked across the table at her, but the commotion outside saved her the necessity of answering. "It sounds like Milord," Pompee said.

Athenée heard Armes' voice giving hurried instructions to the servants and tried to stifle the fear Pompee's words had produced. True, she had desired death, but now she feared it. Yet whatever was coming she must accept it—there was no other way. By the time Armes arrived in the dining room, she felt she presented quite a normal appearance, although she was quite unaware of her extreme pallor.

Armes slumped down in his chair at the table, sweaty and travel-stained. Without noticing the shaking of her hand, he accepted the coffee which she passed him.

"Now what do you think Henry has cooked up for me?" he asked petulantly, biting his lower lip in annoyance.

Pompee's eyes met those of Athenée for a fleeting second, and his look alerted her to the fact that whatever Henry had cooked up, it had been at Pompee's instigation.

"Knowing Henry as I do, it is probably something fantastic," she replied.

"I have to leave in an hour, and this is not just for a day or two days. It's liable to stretch out into a week or even more. I've got to go to Jamaica, of all places."

Pompee rose and stood for an instant behind Armes' chair. He nodded slowly.

"Oh darling, whatever for?" Athenée wondered if her words covered up the relief she felt that Armes would be so far away. She could see the pieces fitting together.

"Sir Home Popham, Admiral of his Britannic Majesty's Fleet, has arrived in Kingston, and Henry wishes me to go there to invite him to come to the Cap to attend the coronation. Whitehall has advised Henry that Popham will officially represent the Court of St. James, and Henry wants me to deliver a personal invitation to him. And, by the way, unbeknownst to me, Henry invited Mr. and Mrs. Frothingham, and they have accepted. I'm so glad, because I want them to know you. But, to get back to Popham. Henry says that I speak English better than anyone else at court *and* I am the Prince Royal *and* I am white *and* he does not know how a

464

Negro or even a mulatto would be received in Jamaica *and* for a dozen other good reasons, he insists that I go. Each time I refused he brought up another logical reason."

"I think you should too." Athenée nodded in approval. "Who is better suited? You have the education, the good looks, and the rank. And furthermore, as Prince Royal it would seem to be your duty."

"Then as Princess Royal you should accompany me."

"How?" She managed a smile. "As your sister, your voodoo wife, or your mistress? My title comes by reason of my being *sister* to the king, not as wife of the Prince Royal, so there would be complications. Furthermore, I do not speak English, which would make it awkward. But most important of all, Henry did not bid me go, and we must not forget that Henry is King and we must do his bidding."

"I'm no lackey to run at Henry's beck and call. However, I told him I would go if, and only if, you granted your permission. Just say the word and I'll defy Henry and stay here."

"But of course you must go, my love. The honor Henry has paid us brings obligations with it. Sir What's-His-Name will be pleased to receive his invitation from the hands of the Prince Royal himself. And, darling, you are such a little boy at times. You know I'll be waiting here for you when you return." She closed her eyes. "Oh, God, let me be waiting for him," she prayed.

"But think of all the nights I shall be away."

"I do, but it will not be as long as when you were with Leclerc, and I shall not worry about you. Then you were in danger. Now you go on a mission of peace, loaded with honors. Eat your breakfast, and I shall help you pack. Will you take your court dress or your uniform as a colonel of the Dahomeys?" She was finding it difficult to speak with complete assurance. "As though a miracle were to happen," she thought, "but if the miracle doesn't happen, I shall not be here to see him when he comes back, running up the stairs, searching for me." But she contrived a happy smile and rose from the table, took his arm, and walked out of the room with him. When she passed Pompee in the doorway, she lowered her eyelids, conveying to him that she understood. By helping Armes to pack his trunks, seeing that he had all the necessities for so long a voyage, and gathering together toilet articles, kerchiefs, and smallclothes, she succeeded in concealing her feelings. When he was ready to leave she walked with him out onto the balcony.

He kissed her good-bye, embraced her as usual, and started down the steps, but she followed him and, at the foot of the steps, she put her arms around him closely and hungrily, drew his head down to hers, and opened her lips as his touched them. She was loath to release him. Her hand clung to him even as they parted, and, when he was astride his horse, she stood beside him, her hands clasped around the calf of his leg just above his riding boot.

"You seem pale, darling, are you well?" He started to swing his leg over the pommel. "Look, if you don't want me to go, I'll stay, and to hell with Henry and all this Prince business."

"I'm just being sentimental. How would you feel if I didn't make any fuss at all about your going so far and for so long? Just don't start ogling those pretty English girls or I shall have TiTonTon report to me."

"TiTonTon can't go with me. Henry says he needs him. Valentin is going with me—he's almost white, and with his red hair, Henry thinks he'd make a better impression than TiTonTon."

She released him. "Give my love to Henry and Marie Louise. Tell them that the Princess Royal sends greetings to her brother the King and to her sister the Queen and . . ." She started to laugh. "Oh, Armes! What are we all doing? Are we acting in an *opéra bouffe*? I just can't make it seem true that we have suddenly become royalty. Really, it's too ridiculous."

"Not if you were to see the Cap and all the preparations for Henry's coronation, including the new cathedral which will never be finished in time. No, your Royal Highness, it's all very real, and when I stand beside Henry and hear the cries of 'Vive le roi,' I really do believe, and I must confess I am proud to be a royal personage. Me, Armes Holbrook, a prince!"

"Then all the more reason why you must go." She carried his hand to her lips as he started, then watched him as far as the gates. She saw them open and close after him and then she ran up the steps, her eyes blinded by tears. Pompee met her inside the door, put his arm around her, and comforted her.

"Henry did this for you. Now be brave, madame. Bear this parting from Milord, because it may be the means of a joyous reunion."

She lifted her face in assent as he helped her to her room.

466

Pompee had made all preparations for their own journey without her knowing it. TiTonTon appeared from his little office below stairs where he had been in hiding from Armes, and Maman lumbered in from the kitchen to envelop Athenée in her ponderous embrace. Soon they were ready to go, but their little party was no royal entourage. They were dressed soberly, like petty bourgeoisie. Gone were the white tricot trousers and the gold-laced coats that TiTonTon and Pompee had been wearing at court; now they were dressed simply in dark cotton suits. Athenée had chosen a simple dress of dove-gray linen and a large straw hat with a gray veil. Maman, monumental in blue denim, sat side-saddle on a giant Percheron Norman horse, looking for all the world like a bronze statue of an Amazon. As Pompee helped Athenée mount Lalla, he spoke softly, telling her it was not too late if she wished to change her mind and with-draw. He assured her he could call the whole thing off, but she shook her head and promised him that whatever lay ahead of her, she would go through with it, willingly and gladly. Even as she spoke the words, however, she longed for the comfort and security of her own room which was still so near. Oh, to slip off the horse, dash up the steps to safety! Safety? She could never be safe now. Better to go on. Whatever lay ahead could not be worse than what she had desired and planned for herself. The gate of Papa Legba was not as fearsome as the gate of Guede Nimbo, even though Pompee did not know which of the two would open for her.

It was a long and difficult journey from Milot to Mire-balais, and the route lay through the mountains. It was late afternoon when they reached the little town of Pignon high in the mountains, and dusk when they arrived at Hinche, where they remained overnight in the *caille* of a *mamaloi* who departed with them the next morning. One reason for the length of their trip was that they had been stopping at many *cailles* along the way, and at each house a man or woman was waiting for them, seated on a mule or a donkey, ready to accompany them. Pompee introduced her to all of them, and she discovered that all were local priests or priest-esses.

By the time they had come down out of the mountains through Lascahobas and into the city of Mirebalais, their retinue stretched a mile or so down the road. At Mirebalais, they were welcomed at a fine old home, where Athenée was received with all the honor due her rank. Her hostess, a tall mulatto woman of great charm who spoke fluent French instead of the slurred Creole, showed her to a large, well-furnished room, and while Athenée rested on the bed, Maman fussed over her, washing her face, cooling her arms with eau de cologne, and feeding her spoonfuls of rich chicken soup. The lady of the house, who introduced herself as Madame Brantome, came in to talk with her, and maids and footmen stole looks at her through the door. Athenée felt that they all knew why she was there and she felt a special love emanating from all of them.

"Now, you go to sleep, pretty one. Maman will wake you when it's time to go. Maman isn't going with you. That Pompee said Maman can't go. Who does he think he is, huh?"

"He's a count now, Maman. Better mind what he says."

"Count, is he? I can slap down a count just as easily as I can any man. I will, too, if he doesn't let me go with you. How do I know what he and that TiTonTon and all the rest of those crazy niggers are going to do to you?"

"No, Maman, you stay here and have things all ready for me when I come back." She looked up at the kindly face grinning down at her. "If I come back, Maman."

"Of course you're coming back. And you're going to be prettier than any niece I ever had. And I got some pretty ones, too." Maman bit her tongue. She had almost added, "If you don't believe me, ask M'sieu TiArmes."

56

AN hour's rest was all that Pompee permitted Athenée before they started out again. Now there were still more people riding behind them—*papalois* and *mamalois* from Pétion's crumbling republic who had heard the message of the drums and responded to Pompee's appeal for help. The long procession advanced slowly and in silence, following the trail that led to the waterfall of Saut d'Eau, some ten miles distant from Mirebalais. Athenée had heard of this spot—a sacred grove of tall maupou trees which bordered the plunging cataract. It was the holy ground of Haiti—the Olympus of the voodoo gods; the Mecca of penitent Dahomean pilgrims; the St. Peter's of the African pantheon.

The short tropical twilight was over when they neared the spot, but even in the darkness, Athenée could tell by the sound of falling waters that this was indeed the place. From a distance she could see thousands of tiny lights on the branches of the great trees; it appeared as though the rising shower of sparks from the blazing fire on the shore had attached themselves permanently to the leaves. In addition to the fire and the twinkling lamps in the trees, hundreds of flambeaux had been stuck in the ground in a wide semicircle. When they arrived and her eyes became accustomed to the light, she could see row on row of shining black faces, partly in shadow and partly gilded by the yellow light of the flaming torches. An unearthly stillness prevailed; no greetings were exchanged; no welcomes uttered. Those who accompanied them dismounted and took their places with the earlier arrivals, and after the bustling of their settling down there was no sound but the snap of branches in the fire, the crackle of flames of the torches, and the splash of falling water.

Pompee took her arm, and although he did not enjoin silence, Athenée did not speak but followed his directions dumbly. His leave-taking was brief as he handed her over to TiTonTon.

"I go now, madame," he whispered. "I cannot tell you now what may happen tonight. I can only say this, that everyone here tonight has come at my special bidding, and they are here for one reason—to help you. Never before has there been such a gathering of those learned in the arts of voodoo. Never before! No matter what happens, try not to be afraid. You may think there is much to fear, but really there is not. Remember what I said—act as though a miracle were to happen—and have faith in me and the love I have for you and Milord. TiTonTon will take care of you and as he cannot speak here is Vandale, another of my *hunsis,* to speak for him." He disappeared into the shadows.

She allowed herself to be led by the gentle pressure of TiTonTon's and Vandale's hands on her arm, stumbling over tree roots and through the branches until she came to the center of the assemblage where the fire was and from which the vast semicircle of faces radiated. A chair was awaiting her—merely a rough peasant chair, but a length of red satin had been draped over it to distinguish it. TiTonTon pointed to it and she collapsed into it. He sat on the ground on one side of her with Vandale on the other, and she reached out and placed her hand on TiTonTon's head. The old gesture which had formerly comforted him at Mon Repos now gave her assurance, and the coarse, rough texture of his hair seemed a homely reality in the midst of so much strangeness. Noticing her gesture, Vandale reached for her other hand and placed it on his own head.

Far out on the perimeter of the circle a drum began with a hollow boom which seemed to make the fire leap higher. Another followed it, then still another, until the outer edge of the assembly was vibrating with the throbs of the big *arada* drums, which were hidden from Athenée because they were far too sacred for a white woman to behold. Although she could not see the drums themselves, she could catch fire-lit glimpses of the leaping men and the flailing arms which surrounded them. With the *arada* drums setting the tempo, the tall *maman* drums joined in, followed by the *papa* drums and then the *bébés*. The night suddenly came alive with their cacophony, which increased in volume until it so dominated the night, filling all space, occupying all time, extending from heaven to earth, that Athenée felt she could cut it in pieces with a knife.

Soon, above the booming of the drums, she heard the high-pitched chant of men and women, and as she looked past the orange blaze of the fire, she could discern the slow weaving back and forth of seated bodies, moving in a changing pattern of light as they followed the rhythm of the drums. Occasionally one voice would rise an octave higher than the rest; a body would disentangle itself from the sooty, swaying mass and stand up. A weird spouting of unknown words would struggle through the pounding of the drums, only to lose itself in their reverberations. The shrieking falsetto would stop and the singer would drop to his seat, but almost immediately another would rise, howl some wordless chant of supplication, and then sink to earth again. As the continuous barrage of drums and voices continued, it seemed that she could almost understand the message of the drums and the wailing. It spoke a message of utter despondency, absolutely without hope. The monstrous music embodied all the sorrow of the world from its very conception to the present, and stretched out to include millenniums to come. She felt strangely akin to the music. It explained exactly how she had felt —hopeless, exhausted, beaten. It desired only death. The screams of the singers were caused by the torture of some unbearable pain; agonized wails of anguish carried into infinity on an interminable high note until the struggling soul could bear it no longer and dissolved into primeval night.

As if lifted by some invisible hand which had reached down from the high maupou trees, the congregation arose to join together in one final lament which ceased abruptly, leaving Athenée expectant for the next note which never came. The drums stopped. The multitude was motionless. It became so quiet she could hear TiTonTon's labored breathing beside her, so quiet she could hear the beating of her own heart. His hand sought hers in silent encouragement, and she welcomed the moist warmth of his palm.

"The *loa* of every god has been asked to come to earth," Vandale whispered. "Some of them I have never heard of, for they are gods of the Ashantis, the Ibo, the Mandingoes, and many others which only a few people know about." A sharp metallic note splintered the silence. "The gods come." TiTonTon clutched her hand more tightly. "Now we welcome them," Vandale added.

A young boy entered the circle of light, holding two pieces of iron—the voodoo *ogans*—in his hand which he struck together. Following him an old crone, her wrinkled skin hanging from her bones, capered into the light, her ancient body bent nearly double from the weight of the strange, crude white beads which rattled about her as she hopped along.

Athenée became aware that the drums had started again, low, distant, and scarcely perceptible. As the old woman stumbled to the center, two stalwart young Negroes, naked except for strings of the same chattering beads the old woman wore, materialized from out of the shadows. Each of them carried an *asson*—a sacred gourd, netted with the vertebrae of snakes. With the *assons* they set the tempo for the drunken gyrations of the old woman. The thin sharp notes of a bamboo *vaccine* rose flutelike above the dry rustle of the *assons* and the beating of the *ogans*. The music increased in intensity, timed by the *asson* shakers, who were dancing to their own metronomic beat, while the old hag pranced crazily alone in circles, lifting her arms so that the white beads cascaded down over her withered dugs. When they danced nearer to Athenée, she could see that the white beads were also snake vertebrae. Directly in front of her all three dancers halted, breaking the music, and looked down at her. Their eyes were hauntingly sad. They seemed to be bidding her a final adieu.

"The gods are here," Vandale whispered. "Now they must be entertained."

Gradually the drums faded in volume to a metrical booming which paced the steps of several tall young Negresses with varicolored silks wrapped around their loins, who marched slowly into the circle of yellow light, carrying crude earthen jars in their hands. They too stopped before Athenée, gazed at her round-eyed for a moment with pitying horror, then deposited the jars some little distance from her, stripping the silk from their bodies to cover them. Timing their movements to the drums, their long bodies stretched out straight behind the veiled jars like the ebony sticks of a fan.

Now a sudden thunderous roll of the drums brought a leaping figure into the half-circle of earthen pots. Athenée shuddered at the weird apparition, but TiTonTon's hands closed tightly over hers, and as she stared down at the boy, his lips formed the name "Pompee." The weird, gyrating figure had little resemblance to the gentle Pompee she had known. His face was entirely covered by a hideous mask, several feet tall, conical in shape, with carven distorted features and huge unseeing eyes of staring white shell. Curving white cock feathers decorated its entire length, and its base was fringed with dried grass. Pompee's upper body was painted in arabesques of white; a sulfurous yellow sash cinched his waist; and his legs were encased in trousers of white velvet which glittered as the firelight caught the reflections of gold coins sewed on the cloth.

Even Pompee's familiar voice was altered as he raised it in a howl which soared above the drums and the chattering *assons*. It seemed impossible that any person could maintain a sound for so long. When it did die out on a high note, Pompee strode over and stood in front of her, then turned his back on her and faced the fire. He was so near to her that the bulging calves of his legs touched her knees, and she could see the sweat, running in rivulets down his back, streaking the arabesques of white paint. His reassuring hand stole behind him and she clutched at it, but he snatched his hand away immediately. It had served its purpose; she knew that under that fantastic garb, the loving Pompee was protecting her.

At his barked command, accompanied by arm gestures, a strange procession started. One by one the bodies of the semicircle stood up and made their way to kneel before Pompee.

472

"Each one is being ridden by his own *loa*," TiTonTon whispered.

The line seemed interminable, and although Pompee blocked her view, Athenée could see them come, kneel, and depart, as well as hear the words they uttered while they knelt before him—words which she could not understand, however. Some of the women spoke like men and some of the men lisped like women. How long it took them all to come forward, kneel, and return to their seats, she could not judge, but it seemed interminable, and all the while the tireless drummers filled the night with pulsating rhythm. Each *papaloi* and *mamaloi* had his or her moment to stand before them all and add the strength of his personal *loa* to the *mystère* that was being prepared. Nobody in the assemblage was slighted: each had a distinctly personal responsibility, a definite role to play. When the last old man had departed, Pompee walked over to the young women on the ground and touched each of them. Athenée leaned forward in her chair to get a clearer view and, while she stared, she saw Pompee turn their bodies over with his foot, place his weight on them, and trample them. Their faces remained impassive, entranced. Apparently he was testing them, for she could now understand that they were in some sort of a hypnotic trance.

Again Pompee started to sing. He whirled toward one of the nude youths and grabbed the *asson* from his hand. After brandishing the gourd wildly, he held it high in the air and stopped its chattering. It was a signal for the drums to cease while a white goat, beribboned and befeathered, with gilded horns supporting lighted candles, was led in and held tightly by a young girl, who seated herself by the largest of the pottery jars, her black hands firmly clutching the white fur of the animal.

"Damballah Weydo," Pompee cried out, and lifted the *asson*, starting the drums again. But he silenced them as another girl led a second goat to stand before another jar. "Ayda Weydo," Pompee screamed.

One by one the goats were led in. There was a third white one—this for Erzuli; a bluish gray one for Agwe Weydo, the god of the sea; a jet-black one for Guede Nimbo, opener of the gate of death; a piebald one for Papa Legba, the gate-opener of heaven; two kids for Loco Attiso and his wife Aizam, protectors against black magic; a sleek dun-colored animal for Papa Zaca of the fields; and finally a huge red

473

goat for Ogoun Feraille of war. The animals were restless, as though they already scented death. Their eyes were wide and wondering, and they kept up a continuous tattoo with their polished hooves while their several attendants tried to hold them in their places.

A very old man, stooping under the weight of several iron pots, entered into the circle of light and deposited one of the pots before each of the goats. He drew a long machete of polished steel from his belt and presented it to Pompee in an elaborate ritual. Once again the drums increased in volume, and the throats of hundreds spewed out a savage chant. From having been a song of *tristesse*, it had now become commanding, instructing the gods in no uncertain terms exactly what was expected of them. Pompee started to dance, waving the machete in wide, fire-splintering circles, and without interrupting the rhythm of his dance his flashing knife found the throats of the sacrificial goats, and as each one died, the attendant maiden reached for the iron pot and caught its jugular blood. With the iron pots spilling the crimson liquid, they held them out at arm's length, dancing with measured steps, sprinkling the drops on the waiting congregation.

All but one! She who had caught the blood of the first white goat—the one dedicated to Damballah Weydo—advanced before Athenée, accompanied by Pompee. Together they stood directly before her, and Pompee removed the tall mask, handing it to TiTonTon, who placed it on the ground. Pompee's fingers dipped in the bowl and flicked the blood on Athenée's face. She shrank from the warm, thick liquid as it streamed down her cheeks, and would have risen from the chair, but TiTonTon's hand gently but firmly encircled her ankles. A gasp of horror came through her clenched teeth as she felt two arms come from in back of her chair to encircle her. They passed under her armpits, and the black hands attached to the muscular arms were clasped tightly in front of her. She was powerless to move. Now the two young men of the *assons* crawled out on their stomachs from behind her chair, and she could see their bodies shining in the firelight as they relieved TiToTon of the firm grip on her ankles. Once more TiTonTon's hand sought hers and pressed it gently. His friendly eyes and his frightened smile did their best to alleviate her terror, but she knew that she was a prisoner. The arms of the man behind her and the tight grip on her ankles proved that she could not stand up nor run away.

"Do not fear, madame," Vandale tried to comfort her, "the gods have eaten and now they must love. Pompee asks a great favor of them, so he must do everything possible to make them happy."

While he was speaking the drums changed to an orgiastic tempo which seemed like the heartbeat of the earth itself. The faces which had been quiescent were now swaying again in some seated ritualistic movement. The outstretched girls behind the *govis* each came to life and stood up to dance nude in front of the fire, before they were joined by an equal number of youths, also naked, each of whom found a partner. The dance was obscenely priapic, but even in its utter abandon, it partook of a ceremonious worship. Athenée wanted to close her eyes; it was too sexually primitive for her to watch, but fear forced her to keep her eyes open so that she might know what was about to happen. She stared at the rampant mating until its culmination, when couple by couple the performers dropped to the ground to lie in tired, satiated embraces, quiet now except for the nervous twitch of arms and legs and the heaving of chests.

Pompee moved nearer to stand before her again, this time facing her. Two attendants came and removed the strings of beads from around his neck and the heavy gold bracelets from his arms. She felt relieved to see his familiar face looking at her. It gave her confidence, and she was not quite so aware of the restraining hands. He leaned slightly toward her and whispered to her—the first words he had spoken during the ceremony.

"Do not fear, madame, the gods are good tonight. They are pleased with our sacrifices. They have drunk the blood, they have lain with women, and now they are in the mood to grant our request. Drink this!" He reached for a small glass bottle that TiTonTon held out to him. Athenée could see that it was filled with some dark liquid, and as he removed the stopper and applied it to her lips, he spoke again. "This will help you endure what lies ahead. Drink it!"

It was sweet and syrupy but bitter, and after she had swallowed it, a burning taste remained in her mouth. Almost immediately it had an effect on her. She could feel her tenseness departing, and a strange relaxation possessed her. She seemed to float outside her own body and view it objectively. To her surprise she discovered that she cared nothing about

475

it, for it seemed no part of her. She even pitied it—that poor envelope of flesh which had enclosed her spirit for so long.

The arms around her loosened their grip and the pressure on her ankles relaxed, but she could still see the veined black hands clasped around her waist and the flickering firelight on the faces of the boys at her feet. Her hand stole out of TiTonTon's and rested on his head. She felt at peace.

An attendant brought a long length of green silk to Pompee, which he handled carefully, as if it were something holy. One end he tucked into his waistband, then whirled himself around until the green silk covered him in a glittering sheath. Athenée was able to follow his actions with her eyes, even to seeing him take some object from the attendant which he placed inside the silk, but even while she watched him, whatever he did mattered very little to her. She was aware that the tempo of the drums was rising, and that while the piercing shrieks of the congregation shattered the night, Pompee was approaching her with a sinuous writhing of his body under the green silk. Once more she felt the arms around her tighten; again the youths fastened her ankles with a grip of steel.

Pompee had something in his hand—something cold, green, and ophidian; something that writhed and circled over his fingers; something that hissed. Even in her drugged state, its writhings terrified her, and she struggled to free herself. She saw TiTonTon cover his face with his hands as Pompee glided nearer. Terror was driving away the effects of the drug, and had it not been for the restraining hands, she would have leaped up and fled into the darkness. Pompee's black hands came nearer, and even in the dim light she could see the tiny eyes of the reptile and hear its soft hissing. She screamed—one piercing cry of horror—as the reptile, released from Pompee's hands, darted toward her and fastened its fangs in her cheek. In her delirium of fright and revulsion, she saw Pompee lunge for it, squeeze it in his mighty hands, and fling it backward into the fire. Then his voice came to her, clear and triumphant above the riotous clamor.

"Damballah has kissed her! Damballah Weydo! Damballah has come to earth. He has kissed this woman with the kiss of death which removes all impurities and blemishes from the body and brings life. Come quick. Quick, I say!"

There was a sound of running feet. Women came scurrying to her—women with steaming kettles, women with cloths, women with bottles and glasses. She felt something hot and moist on her face; she felt wet compresses wound around her head, leaving just a space for her to breathe and see. Someone pushed a glass to her lips, and she gagged on the fire of raw brandy. Followed then more applications of hot moist poultices; a strange aromatic odor which stifled her; and after that hands lifted her tenderly and placed her on a crude stretcher. That was all she remembered—the stretcher with herself on it being hoisted on the shoulders of men and the sound of hundreds of triumphant chanting voices that followed her through the throbbing night.

57

IT was daylight when the effects of the drug wore off and Athenée regained her senses. She opened her eyes to see the vague outlines of a room which she recognized as the one she had been in the day she arrived at Mirebalais. A black mountain on the side of her bed resolved itself into the form of Maman, and the dark shadow on the other side turned out to be Pompee. Madame Brantome was seated in a chair, and she leaned forward as Athenée opened her eyes. She could not open them wide because of the bandages over them, but she could sense the nervous tension of all who were there, and see the relief in Pompee's eyes as she stared at him through half-closed lids.

He leaned over her. "Just one question. Are you all right, madame? Just nod your head if you are, and then try to get more sleep. I shall not leave you."

"And I'm not going to either." Maman's big hand was clasping Athenée's. "I'm not going to leave my baby. Going to sit right here in case she needs something."

Through the thick folds of the bandages, Athenée mumbled her thanks and nodded her well-being to Pompee. She was possessed by a delicious unconcern and discovered in this unaccustomed lethargy that the only thing she desired was to return to the blessed oblivion of sleep.

Although she did not know it, the sun had risen four times and set as many more while she occupied the big mahogany bed. At times she had regained a semi-consciousness when she felt her head lifted and drank from the goblet that was put to her lips. Sometimes it would be filled with cool goat's milk flavored with anisette, and at other times she would taste the same sweet medicine which she had taken on the night of the *mystères*. But it mattered little, for she was beyond caring, even when she opened her eyes to see Maman and Pompee apply warm poultices to her face. It was enough to lie back on the pillow and let them minister to her.

On the fifth day, however, she did not take the medicine, and her wakings were more frequent. Her thoughts, although still confused, began to sort themselves out into some orderly sequence. During the day, as the shadows crept across the floor she felt her senses returning to her, and throughout the night, she began to think normally again. It was as though she had been a great distance away and was plodding slowly back into an orbit of understanding. She raised one hand with effort and felt the bandage on her face. Little by little the events of that fateful night appeared in her memory, and she shuddered at the remembrance of them. But she felt secure. Then she awoke fully. Maman was on one side of her and Pompee on the other, and this one was the same beloved Pompee she had always known. His familiar face was not concealed under a savage mask, and the outlandish clothes were replaced by his sober gray suit.

"Tell me, Pompee, tell me!" Her words came thickly through the folds of linen. "Tell me what has happened. I'm still alive."

"Thanks be to your God and mine," he whispered.

"Then . . ."

"Rest, madame. As soon as you feel strong enough to sit up, we shall . . ."

Suddenly she felt wide awake, even strong, and struggled to sit up with Maman's arm supporting her. TiTonTon had been sitting on the floor by the bed, but she had not noticed him until he rose and supported her by placing pillows behind her back. She acknowledged him with a weak smile.

"I'm quite all right, Pompee. Really. So tell me all that has happened. But first tell me how long I have been here."

"Five days, madame."

"And Armes, has he returned to Haiti?"

"Not yet. Henry has sent daily couriers to inquire about you."

She sighed with relief and patted Maman's hand.

"I remember a little. Dear Maman, you've been so kind."

"I've never left you."

478

"Now tell me, Pompee! Why is this bandage on my face?"

"In a moment." He smiled indulgently. "Wait until Ti-TonTon fetches Madame Brantome." His eyes on TiTonTon, he nodded his head in the direction of the door, and Ti-TonTon ran out.

"Oh, Pompee," she sighed, "it was a terrible experience."

"Terrible, madame? Really, it was not. It was a wonderful experience. It took the power of three hundred and eighty *papalois* and *mamalois* to bring Damballah and all the other gods to you at Saut d'Eau that night."

"It may not have been terrible for you, Pompee, but it was for me."

"Wait, madame! Perhaps you will change your mind." He caught the sound of footsteps in the hall. "Wait, TiTonTon brings Madame Brantome now."

Athenée turned her head as the door opened, and the tall mulatto woman entered. She was carrying a square object wrapped in a cloth, which she deposited carefully on the bed.

"Is she strong enough now?" she asked Pompee, with a searching look at Athenée. "It will be a shock to her."

Pompee nodded. "She seems to be entirely recovered."

"Then?"

"Undo the bandages," Pompee commanded.

Maman, her big hands strangely gentle and her touch soft, reached over and started to unwind the bandages. Under them appeared a dark green gelatinous mass with the same aromatic fragrance which Athenée realized now had possessed her nostrils for days. When Maman had finished unwinding the cloths, she went to a washstand in the corner, wrung a towel out, and came back to the bed. Her eyes questioned Pompee.

He nodded his head slowly, and she started to sponge Athenée's face lightly until all the green paste was removed. Pompee leaned over to watch the operation closely. She saw him clutch at TiTonTon's hand and pull him nearer. TiTonTon laughed gutturally; Pompee smiled with satisfaction; Maman giggled through the tears that ran down her cheeks; and Madame Brantome dabbed at her eyes with a handkerchief.

"What is it?" Athenée looked from one to the other.

"Only this, madame." Pompee reached for the square package that Madame Brantome had placed on the bed and whipped the cloth from it. It was a mirror. Slowly his trembling fingers brought it before Athenée. She hesitated, fearful, and then turned her eyes toward the reflection—one long anguished look which caused her to grab the mirror from Pompee's hands. Shaking her head in utter disbelief, she stared at the image in the glass, then let the mirror fall onto the pillows beside her.

"It can't be true, it can't be true. That which I just saw in the glass cannot be me. Oh, Pompee, are you playing tricks on me? Tell me the truth."

Madame Brantome stroked Athenée's hair gently.

"Madame weeps," she said gently, "but perhaps Madame is not accustomed to seeing such beauty. Indeed Madame la Princesse Royale is the most beautiful woman in the world."

"She sure is." Maman wagged her head so vehemently that her headcloth came loose. "She's prettier than any niece I ever had—prettier than that goddam French bitch Pauline."

Athenée held back her sobs. "Is it true, madame? Am I dreaming? Shall I wake up to find that this is all some fanciful dream—some weird experience—some death that I have died and some afterlife I have passed into?"

"No, your Royal Highness, it is no dream. I am very real and this room is real and so is the Comte de Milot and the Baron de Destinée. And you must forgive me for addressing you as 'madame.' In my excitement I forgot that you were the sister of the King."

Athenée picked up the mirror again and looked at her face once more. It was impossible to believe, but where the ugly purple blotch had once crawled across her face there was nothing now but smooth whiteness, except for two tiny red pinpoints. True, it was almost too white—like unveined marble—but she knew that this bloodlessness was the result of the wet poultices, like the whiteness of hands that had been too long in water. That would disappear. Her fingers came to her cheek and lingered there, feeling only a warm smoothness. Almost unwillingly she relinquished the mirror and smiled up at Pompee.

"As if a miracle would happen . . ." she said. "Oh, Pompee, you have done all this for me."

"Not I, madame, but my gods."

"But without you, Pompee, your gods would not have been interested in my poor face."

"But they were, madame. The miracle did happen."

"Yes, it did, and how can I ever thank you?"

"You already have, madame. You did so a long time ago

when you came to the poor hovel where TiTonTon lay on the floor suffering from the cruel torture your husband had inflicted on him. You had him moved to the kitchen of the big house and you nursed him. Then again, you thanked me when you stood before the Vicomte and all those cruel men and begged for the life of another tortured slave who happened to be me. Do you think that TiTonTon and I could ever repay you and Milord? We shall always be in your debt."

Athenée took his hand and placed it alongside her cheek, as she sank back onto the pillows and closed her eyes.

Madame Brantome walked around the room, quietly closing the jalousies.

"She will sleep now, your Excellency," she said to Pompee, "and by morning she can start on her trip home." She smoothed Athenée's pillows, gave her a little pat on the shoulder, and left the room. Pompee put his arm around TiTonTon's shoulder and guided him toward the door. Before he reached the threshold, TiTonTon turned, slipped out from under Pompee's arm, and ran back to the bed. He whipped out his pad of paper and pencil.

"The Princess Royal is the most beautiful woman in the world," he scribbled hastily, and tucked the paper in her hand, then skipped back across the room to Pompee. They watched her from the door as she read it; saw her happy smile and the tired wave of her hand. She closed her eyes as they closed the door. Almost immediately she opened them again and looked at Maman sitting beside the bed.

"Another look, Maman." She pointed to the mirror. "I still can't believe it is true."

"You'd just better believe it, you pretty little thing. Um-um," Maman started to giggle, "do you suppose if I got myself snakebit I would turn white all over like you?" Her giggling stopped and she sighed. "I would need a whole parcel of snakes to get me white, and then, maybe that Simon wouldn't like a white woman. Better off black, I guess." She removed two of the pillows from under Athenée's head. "You just drift off. Maman's here to watch you."

Athenée handed her the mirror. It was true! She believed it now. She drifted off contentedly.

58

WHEN Athenée awoke again, the lengthening shadows of the slatted jalousies informed her that it must be late afternoon. It took her a few moments to orient herself—the room with its stark white plastered walls and the huge mahogany bed seemed strange and unfamiliar, but then it all came back to her and she hugged herself in joy. Maman was not there, and Athenée welcomed these few moments alone with her now lucid thoughts. She slipped out of bed, felt the coolness of the polished floor on the soles of her bare feet, and ran across the room to the mirror which was propped up on a chair beside the armoire. She felt no weakness; only strength and expectant joy.

One look convinced her that it was not a dream. No, it was true. The mirror did not lie. Her face was as smooth and unblemished on one side as it was on the other. Even the two small pinpricks of blood had almost entirely disappeared. Once more she put her hand to her face in disbelief, as though the mirror might be telling a falsehood, but her fingers reassured her. She crossed the room to where a crucifix with an ivory Christ stood on a chest and knelt on the *prie-dieu,* but the prayer of thanksgiving would not come, and she could only repeat over and over again the one word, *merci.* Then she bethought herself of those other gods—the gods of Pompee—and she became confused in her desire to pray. Whom should she pray to? What could she say? Finally her prayers resolved themselves into one, and she found her lips repeating the familiar "Our Father." For there *was* a supreme Father, even though her confused thoughts could not name Him. Never before had the simple prayer meant so much to her. This time each word stood out like a separate jewel, filled with beauty and meaning. When she had finished she felt renewed and refreshed. She needed no more rest; now she desired action. Her clothes were nowhere in sight and she had nothing but the flimsy nightgown evidently supplied by Madame Brantome. An embroidered bell cord, with faded roses in petit point, hung beside the bed, and she pulled it vigorously. The sluff-sluff of bare feet sounded in the hall; there was a rap on the door and Maman, her round face aglow with a smile which split it like a watermelon, entered.

"Your Highness! My, my, but you sure are a pretty sight. I would bow to you if I could but I'm too big-assed."

"Maman, ask Madame Brantome or the Comte de Milot or the Baron de Destinée to come here, will you?"

"Right this minute, Highness." Maman essayed a jiggle of her enormous breasts, which passed for a curtsy. "I'll call that Pompee Count. He's downstairs."

"And in the meantime, get me a robe or something to put on," Athenée called as Maman backed to the door.

It was far too much, Athenée thought, suddenly to become the second lady of Haiti—a member of the Royal Family, a princess—and then, on top of that, to have this miracle happen. She must get accustomed to being a Highness. Just how did a Highness act? She tried to remember her former experience at the small grand ducal court where she had met René. If a servant curtsied to the Grand Duchess did the Duchess acknowledge it? She seemed to remember that that exalted personage did, but only by a slight inclination of the head. But how about Madame Brantome, who was not a servant? In that case perhaps a little deeper inclination of the head would be in order. And another thing! Did she speak in the first person plural? Was she a *we* or an *I*? No, *we* was only for kings and queens —she was quite certain of that. Now, how should she address Armes in public? Must she always say *sire* to Henry? Must she curtsy to Marie Louise and address her as "your Majesty"? Yes, undoubtedly she must in public, but they would still be Henry and Marie Louise to her, and if Armes were king himself, he could be nothing more than he was.

Maman returned, like a frigate under full sail, with a wrap for Athenée, then again maneuvered herself backward out of the room. "I'll go call that Pompee Count now." She hesitated at the door and grinned. "My goodness, just think, poor old Maman just held the robe for the Princess. Goddamn! That no-good Simon is going to call me Princess now or I'll break his goddamn head."

A plan was beginning to form in Athenée's mind, and it was a plan which required quick action. She ran across to the door and called to Maman, who was halfway down the stairs. "Call the Baron de Destinée also." Maman bobbed her head in acknowledgment and disappeared.

Athenée's tempestuous pacing of the room had stopped by

483

the time Pompee and TiTonTon appeared, and she was sitting restlessly in one of the high-backed chairs. This time Pompee bowed before her.

"Your Royal . . ."

"Pompee," she exclaimed indignantly, "I know you've been coaching poor Maman, but must you go through that rigmarole, too?" She motioned him to come nearer. "Pouf, we've spent too many hours together, you and I and TiTonTon, to bother with such trifles. I'm no different now than I was before Henry wrote a few words on a piece of parchment. As far as you and TiTonTon and I are concerned when we are together, we'll forget all these titles, as I am sure you and TiTonTon do when you are alone. When others are around we shall remember it, but I shall never be able to think of you, Pompee, as the Comte de Milot, and as for you, TiTonTon, I love you too much as TiTonTon to start loving you all over again as the Baron de Destinée. But come, we have a lot to do."

They both remained standing until she waved toward chairs. Pompee looked at her carefully. "Do you feel all right now, madame?"

She flung her arms wide. "I've never felt better in my life. All thanks to you. Oh, Pompee! What can I say or do to tell you how grateful I am? How can I ever repay you?"

"The debt is already paid, madame. Now, what can I do for you? You sent for me."

"So I did. We have a lot to do. First I must have my clothes."

"Madame Brantome has them all ready for you. There were some spots of blood on the dress, you know, but she had it washed and ironed."

Athenée shuddered inwardly. Once more she felt the hot sticky liquid on her face. "I'll dress at once, but before I do I must ask you some questions."

Pompee nodded.

"Do you know when Armes will return?"

"He arrives tomorrow on the British cruiser *Bridgetown*, with Sir Home and Lady Popham. Henry's courier came this morning with the news."

"Then it will be tomorrow night that Henry gives the state dinner for the English ambassador?"

"*Oui*, madame."

"How long will it take us to get from here to the Cap?"

"A long day's hard riding, madame."

She thought for a moment. "I do not feel like making the journey on horseback. Would there be a carriage of some sorts for a conveyance?"

"I am sure there would be, especially for the Princess Royal."

"Find one and let us start as soon as possible. We should arrive in the Cap sometime tomorrow."

"But we cannot take Maman in a carriage."

"We can send for her later. She will not mind, and I want to get to the Cap quickly."

"The Cap?" Pompee was surprised. "You are not going to Sans Souci?"

"No, to the Cap. Armes will be at the Cap and that is where I am going, but Armes must know nothing about this, understand?"

Again Pompee nodded and smiled, for he had an inkling of what Athenée had in mind.

"And you, TiTonTon," she said. "I want you to ride to Sans Souci. You must arrive there by morning. Can you do it?"

His wide grin told her that he most certainly could.

"Then write this down! Oh dear! Can any of the maids at home read?"

TiTonTon traced letters in the air.

Athenée read them. "Oh yes, Yolande. Well, give this paper to Yolande. Now write! I want the new dress of white and silver tissue. Yes, tissue—t-i-s-s-u-e. She'll understand. Then the long scarf of rosepoint." She waited for him to write the words. "Tell Yolande to pack everything that I shall need—toilet articles, underthings, silk stockings, and my silver slippers." She made a mental inventory of her jewels. "And with the silver—yes, with the silver tissue it must be diamonds. The larger tiara for my hair—the one with the diamond egret—the necklace, and the diamond fringe. Oh yes, two bracelets. But that will mean I shall be all in silver and white and diamonds, and it will look too cold. Tell Yolande to take the long ruby velvet train from the shoulders of the other white gown and fasten it to the silver one. Have you got that?"

He looked up at her and nodded.

"Then let me see what you have written. Oh, TiTonTon, you have spelled 'egret' wrong. No, I'll change it. Now, off with you! Collect these things at Sans Souci, and bring them all to the Palais Royale at the Cap. Take them directly to Marie Louise's apartments, and tell nobody but Marie Louise about it. If you should see Armes, hide, run away, disappear into thin air. Don't let him see you, and if by chance he comes to Sans Souci, have the servants tell him I am at the Cap but cannot see him because I am in the hands of my hair-dresser."

TiTonTon came over to her chair and knelt in the old position, which had become symbolic of their relationship. He leaned his head against her knee and waited for her hand to find his hair.

"Now run along." She pushed him tenderly with both hands. "And I shall see you when I arrive in the Cap. Wait in the Queen's anteroom for me. And, TiTonTon, dress yourself in your court regalia and bring Pompee's clothes with you. Come in from Sans Souci by coach so as not to muss my dress or your clothes."

He pressed his lips to her hand and hurried to do her bidding. She was left alone with Pompee.

"You are going to surprise Milord," he said.

"Perhaps I should not do it," she mused. "Perhaps I should first come to him alone. But no! I want him to see me first among people, so that he will understand that all the old fears and timidity have left me. I want him to see me tomorrow night as the Princess Royal—then he will know that the only barrier that has ever existed between us has been removed, and through your goodness. Now hurry, Pompee! See if you can find a carriage somewhere, and break the news to Maman that she is not going, have her bring my clothes, and return as soon as you can."

Within a few moments the Brantome house started to hum with activity. A tray with a tempting dinner appeared in Athenée's room. Madame Brantome herself came up with Athenée's clothes, freshly pressed and laundered. Maman sent maids scurrying about the house, and soon a rattle of wheels in the courtyard below proclaimed Pompee's acquisition of a conveyance. Athenée took a moment to look out the window and saw a trim little chaise and the two fine horses. She had only time to taste the hot soup and the cold chicken and dress hurriedly. Then came the leave-taking. When she kissed Madame Brantome on the cheek, she noted that Madame was properly awed at being kissed by a princess. Maman engulfed her with tears and recriminations, but Athenée assured her that she would be sent for immediately and dashed down the stairs.

That night they crossed the valley of the Artibonite, then came up through the mountains over the same route they had come. From Hinche they came down through the mountains and across the great Plain du Nord, only to climb again through other mountains which encircled the Cap. The brilliance of the moon lighted their way. They stopped somewhere high up in the icy air of the mountains at a sleeping *caille*. Pompee awoke the peasants inside, and Athenée waited patiently for the hot coffee which they prepared. While they were sipping the strong, black brew, the old woman advanced awkwardly toward Athenée, wiping her fingers carefully on her dress.

"Moi kapab—may I?" she asked as she reached tentatively toward Athenée's face.

Athenée leaned toward her without knowing exactly what the woman wanted. The aged fingers lightly touched her cheek. The woman turned to Pompee and spoke to him in a dialect which Athenée could not understand.

"She was there that night," Pompee explained to Athenée. "She was one of those who helped, and she is very proud and happy."

Athenée took the woman's work-hardened hand in her own and stroked it. With her other hand, she unclasped the gold and garnet brooch at her throat and placed it in the woman's hand. A torrent of almost unintelligible Creole poured from the woman's mouth as she tearfully tried to thank her. Then they were on their way again, this time with a pair of mules to replace the tired horses.

With the coming of dawn, they stopped again for more hot coffee and freshly baked bread and to exchange the mules for horses. Noon found them at Grande Rivière du Nord, not too far from Milot and Sans Souci, but they pressed on, and by three o'clock in the afternoon they had arrived at Henry's new-old palace in the Cap.

Athenée directed Pompee to drive around to the back, and they halted at the servants' entrance. She managed to slip out of the chaise and through the back door without being noticed. Once inside, she waited only long enough to give Pompee a few instructions, called one of the kitchen maids to her, and asked her to take her at once to the Queen's apartments.

When they arrived, two Bonbons—as Henry called his household guards—stood at attention at the door and would have denied her entrance, had not Marie Louise, on hearing the commotion, opened the door herself. When she saw Athenée standing there she promptly collapsed. Burnt feathers and eau de cologne soon revived her, and she was led, half-hysterical, to a chair, where she sat and stared at Athenée through her tears and the cobweb of lace which was her handkerchief.

"I can't believe it! I can't believe it!" She was laughing now and crying at the same time. "Pompee told Henry and me what he hoped would happen and Henry has been out of his mind with worry awaiting couriers from you, and I have been lighting candles to every saint in the church. Armes is here. He arrived this morning, and we have had the most terrible time trying to keep him from racing out to Sans Souci. Finally Henry threatened to place him under arrest if he left Sir Home for five minutes so he's still here, and two Bonbons watch his every move." She had stopped crying. "Oh, Athenée, I'm so happy, so very happy, I cannot find words to tell you, and I thank God that you are safe."

All of which was enough to start Athenée weeping, and she dissolved into Marie Louise's arms, providing an impetus for all the ladies-in-waiting to start sniffling and dabbing at their own eyes, until finally Athenée got command of herself and told them all to stop. "At once!" she demanded. "What will the British ambassador think if he sees every woman in the Haitian court with eyes red from weeping?"

Just as suddenly as they had cried, they all started to laugh. Introductions came next, for although they had all heard of the Princess Royal, they had never seen her. Marie Louise took much pleasure in showing off "my dear sister" to the Princess of Limbe—who after all was only a Serene Highness—the Comtesse de la Bande du Nord, the Comtesse de Limonade, and the Duchess of Marmelade—who was only a Your Grace. They all made a deep curtsy to her Royal Highness. Marie Louise waved them all away and they fluttered out the door.

"Now, *ma soeur*." Athenée sank gratefully into a chair. "I am going to need your help."

"In any way I can."

"Tonight is the dinner for the English ambassador?"

"Well, he is really not an ambassador. He's just an admiral whom England has sent here for Henry's coronation. England does not consider Henry worthy of an ambassador yet, but Henry likes to call him that."

488

"Well, whoever he is, I want to go to the dinner."

"*Mais oui.* Pompee said he thought you would be here, so we have laid a place for you, praying that you would be. See!" Marie Louise rummaged through a buhlwork desk and produced a sheet of paper. "This is the table plan."

Athenée followed the spidery handwriting that ran around the edges of the long oblong.

"*Le roi.*" She pointed to the end of the table. "Henry's here, and this must be me at his left because it says *La princess royale.*"

"That is you, Athenée," Marie Louise corroborated. "And here am I"—she pointed to *La reine* at the other end of the table—"with Sir Home on my right and Armes on my left." She fluttered her handkerchief. "Oh, Athenée, he's a white man and he's English and whatever shall I say to him?"

"Ask him about the weather in Jamaica—that's always safe. Now, who is on Henry's right? Oh, Lady Popham, of course."

"She came from Jamaica with the admiral."

"And this"—she pointed—"Mr. Frothingham on my other side. That must be . . ."

"Armes' guardian from Boston, and Madame Frothingham sits beside Armes. They arrived yesterday and dined with us last night. Such a delightful old couple, and they speak the most exact French. Poor Mr. Frothingham, he's lost without TiArmes here, but he and Henry talked business and pretty soon Madame Frothingham thawed out and she gave me the recipe for Boston baked beans and fish chowder which she says Armes loves."

Athenée put the paper slowly back on the desk. So Pompee had believed all along that she would return. He had told Marie Louise that she would be at the dinner. Dear, wonderful, faithful Pompee, to give her this overflowing joy.

Marie Louise took Athenée's arm and guided her to a door, smaller than the formidable double ones which opened onto the hall. "Your room is right here next to mine, so that we can leave the door open and talk while we dress. I must know everything that has happened, my sister. Oh! I've got the most wonderful coiffeur to do your hair in *la mode Italienne* which goes so well with a tiara. And your dress is lovely. TiTonTon brought it this morning, and I peeked and your jewels are wonderful—lovelier than mine."

"Armes bought so many for me and I never thought I would wear them in public."

"Well, you shall now and"—Marie Louise leaned forward and touched Athenée's cheek—"oh, it's the greatest miracle in the world since our beloved Lord raised Lazarus from the dead."

Athenée kissed her and turned the knob of the door. "It was a miracle, Marie Louise, a miracle of love—your love and Henry's love and my dear Armes' love, Pompee's love and TiTonTon's. But even more than that, it was the love of all those dear people who were there that night; who traveled many miles over the mountains out of love for me. I can never forget the people of Haiti, Marie Louise. They are here, *ma soeur*, deep down in my heart, and if any people were worthy of love, they are."

59

BY breaking down the walls between the three houses that he had thrown together to make his palace, Henry had fabricated an enormous room that extended the whole length of the three buildings. Tall windows, balconied with wrought-iron, faced out over the Champ de Mars. It was a useful room, serving at various times as an audience hall, a ballroom, and a throne room, but tonight a vast table, running almost the entire length, converted it into a banquet hall.

This dinner was a milestone for Henry. England had deigned to look across the sea and recognize another majesty in the new world—a black one to be sure, but nevertheless a king. With increased commerce in sight, they reasoned, it might be well to send a representative to this little upstart. The stuffy House of Hanover smiled a little at the idea of a black king and the Prince Regent joked about it among his cronies at Carlton House, but the Haitian exports would be of value to England and a deprivation to France, hence the presence of Sir Home and Lady Popham. Henry was well aware of the newness of his dynasty, and he had determined that this night, above all others, Haiti must show the proud English that a black king, even though born a slave, was familiar with the prerogatives of kingship.

490

Tonight the room was ablaze with hundreds of wax tapers that marched in an uninterrupted procession in silver gilt candelabra down the length of the white table. The crystal girandoles above were sunbursts of light, and the wall sconces were reflected in countless mirrors. The gold plate that Marie Louise had saved from the burning Cap gleamed on the table. To furnish such a large number it had been complemented with silver, dipped in gold and burnished to match the rest. Crystal epergnes filled with roses and orchids alternated with silver baskets of tropical fruits. Behind each chair, one of Henry's Bonbons stood stiffly at attention. They had exchanged their military uniforms for white satin breeches and black, silver-braided coats and, incongruous as it might seem, white powdered wigs covered their kinky black wool.

Henry's majordomo—an immense Negro who had been a sergeant in the Dahomeys—took a last look at the big room and the long table. He walked up the few steps between the gilded pillars to the closed doors leading into a smaller salon and listened, his ear at the keyhole. A faint strain of music filtered through the door. It was the orchestra that Henry had imported from Germany and, while the man listened, he nodded his head in time to the music. When the tune came to an end, he held up his hand in warning and each of the footmen squared his shoulders, sucked in his belly and stared straight ahead with unblinking eyes. Then the big majordomo heard what he had been waiting for—the opening bars of the "Chanson Henri," the new royal anthem. He lifted the tall ebony staff and pounded three times on the floor as a last warning to the footmen, grasped both handles of the big double doors, flung them open, and let in the hum of conversation from the salon.

"His Majesty, King Henry the First of Haiti," he announced to the empty room, "and his Excellency, Lady Popham."

Henry hesitated for a moment at the top of the steps and, as he surveyed the room, his pride overcame all other feelings. Everything looked perfect. The stout, red-faced lady on his arm gave a gasp of uncontrolled admiration and looked up at Henry as they descended the steps together. It was the first time in her life she had had bodily contact with a Negro, and her pudgy fingers twitched like fat white mice on the smooth broadcloth on Henry's arm. She had dreaded this intimacy of touch. She understood that Negroes were prone to smell badly, but, having discovered that Henry smelled only of soap and Parfum de Jockey Club, she had relaxed a bit. Indeed, Henry was such a perfect gentleman she was beginning to forget he was Negro.

The ebony staff rapped again.

"Her Majesty, Queen Marie Louise of Haiti, and his Excellency, Sir Home Popham, representing his Britannic Majesty." Sir Home's jowls were heavy with the prestige of England, and Marie Louise seemed inches taller as they slowly descended the steps.

"His Royal Highness, the Prince Royal of Haiti, and Madame Frothingham of Boston, Massachusetts in the You Ess Ay." Armes appeared on the steps with a stout, comfortable-looking lady on his arm. Not for Mrs. Frothingham were the high-waisted, bust-revealing French dresses. She was completely covered by a voluminous gown of pale gray satin, but the diamonds in her ears were as big as hazelnuts.

"His Excellency, Monsieur Frothingham of Boston in the You Ess Ay, and her Grace the Duchess of Gonaïves." Mr. Frothingham, his spindly legs encased in black satin knee breeches, escorted an elderly Negress whose tiara of amethysts shot purple flames in her steel-gray hair. It was difficult to realize that this distinguished woman had started life as a scullery maid at the Roncourt plantation.

Two by two they descended the steps from the salon to the banquet hall; the dukes, the counts, and the barons with their ladies. Henry had elevated them all from the status of field hands, coachmen, cooks, and maidservants. They varied in color from pale cream to jet-black, but they were all in correct court costume, the men in gold-embroidered short blue coats with long tails, the jeweled star of the Order of St. Henry on their chests; the women in gowns which the leading couturiers of Paris had finished a few weeks before. Among those announced were the distinguished Comte de Milot and the young Baron de Destinée, with ladies of the court on their arms.

Only five white people graced the assembly—Armes, Sir Home and Lady Popham, and Mr. and Mrs. Frothingham. The representatives of the other nations had not arrived as yet. Both Sir Home and his Lady were most correct in their deportment. Not a single glance or gesture betrayed the fact that they were not at Whitehall or Carlton House and, truth to tell, they were even more awed by the black majesty of Henry and Marie Louise than they ever would

492

have been in front of the Prince Regent or the vulgar Princess of Wales.

The music floated down from the salon as the assembly sought their appointed places at the table. As the last bar of the "Chanson Henri" drifted away, the ebony stick pounded again and Henry and Marie Louise sat down, followed, after an almost imperceptible interval, by the rest. Armes, from his place between the Queen and Mrs. Frothingham, looked down the length of the table and noticed an empty place at Henry's left hand. He wondered who the important guest might be who could so carelessly flout protocol as to be late or absent. Surely he or she must have realized that Henry's royal command could not lightly be ignored.

Henry himself glanced at the empty place and whispered to the footman who stood behind his chair. The man left unobtrusively, only to return a moment later and whisper a reply in Henry's ear.

"I have just been informed," he said, "that her Royal Highness, my sister, has been delayed by a slight accident to her coach on the road from Sans Souci. Another coach has been dispatched and she will be here momentarily. She has sent her regrets and begs that we do not wait for her."

As the doors at the end of the hall opened and the palace footmen came in bearing huge silver trays, Armes turned to Marie Louise, his face tense with bewilderment and fright.

"Athenée? Does he mean Athenée?" he whispered hoarsely.

"There is only one Princess Royal of Haiti," she smiled back.

"Athenée? You know she will not come."

"*Mon frère.*" She lifted her hand, heavy with rings, and placed it on his arm. "Henry is a king. When Henry commands, there is no possible way to disobey him. Henry commanded you to remain here today and you stayed, *n'est-ce pas?* Henry commanded Athenée to come here tonight, so she comes. She has no choice in the matter."

Armes clenched his fists under the table. "But it is cruel. Henry knows how she will suffer. Why did he place her in such a position?"

"Sh-h-h-h! Do not worry. It will be all right. I know." She nodded her head so that her earrings made flashing arcs. "Wait!" She turned to Sir Home, terminating her conversation with Armes.

Armes glanced at the gold bowl, piled high with chilled

fruit, which the footman had just placed before him. He heard the gurgle of wine as it filled his glass and he mechanically picked up a spoon and started to eat, but there was no taste to the fruit. Mrs. Frothingham spoke to him and he answered her mechanically. His mind was on Athenée and the ordeal ahead of her. Naturally, despite all the rules of court etiquette, she would find some pretext to wear her veil. The thought that she would be sheltered from curious eyes calmed him, and he dipped his spoon in the compote again. The hum of conversation increased around the table. There was a popping of corks and the subdued sounds of eating. The bowl of fruit was whisked away, and, just as the Bonbon behind Armes was placing a Sèvres plate with a succulent morsel of white fish before him, he heard the rap of the ebony staff again and the stentorian voice of the majordomo.

"Her Royal Highness Athenée, Princess Royal of Haiti."

Armes scarcely dared to lift his eyes. For once he prayed that she had worn her veil, otherwise he could not endure seeing the suffering that must be on that beloved face. The orchestra in the next room started to play. Marie Louise nudged him sharply, and against his will he raised his head and looked toward the door. As he stared, his whole body started to tremble. His hands clutched at the edge of the table—clutched it so tightly that his knuckles showed white through the heavy tan.

"Courage, mon frère," Marie Louise whispered to him. He dared another look. It was Athenée! Oh, dear God, it was Athenée. And . . . she was radiant, beautiful, regal. The silver of her dress enveloped her figure like the water of a slender fountain, molding her breasts above the narrow girdle. A white fire of diamonds blazed on her skin. There was a circle of gems in her hair, and the tall white egret plumes added to her height. As she descended the steps, red velvet flowed behind her like wine poured from a bottle, the weight of the train pulling back her shoulders a little, giving her a proud, imperious bearing. But her face! Oh God, her face! That face he had loved so much, had kissed so often. Oh, her poor dear face! What mattered the gown or the jewels? Her face! Everything else faded into nothingness. He saw the snowy whiteness of her cheeks—*both* cheeks. And then he saw the red curve of her lips and the black brows like two sleek birds poised over her eyes which were proud and happy.

"*Mon Dieu*," he cried, clutching at Marie Louise's hand, oblivious of the fact that Sir Home could both see and hear him. "Tell me! Tell me!"

"Hush," she whispered. "Just be glad and ask no questions now. There's been a miracle, Armes, truly a miracle. God has been good. Now eat, or people will start looking at us. Remember, nobody has ever seen Athenée before, so nobody has noticed anything except her beauty. Do not give them an opportunity to."

Mrs. Frothingham leaned toward Armes.

"Who is she, Armes? I must say she's the handsomest woman I ever saw."

"My wife, your new niece," Armes answered proudly, as the entire assembly arose.

"Is she white?" Mrs. Frothingham whispered.

"Of course. Didn't you see her?"

Further conversation was cut short by Henry's rising from his chair as Athenée came to the table. He embraced her and kissed her on the cheek. As they were both standing there, he held up his hand for silence. All looked toward him.

"*Messieurs et mesdames.*" He caught their attention with his eyes. "Please remain seated. I do not think you have ever had the honor of meeting my beloved sister, the Princess Royal. May I present her to all of you?" Athenée smiled serenely—a smile that enveloped them all—and slipped into her chair, but Henry remained standing. "As you are all assembled together here tonight, we have deemed this a fitting night to celebrate a most important occasion. Immediately after dinner, carriages will be waiting at the door to transport you to the cathedral, where his Eminence the Archbishop Duke of Anse will celebrate a nuptial Mass for my brother, the Prince Royal, and my sister, the Princess Athenée."

There was a gentle clapping of hands, and glances were divided between Armes and Athenée.

Marie Louise's satin shoe nudged Armes. "A toast." Her lips barely moved to form the words. "Get up!"

Armes clutched the table for support as he stood up and raised his wineglass.

"*Vive le roi*," he cried, and all the others around the table' echoed the words. "Thank you, your Majesty," he added.

When he sat down, he caught Marie Louise's eye. "This is just as much of a surprise to me as it is to you," she laughed.

495

"Henry must have planned it all after he saw Athenée this afternoon. Is it all right?"

"All right? Oh, Marie Louise, is it all right? It's my dream come true. It's heaven and earth and all the angels singing together. It is life and love and the music of the spheres. It is . . ."

Her little satin slipper bore down on his boot as Sir Home, begging the Queen's pardon, spoke to Armes.

"My congratulations, your Royal Highness, my congratulations."

"And mine, dear boy." Mrs. Frothingham's hand closed over Armes.

Across the long table, Armes' eyes met those of Athenée. For a long moment they spoke to each other without words, until Mr. Frothingham claimed her attention. Armes relaxed in his chair.

"Pompee did it," Marie Louise whispered.

60

HENRY'S big gilded coach was waiting for Armes and Athenée as they descended the steps of the cathedral after their wedding ceremony. Flambeaux blazed outside the church, making the Champ de Mars as bright as noon, and a double line of Bonbons in full-dress uniform formed an arch of drawn sabers on either side of the red carpet which stretched from the church to the coach. All the inhabitants of the Cap must have been outside, for as far as Armes and Athenée could see there was a mass of black faces split by white-toothed smiles. The air was filled with cries of "Vive le prince" and "Vive la princesse." After they had entered the coach, Henry and Marie Louise walked down the carpet, and the shouts changed to "Vive le roi" and "Vive la reine." Some, however, forgot the titles and shouted "Vive l'homme Henry Christophe."

Armes was wearing a cornet of gold—a design of palm trees, interspersed with the arms of Haiti—which had slipped down over one eye. He pushed the heavy weight of gold back into position as he leaned from the window to grasp Henry's hand. Athenée, whose coronet had replaced the tiara she had worn earlier, leaned across Armes and laid the tips of her fingers on Henry's hand. The king's eyes twinkled at the successful outcome of his coup, and Marie Louise reflected his joy.

"Au revoir, mes enfants." Henry spoke softly so that none of the courtiers might hear. "I wish I could be with you at Sans Souci tonight, but there are some places where even the King of Haiti would not be welcome, and Sans Souci tonight is one of them. You will find it all in readiness for you. May your wedding night be as happy as mine was." He looked down at the Queen, who smiled in agreement. Then Sir Home and Lady Popham came out of the church to the tune of "Rule Britannia" to add their congratulations, and finally Mr. and Mrs. Frothingham, trying to keep in step to "Yankee Doodle," marched down the red carpet.

"Never thought I'd see you in a gold coach with a crown on your head, my lad." Mr. Frothingham allowed his pride in Armes to show.

"And married to a princess!" Mrs. Frothingham clapped her mitted hands together, and smiled up at Athenée. "But I'm going to call you my niece."

"What do you think Boston will say to Athenée?" Armes pushed her a little forward, closer to the window.

"All Boston will love her as we do." Mrs. Frothingham managed to touch Athenée's fingers. "And now, you two children run along with our blessing."

"And ours." Lady Popham actually smiled.

"And ours, darlings," Marie Louise added.

A roll from the drums signaled twelve of Henry's tallest Bonbons to draw up their horses behind the coach. Another roll and Pompee and TiTonTon, also in the uniform of the Bonbons, wheeled their horses into position, one on each side of the coach. Henry raised his hand; the long line of soldiers in the square flashed swords from scabbards; a bugle sounded; the drums rolled again; and through the huzzas of the multitude and rain of flowers, the big coach started to roll.

All the carriages of the court followed them as far as the big-city gates, but as the gates opened wide to let them and their escort pass, the other carriages remained behind. They were alone, except for the coachman up in front and the footmen behind; except for TiTonTon on one side and Pompee on the other; except for the galloping Bonbons behind them.

Armes removed the heavy coronet from his head. "I'll feel

497

better without this and so will you." He reached over and disengaged the little crown which was pinned to Athenée's curls. "Thank God we do not have to be royalty all the time. I'd as soon wear an iron pot on my head as that contraption of mine."

"It's most becoming to you, but I agree it's more comfortable without it." She sighed and patted her hair back into place where Armes had disarranged it. "Oh, do not ask me to think, darling, my mind is in a whirl. No woman ever lived through anything like I have these past few days. And tonight! Never has anyone been quite as happy as I am." She placed his fingers on the gold band on her finger. "You and I together always."

"Yes, you and I together always. That I can understand, but there are so many things I cannot understand. This, for instance." His fingers caressed her cheek.

"I can answer in one word—Pompee."

"But that doesn't explain."

"There is much about it, Armes, that can never be explained. I can only tell you what happened, then you must judge for yourself, but you will never understand any more than I do."

She started at the beginning, from the morning he had left Sans Souci to depart from Jamaica.

"That Henry! He sent me there on purpose."

"Of course! He and Marie Louise both knew about it, but they did not know what the outcome would be, nor I, nor TiTonTon nor Pompee."

She continued with her story, reliving the long ride through the night over the mountains to Mirebalais and the stop at the house of Madame Brantome. Then she took him with her on the journey to Saut d'Eau. Through her words he sat in her chair; saw the semicircle of lights; heard the pulsing drums; felt the sticky blood on his own face and recoiled from the serpent's fangs. He saw her hoisted on the rude litter and borne back to Mirebalais, and he awakened with her and looked into the mirror which Madame Brantome held before her. When she had finished, although she had neglected no detail, he continued to shake his head in bewilderment, and was forced to admit that it was all beyond his comprehension.

"But, my dear," she added gently, "isn't there much we do not understand? Many things that have happened here in Haiti cannot be explained."

498

He agreed, his thoughts reverting to the night Ali had returned to him through Pompee and warned them to go to the mountains. He remembered the night when Bouckman had aroused the blacks, and the message of the drums which he had been able to understand. He recalled all the other things which he had seen and heard and which could not be rationalized. "There is only one answer." His lips sought hers in the darkness of the coach, and for a long moment neither of them were able to speak. "Only one answer, darling, and there can be no questions. Who are we to question the work of the gods? We can only be humbly grateful for all this love we have found here—grateful to Pompee and TiTonTon and their gods."

"And to Henry and Marie Louise," she reminded him.

He fingered his coronet in the darkness. "Think of Henry arranging our marriage and not even letting Marie Louise know. But, are you sure you didn't marry beneath you? After all, you are a princess and the sister of a king."

She placed her finger against his lips. "Sh-h-h!" she cautioned, "that is the only weak spot I can find in my marriage. Are you sure it is legal?"

"Legal? *Mon Dieu,* why not?"

"Well," she considered the matter with mock gravity, "Henry has adopted you as his brother, right?"

He agreed.

"So, if Henry is my brother and Henry is your brother that makes us . . ."

"Man and wife," he shouted, "and if you think for one moment we are not actually married because we might be brother and sister, I'll prove to you that you are mistaken." He kissed her again. "What's that?" he asked.

"A kiss," she admitted.

"But what kind of a kiss?"

"Oh, a most charming kind."

"Was it the sort of kiss a brother would give a sister?"

"How do I know? I've never had a brother."

"Then, my dear, I'll show you." He pecked lightly at her cheek. "There, that is the way a brother might kiss a sister," he explained.

"*Mais non,* that is certainly not the way you kiss, Armes. Not at all. But I must make a real comparison. Show me again *exactly* how you kiss me."

He found her lips wide open and their exploring tongues

499

touched. "That," he said when he could speak again, "is how Armes kisses his wife Athenée."

"*Hélas*, there is a great difference," she laughed. "It does prove most conclusively that we are not brother and sister."

"Shall I prove it to you again?" he leaned closer.

"I doubt if you will ever be able to prove it to me sufficiently. I think I shall require a demonstration every hour for the rest of my life so that I shall never forget."

"One more demonstration, *ma tentatrice*, and you'll be spending your honeymoon on the seat of Henry's royal coach instead of in our room at Sans Souci. A man's flesh can stand only so much, so I advise you to move close to your window and I shall move close to mine, and perhaps the night breeze will cool us off." He moved to the window, but her hand caught his and held it.

The high wheels of the coach rolled on through the purple night. They passed fields of cane, silvered by the moon; they rode under the ragged shadows of tall palms; they heard the sound of rushing water and caught the distant sound of drums. Athenée leaned out of the window, breathing in the soft night air, staring into the blackness, loving this mystic land of Haiti, loving the night and the stars and the silver moon, but most of all the man beside her whose hand pressed hers.

"This St. Domingue, this Haiti." Her fingers clutched his hand more tightly. "Can we ever forget it?"

"No, because Haiti is the *pays du revenant*—the land of return. He who has stepped on Haitian soil must return; he can never stay away."

"And we shall return, Armes, even though we go away. Haiti has done much for us. We cannot ask her to do more. We must not tempt the gods by remaining. Let us go to your Boston and to my France. That is"—she hesitated—"if we have money enough. Do we or don't we, Armes? I do not know. I've never thought much about money before. I know that once I did have money—a great deal, but where it is now I do not know."

"Safely invested in Boston," he assured her. "Henry's government has reimbursed you for the loss of St. Gabriel, and he has insisted on paying me for Sans Souci, even though I protested. He got around it by calling it a wedding gift. That, and this!" He fingered the enameled star of St. Henry. "So

500

Sans Souci belongs to Henry and he intends to build his palace there, but I know we shall always be welcome."

The coach neared Milot and, as they turned into the cobbled street, Armes saw the spherical dome of the little church silhouetted against the black sky. He leaned out of the window and called TiTonTon to the side of the coach.

"Tell the coachman," he said, "to stop at the church. Go in, and if you can find your way in the darkness, light the candles. When they are lit, come out and let us know."

The coach drew up in front of the little church and stopped. Athenée darted a questioning glance at Armes, but he laid his hand on hers. His flint struck a spark and lighted a candle in the tiny gilded sconce by the door of the coach. The seat facing them was banked with flowers—thick-petaled red roses, waxy lilies, and sprays of ferns. He gathered them together in his arms, and when TiTonTon reappeared Armes called Pompee to let down the steps. Pompee assisted Athenée down after Armes.

They walked up the steps of the circular church and down the aisle to the altar where they knelt. After a few moments, Armes stood up and with his free arm led Athenée to a little chapel at the side of the main altar. Pompee had lighted the candles here also, and their light crept up the wall to the picture of a saint which hung against a shimmer of red brocade. The ruddy light of the flames turned the white flesh of the painted youth in the picture to a golden shade.

"The Saint Sebastian of your religion," Armes said quietly as he laid the armful of flowers down before the picture.

"I know, my dear." Atheneé knelt again, and he dropped to his knees beside her. "I see the arrows which are the sign of his martyrdom."

"Don't look at the arrows. Look at his face."

"It is wonderful." She studied it carefully. "Fresh and beautiful with youth. It also seems that he does not feel the arrows."

"It is the face of Ali." Armes shook his head sadly. "I described it to the artist who painted it, and he caught an exact likeness. I pray that Ali did not feel the arrows either."

She bowed her head.

"Little fellow." Armes' words were scarcely audible as he spoke directly to the painted face. "I wanted you to share this moment with us, because I know you would be happy in my happiness. So we have come, Athenée and I, to ask your blessing, and to thank you for saving us on the mountain. These poor flowers are all that I can offer you, except the love in my heart and the love in Athenée's heart, because I know that she loves everything that I do."

The wick of one of the candles flickered and the tip broke off and fell into the molten wax. For a brief moment the flame streaked up, lighting the painted face of the saint on the wall, and in that brief radiance, Armes thought he saw the lips part in a smile.

He lifted Athenée gently from her knees and they walked slowly out of the church. TiTonTon extinguished the candles and clutched at Pompee's arm as they followed. The lights of Sans Souci were shining in the darkness as they seated themselves in the coach—lights which beckoned to them as they rode on through the darkness.

61

ARMES and Athenée had nearly two months to get ready for Henry's coronation, but it was hardly enough. Henry demanded Armes' almost constant attention to settle as many matters as possible before he left. With Athenée spending most of her time with Marie Louise, neither she nor Armes had much time to attend to their own affairs, and there was so much to do. Haiti had been their home for years, and they discovered that they had become Haitians, if not in color at least in their manner of thinking. As a matter of fact, the color of a man's skin, which had once seemed so important, mattered little to either of them now, and Armes, bronzed by the sun until he could easily be mistaken for an octoroon, found himself looking at visiting Europeans and Americans with their fish-belly whiteness quite as though they belonged to a different race from himself.

Not so Mr. and Mrs. Frothingham! Having come so far they had thought to remain for Henry's coronation and return with Armes and Athenée to Boston, but a few weeks of seeing only black faces and the enervating sun of Haiti combined to send them back to Boston, with its pale pinched faces and its salty east wind. Mr. and Mrs. Frothingham had welcomed Athenée as a daughter, but they were not *en rapport* with Haiti and its citizens. Mr. Frothingham recognized a kindred soul in Henry with his aptitude for business, but he found it difficult to address this black man as "Majesty." Mrs. Frothingham sat stiffly through interminable court receptions, and although she was always awarded a place of honor and extreme deference, she never felt at home in Marie Louise's court. Yet, on the day they sailed, when Henry and Marie Louise came to the *quai* to bid them *bon voyage,* Mrs. Frothingham found herself kissing Marie Louise on the cheek and curtsying to Henry, while Mr. Frothingham proudly fingered the Cross of St. Henry which hung from a black and white ribbon around his neck.

With the Frothinghams gone, Armes started to work in earnest. As Henry so often remarked, "There is so much to do and so little time in which to do it." Armes agreed with him. Whenever he and Henry had an extra moment, Henry insisted that Vastey read to them in order to acquaint them with court procedures of other coronations—Napoleon's, George III's, those of the new royalties of Spain, Naples, and the Netherlands—and even with papal rites. Henry would interrupt from time to time and motion to TiTonTon to copy down some pertinent detail of costume, decoration, rite, or procedure. Gradually from these copious notes, a plan for Henry's own coronation developed. Robes were designed by competent artists, sketches were made for decorations, ciphers were designed, protocol established, and a rigorous court etiquette evolved.

The cathedral in the Cap was far too small to accommodate all the Haitian court and the foreign dignitaries that Henry wanted to invite, so architects hurriedly designed a temporary church-pavilion to be erected in the Champ de Mars of the Cap, which was now rechristened Cap Henry.

The crowns of Haiti had arrived, each in its velvet-lined leather box. The rayed black sun, which was to be Henry's emblem, was attached to everything which would support it. The coronation robes for Henry and Marie Louise as well as those for Armes and Athenée came over on a ship from Paris, and were steamed and pressed to remove the wrinkles in them. Gradually, from out of the confusion, some sort of order began to prevail, and Armes was gratified to see all the small details falling into their proper places. Both he and Athenée came to realize that being royalty carried with it a considerable burden of hard work. Perhaps the thing that chafed Armes more than anything else was his compulsory attendance at all Henry's *levées* and court functions. Henry was a stickler for etiquette, with the result that all his receptions were so hedged in with protocol that they were extremely tiresome. Usually they involved sitting for hours in a straight chair—only Henry and Marie Louise were permitted the comparative comfort of an armchair. But at least Armes and Athenée had chairs, for although those of ducal rank were permitted simple *tabourets,* the counts, barons, chevaliers, and their wives were compelled to stand. Armes pitied the poor feet, so recently bare, now encased in tight boots and satin shoes, as the tired courtiers shifted their weight from one foot to another while deep stains of perspiration spotted their resplendent uniforms and elaborate *toilettes.*

Gradually Armes was able to settle his own affairs. The generous grants that Henry had made to Athenée for St. Gabriel and to Armes for Sans Souci were finally transferred to Boston through Durham, Brown. Not everything, however, went to Boston. Armes purchased a fine mansion for Pompee, for certainly the pope of voodoo deserved as fine a dwelling as the Archbishop. Here Pompee installed himself with his *hunsis* and of course TiTonTon.

Despite TiTonTon's great happiness, Armes felt a responsibility for the boy. Not that he was friendless, for he had Pompee whom he worshiped, and Henry whom he greatly respected. Now, as a baron, with his entree at court, he was far different from the illiterate boy of the mountain, and he had progressed far in the *mystères* under Pompee's guidance. But Armes felt that there were far greater potentialities to TiTonTon than anyone suspected, and that in becoming a voodoo *papaloi* or a scribe for Henry he would not realize them. TiTonTon had an amazing capability for learning and a quick intelligence. His physical defect, however, had made him shy and reticent, and he avoided mingling with strangers. Armes wanted to help him overcome this and take his place in the world. He considered sending TiTonTon to Paris to complete his education.

In one of his free moments, Armes discussed the matter with Pompee. He desired the other's advice, for he realized the close bond that existed between TiTonTon and his mentor. Pompee deliberated the matter carefully before he replied.

"I would not have mentioned it, milord, if you had not spoken first, but now that you have, may I feel free to speak?"

"*Certainement,* Pompee! Since when have you needed to ask my permission to speak? If there is anything you desire you have only to ask for it. You have so few wishes and there is so little I can do for you . . ."

"There is something you can do for TiTonTon and that would be doing something for me."

"Tell me and I shall do it," Armes promised with enthusiasm, but Pompee checked him with a wave of his hand.

"Perhaps it is something you will not want to do. I am about to ask you to take TiTonTon with you to Boston when you and Madame leave."

"Will that make him happy, and you?"

"No, milord." Pompee shook his head. "I shall be desolate to be parted from him and he will be lonely without me, but he will be with you and Madame and, next to me, he loves you two best. You have spoken of a college you attended in Boston. It is my desire that TiTonTon should go there. Now that he can read and write, it should not be too difficult."

"But why not to Paris, to the Sorbonne, where he can speak the language?"

"In Boston he would be near you and Madame. In Paris he would be alone. TiTonTon has great attractiveness, which you may not be aware of, and I fear that in Paris he might get into unscrupulous hands and never return to me."

Armes weighed the pros and cons of the matter. "Reading and writing is only the beginning, Pompee. TiTonTon would have to learn English."

"He is quick to learn, you know that."

"And then there would be many other things he would have to know before he could enter college—mathematics, geography, history, Latin, Greek, and a host of other subjects."

"Again I say he would learn quickly."

"But he would be lonely in Boston, too. Outside of Athenée and myself he would have no friends, and there is a distinction between Negro and white in Boston."

"As the Baron de Destinée of Haiti, TiTonTon would take a manservant with him—one of my *hunsis*—who would be a companion as well as a servant."

"But it might be possible that Harvard would not admit him. There are heavy restrictions on a colored man in a white society."

"If the King of Haiti were to request the authorities of your university to accept a Negro—a baron of his court, and accompany it with a generous donation, he might be admitted, *n'est-ce pas?*"

"He'd stand a pretty good chance," Armes admitted.

"Then let us try, milord. We need educated men in Haiti. That is our country's greatest lack. Allow TiTonTon to accompany you. Let him learn. Let him become versed in all the arts which your Harvard can teach him. Then let him return to Haiti—we shall need him here."

When the matter was broached to TiTonTon, he at first refused to leave unless Pompee accompanied him, but gradually Pompee brought him over to his way of thinking, and TiTonTon became convinced. Armes explained the situation to him carefully—the years of hard work and study; the certain social ostracism; and the poignant longing he would have for Pompee and the hot sun of Haiti. But TiTonTon became enthusiastic over the prospects of leaving, and it was decided that he would accompany them on the ship they were sailing on, which would leave the afternoon following Henry's coronation.

For several days before the coronation, crowds began to gather in Cap Henry, until there was not an available inch of space in the whole city. It seemed as though the entire population of Henry's towns and cities of the North had made their way en masse to the capital. The lesser aristocracy from the outlying towns came in coaches and carriages, the peasants arrived on bourriques and on foot, but they all found their way to the Cap to see *l'homme Christophe* enthroned. Beds were set up in every room in all the houses, pallets were made up on floors, and some even slept in doorways and in the street. The influx of crowds kept the Cap in a violent uproar day and night. But it was a happy crowd; there were sounds of laughter everywhere; songs, dancing, and music filled the streets; jugs of *clairin* and *tafia* circulated everywhere; couples embraced in the shadows; and there was a general air of carnival about the whole city.

Armes awoke early the day of the coronation. He stretched his long body as he had so many times before on so many mornings in this same bed, then raised himself on one elbow and looked down at Athenée beside him. Her cheek, which had once been so blemished, was now faintly flushed with pink. Violet shadows lurked under the fringe of her long lashes, and her hair was arranged across his bronze arm in blue-black arabesques. This morning was so much like all other mornings at Sans Souci, yet so very different. In a few hours they were about to leave this house forever. Henry had given orders for workmen to start demolishing it immediately after their departure. The plans for his new

506

palace were ready; the lumber cut; the stones piled in orderly rows in the field, just waiting for them to leave.

This then was good-bye. It was their last morning at Sans Souci. Armes' eyes swept the familiar room, that he might photograph it indelibly and forever in his mind. They rested on each familiar object but always returned to the woman at his side—the one whose love had never surfeited him—who daily presented a new and intriguing facet of herself to widen and deepen his love for her.

She opened her eyes and drew his face closer to hers—so close that he could feel the sweep of her eyelashes on his cheek. Her hand clutched the curling tendrils of his chest and then moved over his body, seeking his strength and his entirety, until all she sought in him responded to her. It was their last morning at Sans Souci, but not the last they would awaken to love and life in the massive mahogany bed. That was a souvenir they would not part with. As soon as they quitted it this morning, the servants would dismantle it and transport it to the ship which was waiting at the *quai*. In the chilly nights in Boston, close together under the heavy blankets, they could imagine themselves back in the warm Haitian night, timing their love to the rhythm of distant drums.

Between them there was no need for words. Such a perfect understanding existed between them that it produced a complete union of bodies, desires, and responses. This last act of love between them at Sans Souci was a silent ritual, identified with a far deeper meaning than the mere joining of flesh to flesh, and when they arose, neither spoke because of the burden of joy in their hearts.

A simple breakfast awaited, after which they both dressed in plain white linen. There was nothing else to take with them, as all their trunks and boxes had been sent to the ship, and their coronation robes awaited them in the palace at the Cap. Slowly they made a circuit of the house, hand in hand, mentally bidding farewell to every object that had been a witness to their love. But their farewells, although sentimental, were not sad. They might be finding it difficult to part with a way of life which had held supreme happiness for them, but they were not parting from each other.

Pompee and TiTonTon were living at Pompee's mansion at the Cap, and there was nobody to bid them *adieu* except a few servants, who were in a hurry to finish their work and go to the Cap. Maman and Simon had come down from Mon

507

Repos, but they too were waiting to go into the city, so their farewell, although tearful, was short. Even the inhabitants of Milot were all in the city, and the village was deserted, although Armes remembered that the painted figure of the tortured boy still kept vigil in the domed church. As they drove along the road, the granite peak of the Bishop's Hat towered above them, and that too held memories for them, as did the road to the city. It was a long procession of farewells —farewell to the sun, the palms, the distant blue mountains, and the grinning blacks who thronged the roads.

When they arrived at the palace it was a maelstrom of activity. A sweating usher hustled them to their apartments, where maids and valets were waiting in attendance. Dressing was a long and complicated process, and when they were nearly finished, the door opened and Henry and Marie Louise entered. Athenée's maid was affixing the coronet to her hair—the little round crown with the royal cipher atop it. Armes was already dressed, and as Henry and Marie Louise entered, he knelt. It was entirely instinctive. For the first time, he realized that Henry was his King—his sovereign. His thoughts raced back to the day he reached Domingue when he had offered the big, handsome slave his hand and his friendship. Both of them had come a long journey. The slave was now King: the white man was his subject.

Marie Louise rushed to embrace Athenée but Henry stood, shaking his head, before Armes.

"It is not fitting that you should kneel before me, Ti-Armes," Henry said solemnly. "I have purposely raised you to such rank that you need never kneel before me or any other man in the world."

Armes looked up at him. "I do not kneel before *you*, Henry Christophe, for you are my brother and my friend. I kneel before his Majesty Henry the First of Haiti and all that he has accomplished—all that he is and all that he shall be. I kneel out of respect both to the man and the crown he wears. But to Henry Christophe, I offer my hand."

Henry looked at it and ignored it. "Once you offered that hand to me years ago, TiArmes, and I took it. It was the wisest and the happiest move I ever made. But today I shall not take your hand. No! That is not enough. Here!" Henry opened his huge arms wide. "Let me embrace you, my brother. We are soon to part. I hope you will not stay away from me long, although I understand the wisdom of your leaving. But always remember this. Haiti is yours, along with the heart of Haiti's King."

He enfolded Armes closely and when they separated, Armes thought he saw tears in the King's eyes. Henry backed away. "Now let me see you, TiArmes, and you too, Athenée, and while my Queen and I admire you, look at us and tell us if we appear like a king and queen, or are we still the stableboy and the chambermaid from the Couronne?"

Henry and Marie Louise stood before them. Henry was in full court regalia, a coat of fine white broadcloth, lavishly embroidered with gold. The black ribbon of the Order of St. Henry stretched tightly across his massive chest. His long legs were molded in tight white trousers, which were also embroidered with a tracery of gold. Over this, he wore a long black mantle, ermine-edged, with a gigantic Cross of St. Henry in gold upon it.

Black and white for the King of Haiti! Black skin and flashing white teeth! Black satin and white broadcloth! Let other monarchs trick themselves out in purple and scarlet —the King of Haiti would don black to match his skin. His head was bare except for the tight skull-cap of crinkly wool, now silvered a little at the temples. He would go to his coronation bareheaded, knowing that the massive crown of Haiti was waiting with the Archbishop in the church—the first gold crown ever to rest on kinky wool such as his.

Armes' robes duplicated Henry's except that the colors were reversed. His coat and trousers were black, but his heavy mantle was of white velvet, with the Cross of St. Henry in silver. He was already wearing his coronet. Marie Louise and Athenée were both in white. Marie Louise's gown was embroidered in gold with her own royal cipher: the intertwined "M" and "L" surrounded by a crown. Athenée's had the entwined "A"'s which she and Armes were permitted to use, embroidered in silver.

"We shall bid each other *adieu* here," Henry said. "We four who have been so close to each other cannot show our feelings in public. I have heard that a monarch must never show his emotions, therefore I do not trust myself to bid you farewell in front of other people. After the ceremony, Marie Louise, the children, and I shall retire behind the altar and do, my loved ones, go then, so that I may not see you leave me. You two have precedence over all the court, so you shall lead the procession of my nobles down the aisle. My coach will be waiting for you with Pompee and TiTonTon in it. They will accompany you to the ship. I am glad you are taking TiTonTon to Boston, but I am glad that Pompee remains here. The Archbishop will crown me, but it will be Pompee's *papalois* who will uphold my throne." Henry placed his right hand on Armes' shoulder and his left on Athenée's. "Now what more can I say except to wish you all joy and happiness?"

"And stop blubbering, Henry, or your eyes will be all red for the ceremony," Marie Louise said, fighting back her own tears. "Look at me. I'm not crying, at least not much." She wiped her eyes and looked at Armes and Athenée and then completely dissolved in tears. "Oh, what are we going to do without you?"

The bells in the church started to toll, and Henry turned and walked out of the room. He hesitated at the door but did not turn back, although Marie Louise did. Despite her cumbersome robes, she ran back and kissed them both, then gathered up her ermine train and ran after Henry. The court chamberlain entered, inspected both Armes and Athenée from head to toe, then folded Athenée's train and placed it on her arm. He straightened Armes' coronet, which still had a tendency to slip over one eye, then, with his hand extended toward the door for them to leave, bowed low.

They entered the church through the private passage from the palace, heard a long gasp of admiration from the hundreds already seated there, and found chairs placed for them in the royal enclosure. No sooner were they seated than they had to rise again, for Henry and Marie Louise and their children entered to the solemn strains of the "Chanson Henri." Followed then a scene of regal pageantry which seemed incredible in Haiti or even the New World. The whole ritualistic ceremony had an air of unreality to Armes —it seemed as ephemeral as the church that had been built for the occasion. Armes' eyes beheld a confusion of silken draperies; the tall figure of the Archbishop under his purple canopy; the regal figure of Henry seated on the low throne. He saw the Archbishop move in a billow of violet satin and place the gold crown on Henry's head. He saw Henry's black hands take the smaller crown and place it on Marie Louise's. He heard the low tones of the organ, and he listened to Henry's oath of fealty to the state. At length the herald at arms, in solemn words, intoned:

"His very great and very august Majesty, Henry the First, King of Haiti, is crowned and enthroned."

Athenée nudged Armes, and he looked up to see Henry,

Marie Louise, Prince Victor, and the children departing in a slow processional around the corner of the altar. He came to his senses and stood up, offering his arm to Athenée, and they walked down the aisle together, seeing only the bowed heads of the standing nobles as they passed. Behind them, two by two, came the others—the decorated representatives of Spain, England, Holland, and Denmark, and following them their Serene Highnesses, the Prince and Princess of Limbe, the Duke and Duchess of Gonaïves, the Duke and Duchess of Plaisance, the Duke and Duchess of Marmelade, and the counts, barons, and chevaliers of Henry's court.

The crowd outside was properly awed. They were expecting Henry and his Queen, but when they saw Armes and Athenée, they changed their cries of "Vive le roi et la reine" to "Vive le prince et la princesse," and then went back to cheering Henry as he appeared on a balcony of the palace.

Pompee and TiTonTon stood on either side of the door of the coach, and they too dropped to their knees as Armes and Athenée descended the steps. The little page that carried Athenée's long train handed it over ceremoniously to Pompee, who folded it and placed it on the floor of the coach. Armes assisted Athenée and then entered himself, followed by Pompee and TiTonTon. The coachman cracked his whip, the gilded wheels started to move, and the coach passed through long lines of Henry's Bonbons to the *quai*.

A carpet of red velvet extended from the coach to the ship, and a young Negro, dressed in black, awaited them and opened the door of the coach.

"Hyacinthe," Pompee whispered, "he whom I have chosen to accompany TiTonTon to Boston. You will find him a good boy."

The rail of the ship was lined with Americans returning to the United States from various islands of the Indies. They were staring open-mouthed at the regal pageantry, as if they could not believe that such magnificence existed in black Haiti. The captain appeared at the head of the gangplank to welcome them. Although he had fought to free his own ship from the burden of royalty, he too was properly impressed. He bowed deeply as Armes and Athenée walked up the red carpet to the music of the Bonbons' drums and cornets.

Pompee halted at the foot of the gangplank.

"I shall not go aboard with you," he said. "I do not wish to step foot on the ship that will carry you away. Damballah wills that you should depart, so I cannot bid you stay, and yet, I want you to know how much of me goes with you. I must not remain, or I would snatch TiTonTon from the ship and take him with me. With him, part of me accompanies you. Through this strong union between TiTonTon and myself I shall be able to watch over you and protect you." He regarded them both closely, reached in his pocket, and drew out two tiny silken bags. "Keep these *ouangas* always; they will protect you. Be good to my TiTonTon and watch out for Hyacinthe, for this is all new to him." Pompee choked and he bent his head.

Armes placed his hands on Pompee's shoulders, and Athenée reached up and kissed him. Pompee's hand reached for that of TiTonTon's, clasped it hard for a second, then he turned and walked quickly back to the coach, his long white legs making quick strides on the red carpet, his sword flashing at his side in the sunlight.

There was a mighty roll of drums in the hills behind the city. The huge *arada* drums thundered, the *maman* drums throbbed, and the others took up the beat. The sound echoed through the hills and came out across the water to embrace them as the ship moved slowly away from the *quai*. TiTonTon and Hyacinthe stood by the rail, waving at the receding shoreline. Armes and Athenée, the ermine borders of their robes sweeping the scrubbed deck, followed the captain to their cabin. The captain left, closing the door behind him.

Armes reached up and removed the gold crown that he was wearing and laid it on a chair. With fingers that were not too steady, he undid the clasps of his mantle and let it fall to the floor, standing before Athenée in his black suit, devoid of all the trappings of royalty.

"It would seem that you have married a commoner, my Princess," he whispered. "I have lost my crown; I am no longer the Prince Royal of Haiti."

She drew out the hairpins that held her own coronet.

"And I," she smiled up at him "am merely Mrs. Armes Holbrook of Boston."

He shook his head. "No, not of Boston, nor Haiti, nor St. Domingue, only of my heart," he answered.

Together they walked to the open porthole and watched the purple mountains fade, and as they receded into the distance, the sound of the drums could no longer be heard. The drums of Haiti were stilled and the only sound they heard was the beating of their own hearts. It was enough.

                    67-4-3